THE INTERACTIONS OF HADRONS

THE INTERACTIONS OF HADRONS

HARTMUT PILKUHN

Department of Theoretical Physics
University of Lund

1967

NORTH-HOLLAND PUBLISHING COMPANY-AMSTERDAM

JOHN WILEY & SONS, INC. - NEW YORK
(Interscience Publishers Division)

LIBRARY OF CONGRESS CATALOG CARD NUMBER 67–26463

Publishers:

NORTH-HOLLAND PUBLISHING COMPANY-AMSTERDAM

Sole distributors for the U.S.A. and Canada:

INTERSCIENCE PUBLISHERS, a division of

JOHN WILEY & SONS, INC. - NEW YORK

PRINTED IN THE NETHERLANDS

TABLE OF CONTENTS

APPENDICES

PREFACE

The word "hadron" (from the Greek ἁδρός = large) comprises the strongly-interacting elementary particles (baryons and mesons) as well as the highly unstable states (resonances), which decay into these particles. Hadrons have strong, electromagnetic and weak interactions; this book deals mainly with the phenomenological description of these interactions.

In chapters 1 to 3, the necessary formalism is developed: relativistic kinematics and phase space, the scattering formalism of spinless particles, and the inclusion of spin. A large number of formulae needed in the practical calculations are derived, e.g. the relativistic spin states and propagators for spins $\frac{1}{2}$, 1, $\frac{3}{2}$ and 2. Two chapters on more complex formalisms, namely relativistic S-matrix theory and helicity and decay correlation problems, are deferred to later chapters (6 and 9), to avoid too much formalism at the beginning. Topics of a mathematical nature are collected in the appendices.

The central part (chapters 4, 5, 7, 8, 10–13) is devoted to the classification of hadrons and their interactions, to the symmetries of the various interactions, and to dynamical models. Since 1960, many resonances have been discovered. On the theoretical side, SU_3 symmetry has provided a powerful classification scheme. For example, the baryons form a complete "octet", and even if a few quantum numbers of members of some multiplets have not yet been measured, it is normally assumed that they are correctly predicted by SU_3 symmetry. In this situation, a self-contained book on hadrons and their interactions may be appropriate.

The theory of strong interactions has produced a large number of dynamical models, most of which have been abandoned after a couple of years. This necessitates some caution in the presentation of models. I have decided that the partial-wave dispersion relations for low-energy pion-nucleon scattering have had enough success to be included in this book. Similarly, the K-matrix parametrization of low-energy antikaon-nucleon interactions has turned out to be very convenient. Also, the main features of high-energy collisions are by now so well-known that the inclusion of at least asymptotic theorems and simple parametrizations is justified. Finally, I have included the Born term model, partly because it provides the basis of several more defined models, and partly because Born terms occur in other parts of the book, namely in the decays of hadrons, in electromagnetic scattering and in photoproduction.

Historically, the theory of strong and weak interactions has been developed in analogy with quantum electrodynamics, i.e. from a Lagrangian formalism of quantized local fields. This formalism is relatively complicated even for the interaction of electrons with photons. For the large number of hadrons, stable or unstable, with spins up to $\frac{3}{2}$ or 2, it is certainly inconvenient. I have therefore decided to use instead the more direct *S*-matrix approach. Here also, I have been rather unorthodox and have postulated more than an *S*-matrix theoretician would admit. Approximations necessary for the inclusion of unstable particles have been made very early. In chapter 6, I have included some topics which go beyond the general frame of the book, e.g. three-particle unitarity and anomalous thresholds.

The *S*-matrix approach has been developed primarily for the strong interactions. However, it turns out to be convenient even for the description of electromagnetic and weak interactions of hadrons. Chapters 10, 12 and 13 deal exclusively with these interactions. In particular, the description of weak interactions is developed without recursion to lowest-order perturbation theory. However, some topics in weak interactions have been omitted, e.g. the "current algebra" method.

On the whole, I have tried to "de-operatorize" the formalism as much as possible. No "second quantization" is used. The partial-wave decomposition is defined as a means of solving the unitarity equation, without introducing operators of total or orbital angular momentum. Predictions of SU_3-symmetry are elaborated from *U*-spin invariance, in analogy with the isospin formalism.

The material for this book has been collected mainly from review articles and summer schools. I apologize to all those authors who find parts of their presentation of the subject in the book, without finding their names quoted. Also reference to the original literature is made only occasionally.

The content of the manuscript was first tried out in my lectures at the University of Lund. Professor G. Källén took great care in promoting the project. Part of the book was written at the Institute of Technology at Darmstadt, during a stay there kindly arranged by Professor F. Beck. The suggestions of Dr. B. E. Y. Svensson, freely given throughout the preparation of the manuscript, contributed significantly to its final form. In personal discussions, Professor J. Hamilton gave valuable advice, particularly about pion-nucleon scattering as discussed in chapter 7.

Among the other persons who read the manuscript, special mention must be made of Dr. C. Jarlskog, who also helped in preparing tables and figures. Mrs. I. Belin skilfully typed the manuscript, and the North-Holland Publishing Company printed it quickly and efficiently.

To these persons, I wish to express my sincere gratitude.

Lund, Sweden,
March, 1967

HARTMUT PILKUHN

CHAPTER 1

KINEMATICS AND PHASE SPACE

1-1. Units and 4-vectors

The fundamental constants in relativistic quantum mechanics are the velocity of light,

$$c = 2.997925 \times 10^{10} \text{ cm/sec} \tag{1.1}$$

and $\hbar$, which is Planck's constant divided by 2π:

$$\hbar = 6.5820 \times 10^{-22} \text{ MeV} \cdot \text{sec} = 1.05450 \times 10^{-27} \text{ erg} \cdot \text{sec}. \tag{1.2}$$

For a determination of these and other constants, see COHEN and DUMOND [1965]. The velocity of light appears in the relation between the energy E, rest mass m and momentum p of a particle,

$$E = \sqrt{m^2c^4 + p^2c^2}. \tag{1.3}$$

Planck's constant relates the wavelength of a particle wave to the particle's momentum:

$$l = 2\pi\hbar/p. \tag{1.4}$$

In the theory of hadrons, it is customary to choose the units such that

$$\hbar = c = 1, \tag{1.5}$$

to simplify the formulae. The unit of energy is the MeV (= million electron volt) or the GeV (= 1000 MeV). The masses of electron and proton are then approximately $\frac{1}{2}$ MeV and 1 GeV, respectively. The exact values will be given in table 4-1. The MeV is converted into sec^{-1} using (2), and into cm^{-1} by

$$\hbar c = 1.9732 \times 10^{-11} \text{ MeV} \cdot \text{cm}, \tag{1.6}$$

which follows from (1) and (2).

Although we have put $c = 1$, we shall occasionally write GeV/c for the unit of momentum. This helps to avoid confusion with energy. Lengths are sometimes expressed in fermis,

$$1 \text{ fm} = 10^{-13} \text{ cm} = \frac{1}{197.3 \text{ MeV}} \approx 5[\text{GeV}]^{-1}. \tag{1.7}$$

This unit is useful in nuclear physics, where the theory is formulated in terms of local potentials. The theory of hadrons is most adequately formulated in "momentum space", and the reinterpretation in terms of distances is not only unnecessary, but sometimes also misleading. Although one may speak about the structure of a proton in terms of some radius, one translates back to inverse momentum in the calculations.

Cross-sections are measured in millibarns (1 mb $= 10^{-27}$ cm^2) or microbarns (1 μb = 0.001 mb). When calculating a cross-section, one converts

$$(\text{GeV})^{-2} = 0.389\,35 \text{ mb} \tag{1.8}$$

at the end of the calculation. This number follows from the square of (6).

In the theory of elementary particles, extensive use is made of Lorentz invariance. For this purpose, the momentum vector $\boldsymbol{p} = (p_x, p_y, p_z)$ of a particle is combined with its energy into a four-component vector $P = (E, \boldsymbol{p})$, shortly called the 4-momentum. Its square is defined as

$$P^2 \equiv E^2 - \boldsymbol{p}^2. \tag{1.9}$$

Lorentz invariance tells us that this is a constant, namely m^2, according to (3). Thus, if we accelerate protons to arbitrary momenta, we can always calculate the corresponding energies from (3). This has been verified with considerable accuracy up to energies in the GeV range (see e.g. ALVÄGER *et al.* [1964]). Of course it could be an approximation to a more complicated relation, in the same way as the non-relativistic expression $E = m + p^2/2m$ is an approximation to (3). However, it seems to be the least questionable approximation in the theory of hadrons.

Sums of different 4-vectors are also 4-vectors. Thus, if we have two particles a and b, $(P_a + P_b)^2$ is also Lorentz-invariant, which implies that

$$P_a \cdot P_b = E_a E_b - \boldsymbol{p}_a \cdot \boldsymbol{p}_b \tag{1.10}$$

is invariant, too. Quite generally, physical laws can be expressed in terms of Lorentz-invariants. This allows us to predict decay properties of a particle in flight from those of the particle at rest, cross-sections for colliding beam experiments from those of a fixed target, and so on. Also, in the analysis of a single experiment, it is important to use different "Lorentz-frames". This is worked out in detail in the following sections.

The abstract group of Lorentz-transformations consists of those linear transformations of the time-space coordinates t, x, y, z which do not change the value of the quadratic form $t^2 - x^2 - y^2 - z^2$. Hence the expression "time-like" ("space-like") for a 4-vector whose square is positive (negative). The components of a 4-vector X are usually denoted by X^μ, where $\mu = 0$ represents the "time component" and $\mu = 1, 2, 3$ the "space components". For a 4-momentum P^μ we thus have

$$P^0 = E, \qquad P^1 = p_x, \qquad P^2 = p_y, \qquad P^3 = p_z. \tag{1.11}$$

To eliminate the minus signs in the quadratic form, one often defines another 4-vector X_μ,

$$X_0 = X^0, \quad X_\mu = -X^\mu, \quad \mu = 1, 2, 3, \quad X \cdot Y = X_\mu Y^\mu = X^\mu Y_\mu. \tag{1.12}$$

Summation over repeated indices is understood.

This can be made even more formal by the introduction of a metric tensor,

$$X_\mu = g_{\mu\nu} X^\nu, \qquad g_{\mu\nu} = \begin{pmatrix} 1 & & & 0 \\ & -1 & & \\ & & -1 & \\ 0 & & & -1 \end{pmatrix}, \tag{1.13}$$

which transforms a vector with upper indices into a vector with lower indices. We shall use these symbols occasionally.

Another convention is to define $P^0 = \mathrm{i}E$, $P^2 = P^\mu P^\mu$, which is just the opposite of (9). It avoids the distinction between upper and lower indices. Books which use this "metric" are recognized by notorious minus signs in the definition of the basic Lorentz-invariants, e.g. $P^2 = -m^2$, $(P_\mathrm{a} + P_\mathrm{b})^2 = -s$.

The Lorentz group contains, as a subgroup, the reflections of space and time, in which the three space components and/or the time component change sign. Physical laws are not necessarily invariant under these "improper" transformations. In the following, the term "Lorentz invariance" is used only for invariance under "proper" Lorentz transformations.

Lorentz transformations which do not affect the time-component are called rotations. They form an important subgroup, used for the definition of spin. This group is briefly discussed in the appendix. A general Lorentz-transformation may be decomposed into a rotation and a "boost". The "boost" (also called "pure" or "special" Lorentz-transformation) affects only the time-component and a linear combination of the space components, defined by the "direction" of the boost. Usually we shall define our coordinate systems such that the boost is in the z-direction, in which case the x- and y-components of 4-vectors remain unchanged.

Boosts do not form a group. A product of several boosts in different directions may be a rotation. This is the origin of the "relativistic complications of spin". We avoid these complications by using the helicity formalism of JACOB and WICK [1959], which will be presented in some detail.

So far, we have not mentioned the group of translations in space and time which, together with the Lorentz group, forms the inhomogeneous Lorentz group or Poincaré group. Translational invariance implies the conservation of energy and momentum in any reaction. It provides the basis for the definition of a free particle in terms of a 4-momentum vector. We return to this point in connection with the definition of the S-matrix. More details of Lorentz transformations are given later.

1-2. Lab system and cms

In this and the following three sections, we discuss the relativistic kinematics of various reactions. Prior to this, we mention some basic hadron reactions.

The most frequently encountered hadrons are the proton (p), the neutron (n) and the π-mesons or pions. There are three types of pions, which differ from each other by their electric charge. One writes π^+, π^- and π^0 for a pion of positive, negative and zero electric charge, respectively. The two charged pions have equal masses, whereas π^0 is slightly lighter. The proton is about 6.7 times heavier than the charged pion (see table 4-1). Proton and neutron have equal masses to within 1.3 MeV. A common name for both particles is "nucleon" (N).

In the large proton accelerators, pions are produced in pp and pn collisions. In practice, one usually puts a metal target into a beam of high-energy protons. To be correct, we should therefore speak about p-nucleus collisions. But at the energies of interest, we can, to a first approximation, neglect the binding energies of the protons and neutrons in the target nuclei. Then, we have the following pion production reactions: $pp \to pp\pi^0$, $pp \to pn\pi^+$, $pn \to pn\pi^0$, $pn \to nn\pi^+$, and $pn \to pp\pi^-$. In all these reactions, the total electric charge is conserved. Usually the proton energy is high enough to allow production of more than one pion in the same collision, e.g. $pp \to pp\pi^+\pi^-$. All these reactions are called "inelastic", in contrast with the "elastic" scatterings $pp \to pp$, $pn \to pn$, in which the outgoing particles are identical with the incoming ones.

The pions can be collimated into secondary beams which may be directed towards another target. Here the most important target is hydrogen, often in the form of liquid hydrogen in a bubble chamber. Since the hydrogen nucleus is a single proton, the complications of nuclear physics do not arise in these secondary interactions.

The best studied interactions of pions are the elastic scatterings, $\pi^+p \to \pi^+p$, $\pi^-p \to \pi^-p$ and the "charge exchange" $\pi^-p \to \pi^0n$. Unfortunately one cannot make beams of π^0, because the π^0 decays into two photons immediately after its creation.

Pions make also inelastic interactions, for example $\pi^+p \to \pi^+\pi^0p$. Another possible reaction is $\pi^-p \to K^0\Lambda$, where K^0 and Λ are two new hadrons, called the K-meson and the Λ-hyperon. This may suffice to indicate the variety of high-energy reactions. In addition to the collisions, we also have the decays of hadrons, since all hadrons except the proton are unstable. The π^- for example decays into the μ^-, which is a kind of heavy electron, and a neutrino. Some hadrons decay into three and more particles. We shall develop the kinematics of the various reactions and decays systematically in the following.

Consider a collision between two particles, called a and b. We shall always assume that, in the lab system, particle b is at rest. It is called the target particle. Then the 4-momenta of a and b in the lab system are $(E_a^{lab}, \boldsymbol{p}^{lab})$ and $(m_b, \boldsymbol{0})$, respectively. The cms (centre-of-momentum system or barycentric system) is defined as that Lorentz-frame in which

$$\boldsymbol{p}_a + \boldsymbol{p}_b = 0. \tag{2.1}$$

This definition implies that the total cms energy is Lorentz-invariant. Its square is denoted by s:

$$(E_a + E_b)^2 = (P_a + P_b)^2 \equiv s. \tag{2.2}$$

Without special indication, components of a 4-vector refer to the cms. Evaluation of the invariant (2) in the lab system gives

$$s = (P_a^{lab} + P_b^{lab})^2 = m_a^2 + m_b^2 + 2m_b E_a^{lab}. \tag{2.3}$$

As an application, let us calculate the threshold value of E^{lab} for a reaction with n particles of masses $m_1, \ldots, m_n$ in the final state. At threshold, all n particles have zero momentum in the cms, and the total cms energy becomes equal to the sum of the masses of the final particles. Then (3) gives us

$$E_a^{lab}(\text{threshold}) = \frac{1}{2m_b}\left[\left(\sum_{i=1}^{n} m_i\right)^2 - m_a^2 - m_b^2\right]. \tag{2.4}$$

Next, we calculate the magnitude p of the cms momentum. According to (1), it is the same for both particles. Inserting $(m_a^2 + p^2)^{\frac{1}{2}}$ and $(m_b^2 + p^2)^{\frac{1}{2}}$ for E_a and E_b in (2), we find

$$p = \frac{1}{2s^{\frac{1}{2}}}\sqrt{(s-m_a^2-m_b^2)^2-4m_a^2m_b^2}. \tag{2.5}$$

Inserting this back into E_a and E_b, we get the simple expressions

$$E_a = \frac{1}{2s^{\frac{1}{2}}}(s+m_a^2-m_b^2), \tag{2.6}$$

$$E_b = \frac{1}{2s^{\frac{1}{2}}}(s-m_a^2+m_b^2), \tag{2.7}$$

the sum of which is of course $s^{\frac{1}{2}}$.

Equation (5) can also be used to calculate the decay momentum of a 2-particle decay. In this case, the cms is the rest system of the decaying particle, and p is defined as the magnitude of the momentum of each of the decay products in this system. All we need do is to replace s by m^2, where m is the mass of the decaying particle.

The expression under the square root in (5) will be denoted by $\lambda(s, m_a^2, m_b^2)$ (see e.g. the book by KÄLLÉN [1964]). It is symmetric in the three variables s, m_a^2, m_b^2:

$$\lambda(s, m_a^2, m_b^2) = s^2+(m_a^2)^2+(m_b^2)^2-2sm_a^2-2sm_b^2-2m_a^2m_b^2. \tag{2.8}$$

It can be written as three different products,

$$\begin{aligned}\lambda(s, m_a^2, m_b^2) &= [s-(m_a+m_b)^2][s-(m_a-m_b)^2] &(2.9)\\ &= [m_a^2-(s^{\frac{1}{2}}+m_b)^2][m_a^2-(s^{\frac{1}{2}}-m_b)^2] &(2.10)\\ &= [m_b^2-(s^{\frac{1}{2}}+m_a)^2][m_b^2-(s^{\frac{1}{2}}-m_a)^2]. &(2.11)\end{aligned}$$

Finally, $\frac{1}{4}(-\lambda)^{\frac{1}{2}}$ is the area of a triangle with sides m_a, m_b and $s^{\frac{1}{2}}$. For this reason λ is sometimes called the triangle function. In a real scattering or decay process, the triangle does not exist since $s^{\frac{1}{2}} > m_a+m_b$. But in a "virtual dissociation" of a stable particle of mass $m < m_a+m_b$, it exists. In that case p is imaginary.

Let us see how we can exploit the symmetry of λ. In addition to P_a and P_b we define the total 4-momentum

$$P = P_a+P_b, \tag{2.12}$$

which transforms like the 4-momentum of a particle of mass $s^{\frac{1}{2}}$. We can change the signs of P, P_a and P_b at will without changing p as given by (5). This leads to the conclusion that whenever one of the three "particles" is at rest, the magnitude of the momentum of each of the other two particles is given by $\frac{1}{2}\lambda^{\frac{1}{2}}$, divided by the mass of the particle at rest. Thus we have

$$\tfrac{1}{2}\sqrt{\lambda(s, m_a^2, m_b^2)} = ps^{\frac{1}{2}} = p^{\text{lab}} m_b = p^{\text{beam}} m_a, \tag{2.13}$$

where "beam" means a system, in which particle a is at rest. Particle b has then the components $(E_b^{\text{beam}}, \boldsymbol{p}^{\text{beam}})$.

1-3. Kinematics of two-particle reactions

Reactions of the type ab → cd with two particles in both initial and final states are called two-particle reactions. Their study is an important topic of hadron physics. Reactions with more than two particles in the final state are usually reduced to a form in which the two-particle formalism applies.

Conservation of energy and momentum yields

$$P_a + P_b = P = P_c + P_d. \tag{3.1}$$

In addition to $P_a^2 = m_a^2, \ldots, P_d^2 = m_d^2$ and the square of the cms energy (2.2), there exists one more Lorentz-invariant. For later use with crossing symmetry, it is useful to introduce three Lorentz-invariants, the so-called "Mandelstam variables":

$$s = (P_a + P_b)^2 = (P_c + P_d)^2 = P^2, \tag{3.2}$$

$$t = (P_c - P_a)^2 = (P_b - P_d)^2 = \Delta^2, \tag{3.3}$$

$$u = (P_a - P_d)^2 = (P_c - P_b)^2. \tag{3.4}$$

These are linearly dependent, since

$$s + t + u = m_a^2 + m_b^2 + m_c^2 + m_d^2. \tag{3.5}$$

The difference $\Delta = P_c - P_a$ is called a 4-momentum transfer. Both t and u are squares of 4-momentum transfers. The scalar product of any combination of P_a, P_b, P_c and P_d can be expressed in terms of the masses and two of the three Mandelstam variables. For the cms momenta in the initial and final state, we shall mainly use the letters q and q':

$$q = \sqrt{\lambda(s, m_a^2, m_b^2)/4s}, \qquad q' = \sqrt{\lambda(s, m_c^2, m_d^2)/4s}. \tag{3.6}$$

We also need the cms scattering angle θ, defined in fig. 1-3. Now we can express t and u as follows:

$$t = m_a^2 + m_c^2 - 2E_a E_c + 2qq' \cos\theta = m_b^2 + m_d^2 - 2E_b E_d + 2qq' \cos\theta, \tag{3.7}$$

$$u = m_a^2 + m_d^2 - 2E_a E_d - 2qq' \cos\theta = m_b^2 + m_c^2 - 2E_b E_c - 2qq' \cos\theta. \tag{3.8}$$

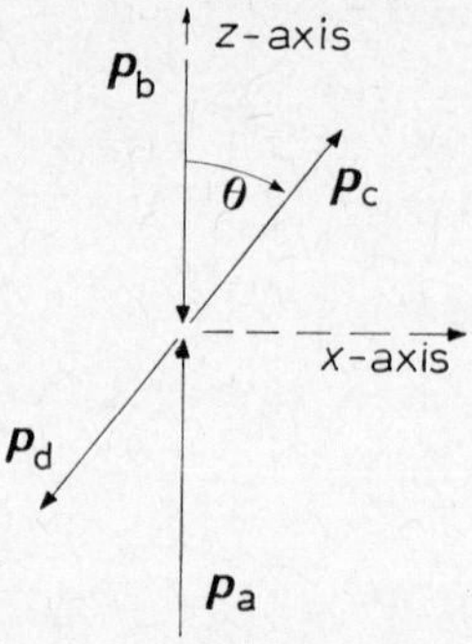

Fig. 1-3. Definition of the cms scattering angle θ. The vectors $\boldsymbol{p}_a$ and $\boldsymbol{p}_b$ are of length q, while $\boldsymbol{p}_c$ and $\boldsymbol{p}_d$ are of length q'. For later use, a coordinate system is inserted. The z-axis lies along $\boldsymbol{p}_a$, the x-axis lies in the reaction plane, with $p_{c,x} > 0$, and the y-axis is along $\boldsymbol{p}_a \times \boldsymbol{p}_c$, i.e. pointing downwards.

We can also express $\cos\theta$ in terms of the Mandelstam variables. From (7) and (8), we get

$$t-u = 4qq'\cos\theta-(E_a-E_b)(E_c-E_d). \tag{3.9}$$

Eliminating the energies by means of (2.6), (2.7), we find

$$\cos\theta = \frac{1}{4qq'}\left[t-u+\frac{1}{s}(m_a^2-m_b^2)(m_c^2-m_d^2)\right]$$
$$= (\lambda\lambda')^{-\frac{1}{2}}[s(t-u)+(m_a^2-m_b^2)(m_c^2-m_d^2)], \tag{3.10}$$

where λ and λ' is a shorthand notation for the two triangle functions of (6). For elastic scattering, we have $m_a = m_c$, $m_b = m_d$, $q = q'$, and (7) simplifies to

$$t(\text{elastic}) = -2q^2(1-\cos\theta) = -4q^2\sin^2\tfrac{1}{2}\theta. \tag{3.11}$$

We shall often need the maximal and minimal values of t. For fixed s, these are given by $\cos\theta = \pm 1$. After some rearrangement, we get from (7)

$$t_{\min}^{\max} = \frac{1}{2s}[2m_a^2m_d^2+2m_b^2m_c^2-(s-m_a^2-m_b^2)(s-m_c^2-m_d^2)\pm\sqrt{\lambda\lambda'}]. \tag{3.12}$$

For large s, this formula is very inconvenient for the calculation of $t_{\max}$, because large cancellations occur. Instead, we introduce the small numbers

$$\varepsilon = \frac{m_a m_b}{s-m_a^2-m_b^2}, \qquad \varepsilon' = \frac{m_c m_d}{s-m_c^2-m_d^2} \tag{3.13}$$

and expand each square root in a power series

$$\lambda^{\frac{1}{2}} = (s-m_a^2-m_b^2)\sqrt{1-4\varepsilon^2} = (s-m_a^2-m_b^2)(1-2\varepsilon^2-2\varepsilon^4-\ldots). \quad (3.14)$$

Up to terms of sixth and higher orders in ε and ε', this gives

$$t_{\max} = \frac{1}{s}(m_a^2 m_d^2 + m_b^2 m_c^2) - \frac{1}{s}(s-m_a^2-m_b^2)(s-m_c^2-m_d^2)[\varepsilon^2+\varepsilon'^2+(\varepsilon^2-\varepsilon'^2)^2]. \quad (3.15)$$

Neglecting also the forth powers of ε and ε', we get finally

$$t_{\max} = -\frac{1}{s}(m_c^2-m_a^2)(m_d^2-m_b^2) - \frac{1}{s}(m_c^2+m_d^2-m_a^2-m_b^2)\left(\frac{m_c^2 m_d^2}{s-m_c^2-m_d^2} - \frac{m_a^2 m_b^2}{s-m_a^2-m_b^2}\right). \quad (3.16)$$

Usually $t_{\max}$ is negative. In elastic scattering it is zero. It is positive for $(m_c^2-m_a^2)(m_d^2-m_b^2) < 0$. The "pick-up" reactions of nuclear physics are of this type.

Finally, we see how t is measured in the lab system. Evaluating the second expression in (3) in that system, we get

$$t = m_b^2 + m_d^2 - 2m_b E_d^{\text{lab}}. \quad (3.17)$$

1-4. Three and more particles in the final state

A reaction with n particles in the final state has $3n-4$ independent Lorentz-invariant variables. We have already seen that for $n = 2$, there are two such variables, e.g. s and t. Adding one particle gives three new variables, for example the momentum components p_x, p_y and p_z of this particle, in a coordinate system defined by the momenta of the remaining particles. Later we shall frequently use such variables. It is however convenient to start with variables which are simply squares of 4-vectors. In the first place, we have the square of the total cms energy,

$$s = (P_a+P_b)^2 \equiv P^2 = (P_1+\ldots+P_n)^2. \quad (4.1)$$

Next, we square the sum of two final state momenta:

$$s_{ik} = (P_i+P_k)^2 = m_i^2+m_k^2+2E_i E_k - 2p_i p_k \cos\theta_{ik}. \quad (4.2)$$

The square root of s_{ik} is called the effective mass of particles i and k. The reason is that in some reactions particles i and k are not produced directly. Instead, they are the decay products of an unstable particle, d. The conservation of energy and momentum in the decay $d \to i + k$ requires $P_d = P_i + P_k$. Since $P_d^2 = m_d^2$ has a fixed value, the effective mass distribution shows a sharp peak at $s_{ik}^{\frac{1}{2}} = m_d$. For extremely short-lived particles and resonances, this is usually the only method of detection.

We can define a separate cms for particles i and k by $\boldsymbol{p}_i + \boldsymbol{p}_k = 0$. In this system we have $s_{ik}^{\frac{1}{2}} = E_i + E_k$. For the case of an unstable particle d, it would be the rest system.

Similarly, we can define effective masses for three and more particles, for example

$$s_{123} = (P_1 + P_2 + P_3)^2 = s_{12} + s_{13} + s_{23} - m_1^2 - m_2^2 - m_3^2. \tag{4.3}$$

If there are only three particles in the final state, we have $s_{123} = s$. In that case, the cms energy of one particle is determined by the effective mass of the other two particles. We find

$$s_{12} = (P_1 + P_2)^2 = (P - P_3)^2 = s + m_3^2 - 2E_3 s^{\frac{1}{2}}. \tag{4.4}$$

In addition to the effective masses, we have n momentum transfers

$$t_{ai} = (P_1 - P_a)^2, \qquad i = 1, \ldots n, \tag{4.5}$$

and n similar transfers t_{bi}. When all the effective masses are given, only two momentum transfers are independent variables (for $n > 2$). This is easily understood in the cms. There, the direction of the initial momenta $\boldsymbol{p}_a$ and $\boldsymbol{p}_b$ relative to the final ones is completely specified by two angles.

Summing up then, a reaction with two particles in the initial state and n particles in the final state has $3n-4$ independent variables. For $n > 2$, $3n-6$ of these may be taken as effective masses, including the total cms energy. The remaining two are necessarily momentum transfers.

In some interactions, the cms momentum of the initial state is zero. This is the case in decays, since these have only one particle in the initial state. It also happens for exothermic reactions, when the two particles in the initial state have no relative velocity. A peculiar example of this type is the antiproton-proton annihilation at rest, which will be discussed later. There, the number of final particles may be quite large. In such interactions, the momentum transfer variables are unnecessary, since the initial state is isotropic (this statement will be modified later, when spin is included). In addition, the total cms energy has some fixed value, namely the sum of the initial masses. Therefore only $3n-7$ variables remain (for $n > 2$). For

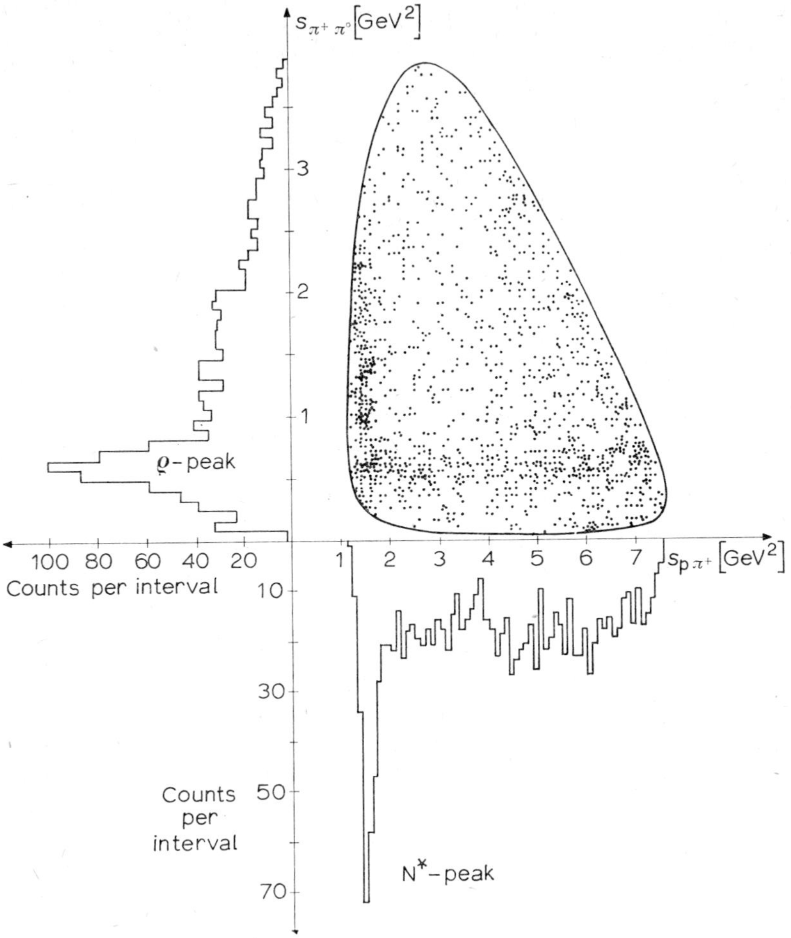

Fig. 1-4.1. Dalitz plot of the reaction $\pi^+p \to \pi^0\pi^+p$ at 4 GeV/c, including the projections on the $\pi^+\pi^0$ and $p\pi^+$ (effective mass)²-distributions (AACHEN-BERLIN-BIRMINGHAM-BONN-HAMBURG-LONDON (I.C.)-MÜNCHEN collaboration, [1964, 1965]. Figure by courtesy of N. Schmitz). The peaks in the (effective mass)²-distributions will be discussed in chapter 5.

$n = 3$ for example, we may take s_{23} and s_{13}, which, by (4), is almost the same as taking E_1 and E_2. In a reaction ab → 123, each event can be plotted as a point in the (E_1, E_2) plane. This is called a Dalitz plot (DALITZ [1953], FABRI [1954]). An example of such a plot is given in fig. 1-4.1. In the cms, the condition $\boldsymbol{p}_1 + \boldsymbol{p}_2 + \boldsymbol{p}_3 = 0$ means that these momenta are coplanar.

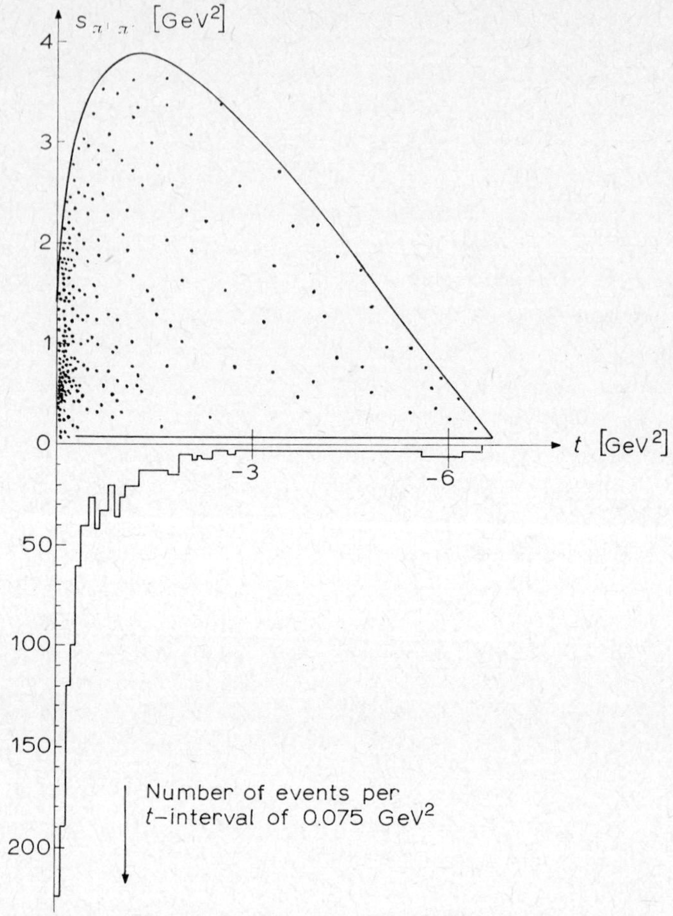

Fig. 1-4.2. Chew-Low plot of the reaction $\pi^+p \to \pi^0\pi^+p$ at 4 GeV/c, including the projection on the square of the momentum transfer from initial to final proton (by courtesy of N. Schmitz, see fig. 1-4.1). Each point in the plot represents 5 events.

The limiting curve of the Dalitz plot corresponds to events which are collinear,

$$\sqrt{E_1^2-m_1^2} \pm \sqrt{E_2^2-m_2^2} \pm \sqrt{E_3^2-m_3^2} = 0. \tag{4.6}$$

Substituting $s^{\frac{1}{2}}-E_1-E_2$ for E_3 and squaring (6), we obtain the following equation for the limiting curve:

$$s-2s^{\frac{1}{2}}(E_1+E_2)+2E_1E_2+m_1^2+m_2^2-m_3^2 = \pm 2\sqrt{(E_1^2-m_1^2)(E_2^2-m_2^2)}. \tag{4.7}$$

In fig. 1-4.1, we have $m_1 = m_2 = m_\pi$, which makes the curve symmetric under the exchange $E_1 \leftrightarrow E_2$.

Another frequently used diagram is the Chew-Low plot (CHEW and LOW [1959]). There, each event is plotted as a point in the (t_{a3}, s_{12}) plane. In this case, the limiting curves are a straight line at $s_{12} = (m_1+m_2)^2$ and a parabola (see fig. 1-4.2). In order to get the parabola, we identify particle 3 with particle c and particles 1 and 2 with the decay products of a fictitious particle d of variable effective mass $m_{12} = m_d = s_{12}^{\frac{1}{2}}$. Then we can identify t_{ac} with t of (3.3). The parabola is given by (3.12), with variable argument m_d^2. For the branch near $t = 0$, (3.16) is often useful, which is also roughly a parabola.

We can now proceed to the evaluation of more complicated Lorentz invariants. Consider the determinant of four 4-vectors, $|P_a P_b P_1 P_3|$ for example. Since a Lorentz transformation does not change the square of a 4-vector, it is a 4×4 matrix of determinant $+1$. (The determinant -1 has been excluded when we excluded space and time reflections. We shall discuss it later.) This implies that determinants of four 4-vectors are Lorentz invariants. For the evaluation of such determinants, the Levi-Civita symbol $\varepsilon_{\alpha\beta\gamma\delta}$ is sometimes useful. It is totally antisymmetric in all four indices, each of which runs over the values 0, 1, 2, 3. Then, according to the definition of determinants,

$$|P_a P_b P_1 P_3| = \varepsilon_{\alpha\beta\gamma\delta} P_a^\alpha P_b^\beta P_1^\gamma P_3^\delta, \qquad \varepsilon_{0123} = 1. \tag{4.8}$$

The phrase "totally antisymmetric" means that $\varepsilon_{\alpha\beta\gamma\delta}$ is $+1(-1)$ if the sequence $\alpha\beta\gamma\delta$ is reached from the sequence 0123 by an even (odd) number of interchanges of adjacent indices. Whenever two or more indices have equal values, ε vanishes.

In reactions ab → cd, the determinant $|P_a P_b P_c P_d|$ vanishes, because these 4-momenta are linearly related by the conservation law (3.1). In reactions ab → 123, we have just one non-vanishing determinant, which can be written in various ways. For example, we can in (8) replace P_1^γ by $-P_2^\gamma$, since $P_1 = P_a+P_b-P_2-P_3$, and since the determinant vanishes if P_1 is replaced by P_a, P_b, or P_3. Suppose we now want to express (8) in terms of cms quantities. For that purpose, we first replace $P_a^\alpha P_b^\beta$ by $-(P_a+P_b)^\alpha P_a^\alpha$. Only the zero-component of P_a+P_b is nonzero, and (8) transforms into

$$|P_a P_b P_1 P_3| = -s^{\frac{1}{2}} |\boldsymbol{p}_a \boldsymbol{p}_1 \boldsymbol{p}_3| = s^{\frac{1}{2}} (\boldsymbol{p}_a \times \boldsymbol{p}_3) \cdot \boldsymbol{p}_1 . \tag{4.9}$$

Next, we apply again the trick of identifying P_3 with P_c and P_1+P_2 with P_d of a fictitious reaction ab → cd. We choose a coordinate system such that $\boldsymbol{p}_a$ points in the z-direction and $\boldsymbol{p}_c$ lies in the (z, x) plane, with $p_{c,x} > 0$, as shown in fig. 1-3. Then (9) becomes

$$|P_a P_b P_1 P_c| = s^{\frac{1}{2}} q q' p_{1,y} \sin\theta \equiv \kappa p_{1,y}. \tag{4.10}$$

The y-axis is of course defined by a right-handed coordinate system. The $(\boldsymbol{p}_a, \boldsymbol{p}_c)$-plane is frequently called the production plane. The y-axis is the normal to the production plane.

Expressing q, q' and $\sin\theta$ by means of (3.6), (3.7) and (3.8), we find the symmetric expression

$$\kappa^2 = sq^2q'^2\sin^2\theta = 2m_a^2m_b^2m_c^2m_d^2(m_a^{-2}+m_b^{-2}+m_c^{-2}+m_d^{-2})$$
$$+stu-s(m_a^2m_b^2+m_c^2m_d^2)-t(m_a^2m_c^2+m_b^2m_d^2)-u(m_a^2m_d^2+m_b^2m_c^2). \tag{4.11}$$

Also $p_{1,y}$ can be expressed in terms of squares of 4-vectors, but that expression involves the second independent momentum transfer, t_{a1} for example. We shall never require it.

In the lab system $p_b^{\text{lab}} = 0$, κ is given by

$$\kappa = m_b(p_a p_c \sin\theta_{ac})^{\text{lab}} = m_b(p_a p_d \sin\theta_{ad})^{\text{lab}} = m_b(p_c p_d \sin\theta_{cd})^{\text{lab}}. \tag{4.12}$$

The two last expressions follow from the first most simply by the fact that in the lab system, $\boldsymbol{p}_a \times \boldsymbol{p}_c = -\boldsymbol{p}_a \times \boldsymbol{p}_d = -\boldsymbol{p}_c \times \boldsymbol{p}_d$. Similar expressions apply in the rest systems of the other particles. In fact, the meaning of κ for four linearly related momenta is analogous to that of $\lambda^{\frac{1}{2}}$ for three linearly related momenta. Whenever one of the four particles is at rest, $|\kappa|$ is the mass of this particle times the magnitude of the only remaining cross product. This is a special case of the invariance of $\varepsilon_{\alpha\beta\gamma\delta}P_a^\alpha P_b^\beta P_c^\delta$ against Lorentz transformations in the production plane.

1-5. Phase space and state normalization

The experimental observation of a particle pertains to a certain momentum region. To calculate the probability of obtaining in some process a particle with momentum in a volume element d^3p around $\boldsymbol{p}$, we have to know the number of states in that momentum space element. This is given by the corresponding phase space element. It is also called the density of states.

One usually starts from the assumption that the states are standing waves in a box of length L. Let the momentum components be p_x, p_y and p_z. Then the periodic boundary condition requires, with (1.4),

$$Lp_x = 2\pi n_x, \qquad n_x = \text{integer}, \tag{5.1}$$

and similar conditions for p_y and p_z. The volume of the phase space corresponding to momenta between $\boldsymbol{p}$ and $\boldsymbol{p}+\mathrm{d}^3p$ is given by the number of states per box volume, in the limit $L\to\infty$. With $n_x/L = p_x/2\pi$ and so on, the phase space element is

$$\mathrm{d}^3p/(2\pi)^3. \tag{5.2}$$

Thus, apart from factors 2π, phase space is the same as momentum space. If we had put $h = 1$ instead of $\hbar = 1$, phase space and momentum space would be identical.

In the relativistic case, certain changes are appropriate. A particle with energy $E = (m^2+p^2)^{\frac{1}{2}}$ sees the box Lorentz-contracted by a factor m/E along the momentum direction. If we want to define the phase space in a Lorentz-invariant way, we have to count the number of states for each particle in the rest system of that particle. This means that we have to multiply (2) by m/E. Remember that for non-relativistic particles, we have $m/E \approx 1$.

To show the Lorentz invariance more clearly, we prove that

$$\frac{m}{E}\,\mathrm{d}^3p = 2m\,\mathrm{d}^4P\,\delta(P^2-m^2). \tag{5.3}$$

The four-dimensional momentum space element is of course Lorentz invariant, and so is the δ-function. According to the rules of δ-functions, we have

$$\begin{aligned}\delta(P^2-m^2) &= \delta(P_0^2-p^2-m^2)\\ &= \frac{1}{2P_0}\,\delta(P_0-\sqrt{p^2+m^2})-\frac{1}{2P_0}\,\delta(P_0+\sqrt{p^2+m^2}).\end{aligned} \tag{5.4}$$

We shall always assume that the integration over P_0 goes over positive values only. In that case, the second δ-function never contributes, and we have $\mathrm{d}P_0\,\delta\,(P^2-m^2) = 1/2E$, where E is the value of P_0 at $(p^2+m^2)^{\frac{1}{2}}$. Some authors prefer to integrate over negative values of P_0 as well, in which case they have to put the step function $\theta(P_0)$ into the integrand. This function is $+1$ for $P_0 > 0$ and zero for $P_0 < 0$.

At this point, the mathematically trained reader might wonder whether the sign of the zero-component of a 4-vector really remains invariant under Lorentz transformations. The answer is that it does so only for timelike vectors, i.e. $m^2 \geqq 0$. Later, we shall also consider particles of zero mass, namely the neutrino and the photon. In those cases, we can always assume a very small and positive m^2, which we put equal to zero in the final results.

In the final formulation of the relativistic phase space, we want to get rid of the factor $2m$ on the r.h.s. of (3). Hence, we define the volume element of the one-particle Lorentz-invariant phase space as

$$\mathrm{d\,Lips}(P) = \frac{\mathrm{d}^3p}{2E(2\pi)^3} = \frac{\mathrm{d}^4P}{(2\pi)^3}\,\delta(P^2-m^2). \tag{5.5}$$

With this convention, the Lorentz-invariant normalization of states is

$$\langle \boldsymbol{p}'|\boldsymbol{p}\rangle = (2\pi)^3 2E\delta(\boldsymbol{p}-\boldsymbol{p}'), \tag{5.6}$$

since it leads to

$$\int \langle \boldsymbol{p}'|\boldsymbol{p}\rangle \mathrm{d\,Lips}(P) = 1. \tag{5.7}$$

For the analogy with the non-relativistic formulae, it would of course be nice to have E/m instead of $2E$. However, we shall see later that definition (5) is much more elegant.

Alternatively, we could always use the non-relativistic phase space (2). In this case, the energy denominator is forced upon us by Lorentz-invariance at some later stage.

For a system consisting of n particles with 4-momenta $P_1, \ldots, P_n$, the phase space element is given by

$$\mathrm{d\,Lips}(P_1, \ldots, P_n) = (2\pi)^{-3n} \prod_{i=1}^{n} \frac{\mathrm{d}^3P_i}{2E_i}. \tag{5.8}$$

In applications, we must pick out final states with a given total 4-momentum P. We therefore define the restricted phase space element

$$\mathrm{d\,Lips}(s; P_1, \ldots, P_n) = (2\pi)^4\delta^4(P-\sum P_i)\mathrm{d\,Lips}(P_1, \ldots, P_n). \tag{5.9}$$

Since it is Lorentz-invariant, it can depend on P only through $P^2 = s$. It is conveniently evaluated in the cms, in which

$$\delta^4(P-\sum P_i) = \delta(s^{\frac{1}{2}}-\sum E_i)\delta^3(\sum \boldsymbol{p}_i). \tag{5.10}$$

Notice that the δ-function of a 4-vector is Lorentz-invariant: two 4-vectors which are identical in one Lorentz frame are identical in any Lorentz frame.

1-6. Two-particle phase space

For two particles in the final state, the restricted phase space element is, according to (5.9) and (5.8),

$$\mathrm{d\,Lips}(s;\,P_c,\,P_d) = (2\pi)^{-2}\,\frac{\mathrm{d}^3p_c}{2E_c}\,\frac{\mathrm{d}^3p_d}{2E_d}\,\delta^4(P-P_c-P_d). \tag{6.1}$$

We can simplify this expression by cancelling δ-functions with differentials. We work in the cms where, according to (5.10), the δ-function of the 3-momenta is $\delta^3(\boldsymbol{p}_c+\boldsymbol{p}_d)$. The first simplification is

$$\mathrm{d}^3p_d\,\delta^3(\boldsymbol{p}_c+\boldsymbol{p}_d) = 1. \tag{6.2}$$

This is a shorthand notation for

$$\int \mathrm{d}^3p_d\,F(\boldsymbol{p}_d)\delta(\boldsymbol{p}_c+\boldsymbol{p}_d) = F(-\boldsymbol{p}_c), \tag{6.3}$$

for any function F. All we have to remember from (3) is that, after the "cancellation", E_d is given by $(m_d^2+p_c^2)^{\frac{1}{2}}$. Next, we go over to spherical coordinates. With $|\boldsymbol{p}_c| = q'$, we have

$$\mathrm{d}^3p_c = q'^2\mathrm{d}q'\mathrm{d}\Omega = q'^2\mathrm{d}q'\mathrm{d}\cos\theta\,\mathrm{d}\phi, \tag{6.4}$$

where θ and ϕ are polar and azimuthal angles respectively. In a reaction ab $\rightarrow$ cd, θ can be taken as the cms scattering angle. In that case the reaction probability will be independent of ϕ, due to the axial symmetry of the initial configuration (see fig. 1-3.1). A ϕ-dependence could arise only if one of the initial particles carries a spin and is polarized along a particular direction. Such cases will be discussed later. At present, we can simply replace $\mathrm{d}\phi$ by $\int \mathrm{d}\phi = 2\pi$.

In order to cancel the energy δ-function, we introduce the new variable

$$E = E_c+E_d = \sqrt{m_c^2+q'^2}+\sqrt{m_d^2+q'^2}, \tag{6.5}$$

$$\mathrm{d}E = \left(\frac{q'}{E_c}+\frac{q'}{E_d}\right)\mathrm{d}q' = \frac{q'E}{E_cE_d}\,\mathrm{d}q\,. \tag{6.6}$$

After elimination of $\mathrm{d}q'$ in favour of $\mathrm{d}E$, our phase space element becomes

$$\mathrm{d\,Lips}(s;\,P_c,\,P_d) = \frac{q'\mathrm{d}\Omega\mathrm{d}E}{(2\pi)^2 4E}\,\delta(s^{\frac{1}{2}}-E) = \frac{q'\mathrm{d}\Omega}{16\pi^2 s^{\frac{1}{2}}} = \frac{q'\mathrm{d}\cos\theta}{8\pi s^{\frac{1}{2}}}\,. \tag{6.7}$$

This important expression can be written in a few alternative ways. From expressions (3.7) and (3.17) for t, we have

$$\mathrm{d}\cos\theta = \frac{\mathrm{d}t}{2qq'} = -\frac{m_b}{qq'}\,\mathrm{d}E_d^{\mathrm{lab}}. \tag{6.8}$$

Inserting this into (7), we find

$$\mathrm{d}\,\mathrm{Lips}(s;\,P_\mathrm{c},\,P_\mathrm{d}) = \frac{\mathrm{d}t}{16\pi q s^{\frac{1}{2}}} = \frac{-m_\mathrm{b}}{8\pi q s^{\frac{1}{2}}}\,\mathrm{d}E_\mathrm{d}^\mathrm{lab}. \tag{6.9}$$

1-7. Recurrence relations

The definition (5.8) exhibits d Lips $(P_1, \ldots, P_n)$ as a product of single-particle phase space elements. The restricted phase space element (5.9) is not quite such a product, but it has a number of useful recurrence relations. Let us first take three particles in the final state:

$$\mathrm{d}\,\mathrm{Lips}(s;\,P_1,\,P_2,\,P_3) = (2\pi)^4\delta^4(P-P_1-P_2-P_3)\mathrm{d}\,\mathrm{Lips}(P_1,\,P_2,\,P_3). \tag{7.1}$$

Introducing the auxiliary 4-momentum

$$P_\mathrm{d} = P_1+P_2, \qquad P_\mathrm{d}^2 = s_\mathrm{d} \tag{7.2}$$

and multiplying (1) by $1 = \mathrm{d}^4P_\mathrm{d}\delta^4(P_\mathrm{d}-P_1-P_2)$, we get after some re-arrangement

$$\mathrm{d}\,\mathrm{Lips}(s;\,P_1,\,P_2,\,P_3) = \delta^4(P-P_3-P_\mathrm{d})\mathrm{d}\,\mathrm{Lips}(P_3)\mathrm{d}^4P_\mathrm{d}\,\mathrm{d}\,\mathrm{Lips}(s_\mathrm{d};\,P_1,\,P_2). \tag{7.3}$$

Now we make s_d an explicit integration variable by writing

$$\mathrm{d}^4P_\mathrm{d} = \mathrm{d}^4P_\mathrm{d}\,\delta(P_\mathrm{d}^2-s_\mathrm{d})\mathrm{d}s_\mathrm{d} = (2\pi)^3\mathrm{d}\,\mathrm{Lips}(P_\mathrm{d})\mathrm{d}s_\mathrm{d}\,. \tag{7.4}$$

Using this expression, we transform (3) into

$$\mathrm{d}\,\mathrm{Lips}(s;\,P_1,\,P_2,\,P_3) = \frac{1}{2\pi}\,\mathrm{d}\,\mathrm{Lips}(s;\,P_\mathrm{d},\,P_3)\mathrm{d}\,\mathrm{Lips}(s_\mathrm{d};\,P_1,\,P_2)\mathrm{d}s_\mathrm{d}\,, \tag{7.5}$$

which is the desired recurrence relation. It can be understood in the following way: the first d Lips on the r.h.s. of (5) is that of particle 3 and a fictitious particle d of effective mass $s_\mathrm{d}^{\frac{1}{2}}$. The second d Lips refers to the "decay" d → 1, 2. We write "decay" because in a proper decay, s_d would have a fixed value. In (5), however, it is an integration variable.

The obvious generalization of (5) to n particles is

$$\mathrm{d}\,\mathrm{Lips}(s;\,P_1,\ldots,P_m,\,P_{m+1},\ldots,P_n) = \frac{1}{2\pi}\,\mathrm{d}\,\mathrm{Lips}(s;\,P_\mathrm{d},\,P_{m+1},\ldots,P_n) \times \mathrm{d}\,\mathrm{Lips}(s_\mathrm{d};\,P_1,\ldots,P_m)\mathrm{d}s_\mathrm{d}\,. \tag{7.6}$$

For $m = 1$, this is an identity. For $n = m+1$, as for example in (5), we can insert the explicit form $(2\pi)^{-2}p_n \mathrm{d}\Omega_n/4s^{\frac{1}{2}}$ for d Lips $(s; P_\mathrm{d}, P_n)$. Here $\mathrm{d}\Omega_n$ is the differential solid angle of the nth particle's momentum in the cms, and

$$p_n = \sqrt{\lambda(s, m_n^2, s_\mathrm{d})}/4s \tag{7.7}$$

is the length of this momentum. Then (6) becomes

$$\mathrm{d}\,\mathrm{Lips}(s; P_1, \ldots, P_n) = \frac{\mathrm{d}\Omega_n}{(2\pi)^3 \cdot 8s} \sqrt{\lambda(s, m_n^2, s_\mathrm{d})}\mathrm{d}\,\mathrm{Lips}(s_\mathrm{d}; P_1, \ldots, P_{n-1})\mathrm{d}s_\mathrm{d}. \tag{7.8}$$

For $n = 3$, we can also insert d Lips $(s_\mathrm{d}; P_1, P_2)$ from (6.7), getting

$$\mathrm{d}\,\mathrm{Lips}(s; P_1, P_2, P_3) = \frac{\mathrm{d}\Omega_3}{(2\pi)^5 \cdot 8s} \sqrt{\lambda(s, m_3^2, s_\mathrm{d})}\, \frac{p\,\mathrm{d}\Omega}{4s_\mathrm{d}^{\frac{1}{2}}}\, \mathrm{d}s_\mathrm{d}. \tag{7.9}$$

where $p = (\lambda(s_\mathrm{d}, m_1^2, m_2^2)/4s)^{\frac{1}{2}}$ now means the magnitude of the momentum of particle 1 (and 2) in the d rest frame, and Ω is the corresponding solid angle.

1-8. Density of states in the Dalitz and Goldhaber plots

In this section we discuss in more detail the density of states for three and four particles. First, we prove that the density of states is constant in the Dalitz plot. For that purpose, we do not use (7.9) but start afresh from the definitions (5.8) and (5.9). We work in the cms and eliminate d^3p_3 by means of $\delta^3(\boldsymbol{p}_1 + \boldsymbol{p}_2 + \boldsymbol{p}_3)$:

$$\mathrm{d}\,\mathrm{Lips}(s; P_1, P_2, P_3) = (2\pi)^{-5} \frac{\mathrm{d}^3p_1 \mathrm{d}^3p_2}{8E_1E_2E_3} \delta(s^{\frac{1}{2}} - E_1 - E_2 - \sqrt{m_3^2 + (\boldsymbol{p}_1 + \boldsymbol{p}_2)^2}). \tag{8.1}$$

As in the case of two particles, we write

$$\mathrm{d}^3p_1 \mathrm{d}^3p_2 = p_1^2 p_2^2 \mathrm{d}p_1 \mathrm{d}\Omega_1 \mathrm{d}p_2 \mathrm{d}\Omega_2. \tag{8.2}$$

The symmetry between all three particles can be restored if we write

$$p_1 \mathrm{d}p_1 = E_1 \mathrm{d}E_1, \qquad p_2 \mathrm{d}p_2 = E_2 \mathrm{d}E_2, \tag{8.3}$$

$$p_1 p_2 \mathrm{d}\Omega_1 \mathrm{d}\Omega_2 = p_1 p_2 \mathrm{d}\Omega' \mathrm{d}\cos\theta_{12}, \tag{8.4}$$

where Ω' now comprises all angles of Ω_1 and Ω_2 except θ_{12}, which is the

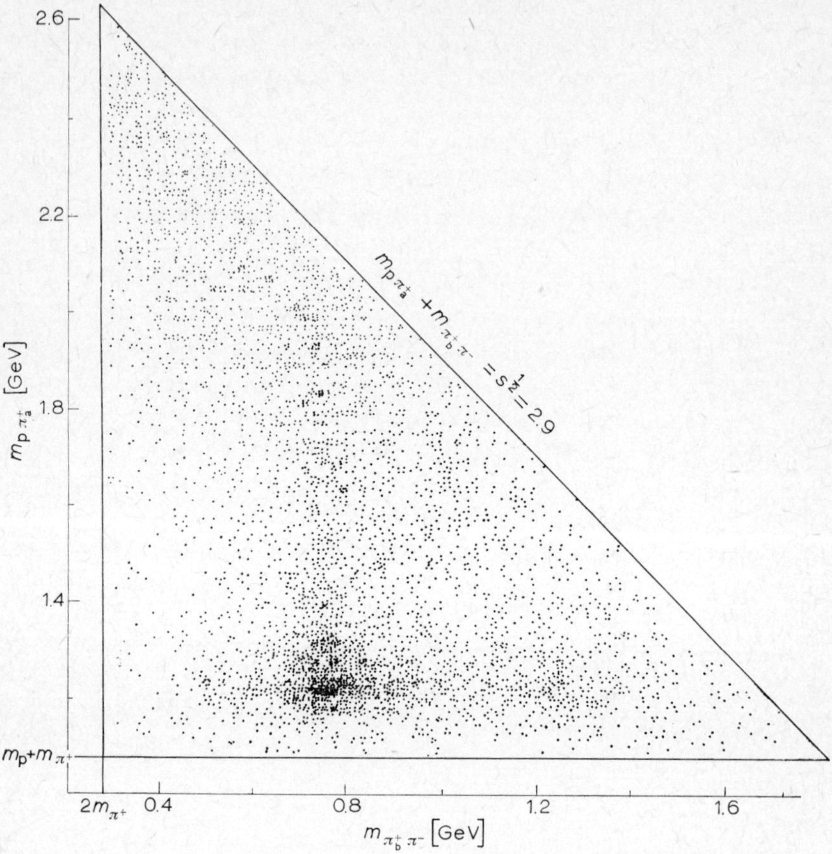

Fig. 1-8. Scatter diagram of $m_{p\pi_a^+} = s_{12}^{\frac{1}{2}}$ versus $m_{\pi_b^+\pi^-} = s_{34}^{\frac{1}{2}}$ for the reaction $\pi^+p \to p\pi_a^+\pi_b^+\pi^-$ at 4 GeV/c (after Aachen-Berlin-Birmingham-Bonn-Hamburg-London (I.C.)-München collaboration, [1965]). Since the final state contains two π^+, there are two points (π_a^+ and π_b^+) for each event.

angle between $\boldsymbol{p}_1$ and $\boldsymbol{p}_2$, and $\int d\Omega' = 8\pi^2$. From

$$p_3^2 = p_1^2 + p_2^2 + 2p_1 p_2 \cos\theta_{12}, \tag{8.5}$$

we get

$$p_1 p_2 \mathrm{d}\cos\theta_{12} = p_3 \mathrm{d}p_3 = E_3 \mathrm{d}E_3. \tag{8.6}$$

Insertion of all these expressions into (1) gives

$$\begin{aligned} \mathrm{d}\,\mathrm{Lips}(s; P_1, P_2, P_3) &= (2\pi)^{-5}\tfrac{1}{8}\mathrm{d}\Omega'\mathrm{d}E_1\mathrm{d}E_2\mathrm{d}E_3\,\delta(s^{\frac{1}{2}} - E_1 - E_2 - E_3) \\ &= \tfrac{1}{8}(2\pi)^{-5}\mathrm{d}\Omega'\mathrm{d}E_1\mathrm{d}E_2. \end{aligned} \tag{8.7}$$

This shows that the density of states is in fact the same for all values of E_1, E_2 and E_3. If, in an actual experiment, the events are not uniformly distributed in the plane of energies (see e.g. fig. 1-4.1), this must be due to truly "dynamical" effects.

With four particles in the final state, the number of two-dimensional effective mass plots becomes quite large. A frequently used plot is the scatter diagram or Goldhaber plot of $s_{12}^{\frac{1}{2}}$ versus $s_{34}^{\frac{1}{2}}$ (CHINOWSKI *et al.* [1962, 1963]). An example of such a plot is shown in fig. 1-8. In this case, the allowed region is limited by straight lines. The line $s_{12}^{\frac{1}{2}} = m_1+m_2$ corresponds to reactions where particles 1 and 2 go together, without relative motion. This is clearly possible for arbitrary values of s_{34}. The third line is given by

$$s_{12}^{\frac{1}{2}}+s_{34}^{\frac{1}{2}} = s^{\frac{1}{2}}. \tag{8.8}$$

It corresponds to events for which both $\boldsymbol{p}_1+\boldsymbol{p}_2 = 0$ and $\boldsymbol{p}_3+\boldsymbol{p}_4 = 0$ in the cms.

In order to calculate the density of states in this scatter diagram, we put $m = 2$ and $n = 4$ in (7.6):

$$\mathrm{d\,Lips}(s; P_1, \ldots, P_4) = \frac{1}{2\pi}\,\mathrm{d\,Lips}(s; P_\mathrm{d}, P_3, P_4)\mathrm{d\,Lips}(s_\mathrm{d}; P_1, P_2)\mathrm{d}s_\mathrm{d}. \tag{8.9}$$

We introduce another auxiliary momentum $P_\mathrm{c} = P_3+P_4$, and apply the recurrence relation once more, this time to d Lips $(s; P_\mathrm{d}, P_3, P_4)$. The result is

$$\mathrm{d\,Lips}(s; P_1, \ldots, P_4) = \frac{1}{4\pi^2}\,\mathrm{d\,Lips}\,(s; P_\mathrm{c}, P_\mathrm{d})\mathrm{d\,Lips}(s_\mathrm{c}; P_3, P_4) \times \mathrm{d\,Lips}(s_\mathrm{d}; P_1, P_2)\mathrm{d}s_\mathrm{c}\mathrm{d}s_\mathrm{d}. \tag{8.10}$$

Obviously, $s_\mathrm{c} = s_{34}$ and $s_\mathrm{d} = s_{12}$ are just the squares of the effective masses plotted in the Goldhaber plot. Inserting (6.7) into each of the three d Lips of (10), we get

$$\mathrm{d\,Lips}(s; P_1, \ldots, P_4) = \frac{q'\mathrm{d}\Omega p_\mathrm{c}\mathrm{d}\Omega_\mathrm{c}p_\mathrm{d}\mathrm{d}\Omega_\mathrm{d}}{4\pi^2(4\pi)^6(ss_{34}s_{12})^{\frac{1}{2}}}\mathrm{d}s_{34}\mathrm{d}s_{12}$$

$$= \frac{\mathrm{d}\Omega\mathrm{d}\Omega_\mathrm{c}\mathrm{d}\Omega_\mathrm{d}}{2(4\pi)^8 s}\sqrt{\lambda(s, s_{12}, s_{34})\lambda(s_{34}, m_3^2, m_4^2)\lambda(s_{12}, m_1^2, m_2^2)}\,\frac{\mathrm{d}s_{12}\mathrm{d}s_{34}}{s_{12}s_{34}}. \tag{8.11}$$

The notation is more or less obvious: p_c vanishes on the line $s_{34}^{\frac{1}{2}} = m_3+m_4$, p_d vanishes on the line $s_{12}^{\frac{1}{2}} = m_1+m_2$, and q' vanishes on the line (8). In other words, the density of states is zero on the whole boundary of the Goldhaber plot. In the interior, it is a smooth non-vanishing function.

Many more phase space elements can be calculated. We refer the reader to the papers of NYBORG *et al.* and NYBORG [1965], in which references to the older literature are given.

1-9. The statistical model

The statistical model was proposed by FERMI [1950] as a simple model of particle production in strong interactions. Originally it was used for the calculation of the relative weights of different channels in high-energy collisions. (A "channel" is here characterized by the number and masses of the outgoing particles.) In this respect, it has not been particularly successful, with the possible exception of antiproton annihilation at rest, which will be mentioned later. In the experimental analysis of a single channel, it is often very useful, since it allows an approximate separation between kinematical and dynamical effects.

Consider a reaction with n outgoing particles of masses $m_1, \ldots, m_n$. The statistical model assumes equal probabilities for all possible final states in this channel. With this assumption, one can calculate the energy distribution of each of the n particles, effective mass distributions, distribution of the angle between two particles, and so on. One merely has to integrate d Lips over those variables which do not enter the distribution. The distributions thus obtained are called "statistical" or "phase space" distributions. As a first example, let us calculate the statistical effective mass distributions of $n-1$ particles in an n-particle channel. The square of this effective mass is denoted by s_d. Its distribution is obtained by integrating (7.8) over all final-state variables except s_d. The result is

$$\frac{\mathrm{d\,Lips}(s;\, m_1 \ldots m_n)}{\mathrm{d}s_d} = \frac{\lambda(s,\, m_n^2,\, s_d)}{(2\pi)^3 \cdot 8s} \int \mathrm{d}\Omega_n \int \mathrm{d\,Lips}(s_d;\, P_1, \ldots, P_{n-1}). \quad (9.1)$$

The first integral on the r.h.s. gives 4π, whereas the second integral gives the *total* phase space of $n-1$ particles at total cms energy $s_d^{\frac{1}{2}}$. This is denoted by Lips $(s_d;\, m_1, \ldots, m_{n-1})$. It depends on the ith particle only through the mass m_i.

We see that the statistical distribution of effective masses involves phase space volumes. In general, the integrals cannot be evaluated in closed form.

The two-particle phase space, however, is very simple. Integration of (6.7) gives

$$\mathrm{Lips}(s_d; m_1, m_2) = \frac{q'}{4\pi s_d^{\frac{1}{2}}} = \frac{1}{8\pi s_d} \sqrt{\lambda(s_d, m_1^2, m_2^2)}. \tag{9.2}$$

Inserting this into (1), we get the distribution of the square of the effective mass of particles 1 and 2 in a 3-particle channel,

$$\frac{\mathrm{d\,Lips}(s; m_1, m_2, m_3)}{\mathrm{d}s_d} = \frac{1}{8\pi^3} \frac{1}{16 s s_d} \sqrt{\lambda(s, m_3^2, s_d)\lambda(s_d, m_1^2, m_2^2)}. \tag{9.3}$$

This function is shown in fig. 1-9. We can convince ourselves that it has the

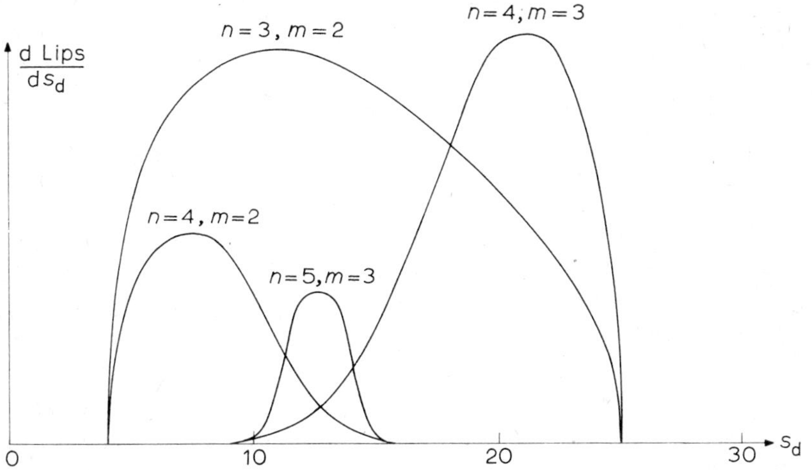

Fig. 1-9. Schematic phase space distributions for (effective mass)^2 of m particles in states of total particle number n, for $s = (6m_i)^2$, and equal masses m_i. Upper and lower limits of the curves are given by $(6-n+m)^2$ and m^2, respectively. The units are arbitrary.

right shape by looking at the Dalitz plot. We remember that $s_d = s_{12}$ and the energy E_3 of the third particle are linearly related by (4.4), and that the density of states is constant over the Dalitz plot. The value of the function (3) at some s_d is therefore proportional to the distance between the two limiting curves at the corresponding value of E_3. This shows immediately that (3) has infinite derivatives at the lower and upper limit of s_d.

We now return to the effective mass distribution (1) for $n > 3$. We can of course always integrate over Ω_n:

$$\frac{\mathrm{d}\,\mathrm{Lips}(s;\, m_1, \ldots, m_n)}{\mathrm{d}s_\mathrm{d}} = \frac{\sqrt{\lambda(s, m_n^2, s_\mathrm{d})}}{16\pi^2 s}\,\mathrm{Lips}(s_\mathrm{d};\, m_1, \ldots, m_{n-1}). \tag{9.4}$$

Although we cannot write down Lips $(s_\mathrm{d};\, m_1, \ldots, m_{n-1})$ explicitly for $n > 3$, we can still make a few comments. The derivative of (4) at the upper limit of s_d remains infinite, whereas the derivative at the lower limit is zero (see fig. 1-9). With increasing n, the distribution becomes more and more skew towards higher values of s_d. These properties can be understood in the following way: Lips $(s_\mathrm{d};\, m_1, \ldots, m_{n-1})$ increases monotonically with s_d. Therefore the only factor which becomes zero at $s_\mathrm{d} = (s^{\frac{1}{2}} - m_n)^2$ is the triangle function in (4), corresponding to the cms momentum of the nth particle. At the lower limit of s_d, however, all relative momenta of $n-1$ particles are simultaneously zero. In fact, one can calculate the phase space in the non-relativistic limit (Lepore and Stuart [1954], see also the review of Milburn [1955]). The result is

$$\mathrm{Lips}(s;\, m_1, \ldots, m_n) = \frac{2^{-n}}{\Gamma(\frac{3}{2}n - \frac{3}{2})} \frac{(\prod_{i=1}^{n} m_i^{\frac{3}{2}})}{(\sum m_i)^{\frac{3}{2}}} \left(\frac{s^{\frac{1}{2}} - \sum m_i}{2\pi}\right)^{\frac{3}{2}n - \frac{5}{2}}. \tag{9.5}$$

The last factor gives the dependence on the total cms kinetic energy. The formula is valid for $n = 2$, as can be checked by comparison with the non-relativistic approximation of (2). Recall that the Γ-function satisfies $\Gamma(\frac{1}{2}) = \pi^{\frac{1}{2}}$, $\Gamma(x+1) = x \cdot \Gamma(x)$. For arbitrary n, (5) is verified by the non-relativistic version of (4).

Much ingenuity has gone into the calculation of phase space integrals. As an example, we mention the statistical method of Lurçat and Mazur [1964], which gives an expansion for the phase space, which converges rapidly for large values of n. The method uses an extension of the central limit theorem of statistical mechanics.

As another example of statistical distributions, we mention the distribution of s_{12} in a 4-particle final state. It is obtained from (8.11) by integrating over all variables except s_{12}:

$$\frac{\mathrm{d}\,\mathrm{Lips}(s;\, m_1, \ldots, m_4)}{\mathrm{d}s_{12}} = \frac{\sqrt{\lambda(s_{12}, m_1^2, m_2^2)}}{2(4\pi)^3 s s_{12}} \int \frac{\mathrm{d}s_{34}}{s_{34}} \sqrt{\lambda(s, s_{12}, s_{34})\lambda(s_{34}, m_3^2, m_4^2)}. \tag{9.6}$$

It has infinite derivative at the lower limit of s_{12}, and zero derivative at the upper limit. The reason is that this time the non-relativistic phase space (5) of particles 3 and 4 and a particle of mass $s_{12}^{\frac{1}{2}}$ appears near the upper limit of s_{12}.

For similar reasons, the effective mass of three particles in a 5-particle channel has zero derivatives at both limits. The general form for the distribution of the effective mass of the first m particles in an n-particle channel is

$$\frac{\mathrm{d}\,\mathrm{Lips}(s; m_1, \ldots, m_n)}{\mathrm{d}s_\mathrm{d}} = \frac{1}{2\pi} \mathrm{Lips}(s; s_\mathrm{d}^{\frac{1}{2}}, m_{m+1}, \ldots, m_n)\mathrm{Lips}(s_\mathrm{d}; m_1, \ldots, m_m). \qquad (9.7)$$

This follows from integration of (7.6).

In general, we do not expect good predictions from statistical distributions. Rather, the discrepancy between the statistical and the measured distributions will be taken as a measure of proper dynamical effects. Only the predictions about zero derivatives are reliable. They indicate "threshold behaviours" which are not so easily destroyed by dynamical effects.

Formulae of type (7) are very convenient for the numerical computation of phase space integrals. Suppose, for example, the total phase space of five particles is needed. We put $m = 3$, $n = 5$ in (7). The two 3-particle phase spaces on the r.h.s. are obtained from (3) by integrating over s_d. Then $\mathrm{Lips}(s; m_1, \ldots, m_5)$ is obtained by integrating the r.h.s. of (7) over s_d.

CHAPTER 2

COLLISIONS AND DECAYS OF SPINLESS PARTICLES

2-1. Definition of cross-sections and lifetimes

In this section we shall define cross-sections and lifetimes in terms of experimental observables like momenta and energies of free particles, number of counts in particle counters or number of interaction stars in a bubble chamber or photographical emulsion. Once this has been done, we may consider the cross-sections and lifetimes themselves as observables. In the next two sections, we shall express them in terms of matrix elements between quantum mechanical states.

Consider a counter experiment. A beam of particles of mass m_a and velocity $v^{lab} = p^{lab}/E^{lab}$ is directed towards a relatively small target, consisting of particles of mass m_b. Behind the target, we have a counter. For simplicity, we assume that this counter registers only particles of mass m_c, $m_c \neq m_a$, $m_c \neq m_b$. For example, we could have a proton beam, a hydrogen target, and a counter which indicates only pions. We also assume that no pion misses the counter. The counting rate, i.e. the number of counts per second, will be denoted by $N(c)/T$. It is proportional to the number N_b of particles in the target, and to the incoming flux, i.e. to the number of particles a per second per unit area perpendicular to the direction of motion. The proportionality constant is called the cross-section for production of particle c in ab collisions, $\sigma(ab \to c \ldots)$. Thus we have

$$\frac{N(c)}{T} = \sigma(ab \to c \ldots) N_b \,\text{flux}(a). \tag{1.1}$$

The flux is the product of the density of the beam particles $\rho(a)$ and their velocity v^{lab},

$$\text{flux}(a) = \rho(a) v^{lab}. \tag{1.2}$$

One may easily convince oneself that σ has the dimension of an area.

Notice that (1) is independent of the shape of the target. We may arrange the N_b particles in a very thin target of large cross-sectional area or in a small but thick target. There are of course limits. The target has to be completely inside the beam, and it has to be so thin that multiple collisions of beam particles or absorption of particles c can be neglected.

In practice, we would like to measure a separate cross-section for each reaction, e.g. $pp \to pn\pi^+$, $pp \to pp\pi^+\pi^-$. Cross-sections also depend in general on the various Lorentz invariants. For two-particle reactions $ab \to cd$, σ will depend on s and t, defined in terms of lab energies by (1-2.3) and (1-3.17), respectively. It is usually denoted by $d\sigma(s, t)/dt$. The momentum transfer can be replaced by the cms scattering angle θ according to (1-3.7). Several forms of "differential" cross-sections are collected at the end of the next section.

Let us now transform (1) into a form which is symmetrical in a and b. For that purpose, we write

$$N_b = \rho_b V, \tag{1.3}$$

where ρ_b is the density of the target, and V is its volume. Inserting (3) and (2) into (1), we have

$$\sigma = \frac{N/TV}{\rho_a \rho_b v^{lab}}. \tag{1.4}$$

This expression is symmetric, if we interpret v^{lab} as the relative velocity $|\boldsymbol{v}_a - \boldsymbol{v}_b|$ of particles a and b.

Now we turn to the definition of the lifetime of an unstable particle. Let us denote the number of decays per second again by N/T. It is proportional to the number N_a of unstable particles which we have under observation. The proportionality constant is called the decay rate or "width" Γ. Thus we have

$$N/T = N_a \Gamma. \tag{1.5}$$

The fact that Γ is time-independent leads to the exponential decay law,

$$N_a(t) = N_a(0) \cdot e^{-\Gamma t}. \tag{1.6}$$

Therefore Γ^{-1} is the lifetime of particle a. The meaning of the name "width" for Γ will appear later. To get (5) in a form similar to (4), we introduce $\rho_a = N_a/V$, where V is the volume under observation. Then we have

$$\Gamma = \frac{N/TV}{\rho_a}. \tag{1.7}$$

To apply (4) and (7), we have to specify to which Lorentz frames the various quantities refer. The particle numbers N, N_a and N_b are of course the same in all frames, and so is the 4-dimensional space-time volume TV. But time and volume separately are not Lorentz invariant. By (5), the lifetime Γ^{-1} is therefore not Lorentz invariant either. In fact, particles a of energy E^{lab} live a factor $E^{\text{lab}}/m_{\text{a}}$ longer than the same particles at rest ("time dilatation"). When speaking about Γ without specification, one always refers to particles at rest.

Similarly, we have

$$\rho_{\text{a}}(\text{lab}) = \rho_{\text{a}}(\text{rest}) \cdot E^{\text{lab}}/m_{\text{a}}, \tag{1.8}$$

in agreement with (7). Now we are ready to define the cross-section (4) in a Lorentz invariant way. The numerator is obviously Lorentz invariant. Insertion of $\rho_{\text{a}}(\text{lab})$ and v^{lab} into the denominator gives

$$\begin{aligned} \rho_{\text{a}}\rho_{\text{b}}v^{\text{lab}} &= \rho_{\text{a}}(\text{rest}) \cdot \frac{E^{\text{lab}}}{m_{\text{a}}} \cdot \rho_{\text{b}}(\text{rest}) \cdot \frac{p^{\text{lab}}}{E^{\text{lab}}} \\ &= \rho_{\text{a}}(\text{rest}) \cdot \rho_{\text{b}}(\text{rest}) \frac{m_{\text{b}}\, p^{\text{lab}}}{m_{\text{a}} m_{\text{b}}} \\ &= \rho_{\text{a}}(\text{rest}) \cdot \rho_{\text{b}}(\text{rest}) \cdot \frac{1}{2m_{\text{a}} m_{\text{b}}} \sqrt{\lambda(s, m_{\text{a}}^2, m_{\text{b}}^2)}. \end{aligned} \tag{1.9}$$

With this expression, (4) is clearly Lorentz invariant and can be used e.g. for colliding beam experiments.

2-2. The *S*-matrix

The quantum theory of scattering is conveniently expressed in terms of the scattering matrix or *S*-matrix. The elements of this matrix give the transition amplitude from a given initial state to one of the possible final states. The final states may be classified into channels, where different channels contain different particles. Within each channel there are infinitely many states, characterized by the values of the particles' momenta. Thus the *S*-matrix is not only a matrix, but also a function of the various initial and final state momenta. Nevertheless, we shall occasionally lump together all quantum numbers of the initial (final) state into one symbol i(f), and treat S as a finite-dimensional matrix of elements S_{if}. This is possible if we work with standing waves in a box of large but finite volume, where the momenta are quantized according to (1-5.1).

Initial and final states are defined at different times; one long before the interaction occurs, the other a long time afterwards. This leads us to consider the time development of quantum states. We start from the Schrödinger equation

$$i\frac{d}{dt}\psi(t) = H\psi(t), \tag{2.1}$$

in which H is the Hamilton operator. We assume that for any time t, $\psi(t)$ can be expanded in terms of free-particle states, in which case H is a matrix in the same sense in which S is a matrix. One can formally integrate (1) by means of a matrix $U(t, t_1)$:

$$\psi_j(t) = \sum_i U_{ji}(t, t_1)\cdot\psi_i(t_1), \qquad i\frac{d}{dt}U(t, t_1) = HU(t, t_1). \tag{2.2}$$

U has the properties

$$U(t_2, t_1) = U(t_2, t)\cdot U(t, t_1), \qquad U(t_1, t_1) = 1. \tag{2.3}$$

Conservation of probability reads

$$\frac{d}{dt}|\psi(t)|^2 = 0, \tag{2.4}$$

from which, for orthonormal states ψ_1,

$$\sum_i |U_{ji}(t_2, t_1)|^2 = 1 \tag{2.5}$$

follows in the first place. Then the same trick which lead to the Lorentz invariance of (1-1.10), also shows that the overlap of two arbitrary states $\psi_i(t)$ and $\psi_j(t)$ is time-independent. For orthonormal states, this implies that U is a unitary matrix:

$$U^+U = 1, \quad \text{or} \quad \sum_f U_{if}U^*_{jf} = \delta_{ij}. \tag{2.6}$$

We cannot write down U explicitly except for a free particle. A particle a is an eigenstate of H, with energy E_a. In that case we have

$$U_a(t_2, t_1) = \exp[-iE_a(t_2-t_1)]. \tag{2.7}$$

For states containing several free particles, we can divide H into a free-particle Hamiltonian H_{free} and an interaction Hamiltonian H_{int}. We may think of H_{int} as some interparticle potential (which also creates new particles), and we assume that H_{int} can be neglected unless the particles are very close to each other. Loosely speaking, we shall be concerned with "short range" interactions. (Electromagnetic interactions will be incorporated afterwards.) Then we have the following physical picture of interactions between particles.

At times $t = \frac{1}{2}T$, long after the interaction has taken place, the time development of an n-particle final state is given by

$$U_{\mathrm{f}}(\tfrac{1}{2}T, 0) = \exp\left(-\tfrac{1}{2}\mathrm{i}T \sum_{j=1}^{n} E_j\right). \tag{2.8}$$

A similar expression $U_{\mathrm{i}}(0, -\frac{1}{2}T)$ applies to the initial state for $t = -\frac{1}{2}T$, long before the beginning of the interaction. Therefore the combination

$$S_{\mathrm{if}} \equiv U_{\mathrm{i}}(-\tfrac{1}{2}T, 0)U_{\mathrm{if}}(\tfrac{1}{2}T, -\tfrac{1}{2}T)U_{\mathrm{f}}^{-1}(\tfrac{1}{2}T, 0) \tag{2.9}$$

is independent of T. It is called the S-matrix element. Since U is unitary, S is also unitary.

From the physical point of view, we could have defined the S-matrix element simply as $U_{\mathrm{if}}(\frac{1}{2}T, -\frac{1}{2}T)$. The purpose of the definition (9) is to get rid of the phases $\mathrm{e}^{-\frac{1}{2}\mathrm{i}E_jT}$, one for each particle. Later we shall see that these phases do not affect observable quantities, and it is therefore convenient to omit them.

A few more remarks are appropriate. The phrase "free particle" includes all stable bound states. Deuteron production in e.g. $\mathrm{pp} \to \mathrm{d}\pi^+$ is treated like a reaction $\mathrm{ab} \to \mathrm{cd}$. In fact, the S-matrix makes no distinction between elementary and composite particles. This comes from the requirement that the eigenstates of H_{free} form a complete set. Since one cannot expand a bound state in terms of unbound states, each bound state must be included as a separate state. This does not exclude the possibility that the binding energy can be calculated in some later approximation scheme. Sometimes the hope is expressed that S-matrix theory may determine the masses of hadrons as well (see e.g. CHEW [1962]).

Although we have assumed the existence of a Hamiltonian, it could be that H does not exist but S is still meaningful. This was the original motivation for studying the S-matrix (HEISENBERG [1943]). There could be a fundamental quantization of time, in which case the time differential in (1) would be meaningless. Since S depends only on large time intervals, it might not be affected.

Finally a word about treatment of time-dependence in general. By definitions of type (2), one can express the whole theory in terms of states at some fixed time t_1, which may be put equal to zero. This is called the Heisenberg picture. Working with states which have the usual time-dependence (1), is called the Schrödinger picture. In states of the type ψU_{f}^{-1}, the time-dependence of a certain free-particle state has been separated off. This is called the interaction or Dirac picture. Our formulae clearly refer to the Schrödinger picture.

In the limit $H_{\rm int} \to 0$, no interaction occurs, and $S_{\rm if}$ as given by (9) reduces to $\delta_{\rm if}$. Also for $H_{\rm int} \neq 0$, most S-matrix elements vanish due to conservation laws. Among the best known conservation laws, we have conservation of the total energy and momentum and of the total electric charge. Several other conservation laws are discussed in chapter 4. It is useful to separate conservation of energy and momentum from the rest:

$$S_{\rm if} = \langle {\rm f}|{\rm i}\rangle + {\rm i}(2\pi)^4\delta^4(P_{\rm i}-P_{\rm f})T_{\rm if}\,. \tag{2.10}$$

To be correct, we should write a Kronecker δ-matrix instead of $2\pi\delta(\ldots)$. The factor i is a matter of definition. It is convenient for weak interactions, where $T_{\rm if}$ is very small. There, unitarity of S implies Hermiticity of T.

We are now ready to establish the connexion between the S-matrix and the cross-section (1.4). If we normalize our quantum states according to (1-5.6), then our theory corresponds to particle densities

$$\rho_{\rm a}({\rm rest}) = 2m_{\rm a}\,, \qquad \rho_{\rm b}({\rm rest}) = 2m_{\rm b}\,, \tag{2.11}$$

and the total number of counts or "events" in (1.4) is nothing but $|S|^2$, integrated over the whole phase space:

$$N = \int |S({\rm ab} \to 1 \ldots n)|^2 \,{\rm d\,Lips}(P_1, \ldots, P_n). \tag{2.12}$$

Inserting (11) into (1.9) and (1.9) and (12) into (1.4), we get the cross-section

$$\sigma = \frac{1}{2[\lambda(s, m_{\rm a}^2, m_{\rm b}^2)]^{\frac{1}{2}}} \int {\rm d\,Lips}(P_1, \ldots, P_n)|S({\rm ab} \to 1, \ldots, n)|^2/TV, \tag{2.13}$$

in the limit of infinite space-time volume TV. The time T is the same as that of (9). The use of (10) and (11) implies already infinite volume. Since we have not carried out the limiting procedure on all quantities simultaneously, we must expect some mathematical difficulties. In fact, from (10) we see that (13) contains the square of the function $\delta^4(P_{\rm i}-P_{\rm f})$, which is mathematically undefined. Formally, we can eliminate this difficulty in the following way. We rewrite one of the δ^4-functions as

$$(2\pi)^4\delta^4(P_{\rm i}-P_{\rm f}) = \int {\rm e}^{{\rm i}x(P_{\rm i}-P_{\rm f})}\,{\rm d}^4x, \tag{2.14}$$

and put $P_i = P_f$ in the integrand, on account of the other δ^4-function. Then we interpret $\int d^4x$ as the total space-time volume VT of the denominator. Finally, we combine the other δ^4-function and d Lips$(P_1, \ldots, P_n)$ into the energy-momentum restricted phase space (1-5.9). Thus the final formula for the cross-section is

$$\sigma = \frac{1}{2[\lambda(s, m_a^2, m_b^2)]^{\frac{1}{2}}} \int \mathrm{d}\,\mathrm{Lips}(s; P_1, \ldots, P_n)|T_{if}|^2. \tag{2.15}$$

If we are interested in differential cross-sections, we exclude the corresponding variables from the integration.

The reason why we did not use the normalization box of volume V more systematically is that this construction does not really correspond to the physical picture which lead to the S-matrix (9). For standing waves in a box, the particle density ρ is uniform over the box at all times, and the statement that the particles are far from each other at $t = \pm\frac{1}{2}T$ makes no sense. Physical particles are always localized by the measurements before and after the interaction, even if this is done on a macroscopic scale. The proper formulation of scattering processes must therefore describe the particles in terms of wave packets, corresponding to a very small momentum spread for each particle. This is explained in some detail in the book of GOLDBERGER and WATSON [1964]. The result (15) is the same. One can also avoid this difficulty by using a box in which the interaction is "switched on" at a time somewhat later than $-\frac{1}{2}T$, and "switched off" shortly before $+\frac{1}{2}T$.

All these tricks become inadequate when the real physical difficulties appear. Namely, all hadrons except the proton are unstable. This means that T has a natural limit. It must be much shorter than the lifetime of the most shortlived particle. At the first sight, it might appear that at least elastic pp scattering would not contain this limit, but in general this is not the case. The point is that the pp channel is connected with channels like ppπ^0 through the unitarity equation. The π^0 decays into 2 photons with a lifetime of the order of 10^{-16} sec. Thus the matrix $U(\frac{1}{2}T, -\frac{1}{2}T)$ in (9) is unitary only for finite times $< 10^{-16}$ sec, unless of course the two-photon states are incorporated explicitly.

From a practical point of view, 10^{-16} sec in infinite compared with typical collision times. From Heisenberg's uncertainty relation $\Delta t \Delta E \approx 1$ and eq. (1-1.2) we find that 10^{-16} sec corresponds to an energy uncertainty of 6.582×10^{-6} MeV. The high-energy physicist is happy if he can determine the energies of his particles to within 1 MeV. Transforming this back to seconds gives collision times well below 10^{-21} sec, whatever the meaning of such unmeasurable time intervals may be. There are, however, resonances in hadron scattering which in many reactions may be treated approximately like particles. In these cases it is important to know how to incorporate some effects of finite lifetimes. A first step in this direction is taken in the next section. We conclude this section by writing down a few alternative forms for the differential cross-section of two-particle reactions. Using the expressions (1-6.7) and (1-6.9), we have

$$\mathrm{d}\sigma = \frac{1}{4s}\frac{q'}{q}\left|\frac{T(s,\theta)}{4\pi}\right|^2 \mathrm{d}\Omega = \frac{\pi}{2s}\frac{q'}{q}\left|\frac{T(s,\theta)}{4\pi}\right|^2 \mathrm{d}\cos\theta$$

$$= \frac{\pi}{4q^2 s}\left|\frac{T(s,t)}{4\pi}\right|^2 \mathrm{d}t = \frac{\pi\,\mathrm{d}t}{\lambda(s, m_a^2, m_b^2)}\left|\frac{T(s,t)}{4\pi}\right|^2. \tag{2.16}$$

The necessary changes for reactions with spin are introduced in section 3-1.

2-3. Unstable particles

Consider the production of an unstable particle, for example the reaction $pp \to pp\pi^0$. As explained in the last section, the π^0 lifetime Γ^{-1} is larger than the typical collision time by a factor of at least 10^5. This also means that the time-interval T which is needed in the definition (2.9) of the S-matrix, can be chosen such that it is negligible with respect to Γ^{-1}. On the time-scale of decay, we may say that the pion is produced at $t = 0$. We now define a new time interval T', which is of the order of Γ^{-1}. Then we can repeat the method of the previous section. Instead of (2.9), we get an S-matrix for the decay

$$S_{\mathrm{df}} = U_{\mathrm{d}}(\tfrac{1}{2}T, 0)U_{\mathrm{df}}(T', \tfrac{1}{2}T)U_{\mathrm{f}}^{-1}(T', 0). \tag{3.1}$$

Except for a change in the argument, U_{f} is again given by (2.8), whereas U_{d} is nothing but $\mathrm{e}^{-\frac{1}{2}\mathrm{i}TE_{\mathrm{d}}}$, where E_{d} is the energy of the decaying particle. In principle, we should take the complete $pp\pi^0$ state as the initial state of the decay interaction, but since the time development of the final protons is trivial, we omit it. Even when we have several unstable particles, we may treat one at a time, since the decays will not interfere with each other. Again we split the Hamiltonian into H_{free} and H_{int}. For a time $t \ll \Gamma^{-1}$, the decaying particle is an eigenstate of H_{free}. The transitions to the various decay states are induced by H_{int}. The differential decay number for a decay $\mathrm{d} \to 1, \ldots, n$ is given by

$$\mathrm{d}N = |S(\mathrm{d} \to 1, \ldots, n)|^2 \mathrm{d}\,\mathrm{Lips}(P_1, \ldots, P_n). \tag{3.2}$$

Inserting this into (1.7) and repeating the various steps of the preceding section, among those the definition of a T-matrix as in (2.10), we get

$$\Gamma(\mathrm{d} \to 1, \ldots, n) = \frac{1}{2m} \int \mathrm{d}\,\mathrm{Lips}(m^2, P_1, \ldots, P_n) |T_{\mathrm{df}}|^2. \tag{3.3}$$

Here we have chosen the rest system of the decay products. Otherwise, we would have m_d replaced by E_d in front of the integral. The total width $\Gamma(\mathrm{d})$ is here the sum of the widths of the various decay channels. The π^0 for example has three decay channels, even if 99% decay into two photons. For a two-particle decay, we have

$$\Gamma = \frac{p}{4m^2} \int \mathrm{d} \cos\theta \left| \frac{T(m^2, \cos\theta)}{(4\pi)^{\frac{1}{2}}} \right|^2, \tag{3.4}$$

according to (1-6.7). Note that the decay matrix element has the dimension of a mass, whereas the corresponding expression in (2.15) was dimensionless.

Our example of π^0 decay is not a good one, since a Γ^{-1} of the order of 10^{-16} sec cannot be observed by the counter method described in section 2-1. The only chance to see a π^0 is in photographic emulsion, but even there it is usually impossible to separate the point of production from the point of decay. So what one really sees are reactions like $\mathrm{pp} \to \gamma\gamma\mathrm{pp}$, $\pi^-\mathrm{p} \to \gamma\gamma\mathrm{n}$, $\pi^-\mathrm{p} \to \gamma\gamma\gamma\gamma\mathrm{n}$ etc., where γ stands for a photon. The identification of photons and neutrons has its own problems, but this need not concern us. The question now is: How can we deduce the existence of π^0 and its lifetime from these reactions?

The most direct method is to study the effective mass distribution of pairs of photons. Let P_1 and P_2 be the 4-momenta of two such photons. If these photons come from the decay of a particle of mass m, we expect $(P_1+P_2)^2 = m^2$. Also, since the unstable state lives only a time of Γ^{-1}, the uncertainty relation $\Delta E \Delta t = 1$ tells us that the effective mass has a distribution around m, with a natural line width of the order of Γ.

Let us see if we can calculate these things. For brevity, we write $\mathrm{i} \to \mathrm{cd}$, $\mathrm{d} \to 12$ for the two-step process $\mathrm{pp} \to \mathrm{pp}\pi^0$, $\pi^0 \to \gamma\gamma$. We work in the cms of particles 1 and 2. There, the effective mass of these particles is given by

$$\sqrt{s_\mathrm{d}} = \sqrt{(P_1+P_2)^2} = E_1 + E_2 \equiv E. \tag{3.5}$$

If particle d were stable, we would have $E = m$. In order to derive the distribution in E, we modify the time-shifting matrix U of (2.8) slightly.

We take the particle at rest and substitute the complex value $m-\frac{1}{2}\mathrm{i}\Gamma$ for the mass,

$$U'_{\mathrm{d}}(t, 0) = \exp(-\mathrm{i}mt-\tfrac{1}{2}\Gamma t), \tag{3.6}$$

to account for the fact that the π^0 intensity decreases by a factor of e during the time interval Γ^{-1}. The S-matrix element of the production process,

$$S(\mathrm{i} \to \mathrm{cd}) = U_{\mathrm{i}}(-\tfrac{1}{2}T, 0)U_{\mathrm{i}\to\mathrm{cd}}(t, -\tfrac{1}{2}T)U_{\mathrm{c}}^{-1}(t, 0)U_{\mathrm{d}}'^{-1}(t, 0) \tag{3.7}$$

is independent of t, whereas $U_{\mathrm{i}\to\mathrm{cd}}(t, \frac{1}{2}T)$ tends to zero for $t \to \infty$. We may say that a small fraction of the probability "leaks" into the channel c12, (i.e. pp$\gamma\gamma$), which is not included explicitly. $|U_{\mathrm{i}\to\mathrm{cd}}(t, -\frac{1}{2}T)|^2$ is the probability that d has been produced at time t, but not decayed. The amplitude for the overall process i → c12 is the product of the U-matrices for production and decay, integrated over the intermediate times t,

$$U_{\mathrm{i}\to\mathrm{c}12} = \int_{\frac{1}{2}T}^{T'} \mathrm{d}t\, U_{\mathrm{i}\to\mathrm{cd}}(t, -\tfrac{1}{2}T)U_{\mathrm{d}\to 12}(T', t). \tag{3.8}$$

(In a classical theory, one would integrate the probabilities instead of the probability amplitudes.) A separation of $S(\mathrm{i} \to \mathrm{c}12)$ into $S(\mathrm{i} \to \mathrm{cd})$ and $S(\mathrm{d} \to 12)$ will be possible only if $\frac{1}{2}T$ may be replaced by 0. Replacing in addition T' by ∞, integral (8) may be calculated explicitly, using the fact that $S(\mathrm{i} \to \mathrm{cd})$ and

$$S(\mathrm{d} \to 12) = U_{\mathrm{d}}^{-1}(0, t)U_{\mathrm{d}\to 12}(\infty, t)U_{12}^{-1}(\infty, 0) \tag{3.9}$$

are both independent of t. With (7) and (9), the matrix element for the overall process pp → $\gamma\gamma$pp becomes

$$S(\mathrm{i} \to \mathrm{c}12) = S(\mathrm{i} \to \mathrm{cd})\int_0^\infty \mathrm{d}t\, U'_{\mathrm{d}}(t, 0)U_{\mathrm{d}}(0, t) \cdot S(\mathrm{d} \to 12)$$

$$= \frac{1}{\mathrm{i}} S(\mathrm{i} \to \mathrm{cd})\Phi(E_{\mathrm{d}})S(\mathrm{d} \to 12), \tag{3.10}$$

$$\Phi(E) = \mathrm{i}\int_0^\infty \mathrm{d}t\, \mathrm{e}^{-\mathrm{i}mt-\frac{1}{2}\Gamma t}\mathrm{e}^{\mathrm{i}Et} = \frac{1}{m-E-\frac{1}{2}\mathrm{i}\Gamma}. \tag{3.11}$$

In $S(\mathrm{i} \to \mathrm{cd})$ and $S(\mathrm{d} \to 12)$, $E = E_{\mathrm{d}}$ may be replaced by $m \equiv m_{\mathrm{d}}$. Therefore, the probability distribution in E is given by $|\Phi(E)|^2$, normalized to unit total probability:

$$W(E) = \frac{\Gamma/2\pi}{(m-E)^2+\frac{1}{4}\Gamma^2}. \tag{3.12}$$

This is the famous Breit-Wigner resonance form for the effective mass E.

It has a maximum $2(\pi\Gamma)^{-1}$ at $E = m$, and drops to half the maximum at $E = m\pm\frac{1}{2}\Gamma$. Hence, Γ is the width of the effective mass distribution. As mentioned at the end of section 2-2, this effect is unimportant for unstable particles, but important for resonances.

Before we continue, we make a slight change in the effective mass amplitude. Instead of (11), we use the so-called propagator,

$$\begin{aligned}\Phi(s_{\mathrm{d}}) &= \frac{1}{m^2-s_{\mathrm{d}}-im\Gamma}\\ &\approx \frac{1/(2m)}{m-E-\frac{1}{2}i\Gamma}+\frac{1/(2m)}{m+E-\frac{1}{2}i\Gamma} = \frac{1}{2m}\left[\Phi(E)+\Phi(-E)\right].\end{aligned} \tag{3.13}$$

This is almost the same as $\Phi(E)/(2m)$, since the contribution of the second term is negligible for E close to m. Later, $\Phi(s_{\mathrm{d}})$ will appear in expressions which are large even for E much smaller than m. There we shall motivate the change.

Using (13), we get the "relativistic" Breit-Wigner form,

$$W(s_{\mathrm{d}}) = \frac{m\Gamma/\pi}{(m^2-s_{\mathrm{d}})^2+m^2\Gamma^2}, \tag{3.14}$$

for the distribution of the square of the effective mass.

We now turn to the study of the over-all process, ab → c, 12. From (10), the equation for the corresponding T-matrices is

$$T = T(\mathrm{ab}\to\mathrm{cd})\cdot T(\mathrm{d}\to 1, 2)\cdot\Phi(s_{\mathrm{d}}). \tag{3.15}$$

We shall see below that the normalization is correct. The cross-section for the over-all process is obtained from (2.15),

$$\sigma = \frac{1}{4qs^{\frac{1}{2}}}\int |T(\mathrm{ab}\to\mathrm{cd})|^2|T(\mathrm{d}\to 1, 2)|^2\frac{\mathrm{d\,Lips}(s; P_{\mathrm{c}}, P_1, P_2)}{(m^2-s_{\mathrm{d}})^2+m^2\Gamma^2}. \tag{3.16}$$

Calling $P_{\mathrm{c}} = P_3$ and making use of the recurrence relation (1-7.5) for $\mathrm{d\,Lips}(s; P_1, P_2, P_3)$, we get

$$\begin{aligned}\sigma &= \frac{1}{4qs^{\frac{1}{2}}}\int |T(\mathrm{ab}\to\mathrm{cd})|^2\cdot\frac{\mathrm{d}s_{\mathrm{d}}}{2\pi}\mathrm{d\,Lips}(s; P_{\mathrm{c}}, P_{\mathrm{d}})\\ &\qquad\qquad\times\frac{|T(\mathrm{d}\to 1, 2)|^2\mathrm{d\,Lips}(s_{\mathrm{d}}; P_1, P_2)}{(m^2-s_{\mathrm{d}})^2+m^2\Gamma^2}\\ &= \int\frac{\mathrm{d}s_{\mathrm{d}}}{\pi}\sigma(\mathrm{ab}\to\mathrm{cd})\cdot\frac{m\Gamma(\mathrm{d}\to 1, 2)}{(m^2-s_{\mathrm{d}})^2+m^2\Gamma^2}.\end{aligned} \tag{3.17}$$

In these formulae, d stands for a particle of mass $s_d^{\frac{1}{2}}$. The last equation implies a redefinition of Γ:

$$\Gamma(\mathrm{d} \to 1, 2) = \frac{1}{2m} \int \mathrm{d\,Lips}(s_\mathrm{d}; P_1, P_2) |T(\mathrm{d} \to 1, 2)|^2. \tag{3.18}$$

Usually the difference between (18) and (3) is small. Only in decays where Γ is large but m is not much larger than $m_1 + m_2$ is it essential to have s_d and not its average value m^2 in d Lips. In these decays, Γ is thus not a constant but a function of the effective mass.

In $\sigma(\mathrm{ab} \to \mathrm{cd})$, we can usually replace s_d by m_d^2, in which case this factor may be put before the integral.

Equation (17) expresses the cross-section for a two-step reaction in terms of the observables of each single interaction. The result is easily generalized to more complicated reactions. Note that the width in the numerator is the partial width, whereas the width in the denominator, which comes from (13), is the total width. From the derivation it is clear that (17) is reliable only for small values of the total width.

Finally we show that for $\Gamma \to 0$, σ goes over into

$$\sigma(\mathrm{ab} \to \mathrm{c}, 1, 2) \approx \sigma(\mathrm{ab} \to \mathrm{cd}) \cdot \frac{\Gamma(\mathrm{d} \to 1, 2)}{\Gamma}. \tag{3.19}$$

The proof goes as follows:

$$\lim_{m\Gamma \to 0} \left\{ \int_{s_1}^{s_2} \frac{m\Gamma\,\mathrm{d}s/\pi}{(m^2 - s)^2 + m^2\Gamma^2} \right\} = \lim_{m\Gamma \to 0} \left\{ \frac{1}{\pi} \tan^{-1} \left(\frac{m^2 - s}{m\Gamma} \right) \right\}_{s_1}^{s_2}$$

$$= \begin{cases} 1 & \text{for } s_1 < s < s_2, \\ 0 & \text{otherwise.} \end{cases} \tag{3.20}$$

This shows that the limit of the integrand has the properties of a δ-function:

$$\lim_{m\Gamma \to 0} \left(\frac{m\Gamma/\pi}{(m^2 - s)^2 + m^2\Gamma^2} \right) = \delta(m^2 - s). \tag{3.21}$$

Insertion of this expression into (17) gives (19). From (19), we can now conclude that the normalization in (15) was correct.

It is customary to illustrate formulas like (15) by little diagrams. Particles are associated with arrows and interactions between particles with bubbles. Lines connecting two bubbles represent propagators of the type (13). At each bubble, the sums of the 4-momenta of incident and out-going particles are equal. The reaction ab → c, 1, 2 and its two-step approximation (15) are illustrated in fig. 2-3. These diagrams were invented by FEYNMAN [1949] in the context of perturbation theory. Roughly speaking, perturbation theory tries to reduce the interactions between any number of particles to successive interactions between a minimal number of particles, usually three (i.e. bubbles with three arrows, like $T(\mathrm{d} \to 1, 2)$). Nowadays, diagrams are used

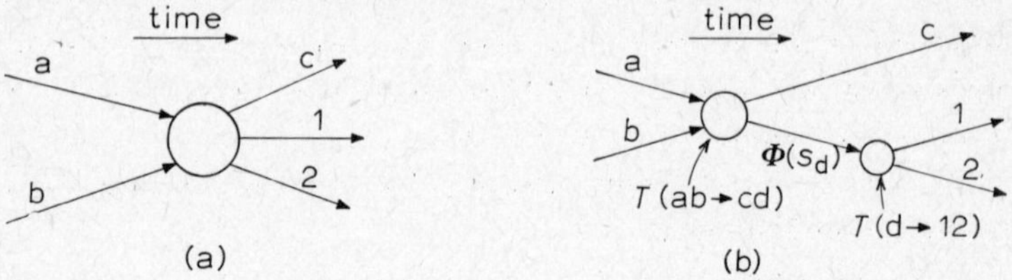

Fig. 2-3. Diagram of (a) reaction ab → c12, (b) its two-step approximation.

with different conventions for different purposes. We shall elaborate our type of diagrams in more detail in chapter 6. There we shall also obtain formulae similar to (15) from another point of view.

2-4. Unitarity and partial wave expansion

The partial wave expansion is a means of handling the unitarity of the S-matrix. In terms of T defined by (2.10), unitarity reads

$$-\mathrm{i}(T_{\mathrm{ii'}} - T^*_{\mathrm{i'i}}) = \sum \int \mathrm{d}\,\mathrm{Lips}(s;\mathrm{f}) T_{\mathrm{if}} T^*_{\mathrm{i'f}}, \tag{4.1}$$

where the sum extends over all channels, elastic and inelastic. For $\mathrm{i} = \mathrm{i}'$, i.e. elastic scattering at zero angle, (1) simplifies to

$$2\,\mathrm{Im}\, T_{\mathrm{ii}} = \sum \int \mathrm{d}\,\mathrm{Lips}(s;\mathrm{f}) |T_{\mathrm{if}}|^2 = 4qs^{\frac{1}{2}}\sigma_{\mathrm{i}}(\mathrm{total}), \tag{4.2}$$

according to (2.15). This is called the optical theorem. In general, (1) is a complicated non-linear integral equation. In this chapter we treat only the case where three- and more particle states can be neglected. The method is generalized later. As stated before, the two-particle amplitude $T_{\mathrm{if}}(s, \theta, \phi)$ is in fact independent of ϕ, apart from spin effects which are easily incorporated afterwards. Working in the cms, we transform (1) by means of the two-particle phase space (1-6.7) into

$$-\mathrm{i}[T_{\mathrm{if}}(\theta) - T^*_{\mathrm{fi}}(\theta)] = \sum_{\mathrm{c}} \frac{q_{\mathrm{c}}}{16\pi^2 s^{\frac{1}{2}}} \int \mathrm{d}\Omega'\, T_{\mathrm{ic}}(\theta') T^*_{\mathrm{fc}}(\theta''). \tag{4.3}$$

Here we have suppressed the argument s of T, since it is the same in all places. The indices i, f and c are now only channel indices, for instance $\mathrm{i} = \pi^+\pi^-$, $\mathrm{f} = \pi^+\pi^-$, $\mathrm{c} = \pi^+\pi^-$, and $\pi^0\pi^0$. We take meson-meson scattering because we have not yet introduced spin. This example is not the best one, not only because $\pi\pi$ collisions cannot be measured, but also because q_c is practically the same for $\pi^+\pi^-$ and $\pi^0\pi^0$. Later, when use is made of isospin invariance, no index in (3) is necessary as long as production of heavier mesons like K^0 can be neglected. The solid angle $\Omega' = (\theta', \phi')$ is that of the momentum in the intermediate state, and the second scattering angle θ'' is that between the intermediate momentum and the final momentum. It is given by

$$\cos\theta'' = \cos\theta\cos\theta' + \sin\theta\sin\theta'\cos(\phi-\phi'). \tag{4.4}$$

Our next step in exploiting unitarity is to expand $T(\theta)$ in terms of Legendre polynomials $P_L(x)$, $x = \cos\theta$:

$$\frac{1}{4\pi}T(\theta) = 2s^{\frac{1}{2}}\sum_{L=0}^{\infty}(2L+1)P_L(x)T_L, \tag{4.5}$$

where the complex numbers T_L depend on s but not on θ. They are called the partial wave amplitudes. The remaining factors have been chosen for later convenience.

The reason for choosing just Legendre polynomials in (5) is the following. Our aim is to decouple the unitarity equation (3) into a set of algebraic equations, one for each value of L. For that purpose we shall need two properties of P_L, namely the orthogonality relation

$$\int_{-1}^{1}\mathrm{d}x(L+\tfrac{1}{2})P_L(x)P_{L'}(x) = \delta_{LL'} \tag{4.6}$$

and the angular decomposition

$$\int \mathrm{d}\phi' P_L(x'') = 2\pi P_L(x)P_L(x'). \tag{4.7}$$

From (4), the latter requirement implies that $P_L(x)$ is a polynomial in $x = \cos\theta$, and we are free to specify that P_L should be a polynomial of degree L. This and the orthogonality relation (6) determines P_L completely (see A-1).

The final form of the unitarity equation for partial waves is

$$-\mathrm{i}[T_{\mathrm{if},L} - T^*_{\mathrm{fi},L}] = 2\sum_{\mathrm{c}} q_\mathrm{c} T_{\mathrm{ic},L} T^*_{\mathrm{fc},L}. \tag{4.8}$$

We derive it by inserting the expansion (5) into each of the T's occurring in (3):

$$-8\pi s^{\frac{1}{2}} \sum_{L_1} (2L_1+1)P_{L_1}(x)\mathrm{i}(T_{\mathrm{if},\,L_1} - T^*_{\mathrm{fi},\,L_1})$$

$$= \sum_{\mathrm{c}} \frac{4q_{\mathrm{c}}}{s^{\frac{1}{2}}} 2\pi \int \mathrm{d}x' [s^{\frac{1}{2}} \sum_{L'} (2L'+1)P_{L'}(x')T_{\mathrm{ic},\,L'}] \times [s^{\frac{1}{2}} \sum_{L} (2L+1)P_L(x)P_L(x')T^*_{\mathrm{fc},\,L}]$$

$$= 16\pi s^{\frac{1}{2}} \sum_{\mathrm{c}} q_{\mathrm{c}} \sum_{L} (2L+1)T_{\mathrm{ic},\,L} T^*_{\mathrm{fc},\,L} P_L(x). \tag{4.9}$$

Here we have used (7) in writing down the second expression, and (6) in writing down the last expression. Equation (8) is obtained by multiplying (9) with $P_L(x)$ and integrating over x. We find

$$T_L = \frac{1}{16\pi s^{\frac{1}{2}}} \int T(\theta) P_L(x)\,\mathrm{d}x. \tag{4.10}$$

A more elegant method of deriving (8) is to define the Legendre polynomials in terms of spherical harmonics Y_0^L, and then use the group properties of Y_M^L under rotations. We shall introduce this group-theoretical method in chapter 3.

If we are only interested in elastic scattering, we can drop the indices i and f in (8) and obtain

$$\mathrm{Im}\, T_L = \sum_{\mathrm{c}} q_{\mathrm{c}} T_{\mathrm{c},\,L} T^*_{\mathrm{c},\,L}. \tag{4.11}$$

In many collisions, only the elastic channel is open at low energies. Then (11) implies that T_L is of the form

$$T_L = \frac{1}{q}\mathrm{e}^{\mathrm{i}\delta_L} \sin\delta_L = \frac{1}{2\mathrm{i}q}(\mathrm{e}^{2\mathrm{i}\delta_L}-1) = \frac{1}{q}\,\frac{\tan\delta_L}{1-\mathrm{i}\tan\delta_L} = \frac{1}{q}\,\frac{1}{\cot\delta_L - \mathrm{i}}, \tag{4.12}$$

where δ_L is a real function of s, called the phase shift. We also define a partial wave S-matrix,

$$S_{\mathrm{if},\,L} = \delta_{\mathrm{if}} + 2\mathrm{i}T_{\mathrm{if},\,L}\sqrt{q_{\mathrm{i}}q_{\mathrm{f}}}. \tag{4.13}$$

As far as two-particle unitarity is concerned, this is now a proper, finite-dimensional matrix. If only the elastic channel is open, it is one-dimensional and, according to (12), it is $S_L = \exp(2\mathrm{i}\delta_L)$. In appendix B-1, we investigate the case of a symmetric S-matrix,

$$S_{\mathrm{if},\,L} = S_{\mathrm{fi},\,L}. \tag{4.14}$$

This symmetry condition can be imposed on the S-matrix as long as it is time-reversal invariant (see section 4-5).

We can express cross-sections directly in terms of partial wave amplitudes. Inserting (5) into (2.16), we get

$$\frac{d\sigma}{d\Omega} = \frac{q'}{q} \left| \sum_L (2L+1) P_L(\cos\theta) T_L \right|^2. \tag{4.15}$$

By means of the orthogonality relation (6), the integrated cross-section is the sum of the "partial-wave cross-sections",

$$\sigma = \sum_L \sigma_L = 4\pi \frac{q'}{q} \sum_L (2L+1) |T_L|^2. \tag{4.16}$$

In the "purely elastic" region, insertion of (12) gives

$$\sigma_L = \frac{4\pi}{q^2} (2L+1) \sin^2 \delta_L. \tag{4.17}$$

For practical calculations, the convergence of the partial-wave expansion (5) is of course important. The first few terms are usually enough, except for energies above one GeV and the elastic scattering of electrically-charged particles at very small angles (Coulomb scattering). One method of estimating the necessary number of terms is to exploit threshold behaviours, which will be discussed in section 2-6.

2-5. Potential scattering

In this section, we treat the purely elastic scattering of two particles by the well-known formalism of potential theory. We shall again arrive at (4.12) and (4.17). In addition, we shall express $\tan \delta_L$ in terms of quantities which will be useful in the parametrization of low-energy scattering, to be discussed in the following section. For this purpose, the fact that potential theory is non-relativistic is of no significance.

Arguments based on potential theory are frequently used in hadron physics. Potential theory has been called a laboratory for hadron theories. The book of De Alfaro and Regge [1965] on potential scattering, for example, contains several formalisms which have become famous models in the theory of elementary particles.

We take a central potential of the form $V(r)/2\mu$, where $\mu = m_1 m_2/(m_1+m_2)$ is the reduced mass. The Schrödinger equation has the form

$$-\nabla^2\psi + V(r)\psi = 2\mu E\psi, \tag{5.1}$$

where $E = q^2/2\mu$ is the total kinetic energy in the cms. The solutions of (1) are expanded in terms of Legendre polynomials:

$$\psi(r, \theta) = \frac{1}{r} \sum_L u_L(r) P_L(x), \tag{5.2}$$

where $u_L(r)$ is the solution of the radial equation

$$u_L'' + \left[q^2 - V(r) - \frac{1}{r^2} L(L+1)\right] u_L = 0. \tag{5.3}$$

We assume that V has a finite range R, i.e. $V(r > R) = 0$. For $r \gg R$, u_L must then be of the form

$$u_L(r) = a_L \frac{1}{q} \sin (qr - \tfrac{1}{2}\pi L + \delta_L); \tag{5.4}$$

where δ_L is the phase shift. The normalization factor a_L/q and the phase $-\frac{1}{2}\pi L$ are included for later convenience. In the same region $r \gg R$, $\psi(r, \theta)$ has the form

$$\psi(r, \theta) = \mathrm{e}^{\mathrm{i}qz} + \mathrm{e}^{\mathrm{i}qr} \frac{1}{r} f(\theta). \tag{5.5}$$

Here the incident plane wave has been taken along the z-axis. It can also be expanded in terms of Legendre polynomials

$$\mathrm{e}^{\mathrm{i}qz} = \frac{1}{qr} \sum_L \mathrm{i}^L (2L+1) \sin (qr - \tfrac{1}{2}\pi L) P_L(x) \quad \text{for} \quad r \to \infty. \tag{5.6}$$

Comparing this with expansions (2), with $u_L(r)$ given by (4), a_L may be determined. We find

$$a_L = \mathrm{i}^L (2L+1) \mathrm{e}^{\mathrm{i}\delta_L}, \qquad f(\theta) = \frac{1}{2\mathrm{i}q} \sum_L (2L+1)(\mathrm{e}^{2\mathrm{i}\delta_L} - 1) P_L(x). \tag{5.7}$$

Comparison with (4.12) and (4.5) shows that

$$f(\theta) = \frac{1}{2s^{\frac{1}{2}}} \frac{1}{4\pi} T(s, \theta), \tag{5.8}$$

and that the phase shifts defined in (4) and (4.12) are identical. The differential cross-section of potential scattering is given by

$$\mathrm{d}\sigma = |f(\theta)|^2 \mathrm{d}\Omega, \tag{5.9}$$

in good agreement with (8) and (2.16). Since we have only considered the region where the potential vanishes, we have only used properties which are also used in S-matrix theory.

Now we drop the requirement $r \gg R$. Then the solution of (3) for $r > R$ (where we have $V = 0$) is a combination of spherical Bessel and Neuman functions (A-3):

$$\frac{1}{ra_L} u_L(r) = j_L(qr) \cos \delta_L + n_L(qr) \sin \delta_L . \tag{5.10}$$

The phase shift can be expressed in terms of the logarithmic derivative of the radial function u/r,

$$\frac{r}{u} \frac{\mathrm{d}}{\mathrm{d}r}\left(\frac{u}{r}\right) = \frac{\dfrac{\mathrm{d}}{\mathrm{d}r} j(qr) + \tan \delta \dfrac{\mathrm{d}}{\mathrm{d}r} n(qr)}{j(qr) + \tan \delta \; n(qr)} . \tag{5.11}$$

We shall see in the next section that we get most information if we take r as small as possible, i.e. $r = R$. We define

$$g_L \equiv \frac{R^2}{u_L} \left[\frac{\mathrm{d}}{\mathrm{d}r}\left(\frac{u_L(r)}{r}\right)\right]_{r=R}, \qquad qR \equiv \rho \tag{5.12}$$

and get from (11)

$$\tan \delta = \frac{\rho j'(\rho) - g j(\rho)}{g n(\rho) - \rho n'(\rho)} = \frac{j(\rho)}{n(\rho)} \frac{\rho \dfrac{j'(\rho)}{j(\rho)} - g}{g - \rho \dfrac{n'(\rho)}{n(\rho)}} . \tag{5.13}$$

This equation will be the starting point of several approximations.

2-6. Threshold behaviour of partial wave amplitudes

Let us assume that somehow we can estimate the range R of an interaction. Then we have a region at small q in which $\rho = qR \ll L$. Here we can use the asymptotic expressions (A-3) for the spherical Bessel and Neuman functions, which give

$$\rho \frac{j_L'}{j_L} = L, \qquad \rho \frac{n_L'}{n_L} = -L-1. \tag{6.1}$$

Expression (5.13) becomes

$$\tan \delta_L(\rho) = \frac{L - g_L(\rho)}{L+1+g_L(\rho)} \frac{\rho^{2L+1}}{(2L+1)!!(2L-1)!!} \qquad \text{for} \quad \rho \ll L. \tag{6.2}$$

The logarithmic derivative $g_L(\rho)$ is a smooth function of ρ which varies very little in the small interval $0 < \rho \ll L$. It can happen that $g_L(\rho)$ is close to or equal to $L+1$, in which case $\tan \delta_L$ may be infinite. This is the case with resonances. It will be discussed later. For $g_L(\rho) \neq L+1$ for all $\rho \ll L$, we can approximate the first factor of (2) by a constant. We thus have

$$\tan \delta_L(qR \ll L) = A_L q^{2L+1}, \tag{6.3}$$

where A_L is called the scattering length. Notice that it has the dimension of a length only for $L = 0$. In the phenomenological analysis of scattering data, it is sometimes useful to go one step further by means of the effective range expansion,

$$q^{2L+1} \cot \delta_L = A_L^{-1} + \tfrac{1}{2} q^2 B_L, \tag{6.4}$$

where B_L is called the effective range. We shall not discuss here why one expands $\cot \delta$ and not e.g. $\tan \delta$. The important thing is that terms linear in q do not appear in the expansion, simply because the differential equation (5.3) depends on q^2 only.

The second factor in (2) can be understood as a penetration factor, caused by the "centrifugal potential" $L(L+1)/r^2$ of (5.3). Inserting (3) into (4.12), we get the low-energy behaviour of the scattering amplitude,

$$T_L(qR \ll L) = q^{2L} \frac{A_L}{1 - \mathrm{i} A_L q^{2L+1}} \,. \tag{6.5}$$

Now we leave potential theory and elastic scattering and try to find something similar in general two-particle reactions. First, we study cases in which the θ-dependence of $T_{\mathrm{if}}(\theta)$ is given by a single pole in the momentum transfer t, $(\mu^2 - t)^{-1}$ say, where μ^2 is called the position of the pole (which has nothing to do with the reduced mass of the previous section). We assume that μ^2 is positive. The origin of such poles will be discussed in chapter 6. Introducing the variable

$$z = \frac{1}{qq'} [E_\mathrm{b} E_\mathrm{d} - \tfrac{1}{2}(m_\mathrm{b}^2 + m_\mathrm{d}^2 - \mu^2)] = \frac{1}{qq'} [E_\mathrm{a} E_\mathrm{c} - \tfrac{1}{2}(m_\mathrm{a}^2 + m_\mathrm{c}^2 - \mu^2)], \tag{6.6}$$

we can write (1-3.7) in the form

$$t = \mu^2 - 2qq'(z - x). \tag{6.7}$$

The partial wave decomposition of the pole is now

$$\frac{1}{\mu^2 - t} = \frac{1}{2qq'} \frac{1}{z - x} = \frac{1}{2qq'} \sum_{L=0}^{\infty} (2L+1) P_L(x) Q_L(z), \tag{6.8}$$

where $Q_L(z)$ are the Legendre functions of the second kind defined in (A-2). When s is near the threshold for the reaction under consideration, q' is very small, z is large and $Q_L(z)$ goes like $(qq')^{L+1}$. We thus find

$$T_{\text{if}, L}(z \gg 1) = (qq')^L A_{\text{if}, L} . \tag{6.9}$$

The most general amplitude $T_{\text{if}}(s, \theta)$ can be expanded as a series of poles in t at various positions:

$$T_{\text{if}}(s, \theta) = \sum_i \frac{c_i(s)}{t - \mu_i^2} . \tag{6.10}$$

In that case, $T_{\text{if}, L}$ is a sum of terms like (9). Each position μ_i^2 gives a value z_i. The smallest μ_i^2 gives the smallest z_i and therefore determines the limit of validity of (9). For $\mu^2 = 0$ (Coulomb scattering), the expansion (8) does not converge. The important physical assumption which has to be made in the derivation of (9) is of course that the coefficients $c_i(s)$ do not increase rapidly for $q' \to 0$. Later we shall see that this is indeed not the case, unless there is a resonance near $q' = 0$.

If we now specialize to elastic scattering and compare (9) with (5), we see that we have only the leading term. The reason is that we have neglected unitarity. Whereas (5) leads to $|S_L| = 1$ for arbitrary real values of A_L, (9) certainly does not. Therefore, for purely elastic scattering, (5) is the "unitary version" of (9). In the inelastic region, unitarity is a matrix equation, and things are more complicated. We shall come back to this point.

For elastic scattering, we have

$$z = \frac{q^2 + \frac{1}{2}\mu^2}{q^2} \approx \frac{\mu^2}{2q^2} . \tag{6.11}$$

It is customary to call

$$R = 1/\mu \tag{6.12}$$

the range of the interaction, in which case we have $\rho^2 = 1/(2z)$ in the non-relativistic approximation. Previously we had defined R as the smallest radius for which the potential is zero. Actually, the two R's are of the same order of magnitude, even if they are not the same. The various μ_i of (10) will be identified with masses or effective masses of hadrons. Since the pion is the lightest hadron, the range (12) cannot be larger than m_π^{-1}. This gives rise to the frequently used phrase, the range of strong interactions is of the order of one pion Compton wavelength. Strictly speaking, this is a misuse of concepts of potential theory.

2-7. Phase shifts in the presence of inelastic channels

In this section we extend the phase shift formalism to the inelastic region. Our starting point is (4.11), which we rewrite in the form

$$\operatorname{Im} T_L = q|T_L|^2 + \sum_r q_r |T_{r,L}|^2. \tag{7.1}$$

The index r runs over the "reaction" channels, i.e. all channels except the elastic one. In terms of the S-matrix elements (4.13), (1) reads as follows:

$$\operatorname{Re}(1-S_L) = \tfrac{1}{2}|S_L-1|^2 + \tfrac{1}{2}\sum_r |S_{r,L}|^2. \tag{7.2}$$

Here again, we mean by S_L not the whole matrix, but only that matrix element which refers to elastic scattering. It can be parametrized in the form

$$S_L = \eta_L e^{2i\delta_L}, \tag{7.3}$$

with positive η_L and real δ_L. Insertion of (3) into (2) gives

$$1-\eta_L \cos 2\delta_L = \tfrac{1}{2}(1+\eta_L^2-2\eta_L \cos 2\delta_L)+\tfrac{1}{2}\sum_r |S_{r,L}|^2,$$

$$\eta_L^2 = 1-\sum_r |S_{r,L}|^2 = 1-4q\sum_r q_r|T_{r,L}|^2. \tag{7.4}$$

Since the sum of $|S_r|^2$ cannot be larger than one, it follows that η lies between zero and one. The partial-wave cross-sections are now expressed as

$$\sigma_L(\text{elastic}) = 4\pi(2L+1)|T_L|^2 = \frac{\pi}{q^2}(2L+1)|1-\eta_L e^{2i\delta_L}|^2, \tag{7.5}$$

$$\sigma_L(\text{reaction}) = \frac{4\pi}{q}(2L+1)\sum_r q_r|T_{r,L}|^2 = \frac{\pi}{q^2}(2L+1)(1-\eta_L^2). \tag{7.6}$$

The sum of these two gives the total partial-wave cross-section

$$\sigma_L(\text{total}) = \frac{2\pi}{q^2}(2L+1)(1-\eta_L \cos 2\delta_L), \tag{7.7}$$

which reduces to (4.17) for $\eta_L = 1$. For obvious reasons, η_L is called the inelasticity coefficient. Instead of (3) one can also use a complex phase shift:

$$\eta_L = e^{-2\operatorname{Im}\delta_L}, \qquad \operatorname{Im}\delta_L \geqq 0. \tag{7.8}$$

Another useful relation is obtained if we eliminate from (1) $|T_L|^2$ and $|T_{r,L}|^2$

in favour of the partial-wave cross-sections,

$$\operatorname{Im} T_L = \frac{q}{4\pi(2L+1)} \sigma_L(\text{total}). \tag{7.9}$$

This is a kind of optical theorem for partial waves.

If there are just two channels, we can write down the S-matrix explicitly,

$$S_L = \begin{bmatrix} \eta_L e^{2i\delta_L{}^{(1)}} & i\sqrt{1-\eta_L^2}\, e^{i(\delta_L{}^{(1)}+\delta_L{}^{(2)}+\gamma_L)} \\ i\sqrt{1-\eta_L^2}\, e^{i(\delta_L{}^{(1)}+\delta_L{}^{(2)}-\gamma_L)} & \eta_L e^{2i\delta_L{}^{(2)}} \end{bmatrix}. \tag{7.10}$$

For the symmetric S-matrix (4.14), γ_L vanishes.

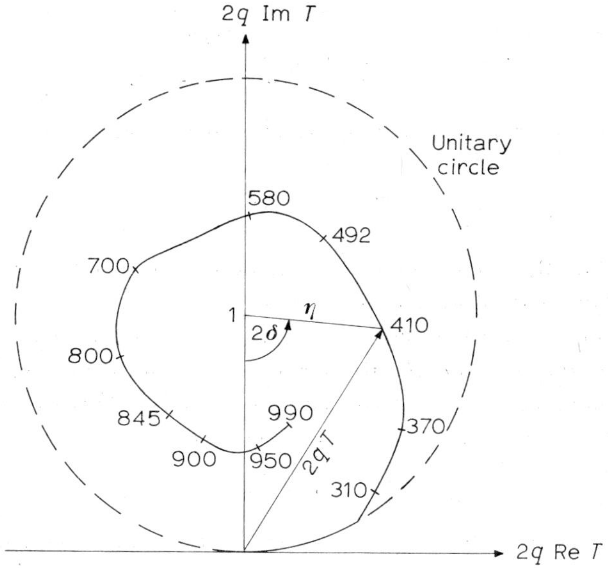

Fig. 2-7. Argand diagram of the P_{11} matrix element for elastic πN scattering, after BAREYRE *et al.* [1965]. The numbers on the curve give the pion lab kinetic energy in MeV.

A graphical representation of $2qT_L$ as a function of energy is given in the Argand plot (see fig. 2-7. The symbol P_{11} means a P-wave, i.e. $L = 1$. Further details are given in section 7-9.). In the elastic region we have $\eta = 1$, and T_L lies on the "unitary circle", according to (4.12). When inelastic reactions begin to contribute, $2qT$ goes inside the circle. The distance from the centre of the circle is given by η.

2-8. Resonance scattering

Consider first the partial wave amplitude $T_L(s)$ in the purely elastic region, where (4.12) applies. We say that we have a resonance if $\cot \delta_L$ goes through zero for some value of s, with a negative derivative. We make the ansatz

$$\cot \delta_L = (m^2 - s)/m\Gamma, \qquad \Gamma > 0, \tag{8.1}$$

where m is called the position or the mass of the resonance and Γ the width. Insertion of (1) into (4.12) gives

$$T_L(s) = \frac{1}{q}\,\frac{1}{\cot \delta_L - \mathrm{i}} = \frac{m\Gamma/q}{m^2 - s - \mathrm{i}m\Gamma}. \tag{8.2}$$

Inserting this into (4.16) and neglecting the other partial waves, we get

$$\sigma_{\text{res}}(s) = 4\pi(2L+1)\frac{m^2\Gamma^2/q^2}{(m^2-s)^2 + m^2\Gamma^2}. \tag{8.3}$$

At resonance energy, the partial-wave cross-section becomes

$$\sigma_{\text{res}}(m^2) = \frac{4\pi}{q^2}(2L+1), \tag{8.4}$$

which is called the unitary limit, since according to (4.17) this is the absolute maximum of a partial-wave cross-section.

The reason why we have chosen once more the symbols m and Γ is that, for small Γ, they have exactly the meaning of the mass and inverse lifetime of an unstable particle, as discussed in section 2-3. This follows directly from the fact that (2) may be written in the form

$$T_L(s) = \Phi(s) \cdot m\Gamma/q, \tag{8.5}$$

where the propagator $\Phi(s)$ is given by (3.13). For example, the uncertainty relation $\Delta E \Delta t = 1$ applied to (5) shows that resonance scattering requires a time interval of the order of Γ^{-1}.

Now let us see if we can learn something more about Γ from potential theory. We can construct a spherical incoming wave packet. Then we can calculate the time delay between the outgoing scattered and unscattered wave packets from the phase shift by means of (5.5), (5.6) and (5.7). It turns out to be Γ^{-1}, which is plausible in view of the uncertainty relation. From this, we can derive an interesting restriction on Γ (WIGNER [1955]). It is possible that the scattered spherical wave comes earlier than the unscattered spherical wave, in which case Γ^{-1} would be negative. Due to causality, however, the scattered wave cannot leave the interaction region $r < R$ before the original wave enters it. The time which the unscattered wave needs to pass through the scattering region is $R/2v$, where $v = q/\mu$ is the velocity. Therefore causality requires

$$\frac{1}{\Gamma} \geqq -\frac{R}{2v}. \tag{8.6}$$

Thus, if Γ is negative, its magnitude has to be larger than $2v/R$. In that case, the cross-section (3) shows no drastic variation with energy, and the phenomenon is not called a resonance. This is the reason for the requirement $\Gamma > 0$ in (1).

Next, we try to calculate the energy dependence of Γ in potential theory. Our basic assumption is again that the logarithmic derivative g_L is a slowly varying function of q^2. Then the zero of the denominator of (5.13) determines the position of the resonance, and the derivative of g_L with respect to s at $s = m^2$ determines the width. For $\rho \ll L$, we find from (6.2)

$$m\Gamma = \frac{(qR)^{2L+1}}{\left(\dfrac{\mathrm{d}g}{\mathrm{d}s}\right)_{s=m^2} [(2L-1)!!]^2}. \tag{8.7}$$

This shows that the threshold behaviour of $\tan \delta_L$ is not completely destroyed by a resonance; it is only modified by a factor $(m^2 - s)^{-1}$. Thus, taking the width independent of energy would be a bad approximation for a resonance close to threshold.

2-9. Multichannel resonances

Many resonances appear in more than one channel. The general multichannel formalism is developed in chapter 8, but the case of one single resonance is so simple that we treat it already here.

As discussed in appendix B-1, the S_L-matrix defined in (4.13) is diagonalized by a unitary matrix. Assuming time-reversal invariance, this matrix is in fact real. We shall denote it by C. Since S is unitary, its eigenvalues are of the form $\mathrm{e}^{2\mathrm{i}\delta}$, where these δ are called the "eigenphases". The physical S-matrix is then of the form

$$S_{\mathrm{if}} = \sum_{\alpha} \mathrm{e}^{2\mathrm{i}\delta_\alpha} C_{\mathrm{i}\alpha} C_{\mathrm{f}\alpha} \tag{9.1}$$

for each angular momentum L. Due to the orthogonality of the coefficients $C_{i\alpha}$,

$$\sum_{\alpha} C_{i\alpha} C_{f\alpha} = \delta_{if}, \tag{9.2}$$

we can write T_{if} as

$$T_{if} = \frac{1}{2i(q_i q_f)^{\frac{1}{2}}} \left(\sum_{\alpha} e^{2i\delta_\alpha} C_{i\alpha} C_{f\alpha} - \delta_{if} \right) = \frac{1}{2i(q_i q_f)^{\frac{1}{2}}} \sum_{\alpha} C_{i\alpha} C_{f\alpha} (e^{2i\delta_\alpha} - 1)$$

$$= \frac{1}{(q_i q_f)^{\frac{1}{2}}} \sum_{\alpha} \frac{C_{i\alpha} C_{f\alpha}}{\cot \delta_\alpha - i} . \tag{9.3}$$

A multichannel resonance is now defined as a resonance in one of the eigenchannels α. Position and width of the resonance are again defined by $\cot \delta_{\alpha_{res}} = (m^2 - s)/m\Gamma$. Let us assume that the eigenphases in all other eigenchannels are negligible. Dropping the index α_{res}, we find

$$T_{if} = \frac{1}{(q_i q_f)^{\frac{1}{2}}} \frac{m\Gamma C_i C_f}{m^2 - s - im\Gamma} = \pm \left(\frac{\Gamma_i \Gamma_f}{q_i q_f} \right)^{\frac{1}{2}} \frac{m}{m^2 - s - im\Gamma} . \tag{9.4}$$

Here we have defined the partial decay widths

$$\Gamma_i = \Gamma C_i^2, \qquad \sum_i \Gamma_i = \Gamma. \tag{9.5}$$

The last equation follows from the orthonormality of the coefficients $C_{i\alpha}$, summed over i.

In the following, we consider only the elastic channel, the partial width of which is denoted by Γ_e. For this channel, (4) is simplified to

$$T = \frac{m\Gamma_e/q}{m^2 - s - im\Gamma}, \tag{9.6}$$

which is similar to (8.2). The elasticity of a resonance is defined as $x = \Gamma_e/\Gamma$. This quantity is often almost independent of s in the interval $-m\Gamma < s - m^2 < m\Gamma$. In such cases, the absolute value of

$$2qT - ix = -ix \left(\frac{m^2 - s + im\Gamma}{m^2 - s - im\Gamma} \right) \tag{9.7}$$

is independent of s in the resonance region, which means that $2qT$ traces a circle of radius x around ix (see fig. 2-9). For $x = 1$, this is the unitary circle. Unfortunately, x is not the same as the inelasticity coefficient η of (7.3). Constant η also gives a circle, but with i as centre.

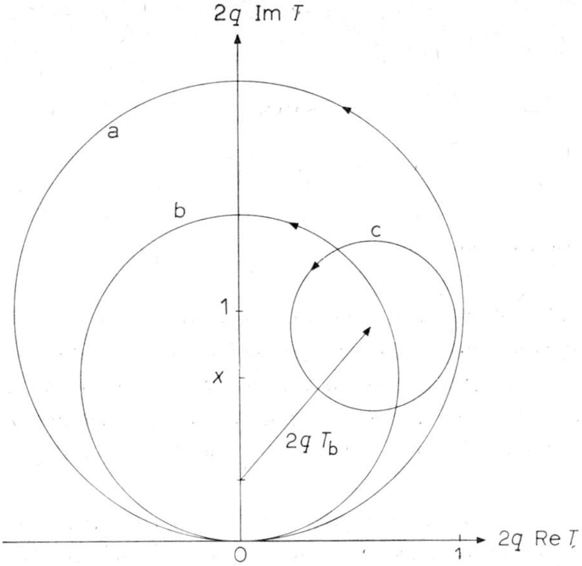

Fig. 2-9. Circles described by resonating partial wave amplitudes; (a) purely elastic resonance, $x = 1$; (b) multichannel resonance, $x < 1$; (c) multichannel resonance, $x < \frac{1}{2}$, including a non-resonant amplitude T_b.

For $x > \frac{1}{2}$ the resonance occurs at $\delta = \frac{1}{2}\pi$. Resonances with $x < \frac{1}{2}$ are sometimes called inelastic resonances. They usually occur at rather high energies. In such cases, the scattering from the non-resonant eigenchannels $\alpha \neq \alpha_{res}$ is no longer negligible. Then one has

$$2qT = 2q(T_b + T_{res}). \tag{9.8}$$

If the background scattering T_b varies slowly with s, then $2qT$ still describes a circle, the centre of which is now shifted to $ix + 2qT_b$. The maximum of $q|T|$, i.e. the "position" of the resonance, now occurs at some odd value of δ_L. Remember that all these equations refer to partial-wave amplitudes. At high energies, many partial waves contribute to the cross-sections. Consequently, the influence of inelastic resonances on cross-sections may be quite small.

CHAPTER 3

SPIN

3-1. Degeneracy of spin states

In this and the following section, we briefly review some basic properties of non-relativistic spin. Then we construct relativistic spin states for spins $\frac{1}{2}$, 1, $\frac{3}{2}$ and 2, and write down Lorentz invariant matrix elements between these states. Pions and kaons are spinless, while nucleons and hyperons have spin $\frac{1}{2}$. Relativistic states of spin 1, $\frac{3}{2}$ and 2 are needed for some of the resonances.

In the last two sections of this chapter, we discuss the partial wave decomposition of meson-nucleon scattering in terms of helicity states. There we construct explicitly matrix elements between total angular momentum eigenstates, in a way which avoids a general discussion of the relativistic extension of the non-relativistic operators $\boldsymbol{S}$, $\boldsymbol{J}$ and $\boldsymbol{L}$ for spin, total and orbital angular momentum. The partial wave decomposition of photoproduction, nucleon-nucleon scattering and more complicated reactions is deferred to later chapters.

As mentioned before, all hadrons except the proton are unstable. The neutron, for example, undergoes the well-known β-decay $\mathrm{n} \to \mathrm{pe}\nu$, whereas the Λ-hyperon, which is a kind of heavy neutron, decays mainly into $\mathrm{n}\pi^0$ and $\mathrm{p}\pi^-$. The first indication about the spin of a hadron usually comes from the observation of its decay angular distribution. By this, one means the fact that the decay probability may depend on the orientation of the momenta of the decay products with respect to the production plane. To be specific, we consider the production reaction $\mathrm{ab} \to \mathrm{cd}$, and the two decay modes $\mathrm{d} \to 12$ and $\mathrm{d} \to 123$. In the rest frame of particle d, the momenta $\boldsymbol{p}_\mathrm{a}$, $\boldsymbol{p}_\mathrm{b}$ and $\boldsymbol{p}_\mathrm{c}$ are sufficient to define a right-handed coordinate system (see fig. 3-1. Notice that the normal to the production plane is the same as in fig. 1-3). The orientation of $\mathrm{d} \to 1, 2$ is now fixed by two angles, for example the polar angle ϑ and the azimuth φ of $\boldsymbol{p}_1$ in this coordinate system. The angles of $\boldsymbol{p}_2$ are then $\pi - \vartheta$ and $\varphi + \pi$. The orientation of $\mathrm{d} \to 1, 2, 3$ is fixed by three angles, for example the polar and azimuthal angles of the normal to the decay plane, and an angle in the decay plane. (For a discussion of the three Euler angles, see e.g. GOLDSTEIN [1951], EDMONDS [1957], ROSE [1957].) We shall not really need these angles. The orientation of an n-particle decay relative to the production coordinate system is also determined by three angles, e.g. the three Euler angles of a Cartesian coordinate system fixed by three of the decay momenta. In addition, there are the relative

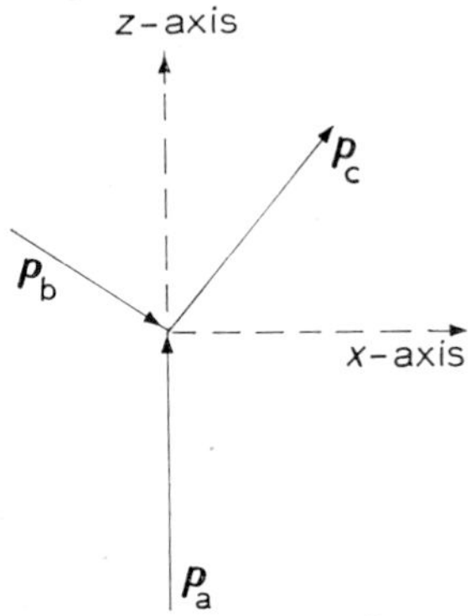

Fig. 3-1. Definition of a coordinate system in the rest frame of particle d. We have $p_{c,y} = 0$ and $p_{c,x} > 0$ as in fig. 1-3.

angles between the decay momenta, for example the angle θ_{12} of (1-8.4). These angles are however independent of the orientation of the decay system as a whole.

Let us now introduce the symbol Ω' for the two or three angles specifying the orientation of the decay system. Then $\mathrm{d}\,\mathrm{Lips}(s_\mathrm{d}; P_1, \ldots, P_n)/\mathrm{d}\Omega'$ is independent of Ω' (see e.g. (1-8.7) for $n = 3$). Since the decay matrix element $T(\mathrm{d} \to 1, \ldots, n)$ in the d rest frame is also independent of the directions of $\boldsymbol{p}_\mathrm{a}$, $\boldsymbol{p}_\mathrm{b}$ and $\boldsymbol{p}_\mathrm{c}$, it follows that the decay probability should be independent of Ω', i.e. completely isotropic. Experiment, however, shows correlations for particles such as n and Λ. We therefore conclude that our description of free states for these particles is incomplete.

The same conclusion can be drawn in the case of the proton from the azimuthal dependence of the scattering of polarized protons. (Remember our reasoning about the angle ϕ in section 2-4.) We clearly have to invent one-particle states which contain orientation also for zero momentum. The concept is, of course, well-known: it is called spin. A particle with spin S has an internal degree of freedom, called the magnetic quantum number M, which may assume $2S+1$ different values. (Unfortunately, we have to use capital letters, because the symbols s and m are already used up.)

We now review the main properties of the spin states of a particle at rest. Our coordinate system is defined by the momenta $\boldsymbol{p}_a$, $\boldsymbol{p}_b$ and $\boldsymbol{p}_c$. Let $|M\rangle$ and $|M, \alpha\beta\gamma\rangle$ denote two states with the same internal quantum number M, but with different orientations. ("Quantization" along different directions in a fixed coordinate system.) By $\alpha\beta\gamma$ we mean the Euler angles of the second orientation with respect to the first. For some values of M, we must have $|M, \alpha\beta\gamma\rangle \neq |M\rangle$, otherwise the decay would be isotropic. We now expand $|M, \alpha\beta\gamma\rangle$ in terms of the complete set of states,

$$|M, \alpha\beta\gamma\rangle = \sum_{M'} D_{M'M}(\alpha\beta\gamma)|M'\rangle. \tag{1.1}$$

The matrices D form a representation of the rotation group. We can put such matrices into reduced form by means of a unitary transformation (see appendix B). We therefore restrict the discussion to irreducible D-matrices. For such matrices, we can prove that all $2S+1$ states $|d_M\rangle$ have the same mass. Consider the free-particle Hamiltonian H_{free}, with matrix elements $H_{MM'}$ between d-particle states. Since H_{free} does not depend on the orientation with respect to the coordinate system (defined by the "external" momenta $\boldsymbol{p}_a$, $\boldsymbol{p}_b$ and $\boldsymbol{p}_c$), it commutes with $D(\alpha\beta\gamma)$ for any values of the Euler angles. Now Schurs' lemma (B-3) says that a matrix which commutes with an irreducible set of matrices is a multiple of the unit matrix. We thus have

$$(H_{\text{free}})_{MM'} = (m - \tfrac{1}{2}\mathrm{i}\Gamma)\delta_{MM'}, \tag{1.2}$$

which is the desired result. We have taken H_{free} as a non-Hermitean matrix to obtain the M-independence of the width Γ at the same time. In addition, from eq. (11) below, we shall find by a definition similar to (2-2.3) that all partial and certain differential widths are independent of the magnetic quantum number.

It can, of course, happen that H_{free} is a multiple of the unit matrix also for the sum of two or more irreducible representations. This is called accidental degeneracy. Note also that, e.g. in a bubble chamber, we should incorporate the magnetic field in H_{free}, in which case (2) is not strictly valid (Zeeman effect).

The irreducible D-matrices are discussed in appendix C. Here we just mention the decomposition,

$$D(\alpha\beta\gamma) = \mathrm{e}^{-\mathrm{i}\alpha J_z}\mathrm{e}^{-\mathrm{i}\beta J_y}\mathrm{e}^{-\mathrm{i}\gamma J_z}, \tag{1.3}$$

where J_z and J_y together with a third matrix J_x form the angular momentum matrix vector $\boldsymbol{J}$. For a single particle at rest, $\boldsymbol{J}$ is called the spin operator.

The fact that the different magnetic states of a particle have the same mass and lifetime has some peculiar consequences. In our derivation of the T-matrix element (2-3.15) for the over-all process ab → c, 1, . . ., n, we started from the factorization of the S-matrix into one matrix for production ab → cd and another one for decay d → 1, . . ., n. This matrix product implies a summation over all possible intermediate states. Up to now, we have had only one intermediate state, namely the one called d. In general, we may have N states d_i of masses m_i and widths Γ_i. Then we must replace (2-3.15) by

$$T = \sum_{i=1}^{N} T(\mathrm{ab} \to \mathrm{cd}_i)T(\mathrm{d}_i \to 1, \ldots, n)\Phi_i(s_\mathrm{d}),$$
$$\Phi_i = (m_i^2 - s_\mathrm{d} - i m_i \Gamma_i)^{-1}. \tag{1.4}$$

This formula is needed e.g. in the discussion of decay interference between two unstable particles of slightly different masses. (If the masses are very different, then all Φ_i except the one with m_i^2 closest to s_d will be negligible.) In the case of spin, we have $2S_\mathrm{d}+1$ states of equal masses and lifetimes, and (4) is rewritten as

$$T = \Phi(s_\mathrm{d}) \sum_{M=-S_\mathrm{d}}^{+S_\mathrm{d}} T(\mathrm{ab} \to \mathrm{cd}_M)T(\mathrm{d}_M \to 1, \ldots, n). \tag{1.5}$$

The differential cross-section $d\sigma(\mathrm{ab} \to \mathrm{c}, 1, \ldots, n)$ for the over-all process is proportional to the absolute square of (4) or (5). Unlike the case of a single intermediate state (2–3.16), it is not simply the product of one production probability and one decay probability. Instead, the absolute square of (5) is

$$|T|^2 = \frac{1}{(m^2 - s_\mathrm{d})^2 + m^2\Gamma^2} \sum_{M, M'} X_{MM'},$$
$$X_{MM'} = T(\mathrm{ab} \to \mathrm{cd}_M)T^*(\mathrm{ab} \to \mathrm{cd}_{M'})T(\mathrm{d}_M \to 1, \ldots, n)T^*(\mathrm{d}_{M'} \to 1, \ldots, n). \tag{1.6}$$

The double sum can be rewritten as the trace of a matrix product. Defining the matrices

$$R(\mathrm{prod})_{MM'} = T(\mathrm{ab} \to \mathrm{cd}_M)T^*(\mathrm{ab} \to \mathrm{cd}_{M'}),$$
$$R(\mathrm{decay})_{MM'} = T(\mathrm{d}_M \to 1, \ldots, n)T^*(\mathrm{d}_{M'} \to 1, \ldots, n), \tag{1.7}$$

(6) is rewritten as

$$|T|^2 = \frac{1}{(m^2-s_d)^2+m^2\Gamma^2} \sum_{MM'} R(\text{prod})_{MM'} R(\text{decay})_{MM'}$$

$$= \frac{1}{(m^2-s_d)^2+m^2\Gamma^2} \text{ trace } [R(\text{prod})R^*(\text{decay})]. \tag{1.8}$$

The trace of each R-matrix is of the form $\sum_M |T(M)|^2$. It is usually known beforehand. The differential cross-section for ab → cd for example is given by a slight generalization of (2-2.16), namely

$$d\sigma(\text{ab} \to \text{cd}) = \frac{\pi}{4q^2 s} \sum_{M_d} \left| \frac{T(s, t, M_d)}{4\pi} \right|^2 dt. \tag{1.9}$$

Since particle d is unstable, it is usually obtained by formula (2-3.19), which we have not proven yet in the case of spin. There is however another method of measuring $d\sigma(\text{ab} \to \text{cd})$, namely by carefully measuring the momenta of particles a, b, and c. Then one can infer the momentum of particle d by energy-momentum conservation, without looking at the decay products $1, \ldots, n$. This method is called the missing mass method. It is independent of the decay modes of particle d. Since the magnetic quantum number is not observed, one has to sum in (9) over all possible values of M_d.

Knowing the trace of R(prod), we now define the production *density matrix* ($M = M_d$)

$$\rho(s, t)_{MM'} = [\sum_M |T(s, t, M)|^2]^{-1} R(\text{prod})_{MM'}, \tag{1.10}$$

which has unit trace. Similarly, we can define a decay density matrix as (7) divided by a normalization constant C. In order to define this constant, let Ω' again denote the two or three angles which determine the orientation of the decay system, and let ξ denote all other variables of the decay. (In two-particle decay, there is no other variable, whereas in three-particle decay, there are two, for example p_1 and θ_{12} or E_1 and E_2, as discussed in section 1-8.) Then one can prove that

$$\int d\Omega' R(\Omega', \xi)_{MM'} = C(\xi)\delta_{MM'}, \quad C(\xi) \equiv \int d\Omega' |T(d_M \to 1, \ldots, n)|^2. \tag{1.11}$$

This follows from (1) and the orthogonality relations of the D-functions. The proof is complicated by the fact that (11) is an integral over two (three) angles for $n = 2$ ($n > 2$). We therefore omit it here. The case $n = 2$ is discussed explicitly in later sections. Instead, we derive (11) from an indirect argument. Suppose that (2-3.19) is valid also when particle d has spin, provided $\sigma(\mathrm{ab} \to \mathrm{cd})$ is calculated from (9). Since (9) contains no interferences between different values of the magnetic quantum number whereas (8) does, (11) is both necessary and sufficient in the derivation of (2-3.19) from (8).

The probability of finding a decay orientation Ω' is now given by the "normalized" version of (8),

$$W(s, t, \Omega', \xi) = \frac{1}{C(\xi)} \operatorname{trace} [\rho(s, t) R^*(\Omega', \xi)]. \tag{1.12}$$

From (11), one sees that

$$\int \mathrm{d}\Omega' \, W(s, t, \Omega', \xi) = 1, \tag{1.13}$$

which justifies the name probability.

We conclude this section by writing down the general form of the differential cross-section when all four particles a, b, c and d carry spin. We shall however assume that the initial particles a and b are unpolarized. The case of polarization will be treated in chapter 9.

The term "unpolarized" implies that the probability of finding an initial particle in a state of magnetic quantum number M is independent of M. Since there are $2S+1$ such states, the probability for each state is $(2S+1)^{-1}$. Therefore, the differential cross-section of unpolarized initial particles is

$$\mathrm{d}\sigma(\mathrm{ab} \to \mathrm{cd}) = \frac{\pi \, \mathrm{d}t}{4q^2 s} [(2S_\mathrm{a}+1)(2S_\mathrm{b}+1)]^{-1} \sum_{M_\mathrm{a}, \ldots, M_\mathrm{d}} \left| \frac{T(s, t, M_\mathrm{a}, \ldots, M_\mathrm{d})}{4\pi} \right|^2 . \tag{1.14}$$

This may suffice as an introduction to some implications of spin. Our main result is (12), which expresses the orientation probability in terms of the two density matrices ρ and $R(\Omega')/C$. Usually the decay density matrix $R(\Omega')/C$ is already known, in which case a measurement of the orientation probability determines the density matrix of the reaction. This allows a determination of the amplitudes $T(\mathrm{ab} \to \mathrm{cd}_M)$, apart from a common phase.

3-2. Spin states in the particle rest frame

The spin states $|M\rangle$ in a particle's rest frame are well-known from the non-relativistic theory of spin. For spin-$\frac{1}{2}$, we have

$$|\tfrac{1}{2}\rangle \equiv \chi(\tfrac{1}{2}) = \begin{pmatrix} 1 \\ 0 \end{pmatrix}, \qquad |-\tfrac{1}{2}\rangle \equiv \chi(-\tfrac{1}{2}) = \begin{pmatrix} 0 \\ 1 \end{pmatrix}, \tag{2.1}$$

when J_z is diagonal. It is customary to write, for $S=\frac{1}{2}$, $\boldsymbol{J}=\frac{1}{2}\boldsymbol{\sigma}$, where the 2×2 matrices $\boldsymbol{\sigma}$ are the Pauli spin matrices:

$$\sigma_x = \begin{pmatrix} 0 & 1 \\ 1 & 0 \end{pmatrix}, \quad \sigma_y = \begin{pmatrix} 0 & -\mathrm{i} \\ \mathrm{i} & 0 \end{pmatrix}, \quad \sigma_z = \begin{pmatrix} 1 & 0 \\ 0 & -1 \end{pmatrix}. \tag{2.2}$$

Thus, the $\chi(M)$ are eigenstates of σ_z with eigenvalue $2M$. In addition to this "quantization along the z-axis", we need rotated states $\chi(M, \vartheta, \varphi)$, in which the quantization axis has polar angle ϑ and azimuthal angle φ. This corresponds to the Euler angles $\alpha=\varphi$ and $\beta=\vartheta$ in (1.3). The third Euler angle γ is unspecified: it corresponds to a rotation about the quantization axis. We put $\gamma=-\alpha$, in which case the rotation matrix reduces to the unit matrix for $\vartheta=0$ (Jacob and Wick [1959]). In the notation of appendix C-2, we have

$$D(\varphi, \vartheta, -\varphi)_{mm'} = d_{mm'}(\vartheta)\mathrm{e}^{\mathrm{i}\varphi(m'-m)}. \tag{2.3}$$

Inserting for $d(\vartheta)$ the values of table C-3, we get from (1.1)

$$\begin{gathered}\chi_m(M, \vartheta, \varphi) = \sum_{M'} D^{\frac{1}{2}}_{M'M}(\varphi, \vartheta, -\varphi)\chi_m(M') = D^{\frac{1}{2}}_{mM}(\varphi, \vartheta, -\varphi), \\ \chi(\tfrac{1}{2}, \vartheta, \varphi) = \begin{pmatrix} \cos\frac{1}{2}\vartheta \\ \sin\frac{1}{2}\vartheta\,\mathrm{e}^{\mathrm{i}\varphi} \end{pmatrix}, \quad \chi(-\tfrac{1}{2}, \vartheta, \varphi) = \begin{pmatrix} -\sin\frac{1}{2}\vartheta\,\mathrm{e}^{-\mathrm{i}\varphi} \\ \cos\frac{1}{2}\vartheta \end{pmatrix}.\end{gathered} \tag{2.4}$$

These states are eigenstates of the rotated σ_z-matrix,

$$\sigma_{z'} = \sigma_x \sin\vartheta\cos\varphi + \sigma_y \sin\vartheta\sin\varphi + \sigma_z\cos\vartheta. \tag{2.5}$$

For spin-1, one usually takes three cartesian vectors as basic spin states,

$$\boldsymbol{\varepsilon} \equiv \begin{pmatrix} \varepsilon_x(M) \\ \varepsilon_y(M) \\ \varepsilon_z(M) \end{pmatrix}, \quad \boldsymbol{\varepsilon}(\pm 1) = \begin{pmatrix} \mp 2^{-\frac{1}{2}} \\ -2^{-\frac{1}{2}}\mathrm{i} \\ 0 \end{pmatrix}, \quad \boldsymbol{\varepsilon}(0) = \begin{pmatrix} 0 \\ 0 \\ 1 \end{pmatrix}. \tag{2.6}$$

In this representation, J^1_z is not diagonal. The reason is that one is more familiar with the transformation properties of a cartesian vector than with the D-matrices for spin-1. Spin states along the axis ($\vartheta, \varphi=0$) in the xz-plane are given by

$$\boldsymbol{\varepsilon}(\pm 1, \vartheta, 0) = 2^{-\frac{1}{2}} \begin{pmatrix} \mp\cos\vartheta \\ -\mathrm{i} \\ \pm\sin\vartheta \end{pmatrix}, \quad \boldsymbol{\varepsilon}(0, \vartheta, 0) = \begin{pmatrix} \sin\vartheta \\ 0 \\ \cos\vartheta \end{pmatrix}. \tag{2.7}$$

The choice of signs in (6) is motivated by eq. (12) below.

For the construction of matrix elements, it is convenient to use spinor and vector indices also for states of higher spin. This is achieved by the

Clebsch-Gordan decomposition of the direct product. For example, the spinors of RARITA and SCHWINGER [1941] for spin-$\frac{3}{2}$ have one spinor and one vector index:

$$\begin{aligned}\chi(\tfrac{3}{2}) &= \chi(\tfrac{1}{2})\varepsilon(1),\\ \chi(\tfrac{1}{2}) &= 3^{-\frac{1}{2}}\chi(-\tfrac{1}{2})\varepsilon(1)+(\tfrac{2}{3})^{\frac{1}{2}}\chi(\tfrac{1}{2})\varepsilon(0).\end{aligned} \tag{2.8}$$

Similarly, the spin-2 states may be described by those direct products of vector states which transform like a traceless symmetric tensor:

$$\begin{aligned}\varepsilon_{ik}(2) &= \varepsilon_i(1)\varepsilon_k(1),\\ \varepsilon_{ik}(1) &= 2^{-\frac{1}{2}}[\varepsilon_i(1)\varepsilon_k(0)+\varepsilon_i(0)\varepsilon_k(1)],\\ \varepsilon_{ik}(0) &= 6^{-\frac{1}{2}}[2\varepsilon_i(0)\varepsilon_k(0)+\varepsilon_i(1)\varepsilon_k(-1)+\varepsilon_i(-1)\varepsilon_k(1)].\end{aligned} \tag{2.9}$$

From the symmetry $C^{j_1, j_2, j_1+j_2}_{M_1, M_2, M} = C^{j_1, j_2, j_1+j_2}_{-M_1, -M_2, -M}$ of the Clebsch-Gordan coefficient of the "stretched" configuration $j = j_1+j_2$, one obtains the states $\chi(-M)$ and $\varepsilon_{ik}(-M)$ from (8) and (9) simply by changing the signs of all magnetic quantum numbers.

Note that the states $|M\rangle$ for each value of the total spin are orthonormal. The scalar products are defined as $\chi^+ \cdot \chi$, $\varepsilon^* \cdot \varepsilon$, $\chi^+ \cdot \chi$ and $\sum_{ik} \varepsilon^*_{ik}\varepsilon_{ik}$, respectively.

Now we can calculate the matrix element for the decay of a particle of spin S and magnetic quantum number M into two spinless particles. In the particle's rest frame, $T(\mathrm{d}_M \to 1, 2)$ of (1.5) must be of the form

$$T(\mathrm{d}_M \to 1, 2) \equiv \langle 12|T|M\rangle = T(\mathrm{d} \to 1, 2)|M\rangle, \tag{2.10}$$

where $T(\mathrm{d} \to 1, 2)$ is composed of the vectors $\boldsymbol{p}_1$ and $\boldsymbol{p}_2$ and transforms under rotations so that (10) is invariant under simultaneous rotations of $|M\rangle$ and $\boldsymbol{p}_1, \boldsymbol{p}_2$. For spin-1, for example, the most general matrix element is

$$T(\mathrm{d}_M \to 1, 2) = G\boldsymbol{p}_1\varepsilon(M), \tag{2.11}$$

where $G = G(s_\mathrm{d})$ is a function of the effective mass $s_\mathrm{d} = (P_1+P_2)^2$. A term $G_2(s_\mathrm{d})\boldsymbol{p}_2\varepsilon(M)$ need not appear explicitly in (11), due to $\boldsymbol{p}_2 = -\boldsymbol{p}_1$. With $\varepsilon(M)$ from (6) and $\boldsymbol{p}_1$ in polar coordinates (p, ϑ, φ), we get

$$\begin{aligned}T(\mathrm{d}_{\pm 1} \to 1, 2) &= \mp\tfrac{1}{2}\sqrt{2}Gp \sin\vartheta\, \mathrm{e}^{\pm \mathrm{i}\varphi} &&= Gp\sqrt{\tfrac{4}{3}\pi}\,Y^1_{\pm 1}(\vartheta, \varphi),\\ T(\mathrm{d}_0 \to 1, 2) &= Gp\cos\vartheta &&= Gp\sqrt{\tfrac{4}{3}\pi}\,Y^1_0(\vartheta, \varphi).\end{aligned} \tag{2.12}$$

Here we have expressed the angular dependence in terms of the spherical harmonics Y^L_M. The result is easily generalized to arbitrary integer spin L. In that case, $T(\mathrm{d} \to 1, 2)$ must transform under rotations like a tensor of degree L. Since there is only one vector available, this tensor is $G(S_d)$ times the Lth direct product of $\boldsymbol{p}_1$ with itself. The result is

$$T(\mathrm{d}_M^L \to 1, 2) = Gp^L L! \sqrt{\frac{2^L 4\pi}{(2L+1)!}}\, Y_M^L(\vartheta, \varphi). \tag{2.13}$$

The numerical factor comes from the normalization of the spin functions $|M\rangle$. For $L = 2$, one may verify (13) by means of (9).

Since one cannot construct a spinor from a vector, a particle of half-integer spin cannot decay into two spinless particles. We cannot yet discuss the decay into particles with spin, since the spin states of particles 1 and 2 would not be at rest in the d rest frame.

Inserting (13) into (1.7), we find that R(decay) really obeys (1.11), due to the orthonormality of the functions Y_M^L on the unit sphere. The constant $C(\xi)$ is $|G|^2(p^L L!)^2 2^L 4\pi/(2L+1)!$.

For the use of (10) and a corresponding product $\langle M|\, T(\mathrm{ab} \to \mathrm{cd})$ in the matrix element (1.5) for the two-step process ab → cd, d → 12, it is convenient to include the spin summation in the definition of the propagator:

$$\Phi_{ij}(s_\mathrm{d}) \equiv \sum_M \frac{|M\rangle_i \langle M|_j}{m^2 - s_\mathrm{d} - im\Gamma}, \quad T(\mathrm{ab} \to \mathrm{c12}) = T(\mathrm{d} \to 12)\Phi(s_\mathrm{d})T(\mathrm{ab} \to \mathrm{cd}). \tag{2.14}$$

Since the last equation is a matrix equation, the ordering matters. (Due to the definition of "bra" and "ket" vectors, the time sequence in such equations goes from the right to the left.) For $S = \frac{1}{2}$ and $S = 1$, $\Phi(s_\mathrm{d})$ is simply a multiple of the unit matrix. For higher spin, it is a projection operator. For spin-$\frac{3}{2}$ for example, it is a 6×6 matrix, in which, by (8), each row and column carries one spinor index and one vector index. We postpone the construction of such matrices until we have found the relativistic generalization of spin states.

We conclude this section by showing that the spin L of an unstable particle d decaying into two spinless particles is the same as the angular momentum of the corresponding resonance in elastic scattering. We use the basic formula (1.5) and insert (13) for the decay d → 1, 2, and its complex conjugate for the "resonance formation" 1, 2 → d:

$$T(1, 2 \to \mathrm{d} \to 1, 2) = \frac{|G|^2 p^{2L}}{m^2 - s - im\Gamma} \frac{4\pi}{2L+1} \sum_M Y_M^{L*}(\vartheta_\mathrm{i}\varphi_\mathrm{i}) Y_M^L(\vartheta_\mathrm{f}\varphi_\mathrm{f}) \tag{2.15}$$

$$= \frac{|G|^2 p^{2L}}{m^2 - s - im\Gamma} P_L(\cos\theta). \tag{2.16}$$

In (15), ϑ_i and φ_i (ϑ_f and φ_f) are the angles of particle 1 in the initial (final) state. The angle θ in (16) is the cms scattering angle. To get (16) from (15), one applies the addition theorem of spherical harmonics (see C-4.4). Writing (16) in the form $8\pi\, s^{\frac{1}{2}}(2L+1)P_L T_L$ analogous to (2-4.5), we have

$$T_L = \frac{|G|^2 q^{2L}}{8\pi s^{\frac{1}{2}}(2L+1)(m^2-s-im\Gamma)} \equiv \frac{m\Gamma/q}{m^2-s-im\Gamma},$$

$$m\Gamma = \frac{|G|^2 q^{2L+1}}{8\pi s^{\frac{1}{2}}(2L+1)}. \tag{2.17}$$

We see that this definition of $m\Gamma$ displays the same threshold behaviour q^{2L+1} as (2-8.7). This entitles us to take G, for small values of qR, as being independent of s. G is called the "coupling constant" of the resonance to its decay products. If several decay channels are open, we get T_L in the form (2-9.4) instead, with one coupling constant G_i for each channel. Note also that G is dimensionless only for $L = 1$.

Now we understand better why we had to use Legendre polynomials for the partial wave expansion (2-4.5). Equation (2-4.7) is a consequence of

$$\int \mathrm{d}\varphi_i\, Y_M^{L*}(\vartheta_i\varphi_i)Y_M^L(\vartheta_f\varphi_f) = 2\pi Y_0^L(\vartheta_i)Y_0^L(\vartheta_f) = (L+\tfrac{1}{2})P_L(\vartheta_i)P_L(\vartheta_f). \tag{2.18}$$

3-3. Relativistic spin one states

Spin states for particles in flight are needed for reactions in which more than one particle carries spin. They are also needed in the partial wave expansion of reactions containing only one spin particle, since the partial wave expansion is restricted to the cms. A systematic study of relativistic spin states has been made e.g. by WEINBERG [1964]. In this book, we follow the more conventional method of studying spin-$\frac{1}{2}$ and spin-1 separately. Relativistic states of spin-$\frac{3}{2}$ and -2 are then constructed from the direct products, analogous to (2.8) and (2.9).

The case of spin-1 is very simple. We have to find three 4-vectors $\varepsilon^\mu(M)$ which reduce to states like (2.6) or (2.7) in the particle's rest frame. This implies $\varepsilon^0(M) = 0$ in the rest frame. Since the time component of a 4-vector is rotation invariant, its rest-frame value describes a state of spin zero. Therefore, if we want to describe the three spin states by means of 4-vectors, we must project out the time component of $\varepsilon^\mu(M)$ in its rest frame. Let P_μ denote the particle's 4-momentum. Then the only Lorentz-invariant generalization of $\varepsilon^0_{\text{rest}}(M) = 0$ is

$$P_\mu \cdot \varepsilon^\mu(M) = 0, \qquad M = \pm 1, 0. \tag{3.1}$$

This is called the Lorentz condition. Together with (2.6) or (2.7) in the system $P_\mu = (m, 0, 0, 0)$, it determines the states $\varepsilon^\mu(M)$ uniquely. For example, for $\boldsymbol{p}$ along the z-axis, only the 0- and z-components of $\varepsilon^\mu(M, \boldsymbol{p})$ differ from those of $\varepsilon^\mu(M, 0, 0, 0)$. If, moreover, (2.6) is to be valid for $\boldsymbol{p} = 0$, then $\varepsilon^\mu(M)$ is given by

$$\varepsilon^\mu(\pm 1) = \tfrac{1}{2}\sqrt{2}(0, \mp 1, -\mathrm{i}, 0), \tag{3.2}$$

$$\varepsilon^\mu(0) = \frac{1}{m}(p, 0, 0, E). \tag{3.3}$$

Here we have introduced the row vectors $(\varepsilon_0, \varepsilon_x, \varepsilon_y, \varepsilon_z)$.

The new orthonormality relations are

$$\sum_\mu \varepsilon^\mu(M)\varepsilon^*_\mu(M') = \varepsilon_0(M) \cdot \varepsilon^*_0(M') - \boldsymbol{\varepsilon}(M) \cdot \boldsymbol{\varepsilon}^*(M') = -\delta_{MM'}. \tag{3.4}$$

The minus sign in front of the δ-function is a consequence of our choice of metric (1-1.9). Being orthogonal to the time-like vector P_μ, ε^μ has to be space-like.

The Lorentz-invariant matrix element for a reaction with one spin-1 particle in the initial state must be of the form $T_\mu \cdot \varepsilon^\mu(M)$, where T_μ is a 4-vector constructed from the spins and 4-momenta of the other particles. For the decay $\mathrm{d}_M \to 1, 2$ for example, the Lorentz-invariant version of (2.11) is

$$T(\mathrm{d}_M \to 1, 2) = -G_1 P_{1\mu} \cdot \varepsilon^\mu(M). \tag{3.5}$$

The Lorentz-covariant generalization of the propagator (2.14) is

$$\Phi_{\mu\nu}(s_\mathrm{d}) = \sum_M \frac{\varepsilon_\mu(M)\varepsilon^*_\nu(M)}{m^2 - s_\mathrm{d} - \mathrm{i}m\Gamma} = \frac{-g_{\mu\nu} + P_\mu P_\nu/m^2}{m^2 - s_\mathrm{d} - \mathrm{i}m\Gamma}. \tag{3.6}$$

The complicated numerator is necessary for the elimination of the spin-0 components:

$$P^\mu \Phi_{\mu\nu} = P^\nu \Phi_{\mu\nu} = 0. \tag{3.7}$$

The only stable elementary particle of spin one is the photon. Since the mass of the photon is zero, the above formalism cannot be applied immediately. The photon has no rest system, and states like (2.6) are a priori meaningless. We treat this problem by assuming a small mass m for the photon, which we put equal to zero in the final formulae. Then we can start as before from (2.6) and impose the Lorentz condition (1) on ε^μ. For "transverse polarization", $M = \pm 1$, this leads again to (2). The state of "longitudinal polarization" (3) on the other hand becomes undefined for $m \to 0$. At this stage, the theory is supplemented by the physical principle of gauge invariance, which requires that all elements of the S-matrix are invariant under the "gauge transformation"

$$\varepsilon^\mu(M) \to \varepsilon^\mu(M) + cP^\mu, \qquad c = \text{arbitrary, complex,} \tag{3.8}$$

of the photon spin states. As a consequence of (8), all matrix elements for $M = 0$ vanish in the limit $m \to 0$. To show this, we replace in $T_\mu \cdot \varepsilon^\mu(0)$ the $\varepsilon^\mu(0)$ as given by (3) by $\varepsilon^\mu(0) - P^\mu/m$. With $E = p + m^2/2p$, we have, according to (8),

$$T_\mu \cdot \varepsilon^\mu(0) = T_\mu \cdot \left(\varepsilon^\mu(0) - \frac{1}{m} P^\mu\right) = T_\mu \cdot \frac{1}{m}\left(-\frac{m^2}{2p}, 0, 0, \frac{m^2}{2p}\right), \tag{3.9}$$

which obviously tends to zero for $m \to 0$.

Note that we did not require gauge invariance of the Lorentz condition (1). For $m \to 0$, (1) is of course gauge invariant for finite c.

The other important observation is that invariance of the matrix element under (8) is required not only for $M = 0$ but also for $M = \pm 1$. Consequently, whenever a photon's spin state is replaced by its 4-momentum P^μ, we have

$$T_\mu \cdot P^\mu_{\text{photon}} = 0. \tag{3.10}$$

One advantage of requiring gauge invariance before going to the limit $m \to 0$ is that the propagator (6) can be used as it stands. In matrix elements of the type $T^\mu_{\text{a}} \Phi_{\mu\nu} T^\nu_{\text{b}}$, the term $P_\mu P_\nu / m^2$ does not contribute, according to (10). Alternatively, one can define

$$\Phi_{\mu\nu} = \frac{g_{\mu\nu}}{s_{\text{d}}} \qquad \text{for} \quad m = 0. \tag{3.11}$$

So far we have no use for this expression, since we need propagators only in connection with unstable particles. As a first example of photon interactions, we treat in section 4-8 the decay $\pi^0 \to \gamma\gamma$.

3-4. Relativistic spin one-half states

In this section we determine the transformation properties of the two-component spinors $\chi(M)$ under Lorentz-transformations. We remember that the connection between the group SU_2 and the rotation group R_3 rests on the fact that the matrices $\boldsymbol{\sigma}$ transform like a 3-vector. Now we extend this correspondence to homogeneous Lorentz-transformations by requiring that the matrices

$$\sigma^{\mu} = (\sigma_0, \boldsymbol{\sigma}), \qquad \sigma_0 = \begin{pmatrix} 1 & 0 \\ 0 & 1 \end{pmatrix} \tag{4.1}$$

transform like a 4-vector. In other words, the quantity

$$\chi^{+}(M')P_{\mu}\sigma^{\mu}\chi(M) = \chi^{+}(M')(E-\boldsymbol{p}\cdot\boldsymbol{\sigma})\chi(M) \tag{4.2}$$

must be Lorentz-invariant. Let us see what consequences this has for the boosts (i.e. the rotation-free transformations) from the particle rest frame to the frame of momentum $\boldsymbol{p}$. We denote by $A(\boldsymbol{p})$ the matrix representing a boost to a state of momentum p along the z-axis, i.e.

$$\chi(M, \boldsymbol{p}) = A(\boldsymbol{p})\chi(M). \tag{4.3}$$

Taking (2) once in the rest frame and once in the new frame, we have

$$m\sigma_0 = EA^{+}\sigma_0 A - pA^{+}\sigma_z A, \tag{4.4}$$

from which we find

$$A_{12} = A_{21} = 0, \qquad (E-p)|A_{11}|^2 = (E+p)|A_{22}|^2 = m. \tag{4.5}$$

Apart from a uninteresting phase factor, (5) requires

$$A(p) = \frac{1}{m^{\frac{1}{2}}}\begin{pmatrix} \sqrt{E+p} & 0 \\ 0 & \sqrt{E-p} \end{pmatrix} = \frac{1}{[2m(E+m)]^{\frac{1}{2}}}(E+m+\sigma_z p). \tag{4.6}$$

For the derivation of the first expression from (5), and the second expression from the first, the following identities are useful:

$$\frac{m}{E \pm p} = \frac{E \mp p}{m}, \tag{4.7}$$

$$E+m \pm p = \sqrt{2(E \pm p)(E+m)}. \tag{4.8}$$

The second expression in (6) is immediately generalized to arbitrary boosts:

$$A(\boldsymbol{p}) = \frac{1}{[2m(E+m)]^{\frac{1}{2}}}(E+m+\boldsymbol{\sigma}\cdot\boldsymbol{p}) = \sqrt{\frac{E+\boldsymbol{\sigma}\cdot\boldsymbol{p}}{m}}. \tag{4.9}$$

We see that boosts are represented by unimodular Hermitean matrices. We may write these matrices in a form similar to the rotation matrices:

$$A(\boldsymbol{p}) = e^{\frac{1}{2}\eta\hat{\boldsymbol{p}}\cdot\boldsymbol{\sigma}} = \cosh \tfrac{1}{2}\eta + \sinh \tfrac{1}{2}\eta\boldsymbol{\sigma}\cdot\hat{\boldsymbol{p}}, \tag{4.10}$$

where $\hat{\boldsymbol{p}}$ is a unit vector along $\boldsymbol{p}$. The comparison with (6) gives

$$\cosh \eta = E/m, \qquad \sinh \eta = p/m. \tag{4.11}$$

Note that the arguments of the hyperbolic functions in (10) and (11) differ by a factor 2.

As an example, let us write down the most general matrix element for the decay $\Lambda \to p\pi^-$. Both the Λ-hyperon and the proton have spin-$\frac{1}{2}$. We know already from section 3-2 that the matrix element must be linear in the spinor $\chi_\Lambda(M)$. By a similar argument, it must be linear in the Hermitean conjugate proton spinor, $\chi_p^+(M')$. According to (2), the most general Lorentz invariant matrix element containing χ_Λ and χ_p^+ is

$$T_p(M, M') = \sum_i G_i \chi_p^+(M') P_i^\mu \sigma_\mu \chi_\Lambda(M), \tag{4.12}$$

where P_i may be any of the available 4-vectors. Due to energy-momentum conservation ($P_\Lambda = P_p + P_\pi$), only two of the three 4-vectors are linearly independent. We thus find two different "couplings",

$$T_p(M, M') = \chi_p^+(M') \left[P_\Lambda^\mu (G-G') \sqrt{\frac{m}{m_\Lambda}} + P_p^\mu (G+G') \sqrt{\frac{m_\Lambda}{m}} \right] \sigma_\mu \chi_\Lambda(M). \tag{4.13}$$

The particular combination of the coupling constants G and G' has been chosen for later convenience. As in (2.11), these constants could in principle depend on $s_d = (P_p + P_\pi)^2$, but due to the smallness of the width Γ_Λ, such dependence cannot be detected.

We evaluate (13) in the Λ rest frame, in which $\chi_\Lambda(M)$ is given by the states of section 2, whereas $\chi_p^+(M')$ is given by $\chi^+(M')A(\boldsymbol{p})$:

$$\begin{aligned} T_p(M, M') &= \chi^+(M') \frac{E+m+\boldsymbol{\sigma}\cdot\boldsymbol{p}}{[2m(E+m)]^{\frac{1}{2}}} \\ &\quad \times \left[(G-G')\sqrt{mm_\Lambda} + (G+G')(E-\boldsymbol{p}\cdot\boldsymbol{\sigma}) \sqrt{\frac{m_\Lambda}{m}} \right] \chi_\Lambda(M) \\ &= \chi^+(M') \left[(G-G')\sqrt{\tfrac{1}{2}m_\Lambda(E+m)} \left(1 + \frac{\boldsymbol{\sigma}\cdot\boldsymbol{p}}{E+m}\right) \right. \\ &\quad \left. + (G+G') \sqrt{\frac{m_\Lambda}{m}} \frac{E^2 - p^2 + mE - m\boldsymbol{\sigma}\cdot\boldsymbol{p}}{[2m(E+m)]^{\frac{1}{2}}} \right] \chi_\Lambda(M) \\ &= \sqrt{2m_\Lambda(E+m)}\chi^+(M') \left(G - G' \frac{\boldsymbol{\sigma}\cdot\boldsymbol{p}}{E+m} \right) \chi_\Lambda(M). \end{aligned} \tag{4.14}$$

This expression can be further simplified if we choose the direction of $\boldsymbol{p}$ as the proton spin quantization axis. The magnetic quantum number of a particle along its momentum is called the helicity, λ. In order to avoid confusion, we now write $\chi^+(\lambda, \vartheta, \varphi)$ instead of $\chi^+(M')$. The states $\chi(\lambda, \vartheta, \varphi)$ are given by (2.4), where ϑ and φ denote the polar and azimuthal angles of $\boldsymbol{p}$ in the Λ rest frame. By the definition of helicity states, we have

$$\boldsymbol{\sigma} \cdot \boldsymbol{p}\chi(\lambda, \vartheta, \varphi) = 2\lambda p\chi(\lambda, \vartheta, \varphi). \tag{4.15}$$

In (14), we need the states $\chi^+(\lambda, \vartheta, \varphi)$, which according to (2.4) are given by

$$\chi_m^+(\lambda, \vartheta, \varphi) = D_{m\lambda}^*(\varphi, \vartheta, -\varphi). \tag{4.16}$$

Here $m = +\frac{1}{2}(-\frac{1}{2})$ denotes the upper (lower) component of the two-component vector χ^+. The Λ-spin is conveniently quantized along the z-axis, in which case we have $\chi_m(M) = \delta_{mM}$. Inserting these expressions into (14), we get

$$\begin{aligned} T(M, \lambda, \vartheta, \varphi) &= \sqrt{2m_\Lambda(E+m)}D_{M\lambda}^*(\varphi, \vartheta, -\varphi)\left(G - G'\frac{2\lambda p}{E+m}\right) \\ &= D_{M\lambda}^*(\varphi, \vartheta, -\varphi)(G\sqrt{2m_\Lambda(E+m)} - 2\lambda G'\sqrt{2m_\Lambda(E-m)}). \end{aligned} \tag{4.17}$$

This is the final result. Remember that m is the proton mass, and $E = (m_\Lambda^2 + m^2 - m_\pi^2)/2m_\Lambda$ is the proton energy in the Λ rest frame (cf. (1-2.6)). As in (2.12), the coupling constants G and G' are dimensionless. We note that the decay matrix $R = T^*(M, \lambda\vartheta\varphi)$. $T(M'\lambda\vartheta\varphi)$ again obeys (1.11), due to the relation

$$\int \mathrm{d}\cos\vartheta\,\mathrm{d}\varphi\, D_{M\lambda}^{\frac{1}{2}}(\varphi, \vartheta, -\varphi)D_{M'\lambda}^{\frac{1}{2}*}(\varphi, \vartheta, -\varphi) = 2\pi\delta_{MM'}. \tag{4.18}$$

A word about the general structure of Lorentz-transformations of two-component spinors may be appropriate. According to (10) and (11), any boost may be written as $\exp(\frac{1}{2}\eta\hat{\boldsymbol{p}} \cdot \boldsymbol{\sigma})$. Similarly, any rotation may be written as $\exp(-\frac{1}{2}\mathrm{i}\varphi\hat{\boldsymbol{n}} \cdot \boldsymbol{\sigma})$, where φ is the rotation angle and $\hat{\boldsymbol{n}}$ the direction of the rotation axis. A general Lorentz transformation may be expressed as the product of a rotation and a boost. On the other hand, any complex 2×2 unimodular (i.e. of unit determinant) matrix C_2 may be decomposed into a product of the form $\exp(\frac{1}{2}\eta\hat{\boldsymbol{p}} \cdot \boldsymbol{\sigma})\exp(-\frac{1}{2}\mathrm{i}\varphi\hat{\boldsymbol{n}} \cdot \boldsymbol{\sigma})$. Therefore the Lorentz group is isomorphic with the group of matrices C_2. From the mathematical point of view, the Lorentz transformations of a 4-vector P_μ form a representation of the unimodular transformations of a 2-component spinor $\chi = (\chi_1, \chi_2)$.

The inverse is not true, since rotations by 2π leave P_μ unchanged, but change the sign of χ. So far we have built our theory on the invariance of scalar products of 4-vectors, $P_a \cdot P_b$. Instead, we could have started by requiring invariance of the determinant of two spinors,

$$|\chi^a, \chi^b| = \chi_1^a \chi_2^b - \chi_2^a \chi_1^b . \tag{4.19}$$

For more details, see e.g. THEIS [1959], ROMAN [1960]. Later, we shall use (19) in connection with charge conjugation.

3-5. Dirac spinors and parity

The wide-spread use of 4-component or Dirac spinors (DIRAC [1928]), for the description of relativistic spin-$\frac{1}{2}$ states has mainly historical reasons. To understand these, we must first discuss the so-called parity operation. This operation reverses the momentum vectors $\boldsymbol{p}$ of particles but not the magnetic quantum numbers of their spin states. In coordinate space, it corresponds to the space inversion $\boldsymbol{x} \to -\boldsymbol{x}$, $t \to t$. The classical correspondence of spin is the axial vector $\boldsymbol{x} \times \boldsymbol{p}$, which remains unchanged under space inversion.

In the terminology of section 1-1, parity is an improper Lorentz transformation. As seen from (1-1.13), it exchanges upper and lower indices on 4-momenta. This does not change the value of Lorentz-invariants like $P_a P_b$, but it changes the sign of the determinant of four 4-vectors (1-4.8). Accordingly, each Lorentz-invariant matrix element can be split into two parts, $T = T_e + T_o$, which are even and odd under "parity conjugation", respectively. Amplitudes $T(\text{ab} \to \text{cd})$ of two-particle reactions of spinless particles are automatically in T_e, since they depend only on s and t (the determinant $|P_a P_b P_c P_d|$ is zero). In fact, the parity transformed state can be reduced to the original state by a rotation of 180° about the normal to the reaction plane. Similarly, the decay of a particle into two spinless particles is in T_e. The decay into particles with spin on the other hand may contain both T_e and T_o. In the decay $\Lambda \to \text{p}\pi^-$, for example, the term $\boldsymbol{\sigma} \cdot \boldsymbol{p}\chi(M)$ of (4.14) changes sign under parity but not under rotations.

Let χ_0 denote a two-component spinor in the particle's rest frame, and let $\chi = A(\boldsymbol{p})\chi_0$ denote an arbitrary spinor, not at rest. The parity-conjugate spinor $\chi^{\mathscr{P}}$ is given by

$$\chi^{\mathscr{P}} = A(-\boldsymbol{p})\chi_0 = A^{-1}(\boldsymbol{p})\chi_0 . \tag{5.1}$$

One easily verifies that $A(-\boldsymbol{p})$ is really the inverse of (4.9), i.e.

$A(\boldsymbol{p})A(-\boldsymbol{p}) = 1$. By applying $A(-\boldsymbol{p})$ twice to χ, we find

$$\chi^{\mathscr{P}} = A^{-2}(\boldsymbol{p})\chi = \frac{1}{m} P_\mu \sigma^\mu \chi. \tag{5.2}$$

From the Lorentz-invariance of (4.2), we conclude that $\chi^{\mathscr{P}}$ transforms under Lorentz transformations inversely to χ^+. (In the notation of VAN DER WAERDEN [1929], spinors which transform like $\chi^{\mathscr{P}}$ are distinguished from spinors which transform like χ by a "dotted" index. See also the reviews of BADE and JEHLE [1953] and CAP [1955].)

Dirac spinors can be introduced in several equivalent ways. Two frequently-used versions are the so-called "high-energy" and "low-energy" representations. The high-energy representation, which is particularly convenient for $m = 0$, is defined by

$$u(\boldsymbol{p}) = \sqrt{m}\begin{pmatrix}\chi\\ \chi^{\mathscr{P}}\end{pmatrix} = \sqrt{m}\begin{pmatrix}A(\boldsymbol{p})\chi_0\\ A(-\boldsymbol{p})\chi_0\end{pmatrix} = \frac{1}{[2(E+m)]^{\frac{1}{2}}}(P_\mu\gamma^\mu + m)\begin{pmatrix}\chi_0\\ \chi_0\end{pmatrix}. \tag{5.3}$$

The last expression contains the definition of Dirac's γ-matrices. In the high-energy representation, these are, according to (4.9),

$$\gamma_0 = \begin{pmatrix}0 & \sigma_0\\ \sigma_0 & 0\end{pmatrix}, \qquad \boldsymbol{\gamma} = \begin{pmatrix}0 & -\boldsymbol{\sigma}\\ \boldsymbol{\sigma} & 0\end{pmatrix}. \tag{5.4}$$

We have chosen γ^μ in anti-diagonal form, since this allows us to combine (2) and its inverse into the famous Dirac equation

$$P_\mu\gamma^\mu u = (E\gamma_0 - \boldsymbol{p}\cdot\boldsymbol{\gamma})u = mu. \tag{5.5}$$

The parity operation $\boldsymbol{p} \to -\boldsymbol{p}$, which exchanges χ and $\chi^{\mathscr{P}}$, simply means multiplication by γ_0:

$$u^{\mathscr{P}}(M) = \gamma_0 u(M). \tag{5.6}$$

We also define the "adjoint" spinor,

$$\bar{u}(M) = u^+\gamma_0 = m^{\frac{1}{2}}(\chi^{\mathscr{P}+}, \chi^+), \tag{5.7}$$

which obeys the adjoint Dirac equation

$$\bar{u}(P_\mu\gamma^\mu - m) = 0. \tag{5.8}$$

By means of the adjoint spinor, the Lorentz-invariant spinor product $\chi^+ P_\mu \sigma^\mu \chi$ of a spinor with itself assumes the simple form

$$\bar{u}(M')u(M) = 2m\delta_{MM'}. \tag{5.9}$$

The factor $2m$ is of course a convention. One could omit it, but then one would get denominators of $2m$ in many other places, for example in the spin summations of the next section. In terms of 4-component spinors, the Lorentz-invariant matrix elements for reactions with one spin-$\frac{1}{2}$ particle in the initial and final state (e.g. $\pi p \to \pi\pi p$ or $\pi p \to K\Lambda$) are of the form

$$T(M, M') = \bar{u}'(M')Qu(M), \tag{5.10}$$

where the primes distinguish the quantum numbers of the final spin-$\frac{1}{2}$ particle, and Q may be a number or a 4×4 matrix. The connection between (10) and (4.12) is established by the projection operators

$$\tfrac{1}{2}(1\pm\gamma_5), \qquad \gamma_5 = \begin{pmatrix}\sigma_0 & 0\\ 0 & -\sigma_0\end{pmatrix} = i\gamma_0\gamma_1\gamma_2\gamma_3, \tag{5.11}$$

which project out the χ and $\chi^{\mathscr{P}}$ components of $u(M)$, respectively. These projection operators are used for the description of parity-non-invariant interactions in terms of 4-component spinors.

We conclude this section by defining the "low-energy representation" of the spinors u:

$$u = \sqrt{E+m}\begin{pmatrix}\chi_0\\ \dfrac{\boldsymbol{\sigma}\cdot\boldsymbol{p}}{E+m}\chi_0\end{pmatrix} = \frac{1}{(E+m)^{\frac{1}{2}}}(P_\mu\gamma^\mu+m)\begin{pmatrix}\chi_0\\ 0\end{pmatrix}, \tag{5.12}$$

$$\gamma_0 = \begin{pmatrix}\sigma_0 & 0\\ 0 & -\sigma_0\end{pmatrix}, \qquad \boldsymbol{\gamma} = \begin{pmatrix}0 & \boldsymbol{\sigma}\\ -\boldsymbol{\sigma} & 0\end{pmatrix}, \qquad \gamma_5 = \begin{pmatrix}0 & \sigma_0\\ \sigma_0 & 0\end{pmatrix}. \tag{5.13}$$

The Dirac equation (5), parity conjugation (6) etc. all remain valid in the low-energy representation. The matrix elements (10) are also independent of the choice of representation. For $\boldsymbol{p} = 0$, the lower components of u obviously vanish. For this reason, the upper and lower components of u are also called "big" and "small" components. With "b" for big and "s" for small components, the matrix Q of (10) is written in the low-energy representation as

$$Q = \begin{pmatrix}Q_{bb} & Q_{bs}\\ Q_{sb} & Q_{ss}\end{pmatrix}. \tag{5.14}$$

Insertion of (14) and (12) into (10) gives $T(M, M')$ in the form

$$T(M, M') = \sqrt{(E+m)(E'+m')}\chi_0'^+(M')$$
$$\times \left[Q_{bb} - \frac{\boldsymbol{\sigma}\cdot\boldsymbol{p}'}{E'+m'} Q_{ss} \frac{\boldsymbol{\sigma}\cdot\boldsymbol{p}}{E+m} + Q_{bs} \frac{\boldsymbol{\sigma}\cdot\boldsymbol{p}}{E+m} - \frac{\boldsymbol{\sigma}\cdot\boldsymbol{p}'}{E'+m'} Q_{sb} \right] \chi_0(M)$$
$$= \chi_0'^+(M')[\sqrt{(E+m)(E'+m')}Q_{bb} - \sqrt{(E-m)(E'-m')}\boldsymbol{\sigma}\cdot\hat{\boldsymbol{p}}' Q_{ss}\boldsymbol{\sigma}\cdot\hat{\boldsymbol{p}}]\chi_0(M)$$
$$+\chi_0'^+(M')[\sqrt{(E-m)(E'+m')}Q_{bs}\boldsymbol{\sigma}\cdot\hat{\boldsymbol{p}} - \sqrt{(E+m)(E'-m')}\boldsymbol{\sigma}\cdot\hat{\boldsymbol{p}}' Q_{sb}]\chi_0(M). \tag{5.15}$$

Here $\hat{\boldsymbol{p}}$ and $\hat{\boldsymbol{p}}'$ are the directions of $\boldsymbol{p}$ and $\boldsymbol{p}'$, e.g. $\boldsymbol{p} = \hat{\boldsymbol{p}}p = \hat{\boldsymbol{p}}\sqrt{(E+m)(E-m)}$. The primes refer to the final spin-$\frac{1}{2}$ particle. In the rest system of the initial spin-$\frac{1}{2}$ particle, the second and third term of (15) vanish, and the remaining two terms are simplified:

$$T(M, M') = \sqrt{2m(E'+m')}\chi_0'^+(M') \left[Q_{bb} - \frac{\boldsymbol{\sigma}\cdot\boldsymbol{p}'}{E'+m'} Q_{sb} \right] \chi_0(M). \tag{5.16}$$

For the decay $\Lambda \to p\pi^-$, (16) is identical with (4.14) for

$$Q_{bb} = G, \qquad Q_{sb} = G'. \tag{5.17}$$

In the 4-component notation (10), this corresponds to

$$T_p(M, M') = \bar{u}'(M')(G + G'\gamma_5)u(M), \tag{5.18}$$

as one may verify from (13). Terms like $G\gamma_0$, which also lead to $Q_{bb} = G$, are excluded on the basis of Lorentz invariance.

The advantage of (18) over (4.13) is that it readily splits into parts of even and odd parity. The disadvantage is that it is more difficult to show that (18) is the most general matrix element for Λ-decay. This requires a systematic study of all possible combinations of γ-matrices and 4-momenta.

3-6. The complete set of Dirac matrices. Spin summation

The matrix Q of the last section can be written as a superposition of the following 16 linearly independent matrices:

$$\begin{aligned}
&1 \text{ scalar matrix: } 1,\\
&1 \text{ pseudoscalar matrix: } \gamma_5,\\
&4 \text{ vector matrices: } \gamma_\mu,\\
&4 \text{ axial vector matrices: } \gamma_\mu\gamma_5,\\
&6 \text{ antisymmetric tensor matrices: } 2\sigma_{\mu\nu} \equiv \gamma_\mu\gamma_\nu - \gamma_\nu\gamma_\mu.
\end{aligned} \tag{6.1}$$

For example, if we try to construct a symmetric tensor from γ_μ and γ_ν, we find the anticommutation rules

$$\gamma_\mu \gamma_\nu + \gamma_\nu \gamma_\mu = 2g_{\mu\nu}. \tag{6.2}$$

In spinor space, $g_{\mu\nu}$ is a multiple of the scalar matrix. From (5.11), it follows that γ_5 and γ_μ anticommute. The name "pseudoscalar" comes from the behaviour in the parity transformation:

$$\gamma_0 \gamma_5 \gamma_0 = -\gamma_5. \tag{6.3}$$

Also the remaining matrices of (1) are either even or odd under parity conjugation.

Next, we turn to the spin summation needed in the propagator (2.14). We have

$$\begin{aligned}\sum_M \chi(M)\chi^+(M) &= \sum_M A(\boldsymbol{p})\chi_0(M)\chi_0^+(M)A^+(\boldsymbol{p}) \\ &= A(\boldsymbol{p})A^+(\boldsymbol{p}) = (E+\boldsymbol{p}\cdot\boldsymbol{\sigma})/m,\end{aligned} \tag{6.4}$$

according to (4.9) and the completeness relation

$$\sum_M \chi_0(M)_i \chi_0^+(M)_k = \delta_{ik}. \tag{6.5}$$

In the 4-component notation, the spin summation and propagator are given by

$$\sum_M u(M)\bar{u}(M) = P_\mu \gamma^\mu + m, \qquad \Phi_{ij}(s_\alpha) = \frac{P_\mu(\gamma^\mu)_{ij} + m\delta_{ij}}{m^2 - s_\alpha - im\Gamma}, \tag{6.6}$$

both in the low-energy and high-energy representation. This may be verified e.g. from (5.12), (5.13) and (5). The spin summation is also needed in the cross-section (1.9). The absolute square of (5.10), summed over M', is

$$\begin{aligned}\sum_{M'} |T(M, M')|^2 &= \sum_{M'} \bar{u}'(M')Qu(M)u^+(M)Q^+(\bar{u}'(M'))^+ \\ &= \sum_{M'} \bar{u}(M)\gamma_0 Q^+ \gamma_0 u'(M')\bar{u}'(M')Qu(M) \\ &= \bar{u}(M)\bar{Q}(P'\cdot\gamma + m')Qu(M).\end{aligned} \tag{6.7}$$

Here we have inserted the spin summation (6). The matrix $\bar{Q}$ is defined as

$$\bar{Q} = \gamma_0 Q^+ \gamma_0. \tag{6.8}$$

As far as the γ-matrices are concerned, $\bar{Q}$ is obtained from Q by writing the

γ-matrices in inverse order. This comes from the property

$$(\gamma_\mu)^+ = \gamma_0 \gamma_\mu \gamma_0, \qquad \mu = 0, 1, 2, 3, 5. \tag{6.9}$$

The coefficients of the matrices in $\bar{Q}$ are of course the complex conjugate of the coefficients in Q.

According to (1.14), an unpolarized target proton implies a second spin summation. In that case, the differential cross-section is proportional to (7), averaged over M:

$$\begin{aligned} \tfrac{1}{2} \sum_{M, M'} |T(M, M')|^2 &= \tfrac{1}{2} \sum_M \bar{u}(M) \bar{Q}(P' \cdot \gamma + m') Q u(M) \\ &= \tfrac{1}{2} \sum_{ii'} (\bar{Q}(P' \cdot \gamma + m') Q)_{ii'} (P \cdot \gamma + m)_{i'i} \\ &= \tfrac{1}{2} \operatorname{Trace} \bar{Q}(P' \cdot \gamma + m') Q (P \cdot \gamma + m). \end{aligned} \tag{6.10}$$

Methods for evaluating traces of products of γ-matrices are given in appendix E-1. The trace method can also be applied for polarized particles, if projection operators on the different spin states are included. It is particularly elegant in quantum electrodynamics and weak interactions, where Q is a sum of relatively few matrices. When Q contains many terms, it is simpler to calculate the elements $T(M, M')$ for each of M and M' separately, to square them, and to sum the squares.

3-7. Relativistic spin-$\frac{3}{2}$ and spin-2 states

Once we have the relativistic states ε_μ for spin-1 and χ or u for spin-$\frac{1}{2}$, we can construct higher spin states from the direct product (see e.g. AUVIL and BREHM [1966]). We merely have to replace the non-relativistic states in (2.8) and (2.9) by their relativistic generalizations. For spin-$\frac{3}{2}$, we use Dirac spinors:

$$u_\mu(\tfrac{3}{2}) = u(\tfrac{1}{2}) \varepsilon_\mu(1), \tag{7.1}$$

$$u_\mu(\tfrac{1}{2}) = (\tfrac{1}{3})^{\frac{1}{2}} u(-\tfrac{1}{2}) \varepsilon_\mu(1) + (\tfrac{2}{3})^{\frac{1}{2}} u(\tfrac{1}{2}) \varepsilon_\mu(0). \tag{7.2}$$

For spin-2, the relativistic generalization of (2.9) is

$$\varepsilon_{\mu\nu}(2) = \varepsilon_\mu(1) \varepsilon_\nu(1), \text{ etc.} \tag{7.3}$$

The Rarita-Schwinger spinor u_μ obeys both the Dirac equation and the condition (3.1) for spin-1 particles:

$$(P_\nu \gamma^\nu - m) u_\mu = P^\mu u_\mu = 0. \tag{7.4}$$

Similarly, we have

$$P^{\mu}\varepsilon_{\mu\nu} = P^{\nu}\varepsilon_{\mu\nu} = 0. \tag{7.5}$$

In addition, u_μ obeys

$$\gamma^{\mu}u_{\mu} = 0, \tag{7.6}$$

and $\varepsilon_{\mu\nu}$ is a symmetric traceless tensor. These conditions come from the elimination of the lower spin values ($\frac{1}{2}$ in the first case and 1 and 0 in the second case) from the direct product. We now turn to the spin summations. The spin-2 summation is expressed in terms of the spin-1 summation, which we abbreviate as $P_{\mu\nu}$:

$$P_{\mu\nu} \equiv \sum_M \varepsilon^*_\mu(M)\varepsilon_\nu(M) = -g_{\mu\nu}+P_\mu P_\nu/m^2. \tag{7.7}$$

The result is

$$\begin{aligned} P_{\mu\nu,\,\mu'\nu'} &= \sum_M \varepsilon^*_{\mu\nu}(M)\varepsilon_{\mu'\nu'}(M) \\ &= \tfrac{1}{2}(P_{\mu\mu'}P_{\nu\nu'}+P_{\mu\nu'}P_{\nu\mu'})-\tfrac{1}{3}P_{\mu\nu}P_{\mu'\nu'}\,. \end{aligned} \tag{7.8}$$

This follows from the fact that $P_{\mu\nu,\,\mu'\nu'}$ is a symmetric traceless tensor in each pair ($\mu\nu$ and $\mu'\nu'$) of indices. The over-all normalization may be found by direct evaluation of the sum in the rest frame. Alternatively, one may exploit the projection property of spin summation:

$$P^2 = cP, \tag{7.9}$$

where c is a number. For (7) we find $c = -1$, which implies $c = 1$ for (8).

For the spin-$\frac{1}{2}$ summation, (6.4) gives $c = 2m$. Combining this with $c = -1$ of the spin-1 case, we get $c = -2m$ for the spin-$\frac{3}{2}$ summation. The result is

$$u_{\mu\nu} \equiv \sum_M u_\mu(M)\bar{u}_\nu(M) = \tfrac{1}{6}(P\cdot\gamma+m)\left(4P_{\mu\nu}+\gamma_\mu\gamma_\nu-\gamma_\nu\gamma_\mu+\gamma_\mu\frac{2P_\nu}{m}-\gamma_\nu\frac{2P_\mu}{m}\right). \tag{7.10}$$

The term $(P\cdot\gamma+m)P_{\mu\nu}$ clearly satisfies the Dirac equation, the adjoint Dirac equation, and the equations $P^\mu u_{\mu\nu} = P^\nu u_{\mu\nu} = 0$. Also the remaining part in (10) satisfies these equations. Finally the relative amount of $P_{\mu\nu}$ in (10) is fixed by the requirement $\gamma^\mu u_{\mu\nu} = u_{\mu\nu}\gamma^\nu = 0$. Inserting $P_{\mu\nu}$ from (7) and using the anticommutation relations (6.2) of the γ-matrices, we get

$$u_{\mu\nu} = \tfrac{1}{3}(P\cdot\gamma+m)\left[\frac{2}{m^2}P_\mu P_\nu-g_{\mu\nu}-\gamma_\nu\gamma_\mu+\frac{1}{m}(\gamma_\mu P_\nu-\gamma_\nu P_\mu)\right]. \tag{7.11}$$

For a particle at rest ($\boldsymbol{p} = 0$), the components of (11) with $\mu = 0$ and/or $\nu = 0$ vanish, and the space components reduce to

$$u_{ik} = \tfrac{1}{3}m(\gamma_0 + 1)(3\delta_{ik} + \gamma_i \gamma_k). \tag{7.12}$$

For spins larger than 2, the construction of spin states from the direct product becomes rather tedious. The relativistic spin projection operators for any spin have been worked out by WEINBERG [1964]. They are expressed directly in terms of the spin matrices $\boldsymbol{J}$ of appendix C.

We conclude this section by discussing a general selection rule, namely the conservation modulo two of fermions. In this context, we define fermions and bosons as particles of half-integer spin and integer spin, respectively.

A fermion of spin S may be described by a generalized Rarita-Schwinger spinor with S-$\frac{1}{2}$ tensor indices and one spinor index. In a Lorentz-invariant matrix element, the tensor indices may be contracted either with 4-momenta or with tensor indices of the spin states of other particles. The spinor index on the other hand must be contracted with the index of the spinor of another particle. Therefore, Lorentz invariance admits only matrix elements in which spinors and therefore fermions appear pairwise.

From expressions like (4.12) or (5.10) one might get the impression that Lorentz invariance requires equal numbers of fermions in the initial and final state. This however is not true, since the determinant (4.19) of two spinors χ^{a} and χ^{b} is also invariant. The reaction $\mathrm{pp} \to \pi^+\pi^+$ for example could be described by a Lorentz-invariant matrix element of the form $|\chi^{\mathrm{a}}(M_{\mathrm{a}}), \chi^{\mathrm{b}}(M_{\mathrm{b}})| T(s, t)$. An additional symmetry principle is required in order to exclude such reactions.

3-8. Partial wave expansion of meson-proton scattering

In this section, we first derive the partial-wave expansion for the elastic scattering of spin-zero particles on spin-$\frac{1}{2}$ particles. The results are then generalized to include inelastic two-particle reactions. Conservation of parity is not required. The important case of parity-conserving elastic scattering will be discussed in the next section.

As in the spinless case, we work in the cms. The directions of the initial and final proton momenta are denoted by $\hat{\boldsymbol{p}}$ and $\hat{\boldsymbol{p}}'$, respectively; their magnitude is denoted by q. In the cms, the most general Lorentz-invariant matrix element can be put into the form

$$T(M, M', \Omega) = 8\pi s^{\frac{1}{2}} \chi_0'^{+}(M')[f_1 + f_2(\boldsymbol{\sigma} \cdot \hat{\boldsymbol{p}}')(\boldsymbol{\sigma} \cdot \hat{\boldsymbol{p}}) + f_3(\boldsymbol{\sigma} \cdot \hat{\boldsymbol{p}}) + f_4(\boldsymbol{\sigma} \cdot \hat{\boldsymbol{p}}')]\chi_0(M), \tag{8.1}$$

where the functions $f_1, \ldots, f_4$ may depend on the Lorentz-invariants s and t (or s and θ). The meson momenta are the opposite of the proton momenta in the cms. In addition we have $\hat{\boldsymbol{p}} \cdot \hat{\boldsymbol{p}}' = \cos\theta$ and $(\boldsymbol{\sigma} \cdot \hat{\boldsymbol{p}})(\boldsymbol{\sigma} \cdot \hat{\boldsymbol{p}}) = 1$. Note the difference between (1) and (5.15). Equation (1) is valid in the cms only, the functions $f_1, \ldots, f_4$ are free from σ-matrices and three-vectors, whereas (5.15) is covariant, and the $Q_{\mathrm{bb}}, \ldots, Q_{\mathrm{ss}}$ may contain scalar products of $\boldsymbol{\sigma}$ and any of the three linearly independent momentum vectors.

Next, we use helicity states, i.e. we use $\hat{\boldsymbol{p}}(\hat{\boldsymbol{p}}')$ as the spin quantization axis of the initial (final) proton. Writing λ and λ' for the initial and final helicities, we may replace in (1) $\boldsymbol{\sigma} \cdot \hat{\boldsymbol{p}} = 2\lambda$, $\boldsymbol{\sigma} \cdot \hat{\boldsymbol{p}}' = 2\lambda'$, and (1) transforms into

$$T(\lambda, \lambda', \Omega) = 8\pi s^{\frac{1}{2}} \chi'^{+}(\lambda')(f_1 + 4\lambda\lambda' f_2 + 2\lambda f_3 + 2\lambda' f_4)\chi(\lambda). \tag{8.2}$$

The symbol Ω finally stands for the pair of angles θ, ϕ, which are the scattering and azimuthal angles of $\hat{\boldsymbol{p}}'$ relative to $\hat{\boldsymbol{p}}$. We take the z-axis of our coordinate system along $\hat{\boldsymbol{p}}$, in which case the spinors of the initial and final proton are given by (2.1) and (2.4), respectively. As in the case of Λ-decay (4.17), we find

$$\begin{aligned} T(\lambda, \lambda', \Omega) &= 8\pi s^{\frac{1}{2}} D^{\frac{1}{2}*}_{\lambda\lambda'}(\phi, \theta, -\phi)(f_1 + 4\lambda\lambda' f_2 + 2\lambda f_3 + 2\lambda' f_4) \\ &= 8\pi s^{\frac{1}{2}} \mathrm{e}^{\mathrm{i}(\lambda-\lambda')\phi} \mathrm{d}^{\frac{1}{2}}_{\lambda\lambda'}(\theta)(f_1 + 4\lambda\lambda' f_2 + 2\lambda f_3 + 2\lambda' f_4). \end{aligned} \tag{8.3}$$

In later calculations, we shall use the same coordinate system as in fig. 1-3, which means that we shall put $\phi = 0$. In the derivation of partial wave unitarity, however, azimuthal angles are needed in the intermediate steps.

In the presence of spin, the unitarity equation (2-4.1) assumes, for elastic scattering, the form

$$-\mathrm{i}(T_{MM'}(\Omega) - T^*_{M'M}(-\Omega)) = \sum_{M''} \frac{q}{16\pi^2 s^{\frac{1}{2}}} \int \mathrm{d}\Omega' T_{MM''}(\Omega') T^*_{M'M''}(\Omega''). \tag{8.4}$$

This is similar to (2-4.3). The indices i, f, and c have been replaced by the magnetic quantum numbers M, M' and M''. In (4), $\Omega = (\theta, \phi)$ denotes the angles of that rotation which transforms the initial momentum direction $\hat{\boldsymbol{p}}$ into the final momentum direction $\hat{\boldsymbol{p}}'$. In T^* on the l.h.s. of (4), initial and final momenta have been exchanged. Therefore, $-\Omega$ stands for the angles of the opposite rotation, which carries $\hat{\boldsymbol{p}}'$ into $\hat{\boldsymbol{p}}$.

To solve the integral equation (4), we expand T in terms of D-functions:

$$\begin{aligned} T(\lambda\lambda'\Omega) &= 8\pi s^{\frac{1}{2}} \sum_J (2J+1) D^{J*}_{\lambda\lambda'}(\Omega) T_J(\lambda\lambda') \\ &= 8\pi s^{\frac{1}{2}} \mathrm{e}^{\mathrm{i}(\lambda-\lambda')\phi} \sum_J (2J+1) d^J_{\lambda\lambda'}(\theta) T_J(\lambda\lambda'). \end{aligned} \tag{8.5}$$

Here we have replaced M and M' by the helicities λ and λ'. This is necessary if we want to get the ϕ-dependence as a simple phase, independent of J. From (3), we convince ourselves that the expansion (5) is really possible. In terms of $f_1, \ldots, f_4$, it means

$$d^{\frac{1}{2}}_{\lambda\lambda'}(\theta)(f_1(\theta)+4\lambda\lambda' f_2(\theta)+2\lambda f_3(\theta)+2\lambda' f_4(\theta)) = \sum_J (2J+1) d^J_{\lambda\lambda'}(\theta) T_J(\lambda\lambda'). \quad (8.6)$$

In view of table C-4 for helicities $\pm\frac{1}{2}$, this implies an expansion of $f_1, \ldots, f_4$ in terms of the derivatives of Legendre polynomials, $P'_{J\pm\frac{1}{2}}$. For parity-invariant matrix elements, this expansion is given in the next section.

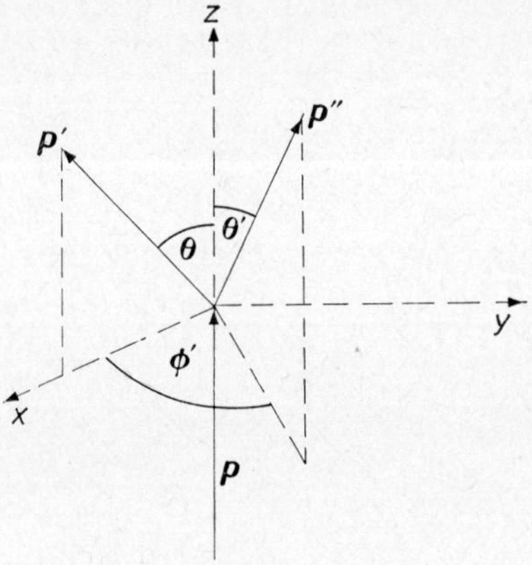

Fig. 3-8. The three momenta **p**, **p**′ and **p**″ occurring in the unitarity equation.

The D-functions in the expansion of $T^*_{\lambda'\lambda}(-\Omega)$ are

$$D_{\lambda'\lambda}(-\Omega) = (D^{-1}(\Omega))_{\lambda'\lambda} = D^*_{\lambda\lambda'}(\Omega), \quad (8.7)$$

i.e. they are identical with those occurring in (5). Inserting the expansion of each T, (4) assumes the following form:

$$-2\pi\mathrm{i} \sum_J D^{J*}_{\lambda\lambda'}(\Omega)[T_J(\lambda\lambda') - T^*_J(\lambda'\lambda)]$$

$$= q \sum_{\lambda''} \int \mathrm{d}\Omega' [\sum_{J'} (2J'+1) D^{J'*}_{\lambda\lambda''}(\Omega') T_{J'}(\lambda\lambda'')]$$

$$\times [\sum_J (2J+1) D^J_{\lambda'\lambda''}(\Omega'') T^*_J(\lambda'\lambda'')]. \quad (8.8)$$

To illustrate the angles Ω' and Ω'', we put $\phi = 0$, i.e. we take the y-axis along the normal to the production plane $\hat{\boldsymbol{p}} \times \hat{\boldsymbol{p}}'$, as shown in fig. 3-8. The angles $\Omega' = (\theta', \phi')$ are now the polar and azimuthal angles of the momentum $\boldsymbol{p}''$ of the intermediate state. Finally, Ω'' represents three angles, two of which specify the direction of $\boldsymbol{p}''$ in a coordinate system in which $\hat{\boldsymbol{p}}'$ is the z-axis. Remember that (3) and therefore also the expansion (5) requires the initial momentum along the z-axis.

Due to the group properties of the rotation matrices, we can express $D(\Omega'')$ as the product of two rotation matrices, the first of which corresponds to the rotation of $\hat{\boldsymbol{p}}'$ back to the z-axis while the second describes the rotation from the z-axis to $\hat{\boldsymbol{p}}''$:

$$D^J_{\lambda'\lambda''}(\Omega'') = \sum_M (D^{-1}(\Omega))_{\lambda' M} D_{M\lambda''}(\Omega')$$
$$= \sum_M D^*_{M\lambda'}(\Omega) D_{M\lambda''}(\Omega'). \tag{8.9}$$

The ϕ'-dependence of the integrand of (8) consists of a factor $e^{i(\lambda-\lambda'')\phi'}$ from the first square bracket, and a factor $e^{i(\lambda''-M)\phi'}$ from the second square bracket, according to (9). Therefore, the ϕ'-integration produces a factor $2\pi\delta_{M\lambda}$, and the r.h.s. of (8) becomes

$$2\pi q \sum_{\lambda''} \int d\cos\theta' [\sum_{J'} (2J'+1) d^{J'}_{\lambda\lambda''}(\theta') T_{J'}(\lambda\lambda'')]$$
$$\times [\sum_J (2J+1) D^{J*}_{\lambda\lambda'}(\Omega) d^J_{\lambda\lambda''}(\theta') T^*_J(\lambda'\lambda'')] \tag{8.10}$$
$$= 4\pi q \sum_{\lambda''} \sum_J (2J+1) T_J(\lambda\lambda'') T^*_J(\lambda'\lambda'') D^{J*}_{\lambda\lambda'}(\Omega). \tag{8.11}$$

The last expression is obtained by means of the orthogonality relations (C-4.1) of the d-functions.

Comparing (11) with the l.h.s. of (8), we find the same ϕ-dependence in both sums. From the orthogonality of the functions $d^J_{\lambda\lambda'}$ and $d^{J'}_{\lambda\lambda'}$ we conclude, analogous to the spinless case, that the coefficients of $d^J_{\lambda\lambda'}(\theta)$ in the two expansions in J must be equal term by term:

$$-i(T_J(\lambda\lambda') - T^*_J(\lambda'\lambda)) = 2 \sum_{\lambda''} q T_J(\lambda\lambda'') T^*_J(\lambda'\lambda''). \tag{8.12}$$

This is the desired partial wave unitarity equation. It is identical with (2-4.8) for the case of two channels, $c \equiv \lambda'' = \pm\frac{1}{2}$. Thus, even in the purely elastic region, it is not possible, on the basis of rotation invariance and unitarity, to express $T_J(\lambda\lambda')$ in terms of a phase shift analogous to (2-4.12). The reason is the degeneracy of spin states. Since q is independent of λ'', there is no energy range in which only one helicity state is "open".

It is not difficult to see that (5) is the only expansion (apart from the factor in front of the summation) which reduces the integral equation to independent matrix equations of 2×2 matrices. To arrive at (12), one needs both the group property (9) and the orthogonality relations of D-functions, which are only valid for *irreducible* representations of the rotation group.

The quantum number J of (5) is called the total angular momentum. The fact that different values of J do not mix in the partial wave unitarity (12) is called the "conservation of the total angular momentum".

In non-relativistic quantum mechanics, one frequently uses states of "orbital angular momentum" instead of helicity states. We can do the same, since (1) is identical with the non-relativistic problem. All "relativistic complications" are hidden in the functions $f_1, \ldots, f_4$. For the derivation of partial-wave unitarity, however, the helicity formalism is the most elegant one. It is true that for the scattering of spin-zero particles on spin-$\frac{1}{2}$ particles, it would have been equally simple to eliminate the d-functions in favour of the derivatives of Legendre polynomials $P'_{J\pm\frac{1}{2}}(\theta)$ according to table C-4. The great advantage of our representation is that the formulae (5) and (7) through (12) are trivially extended to reactions in which all four particles a, b, c, d carry arbitrary spins (JACOB and WICK [1959]). This extension is made in chapter 9.

We conclude this section by extending the above formulae to the region where inelastic two-particle channels contribute to the unitarity equation. For the time being, we assume that also these channels contain one spin-zero and one spin-$\frac{1}{2}$ particle. Then $T(\lambda\lambda', \Omega)$ and $T_J(\lambda\lambda')$ in (5) get two additional channel indices, i and f, and the unitarity equations (4), (8), (10) and (11) contain a summation over intermediate channels c, with different cms momenta, q_c. With these changes, the partial-wave unitarity (12) becomes

$$-\mathrm{i}(T_{\mathrm{if},J}(\lambda\lambda') - T^*_{\mathrm{fi},J}(\lambda'\lambda)) = 2 \sum_{\mathrm{c}} q_{\mathrm{c}} \sum_{\lambda''} T_{\mathrm{ic},J}(\lambda\lambda'') T^*_{\mathrm{fc},J}(\lambda'\lambda''), \qquad (8.13)$$

again in agreement with (2-4.8).

The differential cross-section for unpolarized protons is given by (1.14), with $S_a = \frac{1}{2}$, $S_b = 0$. Insertion of the partial-wave expansion (5) leads to

$$\frac{\mathrm{d}\sigma(s,\theta)}{\mathrm{d}\Omega} = \frac{q'}{q} \frac{1}{4s} \frac{1}{2} \sum_{\lambda\lambda'} \left| \frac{T(\lambda\lambda')}{4\pi} \right|^2 = \frac{q'}{q} \frac{1}{2} \sum_{\lambda\lambda'} \left| \sum_J (2J+1) d^J_{\lambda\lambda'}(\theta) T_J(\lambda\lambda') \right|^2, \qquad (8.14)$$

where q' is the final state cms momentum as in (2-4.15). As expected, (14) is independent of the azimuthal angle ϕ. The integrated cross-section is again simplified by the orthogonality relations of the d-functions:

$$\sigma(s) = 2\pi \frac{q'}{q} \sum_J (2J+1) \sum_{\lambda\lambda'} |T_J(\lambda\lambda')|^2. \tag{8.15}$$

The optical theorem (2-4.2) finally assumes the form

$$\operatorname{Im} T(\lambda, \lambda, \Omega = 0) = 2qs^{\frac{1}{2}}\sigma(\lambda, \text{total}), \tag{8.16}$$

where σ (λ, total) is the total cross-section for a completely polarized proton of helicity λ. To get a theorem for the total cross-section of unpolarized particles, (16) is averaged over the values $\lambda = \pm\frac{1}{2}$:

$$\operatorname{Im} T(\tfrac{1}{2}, \tfrac{1}{2}, \Omega = 0) + \operatorname{Im} T(-\tfrac{1}{2}, -\tfrac{1}{2}, \Omega = 0) = 4qs^{\frac{1}{2}}\sigma\,(\text{total}). \tag{8.17}$$

3-9. Parity conservation in meson-proton scattering

Parity conservation for a general process ab → cd implies invariance of $|T(\text{ab} \to \text{cd})|^2$ under the parity transformation, $\boldsymbol{p}_i \to -\boldsymbol{p}_i$. For elastic scattering, the matrix element $T(\text{ab} \to \text{ab})$ itself must remain invariant. (See section 4-4 below.) For the form (8.1), this implies

$$f_3 = f_4 = 0. \tag{9.1}$$

By means of table C-4, the expansion (8.6) becomes ($x \equiv \cos\theta$)

$$f_1(x) \pm f_2(x) = 2 \sum_J [P'_{J+\frac{1}{2}}(x) \mp P'_{J-\frac{1}{2}}(x)] T_J(\pm\tfrac{1}{2}, \tfrac{1}{2}), \tag{9.2}$$

$$T_J(\tfrac{1}{2}, \tfrac{1}{2}) = T_J(-\tfrac{1}{2}, -\tfrac{1}{2}), \qquad T_J(\tfrac{1}{2}, -\tfrac{1}{2}) = T_J(-\tfrac{1}{2}, \tfrac{1}{2}). \tag{9.3}$$

This symmetry allows a further important reduction of the unitarity equation (8.12). We put $J \equiv L+\frac{1}{2}$ and define partial wave amplitudes $f_{L\pm}$ by

$$\begin{aligned} T_J(\tfrac{1}{2}, \tfrac{1}{2}) &= \tfrac{1}{2}(f_{L+} + f_{(L+1)-}), \\ T_J(\tfrac{1}{2}, -\tfrac{1}{2}) &= \tfrac{1}{2}(f_{L+} - f_{(L+1)-}). \end{aligned} \tag{9.4}$$

In terms of these quantities, (8.12) reads

$$\operatorname{Im} f_{L+} \pm \operatorname{Im} f_{(L+1)-} = q(f^*_{L+} f_{L+} \pm f^*_{(L+1)-} f_{(L+1)-}), \tag{9.5}$$

which decouples into two independent equations,

$$\operatorname{Im} f_{L+} = q f^*_{L+} f_{L+}, \qquad \operatorname{Im} f_{L-} = q f^*_{L-} f_{L-}. \tag{9.6}$$

From these, we conclude as in (2-4.12) that f_{L+} and f_{L-} can be expressed in terms of real "phase shifts",

$$f_{L+} = \frac{1}{q} e^{i\delta_{L+}} \sin \delta_{L+}, \qquad f_{L-} = \frac{1}{q} e^{i\delta_{L-}} \sin \delta_{L-}. \tag{9.7}$$

The "orbital angular momentum" L in (4) has been defined such that f_{L+} and f_{L-} have a threshold behaviour $(qq')^L$, as will be shown below. By definition (4), the "states" $L\pm$ have $J = L\pm\frac{1}{2}$. Later we shall see that in reactions with helicities $> \frac{1}{2}$, parity conservation need not lead to conservation of L. From this point of view, meson-proton scattering is a special case.

Insertion of (4) into (2) gives

$$\begin{aligned} f_1(x) &= \sum_{L=0}^{\infty} [f_{L+} P'_{L+1}(x) - f_{(L-1)-} P'_L(x)] \\ &= f_{0+} + \sum_{L=1}^{\infty} [f_{L+} P'_{L+1}(x) - f_{L-} P'_{L-1}(x)], \end{aligned} \tag{9.8}$$

$$f_2(x) = \sum_{L=0}^{\infty} [f_{(L+1)-} P'_{L+1}(x) - f_{L+} P'_L(x)] = \sum_{L=1}^{\infty} (f_{L-} - f_{L+}) P'_L(x). \tag{9.9}$$

By the orthogonality relations (A-1.10), these equations may be inverted:

$$f_{L\pm} = \tfrac{1}{2} \int_{-1}^{1} dx [P_L(x) f_1(x) + P_{L\pm 1}(x) f_2(x)]. \tag{9.10}$$

The cross-section (8.15) is transformed by (3) and (4) into

$$\sigma(s) = 2\pi \frac{q'}{q} \sum_J (2J+1)(|f_{L+}|^2 + |f_{L-}|^2), \tag{9.11}$$

and the optical theorem (8.16) transforms into

$$\frac{1}{2s^{\frac{1}{2}}} \operatorname{Im} T(\lambda, \lambda, \Omega = 0) = 4\pi \operatorname{Im}(f_1(1) + f_2(1)) = q\sigma(\text{total}). \tag{9.12}$$

The results of sections 2-5 through 2-9 may be extended to meson-proton scattering. The only necessary change is to replace δ_L by $\delta_{L\pm}$ and T_L by $f_{L\pm}$. A resonance in the purely elastic region is again characterized by $\cot \delta_{L\pm} = 0$. The contribution of the resonating partial wave to the total cross-section at resonance energy is

$$\sigma_J(\text{res}) = 2\pi(2J+1)/q^2. \tag{9.13}$$

The threshold behaviour $(qq')^L$ is the same for f_{L+} and f_{L-}. In view of the derivation from (2-6.8), this appears to contradict (10). However, the function f_2 is always proportional to qq'. This factor comes from the "small components" of the Dirac spinors. With $T(M, M')$ in the form $\bar{u}'(M')Qu(M)$ as in (5.10), the most general parity-conserving Q is of the form

$$Q(s, t) = A(s, t) + \tfrac{1}{2}(P_\pi + P_{\pi'}) \cdot \gamma B(s, t), \tag{9.14}$$

where $P_\pi(P_{\pi'})$ denotes the 4-momentum of the initial (final) meson. One easily verifies that this $T(M, M')$ is invariant under the parity transformation $u \to \gamma_0 u$, $\bar{u} \to \bar{u}\gamma_0$, $\boldsymbol{p}_\pi \to -\boldsymbol{p}_\pi$, $\boldsymbol{p}_{\pi'} \to -\boldsymbol{p}_{\pi'}$. From $f_3 = f_4 = 0$, we know already that there are only two independent scalar functions, and therefore (14) is really the most general expression. It gives

$$\left.\begin{matrix} Q_{\mathrm{bb}} \\ Q_{\mathrm{ss}} \end{matrix}\right\} = A \pm \tfrac{1}{2}(E_\pi + E_{\pi'})B, \tag{9.15}$$

$$Q_{\mathrm{bs}} = -Q_{\mathrm{sb}} = -\tfrac{1}{2}(\boldsymbol{p}_\pi + \boldsymbol{p}_{\pi'}) \cdot \boldsymbol{\sigma} B. \tag{9.16}$$

In the cms, (16) may be replaced by $\frac{1}{2}(\boldsymbol{p} + \boldsymbol{p}') \cdot \boldsymbol{\sigma} B$. With this expression, the last square bracket of (5.15) becomes $\frac{1}{2}B$ times

$$(\boldsymbol{\sigma} \cdot \hat{\boldsymbol{p}}')(\boldsymbol{\sigma} \cdot \hat{\boldsymbol{p}})(q'\sqrt{(E-m)(E'+m')} + q\sqrt{(E+m)(E'-m')}) \\ + q\sqrt{(E-m)(E'+m')} + q'\sqrt{(E+m)(E'-m')}. \tag{9.17}$$

Now (5.15) is easily arranged in the form (8.1), and the final result is

$$\begin{aligned} f_1 &= \frac{1}{8\pi s^{\frac{1}{2}}} \sqrt{(E+m)(E'+m')}[A + B(s^{\frac{1}{2}} - \tfrac{1}{2}m - \tfrac{1}{2}m')], \\ f_2 &= \frac{1}{8\pi s^{\frac{1}{2}}} \sqrt{(E-m)(E'-m')}[-A + B(s^{\frac{1}{2}} + \tfrac{1}{2}m + \tfrac{1}{2}m')], \end{aligned} \tag{9.18}$$

and, of course, $f_3 = f_4 = 0$. The square root in f_2 is rewritten as $qq'/\sqrt{(E+m)(E'+m')}$, which displays the factor qq' we were looking for.

Finally, we construct the matrix elements $T(M, M'\theta)$ for the case that both initial and final spin states are quantized along the momentum of the initial proton. With $\phi = 0$ and $\hat{p}'_x = + \sin\theta$, the parity-invariant form of (8.1) is

$$T(M, M', \theta) = 8\pi s^{\frac{1}{2}} \chi_0^+(M')[f_1 + 2Mf_2(\sigma_z \cos\theta + \sigma_x \sin\theta)]\chi_0(M), \tag{9.19}$$

$$\begin{aligned} T(\tfrac{1}{2}, \tfrac{1}{2}, \theta) &= T(-\tfrac{1}{2}, -\tfrac{1}{2}, \theta) = 8\pi s^{\frac{1}{2}}(f_1 + f_2 \cos\theta), \\ T(\tfrac{1}{2}, -\tfrac{1}{2}, \theta) &= -T(-\tfrac{1}{2}, \tfrac{1}{2}, \theta) = 8\pi s^{\frac{1}{2}} f_2 \sin\theta. \end{aligned} \tag{9.20}$$

These matrix elements, frequently denoted by f and g, are called the "spin-nonflip" and "spin-flip" amplitudes. They are useful e.g. for the inclusion of Coulomb scattering (see section 10-1).

CHAPTER 4

SURVEY OF BARYONS AND MESONS

4-1. Classification of elementary particles

In this chapter, we review the main properties of hadrons. Among the most obvious properties, we have the masses, lifetimes and decay modes. The determination of spins and parities is usually more difficult. In addition to these quantum numbers, there exist a few other quantum numbers like baryon number, hypercharge and isospin, which are a priori unrelated to the transformations in space and time. The definition and application of these quantum numbers is the topic of the next few sections.

Elementary particles are classified into hadrons, leptons, and the photon. This classification is based on three different types of interactions, called the strong, electromagnetic and weak interactions. The photon, by definition, has only electromagnetic interactions. In the first place, the photon interacts with all electrically charged particles. The strength of the interaction is characterized by the electric charge e, which is the same, apart from a sign, for all charged elementary particles. It usually appears in the combination

$$\alpha = e^2/4\pi = 1/137. \tag{1.1}$$

The exact value of α^{-1} is 137.036 (PARKER, TAYLOR and LANGENBERG [1967]. Matrix elements for elastic ep (= electron-proton), pp, π^+p or π^-p scattering at small momentum transfer contain a term proportional to α/t, where t is the square of the momentum transfer. This term comes from the "exchange of a virtual photon", which is "emitted" by one particle (coupling constant $\pm e$) and "absorbed" by the other (again coupling constant $\pm e$). It is absent e.g. in pn-scattering. In fact, the term "electromagnetic interactions" means "interactions by means of photons". These interactions are discussed in more detail in chapter 10. Photons may also interact with neutral particles. An example hereof is the decay $\pi^0 \to \gamma\gamma$, to be discussed in section 4-8. Also in such cases, the matrix element is believed to be proportional to α, although it contains other factors which are difficult to calculate.

The lepton class of elementary particles consists of the electron (e$^-$), muon (μ^+), neutrino (ν), and their antiparticles positron (e$^+$), antimuon (μ^-) and antineutrino ($\bar{\nu}$). Particles and antiparticles have identical masses and lifetimes. The particle-antiparticle symmetry is discussed in sections 4-6 and 4-7. For e, μ and ν, the classification into leptons and antileptons poses some problems, which will be discussed in section 12-5.

The approximate masses of e, μ and ν are 0.5, 100 and 0 MeV, respectively. The name "lepton" means "light particle". All leptons have spin-$\frac{1}{2}$.

Leptons have weak interactions, and, of course, the electrically-charged leptons $e^{\mp}$ and $\mu^{\pm}$ have electromagnetic interactions. The weak interactions are characterized by a coupling constant,

$$G_\mu = 1.163 \times 10^{-5}/\mathrm{GeV}^2. \tag{1.2}$$

This number is obtained from μ-decay ($\mu^+ \to e^+\nu\nu$), but it appears to be approximately independent of the types of particle involved. The matrix elements for β-decay ($n \to pe\bar{\nu}$) and Λ-decay ($\Lambda \to p\pi^-$, $\Lambda \to n\pi^0$) contain roughly the same constant. Compared to α, this constant is very small. Note also the difference in dimensions between G_μ and α. In matrix elements, G_μ and α are multiplied by different powers of momenta or energies, which are usually smaller than 1 GeV.

Hadrons finally have weak, electromagnetic and strong interactions. The strength of strong interactions is illustrated by the pion-nucleon coupling constant,

$$G^2/4\pi = 14.9, \tag{1.3}$$

although not all coupling constants of strong interactions are so large.

It is convenient to classify hadrons into baryons, mesons, baryon resonances and meson resonances. Baryons have spin-$\frac{1}{2}$, while mesons have spin zero. Both baryons and mesons decay by electromagnetic or weak interactions and are therefore comparatively stable. The resonances on the other hand decay by strong interactions and are extremely unstable (with one exception, which we discuss below).

There are 8 baryons and 8 mesons. Their masses, lifetimes and decay modes are listed in table 4-1. For later calculations, the square of the mass and the decay momentum

$$\frac{1}{2m}\sqrt{\lambda(m^2, m_a^2, m_b^2)}$$

are also given. For decays into more than two particles, the maximal decay momentum is given instead. This is the momentum of the heaviest decay particle, taken at zero relative momentum of the other decay particles (it is calculated by replacing in (1-2.9) s by m^2 and m_b by the sum of the masses of the other decay particles).

TABLE 4-1

Masses and decay rates of baryons and mesons (after ROSENFELD tables [1967]). The common symbols e, μ, ν are used for leptons and antileptons. Statistical errors are always in the last figure. Resonances are tabulated in tables 5-3 and 5-6, leptons in table 12-5.

Baryons

Symbol	m [GeV] m^2 [GeV^2]	Γ^{-1}[sec] Γ [eV]	Partial mode	fraction	p or p_{max} [GeV]
p	0.93826 0.88032	stable			
n	0.93955 0.88275	1.01×10^{3} 6.5×10^{-19}	peν	1	0.00119
Λ	1.1156 1.2445	2.5×10^{-10} 2.6×10^{-6}	pπ^- nπ^0 peν p$\mu\nu$	0.66 0.34 0.0009 0.0001	0.100 0.104 0.163 0.131
Σ^+	1.1895 1.4149	0.8×10^{-10} 8×10^{-6}	pπ^0 nπ^+ pγ n$\pi^+\gamma$ Λeν	0.53 0.47 0.0019 2×10^{-5} 2×10^{-5}	0.189 0.185 0.225 0.185 0.072
Σ^0	1.1926 1.4222	$<10^{-14}$ >0.1	$\Lambda\gamma$ Λe$^+$e$^-$	1 0.005	0.0745 0.0745
Σ^-	1.1974 1.4339	1.65×10^{-10} 4.0×10^{-6}	nπ^- neν n$\mu\nu$ Λeν n$\pi^-\gamma$	1 0.0012 0.0006 6×10^{-5} 1×10^{-5}	0.193 0.230 0.209 0.079 0.193
Ξ^0	1.315 1.728	3×10^{-10} 2×10^{-6}	$\Lambda\pi^0$	1	0.135
Ξ^-	1.321 1.746	1.7×10^{-10} 3.8×10^{-6}	$\Lambda\pi^-$ Λeν	1 0.002	0.139 0.190

Mesons

Symbol	m [GeV] m^2 [GeV]^2	Γ^{-1} [sec] Γ [eV]	Partial mode	fraction	p or p_{max} [GeV]
$\pi^\pm$	0.13958	2.61×10^{-8}	$\mu\nu$	1	0.0298
	0.019482	2.52×10^{-8}	$e\nu$	0.00012	0.0698
			$\mu\nu\gamma$	0.00012	0.0298
			$\pi^0 e\nu$	1.0×10^{-8}	0.0045
π^0	0.13497	0.9×10^{-16}	$\gamma\gamma$	0.988	0.0675
	0.018217	7.4	γe^+e^-	0.012	0.0675
$K^\pm$	0.4938	1.23×10^{-8}	$\mu\nu$	0.63	0.236
	0.2438	5.33×10^{-8}	$\pi\pi^0$	0.21	0.205
			$\pi\pi\bar{\pi}$	0.056	0.126
			$\pi\pi^0\pi^0$	0.017	0.133
			$\pi^0\mu\nu$	0.034	0.215
			$\pi^0 e\nu$	0.048	0.228
			$\pi\pi^0\gamma$	0.0002	0.205
		$\pi\equiv\pi^\pm$	$\pi\pi\bar{\pi}\gamma$	0.0001	0.126
		$\bar{\pi}\equiv\pi^\mp$	$\pi\bar{\pi}e\nu$	4×10^{-5}	0.204
			$e\nu$	2×10^{-5}	0.247
K^0_S	0.4978	0.87×10^{-10}	$\pi^+\pi^-$	0.69	0.206
	0.2478	7.6×10^{-6}	$\pi^0\pi^0$	0.31	0.209
K^0_L	0.4978	5.2×10^{-8}	$\pi^0\pi^0\pi^0$	0.23	0.139
	0.2478	1.16×10^{-8}	$\pi^+\pi^-\pi^0$	0.115	0.133
			$\pi^\pm\mu\nu$	0.29	0.216
			$\pi^\pm e\nu$	0.37	0.229
			$\pi^+\pi^-$	0.0015	0.206
	m_L-m_S		$\pi^0\pi^0$	0.004	0.209
	$=0.6\Gamma(K^0_S)$		$\gamma\gamma$	0.0007	0.249
η	0.5486		$\gamma\gamma$	0.31	0.274
	0.3010	3×10^3	$\pi^0\gamma\gamma$	0.20	0.258
			$\pi^0\pi^0\pi^0$	0.21	0.179
			$\pi^+\pi^-\pi^0$	0.22	0.174
			$\pi^+\pi^-\gamma$	0.05	0.236

The most short-lived baryon is the Σ^0: π^0 and η^0 are the two most short-lived mesons. These three particles decay by electromagnetic interactions. The remaining baryons and mesons decay by weak interactions.

Of the mesons, π^+ and π^-, K^+ and K^- are treated pairwise, because they have identical masses and decay properties. In section 4-6 we shall show that π^+ and π^-, K^+ and K^- are antiparticles of each other. The antiparticles of baryons on the other hand are not among the baryons. There are in fact two more classes of hadrons, namely the antibaryons and the antibaryon resonances.

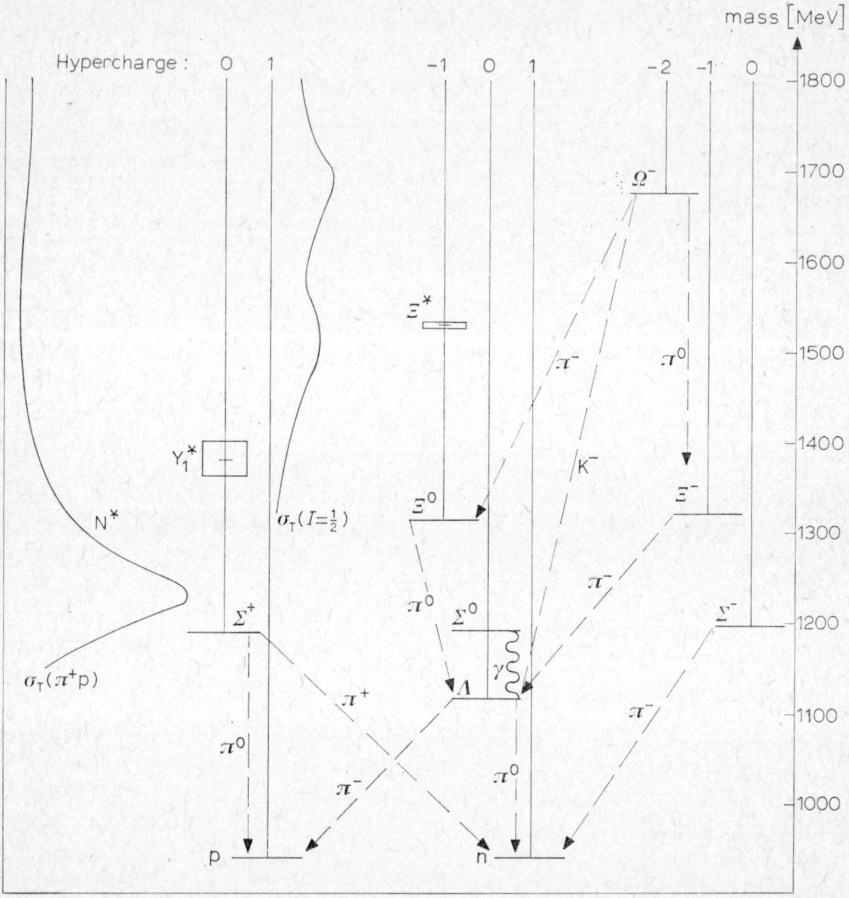

Fig. 4-1. Masses and main decay modes of baryons and some baryon resonances. The curve $\sigma_T(\pi^+p)$ gives the total π^+p cross-section as a function of the cms energy, and $\sigma_T(I=\frac{1}{2}) = \frac{3}{2}\sigma_T(\pi^-p) - \frac{1}{2}\sigma_T(\pi^+p)$. The heights of the squares for Y_1^* and Ξ^* indicate the widths of these resonances.

The decay scheme of the baryons is illustrated in fig. 4-1. Also shown are the positions and widths of some baryon resonances, called N^*, Y_1^*, Ξ^* and Ω^-. We mention these now because the Ω^- is the only resonance which decays by weak interactions. It is therefore a "good" particle, with a lifetime of the order of 10^{-10} sec. Nevertheless, we do not call it a baryon but a baryon resonance, because its internal structure is believed to be the same as that of N^*, Y_1^* and Ξ^* (which all have spin-$\frac{3}{2}$). From a mathematical point of view, any unstable particle can be treated as a resonance of its decay products (see section 2-8). This shows that the distinction between particles and resonances is to some extent arbitrary.

The decays of hadrons obey certain selection rules. The most obvious rule is the conservation of electric charge. In any reaction or decay, the total electric charge is the same in the initial and final states.

Next, we observe that each baryon decays into some other baryon plus additional particles. Decays like $p \to e\gamma$ or $\Lambda \to e\pi$, with no baryon in the final state are absent. From this we conclude that there exists another conserved quantum number, the baryon number. It has the value $+1$ for baryons and baryon resonances, and zero for mesons, leptons and the photon. Like the electric charge, it is strictly conserved.

However, we must be more careful in eliminating alternative explanations. We shall see later that there is a similar quantum number for leptons, called lepton number, which is zero for hadrons and the photon. Decays like $p \to e\gamma$, $\Lambda \to e\pi$ are also forbidden by the conservation of lepton number. Decays like $p \to \pi^+\pi^0$ or $\Lambda \to \pi^+\pi^-$ are already forbidden by the conservation modulo two or fermions. Therefore, the decay scheme of baryons cannot prove the existence of a special baryon quantum number. The conclusive evidence comes instead from the stability of atomic nuclei. The deuteron, for example, could decay into $\pi^+\pi^0$, helium into $\pi^+\pi^+$ or π^+d etc., if the baryon number were not conserved.

The various particles of table 4-1 are discussed in the following sections. A few selection rules for hadron decays are given in section 4-9.

4-2. Nucleons, pions and isospin

The proton, the neutron and the three pions are the oldest and best known hadrons. Long before the discovery of the pion (see the review of POWELL [1950]), YUKAWA [1935] predicted the existence of mesons from his model of nuclear forces. In the same way as electromagnetic forces are due to the exchange of photons, Yukawa postulated mesons as the carrier of nuclear forces. The mass of these mesons can be estimated from the range of the potential, by means of the uncertainty relation $\Delta E \Delta T \geqq 1$. When a nucleon emits a meson, its energy is changed by at least the meson mass μ. According to the uncertainty relation, this "virtual state" can exist only for a time interval $\Delta T \approx 1/\mu$. Since particles cannot travel faster than light, the distance at which the meson can go, i.e. the range R of the force, is of the order of $1/\mu$ (cf. 2-6.12). This shows that the long-range part of the nuclear potential is due to the exchange of the lightest meson, i.e. the pion.

The idea of isospin also originated from the theory of nuclear forces. Because of the smallness of the p − n mass difference, one is tempted to treat these two particles as different states of one particle, called the nucleon (N). Hopefully, nuclear forces are charge-independent, i.e. pp, pn and nn forces are identical.

To make this more precise, let us switch from potential language to scattering cross-sections and matrix elements. The differential pp and pn elastic scattering cross-sections at given s are not expected to be equal for three reasons, namely the mass difference, the Coulomb scattering, and the Pauli principle. We must therefore incorporate these effects explicitly. The mass difference manifests itself as a difference in q^2 at fixed s. It affects relation (2-2.16) between the matrix element $T(s, t)$ and the cross-section. We now assume that $T(s, t)$ is independent of the mass difference.

Coulomb scattering occurs between two protons but not between proton and neutron or between two neutrons. We shall calculate it later, in chapter 10. We therefore put for pp scattering

$$T_{\mathrm{pp}}(s, t) = T(s, t) + T_{\mathrm{c}}(s, t), \tag{2.1}$$

where T_{c} is the Coulomb scattering amplitude, and $T(s, t)$ is the supposedly common amplitude for pn and nn scattering.

Last but not least, the Pauli principle operates for pp and nn scattering, but not for pn scattering. As is well-known, the Pauli principle requires that a state $|\mathrm{n}_1 \mathrm{n}_2\rangle$ consisting of two identical spin-$\frac{1}{2}$ particles is antisymmetric under the simultaneous exchange of the momenta and spin-component quantum numbers, (here denoted by "1" and "2"). If we want to compare pp scattering with pn scattering, we must first split the $|\mathrm{p}_1 \mathrm{n}_2\rangle$ state into an antisymmetric and a symmetric part:

$$\begin{aligned} |\mathrm{p}_1 \mathrm{n}_2\rangle &= 2^{-\frac{1}{2}}|\mathrm{p}_1 \mathrm{n}_2\rangle_{\mathrm{a}} + 2^{-\frac{1}{2}}|\mathrm{p}_1 \mathrm{n}_2\rangle_{\mathrm{s}}, \\ |\mathrm{p}_1 \mathrm{n}_2\rangle^{\mathrm{s}}_{\mathrm{a}} &\equiv 2^{-\frac{1}{2}}|\mathrm{p}_1 \mathrm{n}_2\rangle \pm 2^{-\frac{1}{2}}|\mathrm{n}_1 \mathrm{p}_2\rangle. \end{aligned} \tag{2.2}$$

Only the antisymmetric part can be compared with pp and nn scattering. The symmetric part is not restricted by the principle of charge independence. The S-wave pn state of total spin one, for example, is symmetric. It contains a bound state, the deuteron, which simply cannot exist in the corresponding pp and nn states because of the Pauli principle.

Similar considerations can be applied to three-nucleon states. There, the number of possible charge combinations is $2^3 = 8$, namely ppp, ppn, pnp, npp, nnp, npn, nnp, nnn. Charge independence states that the matrix elements for the totally antisymmetric states are equal. In addition, there are two different groups of symmetry states, each containing two charge combinations. The matrix elements within each group must be equal.

We still need the matrix elements of the S-matrix between states of different symmetry. For that purpose, we define charge independence in the following form. *The S-matrix for the scattering of n nucleons of momentum-spin quantum numbers "1" to "n" does not depend upon which of these quantum numbers belong to protons and which to neutrons.* Stated mathematically, the S-matrix commutes with operators which replace protons by neutrons and neutrons by protons. Consequently, the S-matrix element between a symmetric proton-neutron state and an antisymmetric proton-neutron state vanishes. In general, all matrix elements between states of different symmetries vanish.

The formal study of this symmetry is accomplished by the formalism of isospin. Every particle state is split into a part describing the spin and momentum and an "isospin state" describing the charge. For example, we put $|\mathrm{n}_1\mathrm{n}_2\rangle = |12\rangle\,|\mathrm{nn}\rangle$. Since the charge of a nucleon assumes only two values, the nucleon isospin states can be taken as two-component vectors, like the spin states (3-2.1),

$$|\mathrm{p}\rangle = \begin{pmatrix}1\\0\end{pmatrix}, \qquad |\mathrm{n}\rangle = \begin{pmatrix}0\\1\end{pmatrix}. \tag{2.3}$$

The S-matrix of nuclear scattering is a 2×2 matrix, insofar as the charge of each nucleon is concerned. Charge independence of the S-matrix means that S commutes with the matrix σ_x of (3-2.2) which transforms protons into neutrons. In addition, conservation of charge requires that S commutes with σ_z, since the charge matrix can be written as $\frac{1}{2}+\frac{1}{2}\sigma_z$. If S commutes with σ_x and σ_z, it also commutes with σ_y (by $[\sigma_z, \sigma_x] = 2i\sigma_y$), which means that it commutes with all generators of the group SU_2. From this we conclude (LIPKIN [1965]) that charge independence of nuclear interactions is equivalent with invariance under unitary transformations between neutron and proton states. Hence, the complete formalism of spin can be applied. (Effects such as spin-orbit coupling are of course absent in the isospin case.) The eigenvalues of the square and the third component of the isospin operator $\boldsymbol{I}$ are denoted by $I(I+1)$ and I_3, respectively. Proton and neutron have $I = \frac{1}{2}$ and $I_3 = \pm\frac{1}{2}$, respectively. For two nucleons, eigenstates of the square of the total isospin are constructed by means of the Clebsch-Gordan coefficients. We find

$$\begin{aligned} &\text{for } I = 1\text{:} \quad |\mathrm{p}\rangle|\mathrm{p}\rangle, \qquad 2^{-\frac{1}{2}}(|\mathrm{p}\rangle|\mathrm{n}\rangle+|\mathrm{n}\rangle|\mathrm{p}\rangle), \qquad |\mathrm{n}\rangle|\mathrm{n}\rangle, \\ &\text{for } I = 0\text{:} \quad 2^{-\frac{1}{2}}(|\mathrm{p}\rangle|\mathrm{n}\rangle-|\mathrm{n}\rangle|\mathrm{p}\rangle). \end{aligned} \tag{2.4}$$

If we now invoke the Pauli principle for the protons, we arrive at a generalized Pauli principle for the complete states (i.e. the products of the momentum-spin states and the isospin states): the complete states must be antisymmetric under the simultaneous exchange of all quantum numbers, including the charge quantum numbers. For example, the $I = 1$ states in (4) are symmetric in the charges of the two particles. They therefore belong to an antisymmetric momentum-spin state. The $I = 0$ state is antisymmetric: it is therefore multiplied with a symmetric spin-momentum state.

According to Schur's lemma (B-3), the S-matrix between states of equal I is a multiple of the unit matrix in the I_3 space. The argument is analogous to that which leads to (3-1.2). In addition, S is zero unless I is the same in the initial and final states. This follows from the fact that S commutes with the operator I^2:

$$\begin{aligned} \langle I', I_3'|I^2S|I, I_3\rangle &= I'(I'+1)\langle I', I_3'|S|I, I_3\rangle \\ &= \langle I', I_3'|SI^2|I, I_3\rangle = I(I+1)\langle I'I_3'|S|I, I_3\rangle. \end{aligned} \tag{2.5}$$

Summing up, we have

$$\langle I', I_3'|S|I, I_3\rangle = S(I)\delta_{II'}\delta_{I_3I_3'}. \tag{2.6}$$

Applying this to the states (4), we rediscover the results following (2). The scattering amplitudes for the triplet of states (called "isotriplet") are equal, whereas the scattering in the last state may be different. In addition, (6) tells us that there is no transition between the isosinglet and isotriplet states. This conclusion is trivial, since by definition (2), the $I_3 = 0$ triplet and singlet states have different symmetries.

In the isospin language, the deuteron has $I = 0$. We shall not treat here the three-nucleon states: instead, later in this section, we discuss the three-pion states.

Many relations between the properties of pions follow indirectly from the charge independence of nuclear forces. The three pions must have nearly equal masses, and they must belong to an $I = 1$ representation of SU_2 (KEMMER [1938]). From conservation of I_3 in the emission and absorption of pions by nucleons (or from reactions such as $\mathrm{pp} \to \mathrm{pn}\pi^+$), it follows that π^+, π^0 and π^- have $I_3 = +1$, 0 and -1, respectively. Let us see now what restrictions isospin variance (6) imposes on the amplitudes for the $2\times 3 = 6$ charge combinations of πN scattering. To apply (6), we need the eigenstates of the total isospin. In the notation $|I, I_3\rangle$, these are

$$|\tfrac{3}{2}, \tfrac{3}{2}\rangle = |\pi^+ p\rangle, \qquad |\tfrac{3}{2}, -\tfrac{3}{2}\rangle = |\pi^- n\rangle, \tag{2.7}$$

$$|\tfrac{3}{2}, \tfrac{1}{2}\rangle = \sqrt{\tfrac{1}{3}}|\pi^+ n\rangle + \sqrt{\tfrac{2}{3}}|\pi^0 p\rangle, \qquad |\tfrac{3}{2}, -\tfrac{1}{2}\rangle = \sqrt{\tfrac{1}{3}}|\pi^- p\rangle + \sqrt{\tfrac{2}{3}}|\pi^0 n\rangle, \tag{2.8}$$

$$|\tfrac{1}{2}, \tfrac{1}{2}\rangle = \sqrt{\tfrac{2}{3}}|\pi^+ n\rangle - \sqrt{\tfrac{1}{3}}|\pi^0 p\rangle, \qquad |\tfrac{1}{2}, -\tfrac{1}{2}\rangle = -\sqrt{\tfrac{2}{3}}|\pi^- p\rangle + \sqrt{\tfrac{1}{3}}|\pi^0 n\rangle. \tag{2.9}$$

Our sign conventions are those of CONDON and SHORTLEY [1935]. We see that only two values of I are possible, namely $\frac{3}{2}$ and $\frac{1}{2}$. Consequently, the scattering between all possible charge combinations is described by two amplitudes. The explicit relations will be given in section 5-3. We see immediately that πN scattering is *not* charge independent. For example, the amplitudes for elastic π^+p scattering and π^+n scattering are not the same for identical momentum-spin states. Thus the charge independence of nuclear scattering, which is the same as isospin invariance, by no means implies charge independence of other types of scattering. However, it does imply charge symmetry, which is symmetry under the replacement $I_3 \to -I_3$ for all particles simultaneously. For example, the matrix elements of elastic π^+p and elastic π^-n scattering are equal (after subtraction of the Coulomb part for π^+p).

Isospin states for two and three pions are collected in table 4-2. For two pions, the total isospin can assume the values $I = 0$, 1, and 2. The $I = 0$ and 2 states are symmetric under exchange of the charges of the two pions, whereas the $I = 1$ states are antisymmetric.

The Bose-Einstein principle requires that the $\pi^+\pi^+$ and $\pi^-\pi^-$ states are symmetric under the exchange of the two pion momenta. From the factorization of the general states into an isospin state and a momentum state, we deduce, as a generalized Bose-Einstein principle, that the other product states are symmetric, too. Therefore, the even angular momentum states (S-waves, D-waves etc) of $\pi\pi$ scattering have $I = 0$ or 2, and the odd angular momentum states (P-waves) have $I = 1$.

Three-pion isospin states are usually constructed by adding a third pion to the above two-pion isospin states. Let I_{12} denote the total isospin of the first two pions. Then the total isospin I of all three pions can be 1 for $I_{12} = 0$, it can be 0, 1, and 2 for $I_{12} = 1$, and 1, 2, and 3 for $I_{12} = 2$. Except for the two $I = 1$ states, these are just the states given in the table.

TABLE 4-2

Isospin states of definite symmetry for two and three pions. Three-pion states of negative I_3 are obtained from those of positive I_3 by the substitution $\pi^+ \leftrightarrow \pi^-$. (For $I = 2$, an extra minus sign is needed.)

Symmetry	I	$I_3 = 0$	$I_3 = \pm 1$	$I_3 = \pm 2$
[1 | 2]	2	$6^{-\frac{1}{2}}(\pi^+\pi^- + \pi^-\pi^+ + 2\pi^0\pi^0)$	$2^{-\frac{1}{2}}(\pi^\pm\pi^0 + \pi^0\pi^\pm)$	$\pi^\pm\pi^\pm$
	0	$3^{-\frac{1}{2}}(\pi^+\pi^- + \pi^-\pi^+ - \pi^0\pi^0)$		
[1 / 2]	1	$2^{-\frac{1}{2}}(\pi^+\pi^- - \pi^-\pi^+)$	$\pm 2^{-\frac{1}{2}}(\pi^\pm\pi^0 - \pi^0\pi^\pm)$	

Symmetry	I		$\pi^+\pi^-\pi^0$	$\pi^-\pi^+\pi^0$	$\pi^+\pi^0\pi^-$	$\pi^0\pi^+\pi^-$	$\pi^-\pi^0\pi^+$	$\pi^0\pi^-\pi^+$	$\pi^0\pi^0\pi^0$
[1 | 2 | 3]	3	$10^{-\frac{1}{2}}$	(1	+1	+1	+1	+1	+1	−2)
	1	$15^{-\frac{1}{2}}$	(1	+1	+1	+1	+1	+1	+3)
[1 | 2 / 3]	2	$\frac{1}{2}$	(0	+0	+1	+1	−1	−1)	
	1	$12^{-\frac{1}{2}}$	(2	+2	−1	−1	−1	−1)	
[1 | 3 / 2]	2	$12^{-\frac{1}{2}}$	(2	−2	+1	−1	−1	+1)	
	1	$\frac{1}{2}$	(0	+0	+1	−1	+1	−1)	
[1 / 2 / 3]	0	$6^{-\frac{1}{2}}$	(1	−1	−1	+1	+1	−1)	

Symmetry			$\pi^+\pi^+\pi^-$	$\pi^+\pi^-\pi^+$	$\pi^-\pi^+\pi^+$	$\pi^0\pi^0\pi^+$	$\pi^0\pi^+\pi^0$	$\pi^+\pi^0\pi^0$		$\pi^+\pi^+\pi^0$	$\pi^+\pi^0\pi^+$	$\pi^0\pi^+\pi^+$	$\pi^+\pi^+\pi^+$
[1 | 2 | 3]	3	$15^{-\frac{1}{2}}$	(1	+1	+1	+2	+2	+2)	$3^{-\frac{1}{2}}$	(1	+1	+1)	1
	1	$15^{-\frac{1}{2}}$	(2	+2	+2	−1	−1	−1)					
[1 | 2 / 3]	2	$12^{-\frac{1}{2}}$	(2	−1	−1	−2	+1	+1)	$6^{-\frac{1}{2}}$	(2	−1	−1)	
	1	$12^{-\frac{1}{2}}$	(−2	+1	+1	−2	+1	+1)					
[1 | 3 / 2]	2	$\frac{1}{2}$	(0	+1	−1	+0	−1	+1)	$2^{-\frac{1}{2}}$	(0	+1	−1)	
	1	$\frac{1}{2}$	(0	−1	+1	+0	−1	+1)					

In general, the above coupling scheme treats the three pions in a non-symmetrical way. For the application of the Bose-Einstein principle, it is better to use states of definite symmetry. By definition, such states belong to irreducible representations of the permutation group. In fact, there exist n-particle states which transform irreducibly under unitary transformations SU_2, SU_3 etc. *and* under permutations P_n. The construction of such states is discussed by JAHN and VAN WIERINGEN [1951]. Extensive applications to the many-pion problem have been made by PAIS [1960, 1963]. Instead of discussing the general theory, we show how this works for table 4-2.

Symmetric and antisymmetric two-pion states are denoted by the "Young tableaux"

$$\begin{array}{|c|c|}\hline 1 & 2 \\ \hline \end{array} \quad \text{and} \quad \begin{array}{|c|}\hline 1 \\ \hline 2 \\ \hline \end{array}\,,$$

respectively. This is true even when the two-particle tableau appears as part of a larger tableau. Therefore, whenever 1 and 2 are in the same column, we have $I_{12} = 1$. When they are in the same row, we may have a mixture of $I_{12} = 0$ and $I_{12} = 2$. For the $I = 3$ and $I = 2$ states, however, the triangular inequality of vector addition excludes $I_{12} = 0$. Therefore the only states which need not be eigenstates of I_{12} are those $I = 1$ states which contain the tableau $\begin{array}{|c|c|}\hline 1 & 2 \\ \hline \end{array}$. They are constructed in the following way:

The Young tableau $\begin{array}{|c|c|c|}\hline 1 & 2 & 3 \\ \hline \end{array}$ is completely symmetric in all indices. Denoting by $|I, I_3, I_{12}\rangle$ the states of the ordinary "2+1" coupling, we find that for $I = 1$, the only totally symmetric combination is

$$|1, I_3, \begin{array}{|c|c|c|}\hline 1 & 2 & 3 \\ \hline \end{array}\,\rangle = \tfrac{2}{3}|1, I_3, 2\rangle + \tfrac{1}{3}5^{\frac{1}{2}}|1, I_3, 0\rangle. \tag{2.10}$$

The coefficients in (10) are called fractional parentage coefficients. Note that they are independent of I_3. The remaining symmetry states are now fixed (up to a sign) by the requirement of orthogonality on (10):

$$|1, I_3, \begin{array}{|c|c}\hline 1 & \multicolumn{1}{c|}{2} \\ \hline 3 & \\ \cline{1-1} \end{array}\,\rangle = -\tfrac{1}{3}5^{\frac{1}{2}}|1, I_3, 2\rangle + \tfrac{2}{3}|1, I_3, 0\rangle. \tag{2.11}$$

The symmetries of the various Young tableaux can be read off directly from table 4-2, e.g. from the coefficients of the states ($\pi^+\pi^-\pi^0$+ permutations). The state

$$\begin{array}{|c|}\hline 1 \\ \hline 2 \\ \hline 3 \\ \hline \end{array}$$

e.g. is totally antisymmetric. We could have written down it directly, without knowing any Clebsch-Gordan coefficients. That it has $I = 0$ follows simply from the fact that totally antisymmetric three-pion states require three different charges, i.e. $I_3 = 0$. The first application of three-pion symmetry states is in section 4-9.

We conclude this section by discussing the experimental and "theoretical" accuracy of isospin invariance. The two lightest nuclei of zero isospin are the deuteron and the helium nucleus. The reaction dd → $He^4\pi^0$ has been shown to be absent with a high degree of accuracy (POIRIET and PRIPSTEIN [1963]). In most reactions, one has to separate off electromagnetic interactions before one can speak about isospin invariance. In (1), this was achieved simply by subtracting the Coulomb scattering amplitude. In other reactions, it is more difficult, and in some cases it has so far been impossible. When no separation between electromagnetic and strong interactions is possible, it is of course meaningless to claim that strong interactions are isospin invariant. All one can do in such cases is to quote the deviation of the complete amplitude from isospin invariance.

To indicate how this appears, let us return to the NN-scattering amplitude $T(s, t)$, which was supposed to be charge independent. According to the idea of Yukawa, this amplitude can be calculated from a potential which has the range of the pion mass. The charged pion is 4.6 MeV heavier than the π^0, which means a mass difference of more than 3%. If the range is charge-dependent by 3%, we expect some charge-dependent effects also in $T(s, t)$.

4-3. Strange particles and hypercharge

The four K-mesons or "kaons" K^+, K^-, K^0_L and K^0_S as well as all baryons heavier than the nucleons are called strange particles. This name has historical reasons; from our present point of understanding, all hadrons are equally "strange". However, the physics of strange particles is rather disconnected from the theory of nuclear forces as well as from low-energy pion-nucleon interactions.

The strange baryons are the lambda hyperon Λ, the three sigma-hyperons Σ^+, Σ^0 and Σ^-, and the cascade particles Ξ^0 and Ξ^-. This name for Ξ^0 and Ξ^- is motivated by the cascade of successive decays of these particles, illustrated in fig. 4-1. Sometimes the expression "xi-hyperon" is also used, but we shall reserve the word "hyperon" for Λ and Σ.

In strong interactions strange particles always appear pairwise. In pion-proton collisions, for example, hyperons are produced only together with a K^+ or a K^0. In two-particle reactions, the following combinations are observed ("associated production"):

$$\pi^+ p \to K^+ \Sigma^+, \quad \pi^- p \to K^0 \Lambda, \quad \pi^- p \to K^0 \Sigma^0, \quad \pi^- p \to K^+ \Sigma^-. \tag{3.1}$$

If the lab energy is high enough, production of additional pions is possible, e.g. $\pi^+ p \to K^+ \pi^+ \Lambda$. Reactions such as $\pi^- p \to \pi^0 \Lambda$, which involve only one strange particle, have not been observed.

Another possible type of reactions is the kaon "pair production". Examples of this reaction are the following:

$$\pi^+ p \to K^+ \overline{K}^0 p, \qquad \pi^- p \to K^+ K^- n. \tag{3.2}$$

The states K^0 and $\overline{K}^0$ are related to the particles K_L^0 and K_S^0, as discussed below. Reactions of the type $\pi^+ p \to K^+ K^+ n$ have not been observed.

The first observations of strange particles came from cosmic ray experiments. As a rule, only the decays were observed. Already at that time, when nothing was known about associated production (1) or pair production (2) of strange particles, it was suggested that the production of strange particles was governed by an isospin selection rule. The successful assignment of I and I_3 to these strange particles, together with the introduction of a new quantum number, called strangeness, is due to GELL-MANN [1956] and to NISHIJIMA [1955].

First, the values of I of the baryons are determined. If the interactions which are responsible for the existence of hadrons are isospin invariant, hadrons should always occur in multiplets of $2I+1$ different charge states. We conclude that Λ, Σ and Ξ have $I = 0$, 1 and $\frac{1}{2}$, respectively. This isospin assignment immediately explains the absence of reactions of the type pion + nucleon → hyperon+pions. The total isospin of the final state is integer, whereas that of the initial state is $\frac{1}{2}$ or $\frac{3}{2}$. On the other hand, in hyperon decays of the type $\Lambda \to \pi N$, isospin is clearly not conserved.

Next, the isospin properties of kaons are determined. Since there are four states, one might try $I = \frac{3}{2}$, but this assignment is ruled out by conservation of I_3 in (1) and (2) as follows. From the reactions

$$\pi^+ n \to K^+ \Lambda, \qquad \pi^- p \to K^0 \Lambda, \tag{3.3}$$

we learn that K^+ and K^0 have $I_3 = \frac{1}{2}$ and $-\frac{1}{2}$, respectively. The pair production (2) then requires $I_3 = \frac{1}{2}$ and $-\frac{1}{2}$ for $\overline{K}^0$ and K^-, respectively. Thus the kaons form two doublets of $I = \frac{1}{2}$. From (3), it also follows that K^+ and K^0 are in the same doublet. Since Λ has zero isospin, the total isospin in (3) is $\frac{1}{2}$. From (2.9) we find that the two reactions should occur with the ratio $\frac{2}{3} : \frac{2}{3} = 1 : 1$, in agreement with experiment. Finally, the mesons $\overline{K}^0$ and K^- must form the remaining doublet. The isospin assignments are summarized in table 4-3. Conservation of I_3 in (1) requires $I_3 = \pm 1$ and 0 for $\Sigma^\pm$ and Σ^0, respectively.

TABLE 4-3

Assignment of I and I_3 to hyperons and kaons.

symbol	Λ	Σ^+	Σ^0	Σ^-	K^+	K^0	$\overline{K}^0$	K^-
I	0		1			$\frac{1}{2}$		$\frac{1}{2}$
I_3	0	1	0	-1	$\frac{1}{2}$	$-\frac{1}{2}$	$\frac{1}{2}$	$-\frac{1}{2}$

We still have not explained the states K^0 and $\overline{K}^0$. Experimentally, one finds that K^0-decay occurs with two different lifetimes. The particles associated with the long- and short-lived modes are called K_L^0 and K_S^0, respectively. In their decays, both K^0 and $\overline{K}^0$ manifest themselves as a mixture of K_S^0 and K_L^0. In fact, half of the neutral kaons produced in pion-nucleon collisions decay rapidly, the other half survives much longer. This implies that both K_S^0 and K_L^0 do not have a definite value of I_3, which is indeed possible since I_3 is not conserved in decays. We now *define* K^0 and $\overline{K}^0$ as those linear combinations of K_S^0 and K_L^0 which belong to $I_3 = \frac{1}{2}$ and $-\frac{1}{2}$, respectively:

$$|K_L^0\rangle = p|K^0\rangle + q|\overline{K}^0\rangle, \qquad |K_S^0\rangle = r|K^0\rangle + s|\overline{K}^0\rangle. \tag{3.4}$$

The absolute squares of the complex coefficients p, q, r and s are all of the order of $\frac{1}{2}$. We shall return to (4) in section 4-9 and in chapter 13. Our present aim is to give a preliminary definition of K^0 and $\overline{K}^0$. The final definition will be based on the antiparticle concept. Nonetheless we shall, when needed, use the term antikaons for K^- and $\overline{K}^0$.

At the large proton accelerators, secondary beams of K^+ and K^- are available. The total K^-p collision cross-section is rather large due to the presence of exothermic reactions like $K^-p \to \pi\Lambda$, $K^-p \to \pi\Sigma$. These reactions are studied in detail in chapter 8. The reaction $K^-p \to \pi\pi\Lambda$ is also slightly exothermic.

High-energy beams of K^- are the only practicable means of producing cascade particles. Possible two-particle reactions are

$$K^-p \to K^0\Xi^0, \qquad K^-p \to K^+\Xi^-, \tag{3.5}$$

from which one concludes that Ξ^0 and Ξ^- have $I_3 = \frac{1}{2}$ and $-\frac{1}{2}$, respectively. Reactions such as $\pi^- p \rightarrow \pi^+ \Xi^-$ or $\pi^- p \rightarrow K^+ \Xi^-$ are all forbidden by conservation of I_3.

The selection rules in the production of strange particles are simplified by the introduction of a new quantum number called hypercharge (the older "strangeness" quantum number is mentioned below). For pions and hyperons, the electric charge Q and the third component of isospin I_3 coincide. For other multiplets, the centre of the multiplet may have a net charge. In order to avoid half-integer values of the new quantum number, the charge of the centre of the multiplet is called $\frac{1}{2}$ Y, where Y is the hypercharge. We thus have by definition

$$Q = I_3 + \tfrac{1}{2}Y. \tag{3.6}$$

Nucleons and kaons have $Y = 1$, while antikaons and cascade particles have $Y = -1$. The equivalent strangeness quantum number S is defined by

$$Q = I_3 + \tfrac{1}{2}(S+B), \tag{3.7}$$

where B is the baryon number defined at the end of section 4-1. For mesons, S is the same as Y. The motivation for including the baryon number in the definition of S was to obtain zero strangeness for the nucleons. From the point of view of isospin invariance, Y is the more symmetric quantum number. A plot of Y versus I_3 for baryons and mesons is shown in fig. 4-3.

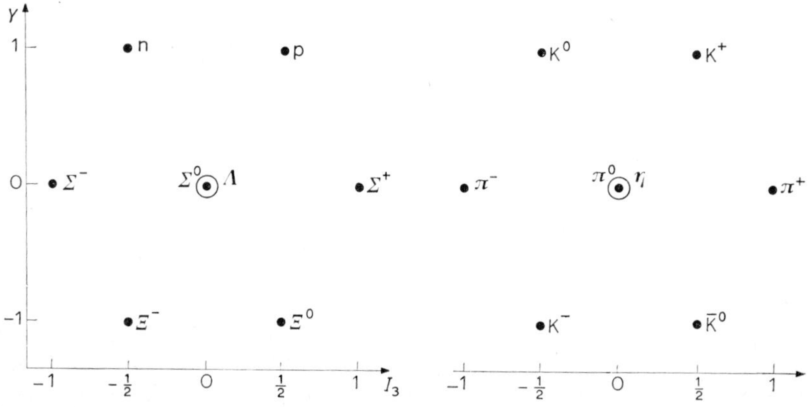

Fig. 4-3. Plot of hypercharge versus third component of isospin for baryons and mesons. The central point $Y = I_3 = 0$ is occupied by two particles, one of which has zero isospin.

It should be mentioned here that the heaviest meson, the η, has $I = I_3 = 0$. It is produced in reactions like $\pi^- p \to \eta n$. One can easily convince oneself that the various forbidden reactions mentioned thus far violate the conservation of hypercharge.

In contrast to I, Y is conserved in electromagnetic interactions. This follows from the absence of decays $K^0 \to \gamma\gamma$, $\Lambda \to \gamma n$ (from table 1-4 we see that the corresponding decays $\pi^0 \to \gamma\gamma$, $\Sigma^0 \to \gamma\Lambda$ which do conserve Y have extremely short lifetimes). From (6) and the fact that Q is exactly conserved in all interactions, we see that I_3 is conserved in electromagnetic interactions as well. This statement was trivial as long as we considered only pions and nucleons, since, for such "non-strange" particles, we have from (7) $I_3 = Q - \frac{1}{2}B$.

4-4. Intrinsic parities

In addition to spin, charge, baryon number and hypercharge, each hadron also has an intrinsic parity, which is either $+1$ or -1. The total parity of systems of particles is conserved in strong and electromagnetic interactions, but usually not in weak interactions.

The parity or "space inversion" operation has been defined in section 3-5. We indicated that any matrix element T can be divided into

$$T = T_e + T_o, \tag{4.1}$$

where T_e and T_o are even and odd under parity conjugation, respectively. Conservation of parity implies that $|T|^2$ is the same for a given transition and its parity conjugate transition. This requires $T_o = 0$ or $T_e = 0$. We now define conservation of parity by the slightly stronger requirement

$$T_e(1+\eta_i\eta_f) = 2T_e, \qquad T_o(1-\eta_i\eta_f) = 2T_o, \tag{4.2}$$

where $\eta_i(\eta_f)$ is the product of the intrinsic parities of the particles in the initial (final) state. Stated differently, $\eta_i\eta_f = +1(-1)$ requires $T_o = 0$ ($T_e = 0$). In elastic scattering for example, one always has $\eta_i\eta_f = 1$, and therefore $T_o = 0$ if parity is conserved. This result was used in section 3-9.

Due to the conservation of charge and baryon number, the parities of proton and neutron may be fixed by definition. It is customary to choose

$$\eta_p = \eta_n = 1. \tag{4.3}$$

With this choice, isospin invariance implies equal parities for the members of an isospin multiplet.

The total parity of a two-particle system of orbital angular momentum L is the product of the intrinsic parities and the orbital parity $(-1)^L$. So far we have defined L only for collisions between a spinless particle and a particle of spin-zero or -$\frac{1}{2}$, (sections 2-4 and 3-9, respectively). For the time being, we assume that the reader is familiar with the orbital parity $(-1)^L$ from non-relativistic scattering theory. Conservation of parity for reactions ab → cd reads

$$\eta_a \eta_b (-1)^{L_{ab}} = \eta_c \eta_d (-1)^{L_{cd}}. \tag{4.4}$$

This implies that $L_{ab} - L_{cd}$ is even for $\eta_a \eta_b = \eta_c \eta_d$ and odd for $\eta_a \eta_b = -\eta_c \eta_d$. The parity of the pions has been determined from the reaction (CHINOWSKY and STEINBERGER [1954])

$$\pi^- d \to nn. \tag{4.5}$$

The π^- is captured from an S-orbit of a π-mesic atom. Since the deuteron is also in an S-state, the total parity of the $\pi^- d$ system is given by the intrinsic pion parity. In the final state, the total parity is determined by the conservation of angular momentum (which must be one since d has spin-1), and by the Pauli principle which excludes triplet S and D states for a system of two neutrons. The only allowed states are thus P-states, which have negative parity. Therefore the π^- has negative intrinsic parity. Having spin zero, it is said to be a pseudoscalar particle.

Isospin invariance of nuclear forces would be astonishing if $\pi^\pm$ and π^0 had different quantum numbers with regard to strong interactions. In any case, CHINOWSKY and STEINBERGER [1955] showed from the reaction $\pi^- d \to nn\pi^0$ that π^0 is also pseudoscalar. The pseudoscalarity of π^+ follows from that of π^- by the antiparticle theorem of section 4-7 below.

In addition to p and n, Λ is also defined to have positive parity. This is possible because hypercharge is conserved in strong and electromagnetic interactions. It is not conserved in weak interactions like the decay $\Lambda \to \pi N$, but since these decays do not conserve parity either, no contradiction can arise.

The parity of kaons has been determined from the production of hypernuclei from K-mesic atoms:

$$K^- He^4 \to {}_\Lambda He^4 \pi^-, \qquad K^- He^4 \to {}_\Lambda H^4 \pi^0. \tag{4.6}$$

The index Λ indicates that one neutron is replaced by a Λ-hyperon. All particles participating in these two reactions have spin zero, and He^4, ${}_\Lambda He^4$ and ${}_\Lambda H^4$ have positive parity. Consequently, conservation of parity requires the same parity for K and π.

The Σ parity has been determined from the electromagnetic decay (COURANT *et al.* [1963])

$$\Sigma^0 \to \Lambda e^+ e^-, \tag{4.7}$$

which is a small fraction of the ordinary decay $\Sigma^0 \to \Lambda\gamma$. The "Dalitz pair" e^+e^- can be thought of as the decay product of a "virtual" photon of non-zero mass. We omit the theory for reaction (7). The result is that Σ particles have the same spin and parity as proton and neutron. This conclusion is confirmed by the analysis of K^-p reactions (see chapter 8). The cascade particles also seem to have spin-$\frac{1}{2}$ and positive parity.

Finally, the parity of the η-meson follows from the existence of the decay $\eta \to \pi^0\pi^0\pi^0$. The Bose-Einstein principle requires that the $\pi^0\pi^0\pi^0$ states be totally symmetric, which in turn implies that all relative angular momenta are even. Since the total intrinsic parity of the final state is negative, the η-meson has negative parity. Of course this argument requires parity conservation in η-decay. A similar argument cannot be applied to the decays $K_L^0 \to \pi^0\pi^0\pi^0$ and $K_S^0 \to \pi^0\pi^0$, since these decays are due to weak interactions, as can be seen from the comparatively long lifetimes of K_S^0 and K_L^0.

A particle's spin S and parity η are usually given in the form S^η. In this notation, the eight baryons are $\frac{1}{2}^+$ and the eight mesons are 0^-.

A parity assignment to leptons is useless. The only transformation between leptons is the muon decay $\mu \to \bar{e}\nu\nu$ which does not conserve parity. The photon on the other hand has negative parity. (Since it has spin-1, it is called a "vector particle", 1^-.) This follows somewhat indirectly from the theory of Coulomb scattering, which will be discussed later. It also follows directly from electromagnetic decays and pion photoproduction.

4-5. Time reversal and detailed balance

The classical definition of time reversal $\mathscr{T}$ is the transformation $(t, \boldsymbol{x}) \to (-t, \boldsymbol{x})$ of the space-time 4-vector. It is achieved by the improper Lorentz transformation matrix $-g_{\mu\nu}$. By the classical correspondence between $\boldsymbol{p}$ and $m(\mathrm{d}x/\mathrm{d}t)$, we require $\boldsymbol{p} \to -\boldsymbol{p}$ under time reversal, as with parity. This time, however, the magnetic quantum number (classically $(\boldsymbol{r} \times \boldsymbol{p})_z$) changes also sign, $M \to -M$. Finally, the reversal of the time sequence transforms initial states into final states and vice versa. We thus find $\mathscr{T}|\boldsymbol{p}, M\rangle = \langle -\boldsymbol{p}, -M|$ for the one-particle states. Since the transformation from ket to bra vectors involves complex conjugation, $\mathscr{T}$ is called an "antilinear" operator, $\mathscr{T}c|\rangle = c^*\mathscr{T}|\rangle$.

In principle, the particles could acquire phases under time reversal, e.g. $\mathscr{T}|\boldsymbol{p}, M\rangle = e^{i\varphi}\langle -\boldsymbol{p}, -M|$. However, since the relative phases between initial and final states cannot be measured, the factor $e^{i\varphi}$ may be absorbed in the definition of the outgoing particle state.

The helicity λ of a particle remains unchanged under time reversal. Summing up, the transformation properties of $|\boldsymbol{p}, M\rangle$ and $|\boldsymbol{p}, \lambda\rangle$ and $\mathscr{P}$ and $\mathscr{T}$ are

$\|\,\rangle$	$\mathscr{P}\|\,\rangle$	$\mathscr{T}\|\,\rangle$
$\|\boldsymbol{p}, M\rangle$	$\eta\|-\boldsymbol{p}, M\rangle$	$\langle -\boldsymbol{p}, -M\|$
$\|\boldsymbol{p}, \lambda\rangle$	$\eta\|-\boldsymbol{p}, -\lambda\rangle$	$\langle -\boldsymbol{p}, \lambda\|$

(5.1)

Invariance of the S-matrix under time reversal requires

$$\langle \boldsymbol{p}_c, \boldsymbol{p}_d, \lambda'|S|\boldsymbol{p}_a, \lambda, \boldsymbol{p}_b\rangle = \langle -\boldsymbol{p}_a, \lambda, -\boldsymbol{p}_b|S|-\boldsymbol{p}_c, -\boldsymbol{p}_d, \lambda'\rangle. \tag{5.2}$$

For the T-matrix element $T(\lambda\lambda', \theta, \phi)$, the symmetry (2) reads

$$T_{if}(\lambda, \lambda', \theta, \phi) = T_{fi}(\lambda', \lambda, \theta, \pi-\phi). \tag{5.3}$$

The replacement $\boldsymbol{p}_i \rightarrow -\boldsymbol{p}_i$ does not affect the cms scattering angle θ. The azimuth ϕ is changed into $\pi-\phi$, since ϕ was defined in a right-handed coordinate system based on the momentum vectors $\boldsymbol{p}_a$, $\boldsymbol{p}_b$ (ϕ is the same in the lab system and in the cms). The replacement $\boldsymbol{p}_i \rightarrow -\boldsymbol{p}_i$ transforms the right-handed coordinate system into a left-handed one. Therefore the new azimuth is not $\phi+\pi$ but $2\pi-(\phi+\pi)$.

For the partial-wave T-matrices $T_J(\lambda\lambda')$ defined by (3-8.5), (3) gives the important symmetry property

$$T_{if, J}(\lambda, \lambda') = T_{fi, J}(\lambda', \lambda), \quad \text{in matrix form} \quad T_J = (T_J)_{tr}. \tag{5.4}$$

This follows from the fact that the expansion (3-8.5) for the r.h.s. of (3) contains the angular functions

$$\begin{aligned} \exp\left(i(\lambda'-\lambda)(\pi-\phi)\right)d^J_{\lambda'\lambda} &= e^{i(\lambda-\lambda')\phi}e^{i(\lambda'-\lambda)\pi}d^J_{\lambda\lambda'}(-1)^{\lambda-\lambda'} \\ &= D^{J*}_{\lambda\lambda'}(\phi, \theta, -\phi), \end{aligned} \tag{5.5}$$

according to (C-2.7). By (4), the l.h.s. of the unitarity equation (3-8.13) is $2\,\mathrm{Im}\,T_{if, J}(\lambda, \lambda')$. For elastic pion-nucleon scattering, the only non-trivial relation of (4) is $T_J(\frac{1}{2}, -\frac{1}{2}) = T_J(-\frac{1}{2}, \frac{1}{2})$. Since this is also implied by parity conservation, it follows that parity-conserving elastic meson-nucleon scattering is automatically time reversal invariant.

From (3), we get

$$|T_{\rm if}(\lambda\lambda', \theta, \phi)|^2 = |T_{\rm fi}(\lambda'\lambda, \theta, \phi)|^2, \tag{5.6}$$

since the ϕ-dependence is only a phase. This equation is the basis of the so-called "principle of detailed balance" (COESTER [1951]):

$$\frac{d\sigma}{dt}(\text{cd} \to \text{ab}) = \frac{d\sigma}{dt}(\text{ab} \to \text{cd}) \frac{q^2}{q'^2} \frac{(2S_a+1)(2S_b+1)}{(2S_c+1)(2S_d+1)}. \tag{5.7}$$

Here we have inserted the relation (3-1.14) between $d\sigma$ and $|T|^2$, and $q(q')$ is the cms momentum in the ab (cd) state. Historically, (7) was applied to the pair of reactions $\pi^+ d \to pp$ (DURBIN *et al.* [1951], CLARK *et al.* [1951]) and $pp \to \pi^+ d$ (CARTWRIGHT *et al.* [1953]) to prove that the π^+ has spin zero.

In (7), we have allowed all four particles to have spin. Evidently, (2) and (3) also apply to such general cases, if $\lambda = (\lambda_a, \lambda_b)$ and $\lambda' = (\lambda_c, \lambda_d)$ represent the pairs of helicities in the initial and final states. Moreover, when we have defined the general partial wave expansion in section 9-4, we shall understand that also $T_J = (T_J)_{\rm tr}$ remains valid. For $S_a = S_b = S_c = S_d = \frac{1}{2}$ (four-fermion interaction), the consequences of time-reversal invariance will be discussed in section 12-2.

4-6. Antiparticles and crossing

The symmetry principles discussed so far are more or less known also in non-relativistic quantum mechanics, for example in nuclear physics. We now come to the last symmetry, the proper account of which requires a Lorentz-invariant theory. This is the particle-antiparticle symmetry. A preliminary definition is that for each particle there is an "antiparticle" having the same mass and lifetime but opposite charge, hypercharge, and baryon number. In fact, we require all additive quantum numbers of particles and antiparticles to be opposite in sign. An additive quantum number Q is generally defined by the conservation law (for a process ab → cd),

$$Q_a + Q_b = Q_c + Q_d. \tag{6.1}$$

I_3 is additive but neither I nor the eigenparity is additive. For π^0 and η all additive quantum numbers are zero, and therefore these particles are their own antiparticle. (The fact that energy and momentum are also additive is neglected for the time being.) Positive and negative pions are antiparticles of each other, as are positive and negative kaons. The antiparticle of K^0 is $\bar{K}^0$, since these particles have opposite hypercharges. K_L^0 and K_S^0 on the other hand cannot be antiparticles of each other, because of their different lifetimes.

Due to the baryon quantum number, the antiparticles of baryons cannot be baryons. They form a new group of hadrons, the antibaryons, with $B = -1$. We thus have the antiproton ($\bar{p}$), antineutron ($\bar{n}$), antilambda ($\bar{\Lambda}$), the antisigmas ($\bar{\Sigma}^-$, $\bar{\Sigma}^0$, $\bar{\Sigma}^+$) and the antixis ($\bar{\Xi}^0$, $\bar{\Xi}^+$). To summarize, the antiparticles of mesons and baryons are

particle	π^0	π^+	K^+	K^0	η	p	n	Λ	Σ^+	Σ^0	Σ^-	Ξ^0	Ξ^-
antiparticle	π^0	π^-	K^-	$\bar{K}^0$	η	$\bar{p}$	$\bar{n}$	$\bar{\Lambda}$	$\bar{\Sigma}^-$	$\bar{\Sigma}^0$	$\bar{\Sigma}^+$	$\bar{\Xi}^0$	$\bar{\Xi}^+$

(6.2)

Note that the definition of antiparticles is reciprocal: π^+ is the antiparticle of π^-, p the antiparticle of $\bar{p}$ etc. It is however customary to define π^+, K^+, K^0 and the baryons as the "particles".

The antiproton has negative electric charge. It was discovered by CHAMBERLAIN, SEGRÉ, WIEGAND and YPSILANTIS [1955, 1956]. The antineutron was discovered soon afterwards. Because of their negative baryon number, antibaryons must be produced pairwise with baryons. In a proton accelerator, the following reactions are possible:

$$\begin{aligned} pp &\to ppp\bar{p}, & pp &\to ppn\bar{n}, \\ pn &\to ppn\bar{p}, & pn &\to pnn\bar{n}. \end{aligned} \tag{6.3}$$

Since the threshold of such reactions is high, antibaryons are difficult to produce. With $m_p = m_n = m$, we find from (1-2.4),

$$E_a^{\text{lab}}(\text{threshold}) = \frac{1}{2m}(16m^2 - m^2 - m^2) = 7m, \tag{6.4}$$

which means a lab momentum of $m\sqrt{48} = 6.5$ GeV. However, even at 30 GeV/c, antibaryons are produced in less than 1% of the inelastic collisions. For comparison, the probability of kaon and hyperon production at high energies is of the order of 5%. Nevertheless, beams of antiprotons are available.

Nuclei should also have antiparticles. However only the antideuteron ($\bar{d}$) has been discovered so far (DORFAN *et al.* [1965], MASSAM *et al.* [1965]).

Reactions of the type $\bar{p}p \to$ mesons are not forbidden by baryon number conservation. They have in fact the largest cross-sections observed in hadron physics. They are called "antiproton annihilation". There is some similarity between these reactions and the reactions $K^-p \to$ hyperon+mesons, which also have large cross-sections. In this latter case, opposite hypercharges "annihilate" each other.

Antihyperons and antideuterons are most conveniently produced by a beam of antiprotons. Possible reactions are

$$\bar{p}p \to \bar{\Lambda}\Lambda, \qquad \to \bar{\Sigma}\Lambda, \qquad \to \bar{\Lambda}\Sigma \text{ etc.}, \qquad \bar{p}p \to \bar{d}d. \tag{6.5}$$

The photon is its own antiparticle. Of the leptons, e^- and e^+, μ^+ and μ^-, ν and $\bar{\nu}$ are particle-antiparticle pairs. The positron e^+ was discovered by ANDERSON [1933]. On the basis of Dirac's equation, there had already been speculations about positively charged electrons. Dirac's theory contained transition matrix elements to states of negative energies. According to the "hole theory", all negative energy states were occupied in vacuo, and the production of an electron-positron-pair was interpreted as the excitation of an electron of energy $-(m^2+p^2)^{\frac{1}{2}}$ to an energy of $+(m^2+p'^2)^{\frac{1}{2}}$. The subsequent "hole-state" at the negative energy was interpreted as the positron. Models of this type are used in solid state physics; even the analogous "energy gap" of $2m$ exists in the theory of superconductors.

However, this picture is incomplete. The Pauli exclusion principle is necessary to prevent electrons from falling into the negative energy states. Therefore the construction does not work for pions, which obey the Bose-Einstein principle. The correct treatment was given by the method of quantized fields, in which antiparticles as well as the connection between spin and statistics appear as consequences of microcausality. Classical or "macro"-causality says that any local perturbation of a system cannot expand faster than light. Microcausality on the other hand is a condition on the commutators between field operators. It ensures macrocausality, but it is a much stronger condition (see e.g. STREATER and WIGHTMAN [1964]).

Since we shall not use field theory in this book, we cannot use microcausality either. Instead, we use the postulate of *crossing symmetry*: "The matrix element for a process containing an *antiparticle* of 4-momentum P_μ in the initial (final) state is identical with the matrix element for the "crossed" process, which contains the corresponding *particle* of 4-momentum $-P_\mu$ in the final (initial) state".

The replacement $P \to -P$ (which includes the energy component) is a consequence of energy-momentum conservation. The S-matrix elements for a reaction ab → cd and one of its crossed processes, a → $\bar{b}$cd, are

$$
\begin{aligned}
S(\mathrm{ab} \to \mathrm{cd}) &= \mathrm{i}(2\pi)^4 \delta^4(P_\mathrm{a}+P_\mathrm{b}-P_\mathrm{c}-P_\mathrm{d}) T(\mathrm{ab} \to \mathrm{cd}),\\
S(\mathrm{a} \to \bar{\mathrm{b}}\mathrm{cd}) &= \mathrm{i}(2\pi)^4 \delta^4(P_\mathrm{a}-P_{\bar{\mathrm{b}}}-P_\mathrm{c}-P_\mathrm{d}) T(\mathrm{a} \to \bar{\mathrm{b}}\mathrm{cd}).
\end{aligned}
\tag{6.6}
$$

At fixed $P_\mathrm{a}, P_\mathrm{c}$ and P_d, equality between the two S-matrix elements at a point where $S \neq 0$ is only possible at $P_\mathrm{b} = -P_{\bar{\mathrm{b}}}$.

In practice, the relation $S(\mathrm{ab} \to \mathrm{cd}) = S(\mathrm{a} \to \bar{\mathrm{b}}\mathrm{cd})$ is of rather restricted use. If particle a is unstable against decay into $\bar{\mathrm{b}}$cd, it will decay before it can make a collision of the type ab → cd. There is one example in nuclear physics, namely the β^+ decay (nucleus → positron, neutrino and another nucleus), which will be mentioned in chapter 12. Here, the crossed reaction "electron capture" (electron+nucleus → neutrino and another nucleus) is actually observed.

Another difficulty of crossing symmetry is that $E_\mathrm{b} = -E_{\bar{\mathrm{b}}}$ requires negative energy either for the particle or for the antiparticle. Therefore, crossing symmetry requires an extrapolation of one of the two matrix elements down to negative energies. For the β^+ decay, this turns out to be very simple, but in general it is a complicated problem. It will be discussed in chapter 6. For the time being, we only investigate the consequences of crossing symmetry for the quantum numbers of antiparticles.

The argument about the conservation of energy and momentum is immediately extended to any additive quantum number (1). Therefore, crossing symmetry requires all additive quantum numbers of particles and antiparticles to be opposite. It also implies equal masses for particles and antiparticles, $m_{\bar{\mathrm{b}}}^2 \equiv P_{\bar{\mathrm{b}}}^2 = (-P_\mathrm{b})^2 = m_\mathrm{b}^2$.

The reader may find the use of negative energies confusing. It is important to remember that crossing symmetry applies to the matrix elements, and not to the phase space element. In section 1-5 we pointed out that the phase space element is zero for negative energies. Therefore, differential transition probabilities to negative energy states do not exist. Processes for which the phase space is zero will be called "unphysical".

In the theory of strong interactions, by far the most important crossing is the simultaneous crossing of two particles, e.g. $S(\mathrm{ab} \to \mathrm{cd}) = S(\bar{\mathrm{c}}\mathrm{b} \to \bar{\mathrm{a}}\mathrm{d})$. This relates the matrix elements of π^+p scattering with those of π^-p scattering and of the reaction $\mathrm{p}\bar{\mathrm{p}} \to \pi^+\pi^-$, which will be discussed below.

By crossing symmetry, the formal discussion of the S-matrix may be restricted to states for which the total energy-momentum, charge, baryon number etc. are zero. Consider for example the matrix element $T(0 \to \bar{\mathrm{a}}\bar{\mathrm{b}}\mathrm{cd})$, where the "0" denotes the vacuum state. By "crossing" two of the four particles $\bar{\mathrm{a}}$, $\bar{\mathrm{b}}$, c, d, we obtain the matrix elements of the reactions ab → cd,

$a\bar{c} \to \bar{b}d$, $\bar{c}b \to \bar{a}d$ and $a\bar{d} \to \bar{b}c$, $\bar{c}\bar{d} \to \bar{a}\bar{b}$, $b\bar{d} \to \bar{a}c$. This approach is particularly elegant. However, in the following, we shall follow the more conventional method of starting from a "physical reaction" such as ab → cd (see section 6-7).

As a first example, we now study the matrix elements of the reaction $p\bar{p} \to \pi^+\pi^-$. The particles' 4-momenta are denoted by $P, \bar{P}, P_{\pi'}$ and $P_{\bar{\pi}}$. The magnetic quantum numbers of proton and antiproton are denoted by M and $\bar{M}$. Since the magnetic quantum number along a fixed direction is additive, it changes sign under crossing. In (3-9.14), the general matrix element of $\pi^+p \to \pi^+p$ was written in the form $\bar{u}(P'M')(A+\frac{1}{2}(P_\pi+P_{\pi'})\cdot\gamma B)$ $\times u(P, M)$. By crossing symmetry, $T(p\bar{p} \to \pi^+\pi^-)$ must be of the same general form, if P', M' and P_π are identified with $-\bar{P}$, $-\bar{M}$ and $-P_{\bar{\pi}}$:

$$T(p\bar{p} \to \pi^+\pi^-) = \bar{u}(-\bar{M}, -\bar{P})[A+\tfrac{1}{2}(-P_{\bar{\pi}}+P_{\pi'})\cdot\gamma B]u(P, M),$$
$$A = A(s, t), \qquad B = B(s, t), \qquad s = (P-P_{\bar{\pi}})^2, \qquad t = (P+\bar{P})^2. \tag{6.7}$$

Note that s is now negative and t is positive. Therefore, the extrapolation of $A(s, t)$ and $B(s, t)$ from the region of physical scattering to the region of antiproton annihilation passes through a large unphysical domain. We keep all four masses different, thereby including reactions such as $\bar{\Lambda}p \to K^+\pi^0$ or $\bar{p}n \to \pi^-\eta$.

The decomposition of the matrix element into big and small components is again given by (3-5.15), with $E' = -\bar{E}$, $M' = -\bar{M}$, and $\boldsymbol{p}' = -\bar{\boldsymbol{p}}$. The formula becomes particularly simple in the cms, where $\bar{\boldsymbol{p}} = -\boldsymbol{p}$ implies $\boldsymbol{p}' = \boldsymbol{p}$:

$$T(p\bar{p}, M\bar{M}) = \sqrt{(E+m)(-\bar{E}+m')}\chi_0'^{+}(-\bar{M})$$
$$\times \left[Q_{bb} - \frac{\boldsymbol{\sigma}\cdot\boldsymbol{p}}{-\bar{E}+m'}Q_{ss}\frac{\boldsymbol{\sigma}\cdot\boldsymbol{p}}{E+m} + Q_{bs}\frac{\boldsymbol{\sigma}\cdot\boldsymbol{p}}{E+m} - \frac{\boldsymbol{\sigma}\cdot\boldsymbol{p}}{-\bar{E}+m'}Q_{sb}\right]\chi_0(M). \tag{6.8}$$

Moreover, if we choose the momentum $\boldsymbol{p}$ of the proton as spin quantization axis both for the proton and the antiproton, we may replace $\boldsymbol{\sigma}\cdot\boldsymbol{p}$ by $2Mp$ when acting on $\chi_0(M)$ and by $-2\bar{M}p$ when acting on $\chi_0^+(-\bar{M})$:

$$T(p\bar{p}, M\bar{M}) = \sqrt{(E+m)(-\bar{E}+m')}\chi_0^{+}(-\bar{M})$$
$$\times \left[Q_{bb} + \frac{4M\bar{M}p^2}{(-\bar{E}+m')(E+m)}Q_{ss} + \frac{2Mp}{E+m}Q_{bs} + \frac{2\bar{M}p}{-\bar{E}+m'}Q_{sb}\right]\chi_0(M). \tag{6.9}$$

Actually, M is the proton's helicity. The antiproton has magnetic quantum number $\bar{M}$ along the proton's momentum, i.e. $-\bar{M}$ along its own momentum.

So far, (8) and (9) apply to annihilation into any number of mesons. For two-meson annihilation, Q is given by the square bracket of (7). From (3-9.15) and (3-9.16), we find for two-meson annihilation,

$$Q_{bb} = A+\tfrac{1}{2}(-E_{\bar{\pi}}+E_{\pi'})B, \qquad Q_{ss} = A-\tfrac{1}{2}(-E_{\bar{\pi}}+E_{\pi'})B,$$
$$Q_{bs} = -Q_{sb} = -\tfrac{1}{2}(-\boldsymbol{p}_{\bar{\pi}}+\boldsymbol{p}_{\pi'})\cdot\boldsymbol{\sigma}B = -\boldsymbol{p}_{\pi'}\cdot\boldsymbol{\sigma}B. \tag{6.10}$$

For annihilation at rest, we have $p = 0$, $E = m$ and $\bar{E} = m'$. Because of the last equality, only the last term of (8) and (9) contributes in this case. More precisely, we replace p by $[(-\bar{E}-m')(-\bar{E}+m')]^{\frac{1}{2}}$, finding that the factors $(-\bar{E}+m')$ cancel in the coefficient of Q_{sb}.

The final formula is

$$\begin{aligned} T(p\bar{p}, M, \bar{M}) &= (-4mm')^{\frac{1}{2}} 2\bar{M}B\chi_0^{+}(-\bar{M})\boldsymbol{p}_{\pi'}\cdot\boldsymbol{\sigma}\chi_0(M) \\ &= (-4mm')^{\frac{1}{2}} Bp_{\pi} Y^1_{M+\bar{M}}(\theta, \phi)(8\pi/3)^{\frac{1}{2}} \quad \text{for } M = \bar{M}. \end{aligned} \tag{6.11}$$

The angles θ and ϕ specify the direction of $\boldsymbol{p}_{\pi'}$. For $M = -\bar{M}$, (11) holds true if the factor $(8\pi)^{\frac{1}{2}}$ is replaced by $(4\pi)^{\frac{1}{2}}$. Instead of the four states characterized by M and $\bar{M}$, we now consider the triplet of states which is symmetric in M and $\bar{M}$. The matrix element for *all three* triplet states is given by (11), whereas the matrix element for the antisymmetric singlet state is zero.

This simple example indicates how to work with negative energy spinors. The fact that $B(s, t)$ is an "unphysical version" of the corresponding amplitude in meson-nucleon scattering is of relevance only in the numerical computation of B. For that purpose, we shall later assume that the scattering amplitudes are analytic functions of their variables.

An important special case of crossing is the simultaneous crossing of all particles of a reaction. This relates ab → cd to $\bar{c}\bar{d} \to \bar{a}\bar{b}$ or d → 12 to $\bar{1}\bar{2} \to \bar{d}$. The simultaneous inversion of all 4-momenta does not affect any of the Lorentz invariants, simply because $s = (P_a+P_b)^2 = (-P_a-P_b)^2$ etc. This implies

$$T(ab \to cd, M_a, \ldots, M_d, s, t) = T(\bar{c}\bar{d} \to \bar{a}\bar{b}, -M_d, \ldots, -M_a, s, t), \tag{6.12}$$

without any extrapolation. The reaction $\bar{c}\bar{d} \to \bar{a}\bar{b}$ is called the *CPT* conjugate of ab → cd. The product of parity $\mathscr{P}$ and time reversal $\mathscr{T}$ exchanges ingoing and outgoing particles and replaces M by $-M$, but it does not change the 4-momentum of the particles. The charge conjugation C, which will be discussed in the next section, exchanges particles with antiparticles, without changing 4-momentum or spin. The difference between *CPT* and the "total crossing" (12) is that *CPT* does *not* invert the 4-momenta. Since this difference does not affect the invariants, it can at most produce a phase. Apart from this, (12) expresses the so-called *CPT* theorem.

Note that the *CPT* theorem does not require additional symmetry principles such as $\mathscr{T}$, *C* or $\mathscr{P}$ invariance. Rather, if any of these three invariance principles is broken, then at least a second one must be broken, too, such that the product of all three remains intact.

For the hadron decays, *CPT* is very useful where it can be combined with $\mathscr{T}$ invariance. In that case we have

$$|T(\mathrm{d} \to 1, 2; M, M_1, M_2)|^2 = |T(\overline{1}\,\overline{2} \to \overline{\mathrm{d}}; -M_1, -M_2, -M)|^2$$
$$= |T(\overline{\mathrm{d}} \to \overline{1}\,\overline{2}; M, M_1, M_2)|^2, \tag{6.13}$$

which implies equality of the various partial and differential decay widths between particle decay and the corresponding antiparticle decay. On the other hand, equality of the *total* widths of particles and antiparticles is a consequence of *CPT* alone. For example, the coupling constants of a multichannel resonance may be complex. In such a case, the resonance amplitude T_{if} of (2-9.4) is

$$T(\mathrm{i} \to \mathrm{f}) = \frac{m\Gamma C_{\mathrm{i}} C_{\mathrm{f}}^*}{(q_{\mathrm{i}} q_{\mathrm{f}})^{\frac{1}{2}}(m^2 - s - \mathrm{i}m\Gamma)} \tag{6.14}$$

and $|T(\mathrm{i} \to \mathrm{f})|^2 = |T(\overline{\mathrm{f}} \to \overline{\mathrm{i}})|^2$ requires the same Γ for $\mathrm{i} \to \mathrm{f}$ and $\overline{\mathrm{f}} \to \overline{\mathrm{i}}$.

Now it is also clear that the form $(m^2 - s - \mathrm{i}m\Gamma)^{-1}$ of the propagator is dictated by *CPT* invariance. In the derivation (2-3.11) of the amplitude $(m - E - \frac{1}{2}\mathrm{i}\Gamma)^{-1}$, E is the energy of the unstable particle. In the treatment of the *CPT* conjugate reaction, the energy of the corresponding antiparticle is $\overline{E} = -E$. However, the derivation analogous to $(2-3.11)$ for the *CPT* conjugate reaction yields $(m - \overline{E} - \frac{1}{2}\mathrm{i}\Gamma)^{-1}$. The only way to avoid a contradiction is to take for the exact propagator an expression which reduces to $(m - E - \frac{1}{2}\mathrm{i}\Gamma)^{-1}$ for $E \approx m$ and to $(m + E - \frac{1}{2}\mathrm{i}\Gamma)^{-1}$ for $E \approx -m$. To lowest order in Γ/m, the result is $2m(m^2 - s - \mathrm{i}m\Gamma)^{-1}$, as shown by (2-3.13).

4-7. Charge conjugation and *G*-parity

The replacement of an antiparticle by its particle (without change of spin or 4-momentum) is called charge conjugation. For the particle states, we have

$$C|\mathrm{a}, P, M\rangle = \eta_{\mathrm{c}}|\overline{\mathrm{a}}, P, M\rangle, \tag{7.1}$$

where $\eta_{\mathrm{c}} = \pm 1$ is called the charge parity. In the matrix elements, charge conjugation implies replacement of $-P$ by P. For ingoing spin-$\frac{1}{2}$ particles, we should also replace $\bar{u}(-M, -P)$ by $u(M, P)$. Such a replacement would break Lorentz invariance; there is however a similar Lorentz-invariant transformation. In terms of two-component spinors, the normally chosen matrix element is of the form (3-4.2) or (3-4.12). Now we make use of (3-4.19) instead. The determinant is constructed by means of the anti-symmetric matrix $\sigma_y = \begin{pmatrix} 0 & -\mathrm{i} \\ \mathrm{i} & 0 \end{pmatrix}$, which also exchanges the spin states (3-2.1). We thus define the charge-conjugate spinor as

$$\chi_c(M, P) = \sigma_2 \chi^*(M, -P) = \sigma_2 \chi^+(M, -P)_{\mathrm{tr}}, \tag{7.2}$$

where tr stands for "transposed". In terms of Dirac spinors, this means

$$u_c(P) = C\bar{u}(-P)_{\mathrm{tr}}, \qquad C = \gamma_0 \gamma_2 . \tag{7.3}$$

The phase could have been chosen differently. Our choice implies $C^{-1} = C$. The adjoint Dirac equation $\bar{u}(-P)(-P_\mu \gamma^\mu + m) = 0$ of the negative energy spinor transforms under charge conjugation (3) into $(P_\mu \gamma^\mu - m)u_c = 0$, as expected. This is due to the property

$$C^{-1}\gamma^\mu C = -\gamma^\mu_{\mathrm{tr}}, \tag{7.4}$$

which follows from the fact that the two matrices γ_1 and γ_3 which commute with C are antisymmetric, whereas γ_2 and γ_0 are symmetric.

As a first application of charge conjugation, we show that the relative intrinsic parity of fermions and antifermions is negative. The reason is that the parity operator γ_0 anticommutes with C:

$$\begin{aligned} \gamma_0 u_c(P) &= \gamma_0 C\bar{u}(-P)_{\mathrm{tr}} = -C\gamma_0 \bar{u}(-P)_{\mathrm{tr}} \\ &= -C\bar{u}(-E, \boldsymbol{p})_{\mathrm{tr}} = -u_c(E, -\boldsymbol{p}). \end{aligned} \tag{7.5}$$

Consequently, a $\bar{\mathrm{p}}\mathrm{p}$ state of orbital angular momentum L has parity $(-1)^{L+1}$. Bosons and antibosons on the other hand have equal parities. This conforms with the known parity invariance of (6.7). Note also the result (6.11) for antiproton annihilation at rest. The initial state is a triplet S-state, since the initial relative momentum is zero. The final two-pion state is obviously a P-state.

Next, we determine the charge parities η_c of the various particles. As in the case of the normal parity, we define $\eta_c = +1$ for the neutron. This time, however, the charge parity of the proton is already fixed by the phase convention of Condon and Shortley for isospin multiplets:

$$\mathrm{e}^{\mathrm{i}\pi I_2}|I, I_3\rangle = (-1)^{I-I_3}|I, -I_3\rangle, \tag{7.6}$$

which we require not only for particles but also for antiparticles. For the states $|n\rangle$ and $|\bar{n}\rangle$, this means

$$e^{i\pi I_2}|n\rangle = -|p\rangle, \qquad e^{i\pi I_2}|\bar{n}\rangle = |\bar{p}\rangle. \tag{7.7}$$

The requirement that charge conjugation commutes with isospin rotations leads to

$$C|p\rangle = -Ce^{i\pi I_2}|n\rangle = -e^{i\pi I_2}C|n\rangle$$
$$= -e^{i\pi I_2}|\bar{n}\rangle = -|\bar{p}\rangle. \tag{7.8}$$

Before we come to the pion charge parity, we mention the FERMI-YANG model [1949] of pions as nucleon-antinucleon bound states. Due to their negative intrinsic parity, pions may be considered as singlet S-wave bound states, namely

$$\pi^+ : |p\bar{n}\rangle, \qquad \pi^0 : 2^{-\frac{1}{2}}|p\bar{p}\rangle + 2^{-\frac{1}{2}}|n\bar{n}\rangle, \qquad \pi^- : |n\bar{p}\rangle. \tag{7.9}$$

So far it has been impossible to calculate the pion mass from a model like this. Nevertheless, the model is useful for remembering the quantum numbers. Equation (9) is the "crossed version" of the old idea of Yukawa that nucleons should emit and absorb single "virtual" pions, $p \to \pi^+ n$ etc. Knowing the opposite charge parities of proton and neutron, we see immediately from (9) that π^+ and π^- have negative charge parity, while that of π^0 is positive:

$$C|\pi^\pm\rangle = -|\pi^\mp\rangle, \qquad C|\pi^0\rangle = |\pi^0\rangle. \tag{7.10}$$

Many textbooks avoid the minus signs in (8) and (10) by defining $-|\bar{p}\rangle$ and $-|\pi^-\rangle$ as the $I_3 = -I$ components of the isospin multiplet. This convention is very dangerous in the vector addition of pions with nucleons (2.7), (2.8), (2.9) or, even worse, with other pions (table 4-2). In such cases the minus sign in front of $|\pi^-\rangle$ is easily forgotten.

For the Λ-hyperon, we define $\eta_c = +1$. We have this freedom since the decay of strange particles is in general not C-invariant. The charge parities of kaons and Σ-hyperons follow now from an extension of Yukawa's idea to $p \to K\Lambda$ and $p \to K\Sigma$. We find that $K^+(K^0)$ has the charge parity of p(n):

$$C|K^\pm\rangle = -|K^\mp\rangle, \qquad C|K^0\rangle = |\bar{K}^0\rangle, \qquad C|\bar{K}^0\rangle = |K^0\rangle. \tag{7.11}$$

Sigmas have the charge parities of pions,

$$C|\Sigma^\pm\rangle = -|\bar{\Sigma}^\mp\rangle, \qquad C|\Sigma^0\rangle = |\bar{\Sigma}^0\rangle, \tag{7.12}$$

and Ξ^- (Ξ^0) has the charge parity of p(n):

$$C|\Xi^-\rangle = -|\bar{\Xi}^+\rangle, \qquad C|\Xi^0\rangle = |\bar{\Xi}^0\rangle. \tag{7.13}$$

Finally, the photon has negative charge parity. The electromagnetic coupling is of the form $e\varepsilon_\mu(M)\gamma^\mu$, inserted between spinors (see chapter 10). Since from (4) γ^μ changes sign under charge conjugation, invariance of the interaction under charge conjugation requires $e\varepsilon_\mu(M) \to -e\varepsilon_\mu(M)$. This, incidentally, is the historical reason for the name charge conjugation. "Particle and antiparticle have opposite electric charges $\pm e$" and "the photon has negative charge parity" are synonymous expressions.

We may check the quantum numbers of the photon by requiring again that protons should emit and absorb virtual photons singly. By crossing symmetry, this implies again the existence of a proton-antiproton state with the quantum numbers of the photon. Due to the unit spin and negative parity of the photon, only the $^3S_1$ and $^3D_1$ states are candidates. (The lower index gives the total angular momentum J, while the upper index "3" refers to the triplet spin states. The upper index is strictly necessary only for states with $L = J$.) We already know that these states are coupled to $\pi^+ - \pi^-$ P-states, which obviously are eigenstates of charge conjugation, with eigenvalue -1.

A general $\bar{p}p$ or $\bar{n}n$ state of total spin S, parity $(-1)^{L+1}$ and total angular momentum J is an eigenstate of charge conjugation, with eigenvalue

$$C = (-1)^{L+S}. \tag{7.14}$$

The exchange of p and $\bar{p}$ brings a factor $(-1)^{S+1}$ from the symmetry of the spin state, and $(-1)^{L+1}$ from the symmetry of the orbital state. The selection rules following from (14) are summarized in the $I = 0$ part of table 4-7, which is discussed below.

TABLE 4-7

States of zero baryon number and hypercharge

$N\bar{N}$	$I=0$				$I=1$			
	ηG	hadron	pions	$K\bar{K}$	ηG	hadron	pions	$K\bar{K}$
$^1S_0$	$-+$	η, η^*	$4P^3$	f	$--$	π	$3S^2$	f
$^3S_1, {}^3D_1$	$--$	ω, ϕ	$3P^2$	a	$-+$	ρ	2P	a
$^1P_1$	$+-$		3SP	f	$++$		$4SP^2$	f
$^3P_0$	$++$		2S	a	$+-$		$5SP^3$	a
$^3P_1$	$++$		$4SP^2$	f	$+-$		$3P^2$	f
$^3P_2, {}^3F_2$	$++$	f	2D	a	$+-$		3PD	a

For the $N\bar{N}$ states, the notation $^{2S+1}L_J$ is used. For each set of quantum numbers J, η- and G-parity, the smallest pion number is given, together with the lowest L-configuration (see text). For the $K\bar{K}$ states, a means allowed, and f forbidden.

Only three particles are eigenstates of charge conjugation, namely the photon, π^0 and η. The positive charge parity of the two mesons follows directly from the decays $\pi^0 \to \gamma\gamma$, $\eta \to \gamma\gamma$. Pairs consisting of a spinless meson and its antimeson, such as $\pi^+\pi^-$, $\pi^0\pi^0$, K^+K^- or $K^0\bar{K}^0$, have

$$C = (-1)^L, \tag{7.15}$$

irrespective of each meson's charge parity.

Another useful quantum number is obtained by combining charge conjugation with a reversal of the sign of I_3. This is called the isospace parity or G-parity (Pais and Jost [1952], Michel [1953], Lee and Yang [1956]. The operator is written as

$$G = C e^{i\pi I_2}. \tag{7.16}$$

By (6) and (10), all three pions are eigenstates of G, with eigenvalue -1. This leads to useful selection rules. A system of n pions (and no other particles) has $G = (-1)^n$. Conservation of G parity in strong interactions therefore implies conservation modulo 2 of the "pion number" in interactions of $B = Y = 0$ states. For $I = 0$, G and C have identical eigenvalues. Thus η has $G = +1$, which forbids the decay $\eta \to \pi^+\pi^-\pi^0$ by strong interactions.

As with hypercharge, the introduction of G-parity is not strictly necessary. If $\eta \to \pi^+\pi^-\pi^0$ were isospin invariant, the three pions should have $I = 0$. We know from table 4-2 that the only $I = 0$ three-pion state is totally antisymmetric. Being antisymmetric under $\pi^+ \leftrightarrow \pi^-$, this state has negative charge parity, as distinguished from the positive charge parity of η. Considerations of this type are summarized by G-parity.

Application of G to nucleons and antinucleons gives, by (6), (7) and (8),

$$\begin{aligned} G|p\rangle &= -|\bar{n}\rangle, & G|n\rangle &= -|\bar{p}\rangle, \\ G|\bar{p}\rangle &= |n\rangle, & G|\bar{n}\rangle &= |p\rangle. \end{aligned} \tag{7.17}$$

Similar relations exist for kaons. Note that $G^2 = -1$ for $I = \frac{1}{2}$ particles. This is an inevitable consequence of (6).

Nucleon-antinucleon states of total isospin I, total spin S and parity $(-1)^{L+1}$ are eigenstates of G, with eigenvalues

$$G = (-1)^{L+S+I}. \tag{7.18}$$

The factor $(-1)^{L+S}$ is the same as occurs in the derivation of (14). There is also a factor $(-1)^{I+1}$ from the symmetry of the isospin state. The product of these sign factors, together with an extra minus sign from (17), leads to (18). In table 4-7, we have collected the $\overline{\text{N}}$N states for $L < 2$. For $I = 0$, we have $G = C$, in agreement with (16). Also listed are η and π in the appropriate places, together with a few resonances, to be discussed later. The column labelled "pions" contains the lowest possible number of pions in annihilation, together with the lowest orbital angular momentum configuration. The notation S, P, D in this column refers to the angular momenta of the subsystem of the first two, three, etc. pions. In one case we see that the allowed minimum of pions is five. The decay of a 0^+ state into three pseudoscalar particles is forbidden by parity conservation. The coupling of three spinless particles to $J = 0$ is of the type 3P^2, which has a positive orbital parity. Due to the negative intrinsic parity, the system's total parity is negative. This argument forbids not only the decay into three pions, but also decay into $\overline{\text{K}}\text{K}\pi$, $\eta\pi\pi$, etc.

The G-transformations of kaons are analogous to (17). Since kaons have zero spin, a $\overline{\text{K}}$K system of angular momentum J and isospin I has

$$G = (-1)^{J+I}, \tag{7.19}$$

analogous to (18). Consequently, the only critical selection rule for $\overline{\text{N}}\text{N} \to \overline{\text{K}}\text{K}$ is that the connection between J and parity must be the "natural" one, $\eta = (-1)^J$.

4-8. The decays $\pi^0 \to \gamma\gamma$ and $\Sigma^0 \to \gamma\Lambda$

The electromagnetic decays of hadrons are limited not only by the conservation of hypercharge, parity and charge conjugation, but also by the principle of gauge invariance. The decay $\eta \to \pi^0\gamma$ for example could have the matrix element $-G_1 P_\eta \cdot \varepsilon^*(M)$ analogous to (3-3.5). Gauge invariance (3-3.10), however, requires this matrix element to vanish when ε^* is replaced by P_γ. Since

$$P_\eta \cdot P_\gamma = (P_\eta - \tfrac{1}{2}P_\gamma) \cdot P_\gamma = \tfrac{1}{2}(P_\eta + P_\pi)(P_\eta - P_\pi) = m_\eta^2 - m_\pi^2, \tag{8.1}$$

the matrix element is gauge invariant only for $m_\eta = m_\pi$.

For the decays $\pi^0 \to \gamma\gamma$ and $\eta \to \gamma\gamma$, two gauge invariant couplings exist:

$$T(\lambda_1, \lambda_2) = g\varepsilon_{\alpha\beta\gamma\delta} P_1^\alpha \varepsilon_1^{*\beta}(\lambda_1) P_2^\gamma \varepsilon_2^{*\delta}(\lambda_2), \tag{8.2}$$

$$T'(\lambda_1, \lambda_2) = g'[(P_1 \cdot P_2)(\varepsilon_1^*(\lambda_1) \cdot \varepsilon_2^*(\lambda_2)) - P_1 \cdot \varepsilon_2^*(\lambda_2) P_2 \cdot \varepsilon_1^*(\lambda_1)], \tag{8.3}$$

where P_1 and P_2 are the photons' momenta, and λ_1 and λ_2 are their helicities. If either polarization vector is replaced by the corresponding photon momentum, then T and T' vanish. Replacement of $\varepsilon_1^*(\lambda_1)$ by P_1 for example gives $\varepsilon_{\alpha\beta}..P_1^\alpha P_1^\beta \ldots$ in T, which vanishes because of the antisymmetry of the ε-symbol (summation over α and β is understood).

Under parity conjugation, T and T' are odd and even, respectively. Due to the negative intrinsic parity of the π^0, we require $g' = 0$. In the pion rest frame, with the decay direction along the z-axis, we have $P_1 = (p, 0, 0, p)$, $P_2 = (p, 0, 0, -p)$, $p = \frac{1}{2}m_\pi$. The only non-vanishing terms in the summation come from the values 0 and 3 for α and γ, which implies 1 and 2 for β and δ:

$$\begin{aligned} T(\lambda_1, \lambda_2) &= -\tfrac{1}{2}gm^2\varepsilon_{0\beta 3\delta}\varepsilon_1^{*\beta}(\lambda_1)\varepsilon_2^{*\delta}(\lambda_2) \\ &= \tfrac{1}{2}gm^2[\varepsilon_{1x}^*(\lambda_1)\varepsilon_{2y}^*(\lambda_2) - \varepsilon_{1y}^*(\lambda_1)\varepsilon_{2x}^*(\lambda_2)]. \end{aligned} \tag{8.4}$$

By (3-3.3), this expression vanishes except for $|\lambda_1| = |\lambda_2| = 1$. The vector $\varepsilon_1^*(\lambda_1)$ is the complex conjugate of (3-3.2). The vector $\varepsilon_2^*(\lambda_2)$ on the other hand is the complex conjugate of (3-3.2) for magnetic quantum number $-\lambda_2$. The reason for this is that helicity is defined as the magnetic quantum number in the direction of the momentum, and that the momentum of the second photon points along the negative z-axis. Observing this, we obtain

$$T(\lambda_1, \lambda_2) = -\tfrac{1}{2}igm^2\lambda_1\delta_{\lambda_1\lambda_2}, \qquad \Gamma = \frac{1}{8m}\sum_{\lambda_1\lambda_2} 2\frac{|T|^2}{4\pi} = \frac{m^3}{8}\frac{g^2}{4\pi}. \tag{8.5}$$

The equality of the two helicities follows trivially from the fact that the pion has zero magnetic quantum number. Γ is computed from (2-3.4).

Next, study the decay $\Sigma \to \gamma\Lambda$. For equal intrinsic parities of Σ and Λ, the most general parity-conserving decay is of the form

$$T(M, M', \lambda) = \varepsilon^{*\nu}(\lambda)\bar{u}'(M')\left[G_\text{v}\gamma_\nu + \frac{G_\text{t}}{m+m'}\sigma_{\mu\nu}P_\gamma^\mu\right]u(M), \tag{8.6}$$

where $P_\gamma = P - P'$ is the photon momentum, $\sigma^{\mu\nu}$ is defined in (3-6.1) and G_v and G_t are called the vector and tensor coupling constants, respectively. For opposite intrinsic parities, $u(M)$ would be replaced by $\gamma_5 u(M)$. By means of the Dirac equations for $\bar{u}'$ and u and the anticommutation relations (3-6.2) for γ-matrices, (6) is rewritten as

$$T(M, M', \lambda) = \varepsilon^{*\nu}(\lambda)\bar{u}'(M')\left[(G_\text{v}+G_\text{t})\gamma_\nu - \frac{(P+P')_\nu}{m+m'}G_\text{t}\right]u(M). \tag{8.7}$$

This shows that terms of the form GP_ν are already included in the square bracket of (6). Replacing $\varepsilon^{*\nu}(\lambda)$ by P_γ^ν, we find that the tensor coupling of (6) is gauge invariant, due to $P_\gamma^\nu\sigma_{\mu\nu}P_\gamma^\mu = 0$. For the vector coupling, we find by the Dirac equations (3-5.5) and (3-5.8),

$$P_\gamma^\nu \bar{u}'(M')\gamma_\nu u(M) = \bar{u}'(M')(P-P')\cdot\gamma u(M) = (m-m')\bar{u}'(M')u(M), \quad (8.8)$$

which vanishes only for $m = m'$. We conclude that the decay $\Sigma \to \gamma\Lambda$ has $G_v = 0$.

From table 4-1 we see that 4 Σ^+ decays per thousand proceed via $\Sigma^+ \to \gamma p$. The fact that this decay does not conserve strangeness indicates that it must involve a weak interaction and therefore need not conserve parity. It is of the general form

$$T(M, M', \lambda) = \varepsilon^{*\nu}(\lambda)\bar{u}'(M')\frac{\sigma_{\mu\nu}}{m+m'}P_\gamma^\mu(G_t+G_t'\gamma_5)u(M). \quad (8.9)$$

In other parts of table 4-1, photons also appear in obviously weak interactions. As a rule, such decay modes are suppressed by a factor α (1.1) or even α/π in comparison with photonless decays.

4-9. Selection rules of $\Delta Y \neq 0$ decays

Although weak interactions need not conserve hypercharge or isospin, they still obey important selection rules. The $|\Delta Y|=1$ or $|\Delta S|=1$ rule states that the hypercharge changes at most by one unit. It forbids decays such as $\Xi \to N\pi$ and $\Xi \to Ne\nu$ and thus explains the "cascade" from Ξ-decay. Further evidence comes from the absence of the decays $\Omega^- \to \pi\Sigma$, $\Omega^- \to \pi\Lambda$, and $\Omega^- \to \pi n$. The last of these decays has $\Delta Y = -3$.

Actually, $|\Delta Y| = 1$ is a consequence of the more specific $\Delta I = \frac{1}{2}$ rule, which states that in hypercharge changing decays, the total isospin changes by $\frac{1}{2}$. As a first example of this rule, consider the decays $\Lambda \to \pi^- p$ and $\Lambda \to \pi^0 n$. Since Λ has $I = 0$, the total isospin of the πN system may be $\frac{1}{2}$ but not $\frac{3}{2}$. From the second equation of (2.9), we get

$$\Gamma(\Lambda \to \pi^- p) : \Gamma(\Lambda \to \pi^0 n) = 2:1, \quad (9.1)$$

which agrees with the experimental ratio (table 4-1).

The derivation of $|\Delta Y| = 1$ from $\Delta I = \frac{1}{2}$ is based on the connection (3.6) between Q, I_3 and Y, which requires

$$\Delta Y = 2(\Delta Q - \Delta I_3). \quad (9.2)$$

In the non-leptonic decays, the total electric charge Q of the hadrons is conserved. With $\Delta Q = 0$, (2) reduces to $\Delta Y = -2\Delta I_3 = \pm 1$. In the leptonic decays, the lepton pair carries away one unit of charge, i.e. we have

$\Delta Q = \pm 1 = \pm 2\Delta I_3$. By (2), the case $\Delta Q = -2\Delta I_3$ requires $|\Delta Y| = 3$, which can only occur for Ω^- decay (see below). For all other decays, we have $\Delta Q = +2\Delta I_3$, and therefore

$$\Delta Y = \Delta Q = \pm 1 \tag{9.3}$$

for the leptonic decays of hadrons. Stated differently, decays such as $\Sigma^+ \to ne^+\nu$, $K^\pm \to \pi^\pm\pi^\pm e^\mp\nu$ which have $\Delta Y = -\Delta Q$, necessarily have $\Delta I_3 = \pm\frac{3}{2}$. Experimentally, such decays have not been detected.

There could be one exception to (3), namely $\Omega^- \to ne\nu$ or $\Omega^- \to n\mu\nu$. Since Ω^- has $I = 0$, the decay fulfills the $\Delta I = \frac{1}{2}$ rule, but it has $\Delta Y = -3$, $\Delta Q = -1$. The decay has not been seen, which however implies very little in view of the small numbers if Ω^- observed so far.

The $\Delta I = \frac{1}{2}$ rule, the $|\Delta Y| = 1$ rule, and the rule $\Delta Y(\text{leptonic}) = \Delta Q$ are combined in the convenient "spurious kaon" rule:

In interactions with $\Delta Y \neq 0$, conservation of hypercharge and isospin is restored by the inclusion of a "spurious" kaon. In the leptonic decay modes, the lepton pair has the isospin properties of a charged kaon. In the hadronic decay modes, a spurious neutral kaon of zero energy and momentum must be added.

Since kaons have $Y = Q = \pm 1$ and $I = \frac{1}{2}$, the specific rules previously mentioned follow immediately. The selection rules of $\Lambda \to \pi N$ for example follow from conservation of isospin in the "reactions" $(K^0)\Lambda \to \pi N$ or $\Lambda \to \pi N(\overline{K}^0)$, where the spurious kaon has been placed in parentheses. A second example is

$$\Gamma(\Xi^- \to \Lambda\pi^-) : \Gamma(\Xi^0 \to \Lambda\pi^0) = 2:1, \tag{9.4}$$

which is obtained from isospin conservation either in the reaction $(K^0)\Xi \to \pi\Lambda$ by (2.4) or in the reaction $\Xi \to \pi(\overline{K}^0)\Lambda$ by (2.9). Remember that $\overline{K}^0$ (K^0) is identical with p(n) as far as isospin is concerned. Similarly, the isospin decomposition of the decays $\Sigma^+ \to \pi^0 p$, $\Sigma^+ \to \pi^+ n$ and $\Sigma^- \to \pi^- n$ is identical with that of the corresponding spurious reactions $(K^0)\Sigma \to \pi N$. It will be discussed in section 9-7.

Electromagnetic interactions conserve charge and hypercharge and therefore cannot modify the $|\Delta Y| = 1$ and $\Delta Y = \Delta Q$ rules. They do however introduce decays with $\Delta I_3 = \pm\frac{1}{2}$, $\Delta I = \frac{3}{2}$. An example of this is $K^+ \to \pi^+\pi^0$. Conservation of J requires an S-state for the two-pion state. By the extended Bose-Einstein symmetry, this could occur with $I = 0$ and $I = 2$, but $I = 0$ is excluded because $I_3 = 1$. The decay $K^+ \to \pi^+\pi^0$ thus has $\Delta I = \frac{3}{2}$ (or $\Delta I = \frac{5}{2}$, since isospins $\frac{1}{2}$ and $\frac{5}{2}$ can also couple to $I = 2$).

If the decay is caused by the emission and re-absorption of a virtual photon, its width should be a factor α^2 smaller than that of $K^0 \to \pi\pi$. From table 4-1, we find $\Gamma(K^+ \to \pi^+\pi^0)/\Gamma(K^0_S) = (0.21/123) \times 0.87 = 0.0015$, which is somewhat too large.

At this point, one may wonder why the ratio $\Gamma(K^0_L \to \pi^+\pi^-)/\Gamma(K^0_S \to \pi^+\pi^-)$ is as small as 2×10^{-6}. The decay $K^0_L \to \pi^+\pi^-$ was discovered in 1964 (Christenson *et al.*). Before that, weak interactions were believed to be invariant under *CP*, the product of charge conjugation and parity operation, in which case the decay $K^0_L \to \pi\pi$ was forbidden. To see this, we split the weak interactions into a *CP* conserving part and a small *CP* violating part, which we neglect for the time being. A kaon at rest is an eigenstate of $\mathscr{P}$, with eigenvalue -1 (the eigenparity). By (7.11), we have

$$C|K^0\rangle = +|\overline{K}^0\rangle. \tag{9.5}$$

Therefore, the linear combinations

$$|K^0_1\rangle = 2^{-\frac{1}{2}}(|K^0\rangle - |\overline{K}^0\rangle), \qquad |K^0_2\rangle = 2^{-\frac{1}{2}}(|K^0\rangle + |\overline{K}^0\rangle) \tag{9.6}$$

are eigenstates of *CP*, with eigenvalues $+1$ and -1, respectively. S-states of $\pi^+\pi^-$ and $\pi^0\pi^0$ are also eigenstates of *CP*, with eigenvalue $+1$. The decay $K^0_2 \to \pi\pi$ is thus forbidden by *CP* invariance. From the decay modes of K^0_S and K^0_L, we conclude that these particles are identical with the combinations K^0_1 and K^0_2 respectively, if effects of the *CP*-violating interaction are neglected. Equation (6) explains why kaons produced in πN collisions decay half as K^0_L and half as K^0_S. On the other hand, in $\bar{p}p$ annihilations at rest, $\bar{p}p \to K^0_1 K^0_2$ is forbidden. According to table 4-7, only the $^3S_1$ state, which has $CP = +1$, can decay into two kaons.

As a final example, we compare the decay rates of the decays $K^+ \to \pi^+\pi^+\pi^-$, $K^+ \to \pi^+\pi^0\pi^0$, $K^0_L \to \pi^0\pi^0\pi^0$ and $K^0_L \to \pi^+\pi^-\pi^0$. Due to the small amount of energy released in $K \to \pi\pi\pi$, we expect all orbital angular momenta of the final state to be zero. In the notation of table 4-7, these are $3S^2$ states, which in fact have negative intrinsic parity. The next allowed configuration would be $3P^2$, which already contains two angular momentum barriers.

The total symmetry of $3S^2$ states requires, by the extended symmetry principle of pions, a totally symmetric isospin state. Such states are denoted by $\boxed{1|2|3}$ in table 4-2. They contain $I = 1$ and $I = 3$. For our purpose, $I = 3$ is excluded by the $\Delta I = \frac{1}{2}$ rule. Therefore the sum of the absolute squares of the matrix elements for the above four decays is proportional to 12/15, 3/15, 9/15 and 6/15, respectively.

According to (2-3.3), the width Γ contains an integration over the three-particle phase space. Since the energy release $m_K - \sum_i m_i$ is so small, one cannot neglect the $K^+ - K^0$ and $\pi^+ - \pi^0$ mass differences in this calculation. One may, however, assume that the matrix element T_{df} is nearly constant over the small range of E_1 and E_2 inside the Dalitz plot (statistical model). Then $\Gamma(K \to \pi\pi\pi)$ is given by $(1/2m)\,\mathrm{Lips}(m^2, m_1 m_2 m_3)|T_{df}|^2$, where m is the kaon mass and m_1, m_2, m_3 are the masses of the three pions. Lips may be calculated in the non-relativistic approximation (1-9.5). The main mass dependence comes from the last factor, $(m_K - \sum_i m_i)^2$. The ratio of $K^+ \to \pi^+\pi^+\pi^-$ and $K^+ \to \pi^+\pi^0\pi^0$ decays for example becomes

$$\frac{\Gamma(K^+ \to \pi^+\pi^+\pi^-)}{\Gamma(K^+ \to \pi^+\pi^0\pi^0)} = \frac{12}{3}\left(\frac{m-3m_+}{m-2m_0-m_+}\right)^2 = 4\left(\frac{0.075}{0.084}\right)^2 = 3.2, \qquad (9.7)$$

which agrees quite well with the experimental ratio 0.056/0.017 of table 4-1. For a further discussion of $K \to \pi\pi\pi$ decays, see e.g. the review of LEE and WU [1966].

The isospin selection rules of weak interactions would be a miracle if the strong interactions were not isospin invariant. In this sense, the $\Delta I = \frac{1}{2}$ rule provides at present the most accurate tests of isospin invariance of the strong interactions of hyperons and kaons.

CHAPTER 5

RESONANCES AND SU_3 SYMMETRY

5-1. The N^*_{33} resonance

The oldest and best-known resonance in the interactions of hadrons is the "nucleon isobar" N*, also denoted by N^*_{33} and Δ. It appears most clearly in elastic π^+p scattering. On the left side of fig. 4-1, we have plotted the total π^+p scattering cross-section as a function of the total cms energy. There is a strong maximum at 1225 MeV. The maximum cross-section 210 mb is very close to $8\pi/q^2$. According to (3-9.13), this implies $J = \frac{3}{2}$. From (4-2.7), π^+p states have $I = \frac{3}{2}$. The two indices of N^*_{33} stand for $I = \frac{3}{2}$ and $J = \frac{3}{2}$.

A check of isospin invariance of strong interactions is provided by the fact that πN scattering in the $I = \frac{1}{2}$ state is very small in the N* region. We have

$$\sigma(\tfrac{3}{2}) = \sigma(\pi^+p), \qquad \sigma(\tfrac{1}{2}) = \tfrac{3}{2}\sigma(\pi^-p) - \tfrac{1}{2}\sigma(\pi^+p). \tag{1.1}$$

The first equation follows obviously from (4-2.7), while the second follows from the fact that π^-p is $\frac{1}{3}$ in $I = \frac{3}{2}$ (4-2.8) and $\frac{2}{3}$ in $I = \frac{1}{2}$ (4-2.9): $\sigma(\pi^-p) = \frac{1}{3}\sigma(\frac{3}{2}) + \frac{2}{3}\sigma(\frac{1}{2})$. The total $I = \frac{1}{2}$ πN cross-section, defined by (1), is also shown in fig. 4-1.

The parity of a πN state of orbital angular momentum L is $-(-1)^L$, the extra minus sign coming from the pion's negative intrinsic parity. We now demonstrate that the N* is $\frac{3}{2}^+$, i.e. a P-wave resonance. The case of a D-wave resonance is a priori unlikely because of the threshold behaviour q^{2L} of the amplitude $f_{L\pm}$. The conclusive evidence about the quantum numbers of the resonance comes from the threshold behaviour of the various terms in the differential cross-section, which include interference with non-resonant partial waves. Insertion of (3-9.4), (3-9.3) into (3-8.14) for elastic scattering gives

$$\frac{d\sigma(s,\theta)}{d\Omega} = |\sum_J (J+\tfrac{1}{2}) d^J_{\frac{1}{2}\frac{1}{2}}(\theta)(f_{L+} + f_{(L+1)-})|^2 + |\sum_J (J+\tfrac{1}{2}) d^J_{\frac{1}{2}-\frac{1}{2}}(\theta)(f_{L+} - f_{(L+1)-})|^2. \tag{1.2}$$

An exchange $L+ \to (L+1)-$, for all values of L, leaves $d\sigma/d\Omega$ invariant (this is called the Minami ambiguity). Clearly, the exchange of $S_{\frac{1}{2}}$ and $P_{\frac{1}{2}}$, $P_{\frac{3}{2}}$ and $D_{\frac{3}{2}}$ etc. changes the threshold behaviour of the resonant partial wave, and that of all other partial waves as well.

We keep only $J = \frac{1}{2}$ and $J = \frac{3}{2}$ in (2). Inserting the d-functions of table C-3, we get

$$\frac{d\sigma}{d\Omega} = \cos^2 \tfrac{1}{2}\theta |f_{0+} + f_{1-} + (1 - 3\sin^2 \tfrac{1}{2}\theta)(f_{1+} + f_{2-})|^2$$
$$+ \sin^2 \tfrac{1}{2}\theta |f_{0+} - f_{1-} + (3\cos^2 \tfrac{1}{2}\theta - 1)(f_{1+} - f_{2-})|^2. \quad (1.3)$$

For comparison with experiment, this is put into the form

$$\frac{d\sigma}{d\Omega} = A + B\cos\theta + C\cos^2\theta + D\cos^3\theta. \quad (1.4)$$

The two sums in (3) are rewritten as

$$f_{0+} - f_{2-} \pm (f_{1-} - f_{1+}) + 3\cos\theta(f_{1+} \pm f_{2-}), \quad (1.5)$$

which gives

$$A = |f_{0+} - f_{2-}|^2 + |f_{1-} - f_{1+}|^2,$$
$$B = 2\,\text{Re}\,(2f_{0+}^* f_{1+} + f_{0+}^* f_{1-} + 2f_{1-}^* f_{2-} - 5f_{1+}^* f_{2-}),$$
$$C = 3(|f_{1+}|^2 + |f_{2-}|^2 + 2\,\text{Re}\,(f_{1-}^* f_{1+} + f_{0+}^* f_{2-})),$$
$$D = 18\,\text{Re}\, f_{1+}^* f_{2-}. \quad (1.6)$$

Experimentally, D is negligible in the resonance region, $A : C \approx \frac{1}{3}$ at resonance, and B goes through zero at resonance. The natural explanation is $f_{1-} = f_{2-} = 0$, and $f_{L\pm} = 0$ for $J > \frac{3}{2}$. The remaining terms in $d\sigma/d\Omega$ are

$$\frac{d\sigma}{d\Omega} \approx |f_{0+}|^2 + |f_{1+}|^2 + 4\cos\theta\,\text{Re}\, f_{0+}^* f_{1+} + 3\cos^2\theta |f_{1+}|^2. \quad (1.7)$$

The fact that $\text{Re}\, f_{0+}^* f_{1+}$ passes through zero near the resonance is explained as follows: For $qR \ll 1, f_{0+}$ is approximated by the real scattering length A_{0+} (2-6.5). At resonances, f_{1+} becomes purely imaginary, and $\text{Re}\, f_{0+}^* f_{1+}$ passes through zero.

The "Minami-transformed" explanation would be $f_{0+} = f_{1+} = 0$, and $f_{L\pm} = 0$ for $J > \frac{3}{2}$. In that case, A, B and C would have the threshold behaviour q^4, q^6 and q^8, instead of q^0, q^2 and q^4. The absence of $S_{\frac{1}{2}}$ and $P_{\frac{3}{2}}$ scattering in the presence of $P_{\frac{1}{2}}$ and $D_{\frac{3}{2}}$ scattering would be difficult to explain.

Another possibility of excluding $D_{\frac{3}{2}}$ from the resonance originates from the polarization of the final proton, which is discussed later.

We now neglect the non-resonant partial waves, in which case $\sigma(s)$ is given by the resonance formula

$$\sigma(s) = 2\pi(2J+1)\frac{m^2\Gamma^2/q^2}{(m^2-s)^2+m^2\Gamma^2}, \tag{1.8}$$

where m is the "mass" of the resonance, and $s^{\frac{1}{2}}$ the "effective mass". For a broad P-wave resonance, the s-dependence of Γ cannot be neglected. For $qR \ll 1$, we expect $m\Gamma$ to be of the form $(qR)^3(\mathrm{d}g/\mathrm{d}s)^{-1}$ according to (2-8.7). This, however, gives a poor fit for the resonance, except for its low-energy tail. For the case of a general qR, the position of the resonance is defined as the zero of the denominator of (2-5.13), that is $qRn'(qR) = gn(qR)$. In order to get the width, one writes (2-5.13) as $m\Gamma/(m^2-s)$, according to the definition (2-8.1). As long as no other details of the interaction but its range R are included, one obtains for Γ (BLATT and WEISSKOPF [1952], p. 311)

$$\Gamma(qR) = qv_L(qR)\gamma, \tag{1.9}$$

where the dimensionless constant γ is the "reduced width", and where the "penetration factor" $v_L(\rho)$ is given by

$$v_L(\rho) = [\rho^2 n_L^2(\rho)+\rho^2 j_L^2(\rho)]^{-1}. \tag{1.10}$$

In this approximation, a resonance is characterized by three energy-independent parameters; m, R and γ. The functions v_L are relatively simple. For $L = 0$, 1 and 2, they are

$$v_0(\rho) = 1, \qquad v_1(\rho) = \frac{\rho^2}{1+\rho^2}, \qquad v_2(\rho) = \frac{\rho^4}{9+3\rho+\rho^4}. \tag{1.11}$$

The name "penetration factor" refers to the penetration of the centrifugal barrier $L(L+1)/r^2$ of (2-5.3). For $\rho \gg 1$, $v_L(\rho)$ becomes unity for any value of L. For $\rho \ll 1$, it reduces to the familiar threshold behaviour $\rho^{2L}[(2L-1)!!]^{-2}$ of (2-8.7).

For the N*-resonance, with $L = 1$, one obtains a reasonable fit for the P_{33} phase shift with

$$m = 1.240 \text{ GeV}, \qquad R = 6.3/\text{GeV}, \qquad \gamma = 0.74. \tag{1.12}$$

The comparison between

$$\Gamma = \gamma q \frac{R^2q^2}{1+R^2q^2} \tag{1.13}$$

and $\Gamma = 2(m-s^{\frac{1}{2}}) \tan P_{33}$ (the tangent of the $I = J = \frac{3}{2}$ phase shift) of ROPER, WRIGHT and FELD [1965] is shown in fig. 5-1. The value of Γ at $s^{\frac{1}{2}} = m$ is 115 MeV. For $s > m^2$, curve (13) rises a little too rapidly.

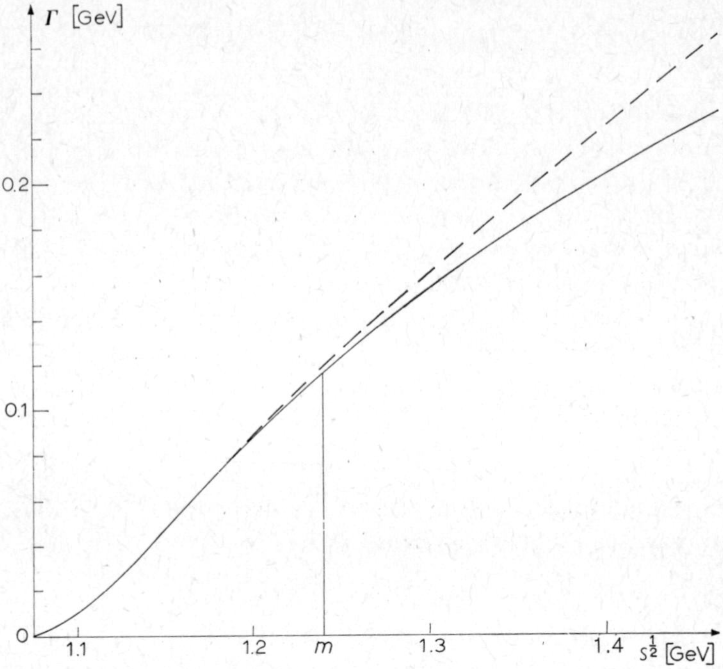

Fig. 5-1. Variation of the N^*_{33} width with cms energy; —— $\Gamma = 2(1.24 - s^{\frac{1}{2}}) \tan P_{33}$ from ROPER, WRIGHT and FELD [1965], - - - $\Gamma = 0.74q \dfrac{(6.3q)^2}{1+(6.3q)^2}$ (eq. (1.13)). (By courtesy of K. D. DRAXLER.)

5-2. Production of resonances and resonance shift

Resonances are copiously produced in inelastic high-energy collisions. The Dalitz plot for $\pi^+p \to \pi^0\pi^+p$ for example (fig. 1-4.1) shows the N* very clearly. As long as no reliable theory of such reactions exists, the best one can do is to treat the N* as an unstable spin-$\frac{3}{2}$ particle of finite, energy-dependent width. The amplitude for N* decay will be denoted by $T(M, \lambda', p, \vartheta, \varphi)$, where $M = \pm\frac{3}{2}, \pm\frac{1}{2}$ is the magnetic quantum number of the resonance, $\lambda' = \pm\frac{1}{2}$ is the decay proton's helicity, and p, ϑ and φ give the magnitude and direction of the proton's momentum in the resonance rest frame. The angular dependence of T is found from the decomposition of $D^{J*}_{\lambda\lambda'}(\Omega)$ in (3-8.5) analogous to (3-2.15):

$$D^{*}_{\lambda\lambda'}(\phi, \theta, -\phi) = \sum_M D_{M\lambda}(\Omega_i) D^{*}_{M\lambda'}(\varphi_f, \vartheta_f, -\varphi_f). \tag{2.1}$$

The derivation of this formula is analogous to that of (3-8.9). This time, the angles Ω_i of the initial state are determined by the group properties of the rotation matrices. For the final state, (1) requires

$$T(M, \lambda', p, \vartheta, \varphi) = T(\lambda', p) D^{J*}_{M\lambda'}(\varphi, \vartheta, -\varphi), \tag{2.2}$$

for any pion-nucleon resonance of arbitrary J and parity. To get the function $T(\lambda', p)$, it is customary to write T in the Lorentz invariant form

$$T(M, \lambda', p, \vartheta, \varphi) = -G^* \bar{u}'(\lambda') P^{\mu} u_{\mu}(M), \tag{2.3}$$

where P^{μ} is the proton's 4-momentum. The "coupling constant" G^* is a function of the effective mass, and $u_{\mu}(M)$ is the Rarita-Schwinger spinor of section 3-7. Since the M-dependence is already known from (2), we calculate T for one value of M only. The value $M = \frac{3}{2}$ is convenient, because of $u_{\mu}(\frac{3}{2}) = u(\frac{1}{2})\varepsilon_{\mu}(1)$. In the resonance rest frame, ε_0 vanishes, and one gets $-P^{\mu} \cdot \varepsilon_{\mu}(1) = \boldsymbol{p} \cdot \boldsymbol{\varepsilon}(1)$, which was already computed in (3-2.12). Using the low-energy representation, we may replace Q_{bb} by $G^* \boldsymbol{p} \cdot \boldsymbol{\varepsilon}(1) = -\frac{1}{2}\sqrt{2}\, G^* p \sin\vartheta\, e^{i\varphi}$ in (3-5.16), which yields

$$\begin{aligned} T(\tfrac{3}{2}, \lambda', p, \vartheta, \varphi) &= -2^{-\frac{1}{2}} G^* p \sqrt{2m(E'+m')}\, \chi_0'^{+}(\lambda') \chi_0(\tfrac{1}{2}) \sin\vartheta\, e^{i\varphi} \\ &= (\tfrac{2}{3})^{\frac{1}{2}} G^* p \sqrt{2m(E'+m')}\, D^{\frac{3}{2}*}_{\frac{3}{2}\lambda'}(\varphi, \vartheta, -\varphi), \end{aligned} \tag{2.4}$$

and therefore

$$T(\lambda', p) = (\tfrac{2}{3})^{\frac{1}{2}} G^* p \sqrt{2m(E'+m')}. \tag{2.5}$$

The width Γ may now be calculated from a formula analogous to the spinless case (2-3.4). We know that Γ must be independent of M, but it may in general depend on the helicity λ'. We then have

$$\Gamma(p) = \frac{p}{4m^2} \sum_{\lambda'} \int \frac{d\cos\vartheta}{4\pi} |T(M, \lambda', p, \vartheta, \varphi)|^2. \tag{2.6}$$

By (C-4.1), the angular integration gives a factor $\frac{1}{2}$. Due to parity conservation in the resonance decay, (5) is actually independent of λ'. The helicity summation thus gives a factor 2. The final result is

$$\Gamma_{N^*}(p) = \frac{1}{6} \frac{G^{*2}}{4\pi} p^3 \frac{2(E'+m')}{m} = \frac{1}{6} \frac{G^{*2}}{4\pi} \frac{(m+m_p)^2 - m_\pi^2}{m^2} p^3. \tag{2.7}$$

In the last expression we have put $m' = m_p$ and $2E' = (m^2+m_p^2-m_\pi^2)/m$. From the discussion of section 2.3 we remember that we cannot distinguish between s and m^2 in (6) or (7). In view of the possible s-dependence of the function G^*, this distinction would be rather meaningless anyway. If we want Γ in the form (1.13), then G^* must depend on s according to

$$G^{*2}(s) = G^{*2}(m^2)\,\frac{1+R^2p^2(m^2)}{1+R^2p^2(s)}, \tag{2.8}$$

$$\frac{G^{*2}(m^2)}{4\pi} = 6\Gamma(m^2)\left[\left(1+\frac{m_p}{m}\right)^2 p^3(m^2)\right]^{-1} \approx 14/\text{GeV}^2. \tag{2.9}$$

If the width Γ were independent of s, then the effective mass distribution would have its maximum at $s = m^2$. The energy dependence of Γ shifts the maximum to smaller values of s. In fact, fig. 4-1 shows the maximum at $s^{\frac{1}{2}} = 1225$ GeV, which is 13 MeV below the m-value of (1.12). In most production reactions ($\pi p \to \pi N^*$ or $Kp \to KN^*$), the maximum occurs even lower, usually around $s^{\frac{1}{2}} = 1215$ MeV.

We now discuss a simple model for the resonance shift (JACKSON [1964]).

For the two-step process $ap \to cN^*$, $N^* \to \pi p$, the dependence of the cross section on the πN effective mass is given by (2-3.17), without the $\int ds_d$. For elastic scattering $\pi p \to N^* \to \pi p$, it is given by (1.8). We assume that $\sigma(ap \to cN^*)$ is independent of the effective mass. The task then is to find the maxima of the two functions

$$F_{pr} = \frac{m\Gamma(x)}{x^2+m^2\Gamma^2(x)}, \qquad F_{el} = \frac{m^2\Gamma^2(x)/p^2(x)}{x^2+m^2\Gamma^2(x)}, \qquad x \equiv m^2-s, \tag{2.10}$$

for production reactions and elastic scattering, respectively. The positions x_{pr} and x_{el} of the maxima are given by the zeros of the derivatives,

$$\Gamma'(x_{pr}^2+m^2\Gamma^2)-\Gamma[2x_{pr}+m^2(\Gamma^2)'] = 0,$$

$$\left(\frac{\Gamma^2}{p^2}\right)'(x_{el}^2+m^2\Gamma^2)-\left(\frac{\Gamma}{p}\right)^2[2x_{el}+m^2(\Gamma^2)'] = 0. \tag{2.11}$$

Taking Γ proportional to p^{2L+1} for small values of pR, we get approximately

$$\Gamma' = (L+\tfrac{1}{2})\Gamma\,\frac{(p^2)'}{p^2}, \qquad (\Gamma^2)' = (2L+1)\Gamma^2\,\frac{(p^2)'}{p^2}, \qquad \left(\frac{\Gamma^2}{p^2}\right)' = 2L\,\frac{\Gamma^2}{p^2}\,\frac{(p^2)'}{p^2}, \tag{2.12}$$

which leads to the equations

$$x_{pr} = \frac{(p^2)'}{p^2}(L+\tfrac{1}{2})(\tfrac{1}{2}x_{pr}^2 - \tfrac{1}{2}m^2\Gamma^2), \tag{2.13}$$

$$x_{el} = \frac{(p^2)'}{p^2}(Lx_{el}^2 - \tfrac{1}{2}m^2\Gamma^2). \tag{2.14}$$

Since we expect x to be small, we neglect the x^2-terms and get

$$x_{el} = -\tfrac{1}{2}m^2\Gamma^2 \frac{(p^2)'}{p^2}, \tag{2.15}$$

$$x_{pr} = (L+\tfrac{1}{2})x_{el}. \tag{2.16}$$

The first equation shows that x_{el} is positive, since $(p^2)' = -\mathrm{d}p^2/\mathrm{d}s$. The exact value of x_{el} does not agree too well with the experimental shift. The second equation tells us that the peak value in the resonance production occurs at a still lower effective mass. For P-wave resonances, the production shift is 50% bigger than the shift in elastic scattering.

5-3. The N^*_{13} and N^*_{15} resonances

In addition to the N^*_{33}, several other resonances are found in elastic πN scattering. The $I = \frac{1}{2}$ curve in fig. 4-1 shows two bumps at 1518 and 1688 MeV, which correspond to resonances in the $D_{\frac{3}{2}}$ and $F_{\frac{5}{2}}$ partial waves. The determination of spins and parities of these resonances is more complicated than in the case of N^*_{33}. The formula $\sigma_J(\text{res}) = 2\pi(2J+1)/q^2$ is useless, because too many non-resonant partial waves and inelastic channels contribute to σ(total).

A convenient notation for pion-nucleon resonances is $N^*_{2I,\,2J}$. For completeness, the resonance energy is often added in parentheses, for example N^*_{33} (1238), N^*_{13} (1518) and N^*_{15} (1688). The main properties of these and a few other baryon resonances are collected in table 5-3.

The first evidence for the N^*_{13} resonance came from the photoproduction reactions $\gamma p \to p\pi^-\pi^+$, $\gamma p \to p\pi^0$ and $\gamma p \to n\pi^+$ (see fig. 10-8). The spin $\frac{3}{2}$ was deduced from the angular distribution. A negative parity was suggested by the proton polarization in $\gamma p \to \pi^0 p$. Today, an extensive phase shift analysis of πN scattering exists (see e.g. ROPER [1964], BAREYRE *et al.* [1965]). The angular distribution in the region of the 1518 and 1688 resonances is described by a polynomial of sixth order in $\cos\theta$. We shall

TABLE 5-3

Masses and decay properties of some low-lying baryon resonances

symbol (m)	LJ^η	m [GeV] m^2 [GeV^2]	Γ [MeV]	partial mode	fraction	p or p_{max} [GeV]
$N^*_{33}(1238)$	$P\frac{3}{2}+$	1.240 1.538	$\frac{0.74p(6.3p)^2}{1+(6.3p)^2}$	πN	1	0.233
$N^*_{13}(1518)$	$D\frac{3}{2}-$	1.518 2.304	80	πN $\pi\pi N$	0.7 0.3	0.454 0.410
$N^*_{15}(1688)$	$F\frac{5}{2}+$	1.688 2.849	145	πN	0.85	0.572
$Y^*_{13}(1385)$	$P\frac{3}{2}+$	1.384 1.915	40	$\Lambda\pi$ $\Sigma\pi$	0.9 0.1	0.208 0.117
$Y^*_{01}(1405)$	$S\frac{1}{2}-$	1.405 1.974	35	$\Sigma\pi$	1	0.142
$Y^*_{03}(1520)$	$D\frac{3}{2}-$	1.519 2.307	16	$\Sigma\pi$ $\bar{K}N$ $\Lambda\pi\pi$	0.55 0.29 0.16	0.237 0.260 0.252
$Y^*_1(1660)$	?	1.660 2.756	50	$Y^*_{01}\pi$	≈ 1	
$\Xi^*_{13}(1530)$	$P\frac{3}{2}+$	1.529 2.338	7	$\Xi\pi$	1	0.148
$\Omega^-(1674)$	$\frac{3}{2}+$	1.674 2.802	4×10^{-12}	$\Xi\pi$ ΛK^-	0.5 0.5	0.296 0.216

not discuss this in general, but remark on one special feature which shows that the first $I=\frac{1}{2}$ resonances is $D_{\frac{3}{2}}$. Namely, the coefficient D of $\cos^3\theta$ in π^-p-scattering passes through zero at the resonance energy, similar to the coefficient B at the 1238 resonance. According to (1.6), this could be interpreted as an interference effect between the 1238 resonance of the amplitude f_{1+} and the 1518 resonance of the amplitude f_{2-}. To discuss this in more detail, we need the isospin decomposition of the π^-p scattering amplitude. Inserting (4-2.7), (4-2.8) and (4-2.9) into (4-2.6), we find

$$T^{\frac{3}{2}} = \langle \pi^+ p|T|\pi^+ p\rangle = \langle \pi^- n|T|\pi^- n\rangle$$
$$= \tfrac{1}{3}\langle \pi^+ n + 2^{\frac{1}{2}}\pi^0 p|T|\pi^+ n + 2^{\frac{1}{2}}\pi^0 p\rangle = \tfrac{1}{3}\langle \pi^- p + 2^{\frac{1}{2}}\pi^0 n|T|\pi^- p + 2^{\frac{1}{2}}\pi^0 n\rangle, \tag{3.1}$$

$$T^{\frac{1}{2}} = \tfrac{1}{3}\langle 2^{\frac{1}{2}}\pi^+ n - \pi^0 p|T|2^{\frac{1}{2}}\pi^+ n - \pi^0 p\rangle = \tfrac{1}{3}\langle 2^{\frac{1}{2}}\pi^- p - \pi^0 n|T|2^{\frac{1}{2}}\pi^- p - \pi^0 n\rangle, \tag{3.2}$$

$$0 = \langle \pi^+ n + 2^{\frac{1}{2}}\pi^0 p|T|2^{\frac{1}{2}}\pi^+ n - \pi^0 p\rangle = \langle \pi^- p + 2^{\frac{1}{2}}\pi^0 n|T|2^{\frac{1}{2}}\pi^- p - \pi^0 n\rangle. \tag{3.3}$$

The two amplitudes $T^{\frac{3}{2}}$ and $T^{\frac{1}{2}}$ describe ten different reactions, namely elastic $\pi^\pm p$, $\pi^\pm n$, $\pi^0 p$ and $\pi^0 n$ scattering, the charge exchanges $\pi^- p \to \pi^0 n$, $\pi^+ n \to \pi^0 p$ and their inverse reactions $\pi^0 n \to \pi^- p$, $\pi^0 p \to \pi^+ n$. Only three of these reactions can be measured accurately, namely elastic $\pi^\pm p$ scattering and $\pi^- p \to \pi^0 n$. From the above equations, we find

$$T^{\frac{3}{2}} + 2T^{\frac{1}{2}} = 3\langle \pi^- p|T|\pi^- p\rangle, \tag{3.4}$$
$$2^{\frac{1}{2}}(T^{\frac{3}{2}} - T^{\frac{1}{2}}) = 3\langle \pi^0 n|T|\pi^- p\rangle. \tag{3.5}$$

At present, we need only the fact that the $I = \frac{3}{2}$ and $I = \frac{1}{2}$ amplitudes occur with the same sign in (4). This shows that the coefficient D of $\cos^3\theta$ has the same sign as $\mathrm{Re}[(f^{\frac{3}{2}}_{1+})^* f^{\frac{1}{2}}_{2-}]$, if our assumption about interference between N^*_{33} and N^*_{13} is correct. Then D should be negative in the region between the two resonances on the basis of the following argument: Inserting the resonance formula (2-8.2) for f_{1+} and f_{2-}, we have

$$f^*_{1+} f_{2-} = \frac{m_1\Gamma_1/q}{m_1^2 - s + im_1\Gamma_1}\,\frac{m_2\Gamma_2/q}{m_2^2 - s - im_2\Gamma_2}$$
$$= \frac{m_1\Gamma_1 m_2\Gamma_2/q^2}{(m_1^2-s)(m_2^2-s) + m_1 m_2\Gamma_1\Gamma_2 + im_1\Gamma_1(m_2^2-s) - im_2\Gamma_2(m_1^2-s)}. \tag{3.6}$$

The real part of this expression is negative for

$$(m_1^2-s)(m_2^2-s) + m_1 m_2 \Gamma_1\Gamma_2 < 0. \tag{3.7}$$

In the region between the resonances, $m_1^2 < s < m_2^2$, and (7) is in fact fulfilled except in the immediate neighbourhood of each resonance.

So far we have neglected the effects of inelastic channels, mainly of $\pi\pi N$ channels, on the resonances. For the N^*_{13} and N^*_{15} resonances, little is known about the branching ratios into the various inelastic channels. However, we get a crude estimate of the elasticity $x = \Gamma_e/\Gamma$ by the method of section 2-9. Neglecting a possible non-resonant background T_b (2-9.8) in the resonating partial wave, insertion of (2-9.4) into f_{L+} or f_{L-} of (3-9.11) gives

$$\sigma_J(\text{elastic}) = \frac{2\pi}{q^2}(2J+1)\frac{m^2\Gamma_e^2}{(m^2-s)^2+m^2\Gamma^2}, \tag{3.8}$$

$$\sigma_J(\text{reaction}) = \frac{2\pi}{q^2}(2J+1)\frac{m^2\Gamma_e(\Gamma-\Gamma_e)}{(m^2-s)^2+m^2\Gamma^2}, \tag{3.9}$$

$$\sigma_J(\text{total}) = \frac{2\pi}{q^2}(2J+1)\frac{m^2\Gamma_e\Gamma}{(m^2-s)^2+m^2\Gamma^2}. \tag{3.10}$$

In the total $I = \frac{1}{2}$ πN cross-section, we have at resonance

$$\sigma_J(\text{res}) = \frac{2\pi}{q^2}(2J+1)x, \qquad x \equiv \frac{\Gamma_e}{\Gamma}. \tag{3.11}$$

If $\sigma_J(\text{res})$ is identified with the bump in the total cross-section, a value of x follows. The two bumps in $\sigma(I = \frac{1}{2})$ of fig. 4-1 are approximately 25 and 37 mb, which gives $x = 0.53$ and 0.83, respectively. However, a reliable determination of x requires a phase-shift analysis.

In principle, the widths of these resonances should again be energy-dependent. However, no detailed investigations of such effects exist so far for resonances other than the N^*_{33}. The widths of table 5-3 are therefore the measured widths of the resonance bumps at half maximum. For the N^*_{13} and N^*_{15}, the cms momentum q is relatively large, and one may hope that the penetration factor v_L (1.11) is close to 1.

The production of N^*_{13} and N^*_{15} in inelastic collisions of the type $\pi p \to \pi N^*_1$ or $Kp \to KN^*_1$ seems to be small. As a rule, only low-lying resonances of elastic scattering produce bumps in the corresponding effective mass distributions of other reactions. In fact, even elastic scattering need not display a maximum at each resonance, if many partial waves or inelastic channels contribute. For this reason, resonances at high energies are relatively uninteresting.

5-4. Production of baryon resonances in K^-p interactions

Baryon resonances with $Y = 0$ and $Y = -1$ are denoted by Y* and Ξ*, respectively. They are conveniently produced in K^-p collisions ($\pi^\pm p$ or K^+p collisions are not suited because of their positive hypercharge). The two lightest Y* resonances, namely the Y*(1385) and Y*(1405), are produced in reactions of the type $K^-p \to \pi Y^*$. The masses of these resonances lie below the threshold $m_K + m_p = 1432$ MeV for K^-p scattering. For this reason, these two resonances cannot be observed in elastic K^-p scattering. The next two resonances, $Y^*(1520)$ and $Y^*(1660)$, are formed in K^-p interactions $K^-p \to Y^*$, but they mainly decay into the pion-hyperon channels, i.e. they are highly inelastic. Of course, this property depends on the initial state. If one could produce pion-hyperon collisions, then one would find the low-lying Y^* resonances mainly in elastic scattering.

The Ξ^* resonances are produced in the reaction $K^-p \to K\Xi^*$. The outgoing kaon is K^+ or K^0, because of hypercharge conservation. In table 5-3 we have included only one Ξ^* resonance, the Ξ^*_{13} (1530), which decays into $\Xi\pi$. The cross-section for $K^-p \to K\Xi^*$ is small, about as small as the cross-section for $\pi p \to KY^*$. Such reactions are suppressed because they are highly endothermic.

We now discuss some properties of the Y^* resonances of table 5-3. The notation is $Y^*_{I,\,2J}$. The Y^*_{13} (1385) was the first strange particle resonance discovered (ALSTON *et al.*, [1960]). It decays into $\Lambda\pi$ and $\Sigma\pi$, with a ratio of 9 : 1. In the Dalitz plot of $K^-p \to \Lambda\pi^+\pi^-$, both the $\Lambda\pi^+$ and the $\Lambda\pi^-$ effective mass distributions show strong peaks at 1385 MeV. Since the total isospin of a $\Lambda\pi$ system is one, it follows immediately that this resonance has $I = 1$. The neutral member of the resonance triplet is produced in $K^-p \to Y^*\pi^0 \to \Lambda\pi^0\pi^0$, which is difficult to identify experimentally. At K^- momenta above 2 GeV/c, $Y^{*-}\pi^+$ production becomes much weaker than $Y^{*+}\pi^-$ production. This is explained by the peripheral model, chapter 11. Note that isospin invariance does not imply equal probabilities for $Y^{*+}\pi^-$ and $Y^{*-}\pi^+$. States of total isospin $|I, I_3\rangle$ are given by (4-2.4), with the second proton (neutron) replaced by a $\bar{K}^0(K^-)$. For $I_3 = 0$, this gives

$$|1,0\rangle = 2^{-\frac{1}{2}}(|p\rangle|K^-\rangle + |n\rangle|\bar{K}^0\rangle), \quad |0,0\rangle = 2^{-\frac{1}{2}}(|p\rangle|K^-\rangle - |n\rangle|\bar{K}^0\rangle), \tag{4.1}$$

$$|p\rangle|K^-\rangle = 2^{-\frac{1}{2}}(|1,0\rangle + |0,0\rangle), \quad |n\rangle|\bar{K}^0\rangle = 2^{-\frac{1}{2}}(|1,0\rangle - |0,0\rangle). \tag{4.2}$$

The $Y_1^{*+}\pi$ states have the same isospin decomposition as the $\pi\pi$ states of table 4-2. The fact that the $Y_1^{*+}\pi^-$ and $Y_1^{*-}\pi^+$ probabilities may be different is due to the possibility of interference between $I = 0$ and $I = 1$ amplitudes in $pK^- \to Y_1^*\pi$. On the other hand, in the decay $Y_1^* \to \Sigma\pi$, the initial state is a pure $I = 1$ state (indicated by

1
2

in table 4-2), which implies

$$\Gamma(Y_1^{*0} \to \Sigma^+\pi^-) = \Gamma(Y_1^{*0} \to \Sigma^-\pi^+) = \Gamma(Y_1^{*\pm} \to \Sigma^\pm\pi^0) = \Gamma(Y_1^{*\pm} \to \Sigma^0\pi^\pm), \tag{4.3}$$

$$\Gamma(Y_1^{*0} \to \Sigma^0\pi^0) = 0. \tag{4.4}$$

The determination of spin and parity of a resonance produced together with a pion, is complicated by the possibility of interference between the decay meson and the "direct" pion. Fortunately, the widths of the Y_1^* (1385), Y_0^* (1405) and Ξ_1^* (1530) are so small that one may treat these resonances in the unstable-particle approximation of section 2-3, at least if the total cms energy is large enough. This approximation neglects interference between "direct" and "decay" particles, and also interference between the resonant partial wave and other, non-resonant, pion-hyperon partial waves.

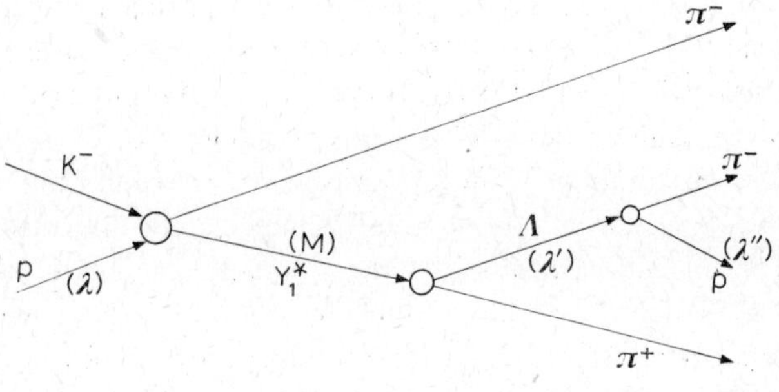

Fig. 5-4.1. The reaction $K^-p \to \pi^-Y_1^*$, followed by the decays $Y_1^* \to \pi^+\Lambda$ and $\Lambda \to \pi^-p$.

The overall process $K^-p \to \Lambda\pi^+\pi^-$ is now the sum of the "direct" process $K^-p \to \Lambda\pi^+\pi^-$ and two two-step processes, $K^-p \to Y^{*+}\pi^- \to \Lambda\pi^+\pi^-$ and $K^-p \to Y^{*-}\pi^+ \to \Lambda\pi^-\pi^+$. The first two-step process is illustrated in fig. 5-4.1 where a decay $\Lambda \to \pi^-p$ has been included too. This final decay facilitates the spin-parity analysis of the Y^*. Since the Λ-decay is not parity-invariant, its angular distribution resolves the Minami ambiguity of the Y^* decay distribution (see section 9-3). For the time being, however, we treat the Λ as a stable particle.

Let λ and λ' denote the helicities of the initial proton and final Λ-hyperon, respectively. The cross-section for $K^-p \to \pi Y^* \to \pi\pi\Lambda$ is proportional to $\frac{1}{2}\sum_{\lambda\lambda'}|T(\lambda\lambda')|^2$, where $T(\lambda\lambda')$ factorizes according to (2-3.15)

$$T(\lambda\lambda') = \Phi(s_d) \sum_M T(K^-p_\lambda \to \pi^-Y_M^*)T(Y_M^* \to \pi^+\Lambda_{\lambda'}). \tag{4.5}$$

Our aim is to determine the spin of the Y* from the decay distribution $W(s, t, \Omega')$ in the resonance rest frame. This distribution is again given by (3-1.12), if the summation over λ and λ' is included in the definition of the density matrices ρ and R/C,

$$\rho(s,t)_{MM'} = \frac{\sum_{\lambda} T(\mathrm{K}^-\mathrm{p}_\lambda \to \pi^-\mathrm{Y}^*_M)T^*(\mathrm{K}^-\mathrm{p}_\lambda \to \pi^-\mathrm{Y}^*_{M'})}{\sum_M \sum_\lambda |T(\mathrm{K}^-\mathrm{p}_\lambda \to \pi^-\mathrm{Y}^*_M)|^2}, \tag{4.6}$$

$$\frac{1}{C} R(\vartheta, \varphi)_{MM'} = \frac{\sum_{\lambda'} T(M, \lambda', p, \vartheta, \varphi) T^*(M', \lambda', p, \vartheta, \varphi)}{\int \mathrm{d}\Omega' \sum_{\lambda'} |T(M, \lambda', p, \vartheta, \varphi)|^2}. \tag{4.7}$$

In the latter equation, p is the Y* decay momentum, and ϑ, φ are the decay angles. From (2.2) and the parity invariance $T(\lambda', p) = T(-\lambda', p)$ we obtain

$$\frac{1}{C} R(\vartheta, \varphi)_{MM'} = \frac{\sum_{\lambda'} D^{j*}_{M\lambda'}(\varphi, \vartheta, -\varphi) D^j_{M'\lambda'}(\varphi, \vartheta, -\varphi)}{\sum_{\lambda'} \int \mathrm{d}\Omega' |D^j_{M\lambda'}(\varphi, \vartheta, -\varphi)|^2}$$

$$= \frac{j+\frac{1}{2}}{4\pi} \mathrm{e}^{\mathrm{i}(M-M')\varphi} (d^j_{M\frac{1}{2}}(\vartheta) d^j_{M'\frac{1}{2}}(\vartheta) + d^j_{M,-\frac{1}{2}}(\vartheta) d^j_{M',-\frac{1}{2}}(\vartheta)). \tag{4.8}$$

From table C-3, we get

$$\frac{1}{C} R(\vartheta, \varphi)_{MM'} = \frac{1}{8\pi} \delta_{MM'} \quad \text{for} \quad j = \tfrac{1}{2}, \tag{4.9}$$

which gives an isotropic decay distribution (3-1.12). Experimentally, the Y_1^* (1385) decay distribution is not isotropic, which excludes the possibility of spin-$\frac{1}{2}$. At high energies, the distribution with respect to the *normal of the production plane* is of the form (BERTANZA *et al.* [1963]) $1+3\cos^2\vartheta$, independent of φ. This form is predicted by the Stodolsky-Sakurai model for production of $\frac{3}{2}^+$ resonances in high-energy meson-nucleon collisions (see section 11-4), which indicates that Y_1^* (1385) is a $\frac{3}{2}^+$ resonance. However, the decisive evidence for $\frac{3}{2}^+$ comes from the BYERS-FENSTER [1963] analysis, which investigates the Λ decay distribution in addition to the Y* decay distribution. The corresponding analysis of the Ξ_1^* (1530) in $\mathrm{K}^-\mathrm{p} \to \mathrm{K}\Xi_1^*$ shows that also this resonance is $\frac{3}{2}^+$.

We now turn to the Y_0^* (1405) resonance, which was discovered in the $\Sigma^-\pi^+$ and $\Sigma^+\pi^-$ effective mass distributions of the reaction $\mathrm{K}^-\mathrm{p} \to \Sigma^\pm\pi^\mp\pi^+\pi^-$.

Later, it was also found in the simpler reaction $K^-p \to \Sigma^{\pm}\pi^{\mp}\pi^0$. The fact that it does not decay into $\pi\Lambda$ and that it occurs only in the zero charge state shows that it has $I = 0$. From the coefficients of the $I = 0$ state of table 4-2 one finds

$$\Gamma(Y_0^* \to \Sigma^+\pi^-) = \Gamma(Y_0^* \to \Sigma^-\pi^+) = \Gamma(Y_0^* \to \Sigma^0\pi^0), \tag{4.10}$$

in agreement with experiment. The decay distribution of Y_0^* is isotropic and therefore, by (9), consistent with spin-$\frac{1}{2}$. The $\frac{1}{2}^-$ assignment comes from the extrapolation of the K^-p S-wave scattering below threshold. This will be discussed in section 8-5. The result is that the Y_0^* is an S-wave "bound state" of the K^-p system. Finally, the Y* (1520) resonance will be discussed in section 8-6.

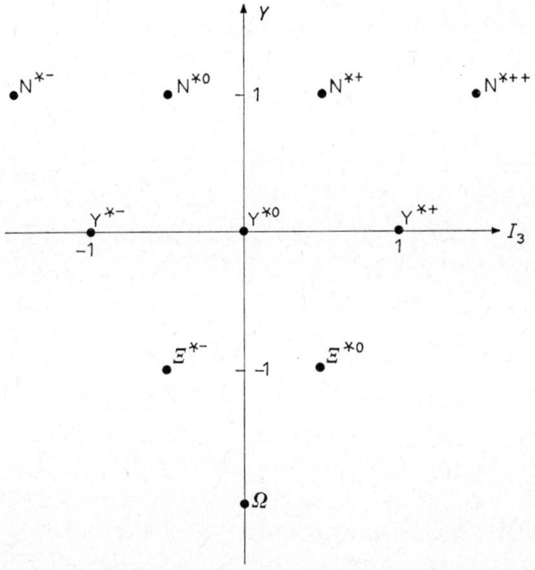

Fig. 5-4.2. Plot of hypercharge versus third component of isospin for the $\frac{3}{2}^+$ baryon-meson resonances.

For each hypercharge considered so far, the lowest baryon resonance occurs in the $\frac{3}{2}^+$ state. Moreover, in the (Y, I_3) plot, these resonances form a triangle if a single resonance of $I = 0$ and $Y = -2$ is added (see fig. 5-4.2). This led to the prediction of the Ω_{03}^-, which was subsequently found in the reaction $K^-p \to K^+K^0\Omega$. The mass of the Ω was predicted from the observation that the masses of the $\frac{3}{2}^+$ N*, Y* and Ξ* resonances occur at equal intervals of 145 MeV. Adding 145 MeV to 1530 MeV, which is the mass of the Ξ^*, one arrives at 1675 MeV, in amazing agreement with the experimental Ω^- mass. This equal spacing is evident e.g. from fig. 4-1.

Hypercharge cannot be conserved in Ω^- decay. The lowest final state of $Y = -2$ is $\overline{\mathrm{K}}\Xi$, but since $m_{\mathrm{K}}+m_{\Xi} = 1808$ MeV, the decay $\Omega^- \to \overline{\mathrm{K}}\Xi$ is energetically impossible.

In the observed decays $\Omega \to \Xi\pi$ and $\Omega \to \Lambda\mathrm{K}^-$, I_3 and I change by $\frac{1}{2}$, in agreement with the "spurious kaon" rule. (From the few events reported so far one cannot test the rule $\Gamma(\Omega \to \Xi^-\pi^0)/\Gamma(\Omega \to \Xi^0\pi^-) = 1:2$.)

The decay matrix element for Ω-decay is obtained from (2.3) by adding a term of opposite parity:

$$T(M, \lambda', p, \vartheta, \varphi) = \bar{u}'(\lambda')(-G-G'\gamma_5)P^{\mu}u_{\mu}(M). \tag{4.11}$$

This is again of the form (2.2), but this time the function $T(\lambda', p)$ is really λ'-dependent. Comparing (11) with (3-5.18), (3-4.17) and (2.5), we find

$$T(\lambda', p) = (\tfrac{2}{3})^{\frac{1}{2}}p(G\sqrt{2m(E'+m')}-2\lambda'G'\sqrt{2m(E'-m')}). \tag{4.12}$$

5-5. SU_3 symmetry

The regularity in the masses of the $\frac{3}{2}^+$ isobars, as well as the Y, I_3 plots of figs. 4-3 and 5-4.2, indicate a new type of symmetry, namely SU_3 symmetry. The group SU_3 of unimodular 3×3 unitary matrices includes, as a subgroup, the group SU_2 of isospin. The first attempt to introduce SU_3 into hadron physics was made by SAKATA [1956]. In the Sakata model, invariance of the theory under unitary transformations of the three states p, n and Λ was postulated.

One difficulty of any such "higher symmetry" is the requirement that various isospin multiplets should group into "supermultiplets" of states with nearly equal masses. Whereas the masses of p and n differ by 1.3 MeV, the $\mathrm{p}-\Lambda$ mass difference is 177 MeV. If this mass splitting is linearly related to the strength of the symmetry-breaking interaction, then the SU_3-breaking interaction should be 100 times stronger than the SU_2-breaking electromagnetic interaction. For this reason, the SU_3-breaking interaction is called "semi-strong". Predictions of SU_3-symmetry are therefore unreliable, unless the corrections due to the semi-strong interactions can be estimated.

Except for explaining some qualitative features in the theory of weak interactions, the Sakata model was unsuccessful. The correct classification into super-multiplets is due to GELL-MANN [1961] and NE'EMAN [1961].

In this classification, called the "eightfold way", all 8 baryons form one supermultiplet, and all 8 mesons form another supermultiplet. As in the case of isospin multiplets, all members of a supermultiplet should have the same spin parity. This rule is satisfied in the eightfold way: the eight baryons are $\frac{1}{2}^+$, while the eight mesons are 0^-. Actually, the existence of the η-meson was not known in 1961; it was predicted by the eightfold way.

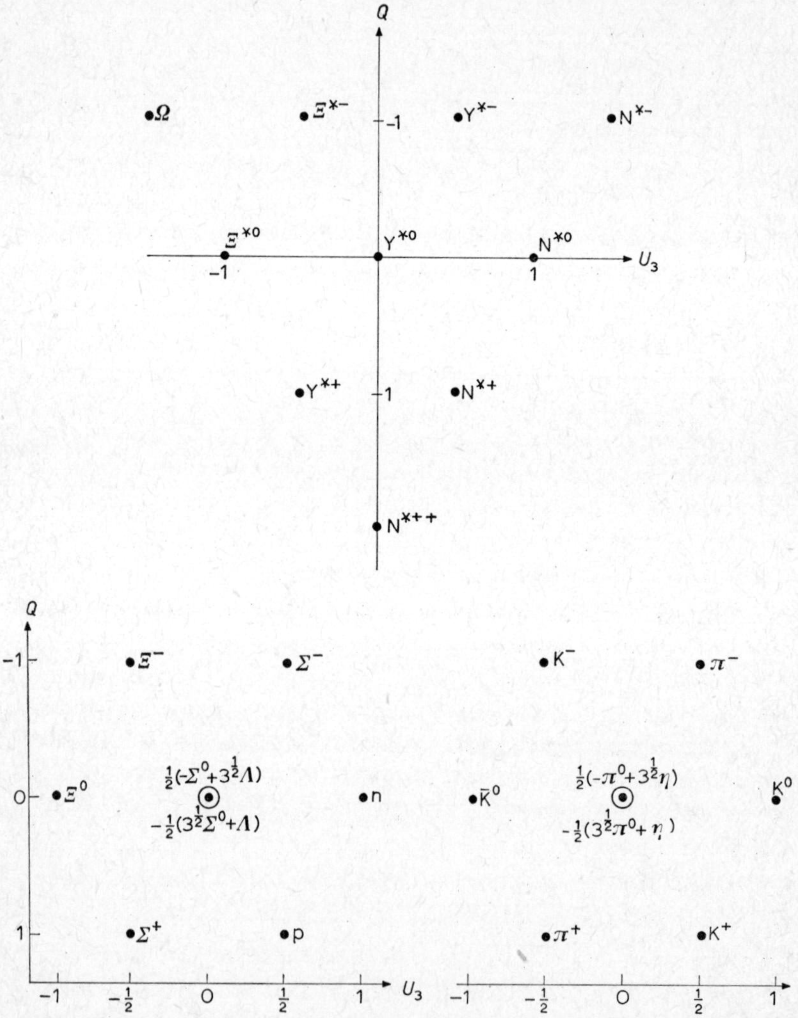

Fig. 5-5.1. Plots of electric charge versus U_3 for the baryon octet, the meson octet, and the $\frac{3}{2}^+$-decuplet.

Similarly, the $\frac{3}{2}^+$ resonances are grouped into the 10-dimensional representation of SU_3. (The representations of SU_3 are evaluated in appendix D-2.) The Ω was predicted as the tenth member of the multiplet of N^{*++}, N^{*+}, N^{*0}, N^{*-}, Y_1^{*+}, Y_1^{*0}, Y_1^{*-}, Ξ_1^{*0} and Ξ_1^{*-}, as explained in the previous section.

Particles which transform under SU_3 according to the basic triplet representation have been proposed by GELL-MANN [1964] and ZWEIG (unpublished). Such particles are sometimes called "quarks". Two of them should form an isospin doublet, while the third should have $I = 0$, as in the Sakata model. For this reason, they are denoted by $\underline{p}$, $\underline{n}$ and $\underline{\Lambda}$ (see D-1.4). However, they have electric charges of $\frac{2}{3}$, $-\frac{1}{3}$ and $-\frac{1}{3}$, as we shall see below. So far, fractionally charged particles have not been found. Nevertheless, "quarks" are convenient for illustrating the mathematical structure of the SU_3 symmetry.

SU_3 transformations contain, as a subgroup, those SU_2 transformations which leave one of the three quark states invariant. Transformations which leave $\underline{\Lambda}$, $\underline{p}$ and $\underline{n}$ invariant are called I-spin, U-spin and V-spin transformations, respectively. The mathematical formalism is the same for all three types of "spin": only the physical meaning is different.

The classification of particles into I-spin multiplets is already known. Next, we observe that all plots of Y versus I_3 considered so far (figs. 4-3 and 5-4.2) are symmetric under rotations of 120° around the origin. Since the SU_3 multiplet structure must be symmetric in I-, U- and V-spin, we conclude that U- and V-spin multiplets are formed by those particles which replace the particles in the isospin multiplets after rotation. By definition, the clockwise rotation gives the U-spin multiplets. The resulting plots are shown in fig. 5-5.1. The I_3-axis is replaced by the U_3-axis, which measures the third component of U-spin. Obviously, the electric charge Q is constant within each U-spin multiplet. Mathematically, this requires that Q commutes with the generators of U-spin transformations, which implies that it is a multiplet of the unit matrix in the space spanned by each U-spin multiplet.

For the basic triplet, Q must have the form

$$Q = \begin{pmatrix} a & 0 & 0 \\ 0 & b & 0 \\ 0 & 0 & b \end{pmatrix},$$

since $\underline{n}$ and $\underline{\Lambda}$ form the basic V-spin doublet. Such a form is expressed in terms of the λ-matrices (appendix D-1) as $-\frac{3}{2}\, b(\lambda_3 + 3^{-\frac{1}{2}}\lambda_8)$. From the definition (4-3.6) of hypercharge, we now find

$$Q = I_3+\tfrac{1}{2}Y, \qquad I_3 = \tfrac{1}{2}\lambda_3, \qquad Y = 3^{-\frac{1}{2}}\lambda_8. \tag{5.1}$$

Thus, p̲, n̲ and $\underline{\Lambda}$ have $Y = \frac{1}{3}, \frac{1}{3}$ and $-\frac{2}{3}$, respectively (see fig. 5-5.2). The resultant charges of the basic triplet are $a = \frac{2}{3}$ and $b = -\frac{1}{3}$. For arbitrary representation of SU_3, Q is expressed in terms of the generators F_3 and F_8 (see B-2)

$$Q = \tfrac{1}{2}(F_3+3^{-\frac{1}{2}}F_8). \tag{5.2}$$

This formula gives integer charges only for the representation 8 and the irreducible representations in the products $8\otimes 8$, $8\otimes 8\otimes 8$ etc.

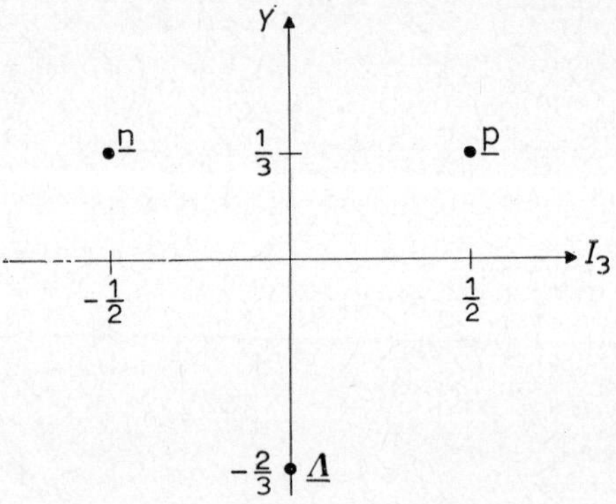

Fig. 5-5.2. The values of Y and I_3 for the basic triplet p̲, n̲, $\underline{\Lambda}$.

By means of (D-1.7), we find

$$U_3 = \tfrac{3}{4}Y-\tfrac{1}{2}I_3 = Y-\tfrac{1}{2}Q, \tag{5.3}$$

which is also evident from fig. 5-5.1).

For the octet representations, the U-spin classification is complicated by the fact that the central point $Q = Y = I_3 = U_3 = 0$ is occupied by two particles, Σ^0 and Λ in the baryon case and π^0 and η in the meson case. The linear combination $\frac{1}{2}(-\Sigma^0+3^{\frac{1}{2}}\Lambda)$ forms a U-spin triplet together with Ξ^0 and n, whereas the orthogonal linear combination $-\frac{1}{2}(3^{\frac{1}{2}}\Sigma^0+\Lambda)$ is a U-spin singlet. To get these combinations, we observe that the basic vectors of the 8-dimensional representation transform like the eight generators λ_i under SU_3 (appendix D-2). Thus the Σ^0 is associated with the third component of the isovector operator, which is $\frac{1}{2}\lambda_3$. The Λ on the other hand, being invariant under isospin transformations, is associated with $\frac{1}{2}\lambda_8$. Correspondingly, the neutral member of the U-spin triplet is associated with the third component of the U-spin vector operator. This component is $U_3 = \frac{1}{4}(-\lambda_3 + 3^{\frac{1}{2}}\lambda_8)$ according to (D-1.7).

For the meson octet, the U-spin classification is analogous. Thus π^- and K^- form a U-spin doublet of $U_3 = +\frac{1}{2}$ and $-\frac{1}{2}$, respectively, K^+ and π^+ form another doublet, and so on.

Having accomplished the SU$_3$-assignment of baryons, baryon resonances and mesons, we can derive a large number of relations between matrix elements, both for scattering and decay (GOURDIN [1967]). As a first application, we look for relationships between the matrix elements for $\pi^- p \to K^+ Y^{*-}$, $\pi^- p \to \pi^+ N^{*-}$, $K^- p \to K^* \Xi^*$, and $K^- p \to \pi^+ Y^{*-}$. The resonances in the final state are in the $U = \frac{3}{2}$ multiplet, whereas the K^+ and π^+ form a $U = \frac{1}{2}$ doublet. Consequently, the total U-spin may be 1 or 2. The value 2 is excluded, however, since both particles in the initial state have $U = \frac{1}{2}$ and thus cannot give a total U-spin larger than one. The initial $\pi^- p$ state is $|U, U_3\rangle = |1, 1\rangle$, whereas the $K^- p$ state is contained in the $|1, 0\rangle$ state with a Clebsch-Gordan coefficient of $2^{-\frac{1}{2}}$, according to (4-2.4). The corresponding coefficients of the four final states are $-\frac{1}{2}$, $\frac{1}{2} \cdot 3^{\frac{1}{2}}$, $-2^{-\frac{1}{2}}$ and $2^{-\frac{1}{2}}$, respectively. As a result, we get

$$
\begin{aligned}
-T(\pi^- p \to K^+ Y^{*-}) &= 3^{-\frac{1}{2}} T(\pi^- p \to \pi^+ N^{*-}) \\
&= -T(K^- p \to K^+ \Xi^{*-}) = T(K^- p \to \pi^+ Y^{*-}). \qquad (5.4)
\end{aligned}
$$

Due to the large mass splittings, this equation does not imply equal cross-sections for $\pi^- p \to K^+ Y^{*-}$, $K^- p \to K^+ \Xi^{*-}$, and $K^- p \to \pi^+ Y^{*-}$. For equal values of s, the cross-sections will vary by the factor q'/q of (2-2.16). The comparison with $K^- p \to K^+ \Xi^{*-}$ is impossible for $s^{\frac{1}{2}} < 2024$ MeV, which is the sum of the masses in the final state. The reaction $K^- p \to \pi^+ Y^{*-}$ has the largest value of q'/q. Experimentally, this reaction has also the largest cross-section. However, the endothermic reactions are usually more suppressed than just by the factor q'/q.

Next, we calculate the widths of the Y_1^* and Ξ^* resonances from the N^* width. We select again the negative charge states Ω, Ξ^{*-}, Y^{*-} and N^{*-}, since these states are in the $U = \frac{3}{2}$ multiplet. In analogy with our previous example, we could take Γ proportional to $p|T|^2$, where p is the decay momentum. Then we could relate the matrix elements T for the various decays by means of Clebsch-Gordan coefficients. However, for P-wave resonances, T contains the additional momentum-dependence of the penetration factor. Due to the large mass splitting, this momentum-dependence of T destroys the SU$_3$-invariance. We expect better results if we rewrite Γ for each resonance in the form (2.7), (2.8), and relate the coupling constants $G^*(m)$ by means of Clebsch-Gordan coefficients.

The U-spin coefficients for the reaction baryon* → baryon+π^- are given by (4-2.7) and (4-2.8), if the π^- is associated with p, and the states n, $\frac{1}{2}(-\Sigma^0+3^{\frac{1}{2}}\Lambda)$, Ξ^0 with π^+, π^0 and π^-, respectively. Thus we obtain

$$G(\mathrm{N}^* \to \mathrm{n}\pi^-) = -6^{-\frac{1}{2}}G(\mathrm{Y}^* \to \Sigma^0\pi^-)$$
$$= 2^{-\frac{1}{2}}G(\mathrm{Y}^* \to \Lambda\pi^-) = 3^{-\frac{1}{2}}G(\Xi^* \to \Xi^0\pi^-). \tag{5.5}$$

By isospin invariance, these coupling constants are now related to the coupling constants for other charge combinations. With $\Gamma_{\mathrm{N}^*}(s^{\frac{1}{2}} = 1240) = 100$ MeV, we obtain the following total isospin widths:

decay	$\mathrm{N}^* \to \pi\mathrm{N}$	$\mathrm{Y}^* \to \pi\Lambda$	$\mathrm{Y}^* \to \pi\Sigma$	$\Xi^* \to \pi\Xi$
$\Gamma(m)$	$\equiv 100$	42	5	13.5

(5.6)

Comparing these with the values of table 5-3, we again find that the widths of the less exothermic decays, especially Γ (Ξ^*), are too large. (For the Y* and Ξ^*, the difference between $\Gamma(m)$ and the experimental full width at half maximum should be small, the latter value being the larger one.)

Finally, we mention the mass rule of GELL-MANN [1961] and OKUBO [1962] for the baryon octet:

$$2(m_{\mathrm{N}}+m_{\Xi}) = m_{\Sigma}+3m_{\Lambda}. \tag{5.7}$$

In the limit of exact SU_3 symmetry, all masses of particles belonging to the same multiplet should of course be equal,

$$m_{\mathrm{N}} = m_{\Xi} = m_{\Sigma} = m_{\Lambda}. \tag{5.8}$$

This relation is badly violated, because the mass difference between N and Ξ is 380 MeV or 35% of the average mass. Relation (7), however, holds with an accuracy of about 1%. It is obtained from an assumption about the SU_3 transformation properties of the medium-strong, symmetry-breaking interactions. For our present purpose, we start from the assumption that the masses of hadrons belonging to the same U-spin multiplet are given by the formula

$$m(U_3) = m_0 - U_3 m_1, \tag{5.9}$$

i.e. the masses within a U-spin multiplet are equally spaced. This assumption is justified by the observed equal spacing of N^{*-}, Y^{*-}, Ξ^{*-} and Ω, for which m_1 equals 145 MeV, according to our calculation at the end of section 5-4. (The equality of masses within each isospin multiplet follows of course from isospin invariance.) Application of (9) to the $U = 1$ triplet n, $\frac{1}{2}(-\Sigma^0+3^{\frac{1}{2}}\Lambda)$ and Ξ^0 gives

$$m_0 = \tfrac{1}{4}(m_\Sigma+3m_\Lambda), \qquad m_1 = \tfrac{1}{2}(m_\Xi-m_\mathrm{N}) = 190 \text{ MeV}, \qquad (5.10)$$

or, in general, eq. (7).

The mass formula for the octet of 0^- mesons is

$$4m_\mathrm{K}^2 = m_\pi^2+3m_\eta^2. \qquad (5.11)$$

By strict analogy with (7), we should take the masses of the mesons, and not their squares. However, the formula $4m_\mathrm{K} = m_\pi+3m_\eta$ is empirically less satisfactory than (11), and we therefore take the freedom to replace the masses by their squares. This argument is of course not convincing. The validity of a mass formula like (9) seems to be restricted to lowest-order perturbation theory. Since the relative splitting of the meson masses is much larger than that of the baryon masses ($m_\eta/m_\pi = 4$), it is possible that no simple mass formula applies to the mesons.

In addition to SU_3, even larger symmetry groups have been used for the classification of hadrons. In particular, SU_3 and the rotation group SU_2 of ordinary spin may be combined in the group SU_6. In the representations of these larger groups, particles of different spins may occur in the same multiplet. For example, the 8 baryons of spin-$\frac{1}{2}$ and the 10 baryon resonances of spin-$\frac{3}{2}$ just fill one 56-dimensional representation ($2\times8+4\times10$) of SU_6. For a review of these developments, see PAIS [1966].

5-6. The 1^- meson resonances

In addition to the meson-baryon resonances (shortly "baryon resonances"), a number of resonances between mesons exist. Since meson-meson collisions cannot be produced experimentally so far, all information about meson resonances comes from production reactions or, somewhat indirectly, from dynamical models of other reactions. Some of the resonances cannot decay into two mesons, in which case the term "resonance" becomes somewhat problematic.

The most important meson resonances are collected in table 5-6. The distinction between mesons and meson resonances is rather meaningless for some objects, especially for the η^*, which is a heavy version of the η-meson.

TABLE 5-6

Masses and decay properties of meson resonances

symbol	$I(J^{\eta G})$	m [GeV] m^2[GeV²]	Γ[MeV]	partial mode	fraction	p or p_{max}	$\frac{G^2}{4\pi}$
ρ	$1(1^{-+})$	0.766 0.587	125	$\pi\pi$	1	0.357	7.8
ω	$0(1^{--})$	0.783 0.613	12	$\pi^+\pi^-\pi^0$ $\pi^0\gamma$ e^+e^-	0.9 0.1 0.01	0.327 0.380 0.392	25/GeV² 0.042/GeV²
K*	$\frac{1}{2}(1^-)$	0.892 0.795	50	$K\pi$	1	0.288	3.3
ϕ	$0(1^{--})$	1.0186 1.0375	4	K^+K^- K_1K_2 $\pi^+\pi^-\pi^0$	0.48 0.40 0.12	0.126 0.109 0.461	} 7.6 0.066/GeV²
X or η^*	$0(0^{-+})$	0.958 0.918	< 4	$\eta\pi^0\pi^0$ $\eta\pi^+\pi^-$ $\pi^+\pi^-\gamma$	(0.27) (0.53) 0.2	0.234 0.232 0.459	
f	$0(2^{++})$	1.25 1.57	116	$\pi^+\pi^-$	1	0.611	22/GeV²
A_2	$1(2^{+-})$	1.306 1.706	81	$\rho\pi$ $\bar{K}K$ $\eta\pi$	93 4 3	0.417 0.425 0.527	

The symbol $J^{\eta G}$ denotes spin, parity, and G-parity. The definitions of $G^2/4\pi$ are as given in the text.

In this section, we discuss the 1^- meson resonances or shortly "vector mesons". Of these, the ρ and ω-mesons are of great importance not only for πN interactions, but also for the theory of nuclear forces (see e.g. BALL, SCOTTI and WONG [1966], CARTER [1967]). An example of ρ production is the reaction $\pi^+ p \to \pi^+\pi^0 p$ in the GeV region. The Dalitz plot of this reaction at 4 GeV was given in fig. 1-4.1, which shows a strong peak in the effective mass distribution of $\pi^+\pi^0$ at the ρ mass. The ρ-meson occurs in three charge states, ρ^+, ρ^0 and ρ^-, which indicates that it has $I = 1$. This is confirmed by the absence of the decay mode $\rho^0 \to \pi^0\pi^0$ (see state

$$\boxed{\begin{array}{c}1\\\hline 2\end{array}}$$

of table 4-2).

By the generalized Bose-Einstein symmetry, the ρ-meson must have odd angular momentum and therefore negative intrinsic parity. The decay distribution of ρ-mesons in the reactions $\pi^{\pm}p \to \rho^{\pm}p$ is approximately of the form $\cos^2 \vartheta$, where ϑ is the polar angle of π^+ in the two-pion rest system, measured from the direction of the incident pion. According to (3-2.12), this indicates $J = 1$ for the ρ-meson (and $M = 0$ in $\pi p \to \rho p$). In the reaction $\pi^- p \to \rho^0 n \to \pi^+\pi^- n$, the decay distribution in the ρ-region is of the form (see e.g. SACLAY-ORSAY-BARI-BOLOGNA collaboration [1965])

$$W(\vartheta, \varphi) = A + B \cos \vartheta + C \cos^2 \vartheta, \tag{6.1}$$

which indicates interference with S-wave scattering in the $I = 0$ $\pi\pi$ state.

Since the ρ-meson decays into two pions, it has positive G-parity. For the neutral member of an isospin multiplet of $Y = 0$, definition (4-7.16) gives

$$C = G(-1)^I \tag{6.2}$$

according to (C-2.8). Thus ρ^0 is a 1^- state of negative charge parity, exactly like the photon. (The negative charge parity also follows directly from the antisymmetry of the

$$\begin{array}{|c|}\hline 1 \\ \hline 2 \\ \hline \end{array}$$

two-pion state.) Taking the Lorentz-invariant decay matrix element in the form (3-3.5), we get the width Γ from (2-3.4) and (3-2.12)

$$\Gamma = \frac{p}{4s} \int \frac{dx}{3} |G_1 p Y_0^1|^2 = \frac{1}{6} \frac{p^3}{s} \frac{G_1^2}{4\pi}. \tag{6.3}$$

The s-dependence of G_1 should be of the form (2.8), but so far this effect has not been measured. Somewhat arbitrarily setting $\Gamma(m_\rho) = 100$ MeV, we get $G_1^2(m_\rho)/4\pi = 7.8$.

The ω-meson was discovered by MAGLIĆ *et al.* [1961] in the antiproton annihilation $\bar{p}p \to \pi^+\pi^+\pi^-\pi^-\pi^0$, as a sharp peak in the $\pi^+\pi^-\pi^0$ effective mass distribution. From the absence of corresponding peaks in the $\pi^+\pi^+\pi^-$ and $\pi^+\pi^-\pi^-$ effective mass distribution, the isospin zero of the ω was inferred. The ω is also produced in a large number of other reactions, e.g. $\pi^+ n \to \omega p$, $\pi^+ p \to \omega N^*$, $K^- p \to \Lambda\omega$. Because of its small width, the ω may be treated like an unstable particle in these reactions.

The spin and parity of ω may be inferred from the distribution of events in the Dalitz plot of $\omega \to \pi^+\pi^-\pi^0$, (STEVENSON *et al.* [1962]). Assuming isospin conservation, the three-pion final state must be totally antisymmetric under exchange of the pions (see the discussion following 4-2.11). Different spin-parity combinations for the resonance produce different threshold behaviours of the three pions' momenta. Since the energy release in $\omega \to \pi^+\pi^0\pi^-$ is relatively low, each threshold behaviour is easily recognized by the probability distribution of the Dalitz plot.

For a 1^- particle, the only totally antisymmetric, parity conserving matrix element for decay into three pseudoscalar mesons may be written in Lorentz-invariant form as

$$T(M, P_+ P_0 P_-) = G_{\omega\pi^3} \varepsilon_{\alpha\beta\gamma\delta} P_+^\alpha P_0^\beta P_-^\gamma \varepsilon^\delta(M), \tag{6.4}$$

where P_+, P_0, P_- denote the 4-momenta of π^+, π^0 and π^-. In the resonance rest frame, (4) becomes

$$T(M, \boldsymbol{p}_+, \boldsymbol{p}_0, \boldsymbol{p}_-) = G_{\omega\pi^3} \boldsymbol{\varepsilon}(M) \cdot \boldsymbol{n}, \tag{6.5}$$

$$\boldsymbol{n} = E_+(\boldsymbol{p}_0 \times \boldsymbol{p}_-) + E_0(\boldsymbol{p}_- \times \boldsymbol{p}_+) + E_-(\boldsymbol{p}_+ \times \boldsymbol{p}_0). \tag{6.6}$$

The vector $\boldsymbol{n}$ lies normal to the decay plane which is spanned by $\boldsymbol{p}_0$, $\boldsymbol{p}_-$ and $\boldsymbol{p}_+$. Whenever these three vectors are collinear, $|\boldsymbol{n}|$ vanishes. From (1-4.6), we remember that the boundary of the Dalitz plot corresponds to collinear events. From the fact that the periphery of the Dalitz plot of $\omega \to \pi^+\pi^-\pi^0$ is indeed depopulated, one concludes that the ω is a 1^- particle. To complete the proof, one should of course demonstrate that other matrix elements do not vanish along the whole boundary of the Dalitz plot. The decay of a 1^+ state into a totally antisymmetric three-pion state for example is of the form

$$G' \varepsilon_\mu(M)[P_+^\mu P_+(P_0 - P_-) + P_0^\mu P_0(P_- - P_+) + P_-^\mu P_-(P_+ - P_0)]. \tag{6.7}$$

This amplitude only vanishes at points where two of the three 4-momenta are equal. As discussed at the end of section 4-7, the 0^+ state is excluded by parity conservation. The 0^- state is excluded by the experimental observation of anisotropic angular distributions of $\boldsymbol{n}$. Note that the angular dependence of the decay matrix element (5) is identical with (3-2.11) for the appropriate two-particle decay. Only the meaning of the decay vector has changed.

Since the ω width is so small, we may neglect the dependence of $G_{\omega\pi^3}$ on $s_3 = (P_+ + P_0 + P_-)^2$. However, for fixed s_3, the effective masses of the $\pi^+\pi^0$, $\pi^+\pi^-$ and $\pi^0\pi^-$ pairs may vary over a considerable range (Dalitz plot), and it would be unrealistic to assume that $G_{\omega\pi^3}$ is constant over the whole Dalitz plot. So far, the dependence of $G_{\omega\pi^3}$ on the effective mass of pion pairs has not been established with certainty, but a simple model has been proposed by GELL-MANN, SHARP and WAGNER [1962]. In this model, ω-decay is approximated by the two-step process, $\omega \to \rho\pi \to \pi\pi\pi$. Although we have $m_\rho + m_\pi > m_\omega$, the ρ-resonance is so broad that its low-energy tail may give a considerable contribution. The absolute magnitude of $\omega \to \pi\pi\pi$ is then fixed by one parameter, the "coupling constant" $G_{\omega\rho\pi}$.

The Lorentz-invariant matrix element for $\omega \to \rho\pi$ may be written in the form

$$T(M, M') = G_{\omega\rho\pi}\,\varepsilon_{\alpha\beta\gamma\delta} P^\alpha_\rho \varepsilon^{*\beta}(M') P^\gamma_\omega \varepsilon^\delta(M). \tag{6.8}$$

This is the "crossed" version of the matrix element (4-8.2) for the decay $\pi \to \gamma\gamma$. We first consider the two-step process $\omega \to \rho^+\pi^- \to \pi^+\pi^0\pi^-$, for which $P_\rho = P_+ + P_0$. Application of (3-2.14) leads to

$$\begin{aligned} T_+(M, P_+P_0P_-) &= G_{\omega\rho\pi}\,\varepsilon_{\alpha\beta\gamma\delta} P^\alpha_\rho \frac{-g^{\beta\mu} + P^\beta_\rho P^\mu_\rho}{m^2 - P^2_\rho - im\Gamma} (-G_1 P^\mu_+) P^\gamma_\omega \varepsilon^{*\delta}(M) \\ &= \frac{G_{\omega\rho\pi} G_1}{m^2 - P^2_\rho - im\Gamma}\,\varepsilon_{\alpha\beta\gamma\delta} P^\alpha_\rho P^\beta_+ P^\gamma_\omega \varepsilon^{*\delta} \\ &= \frac{G_{\omega\rho\pi} G_1}{m^2 - P^2_\rho - im\Gamma}\,\varepsilon_{\alpha\beta\gamma\delta} P^\alpha_0 P^\beta_+ P^\gamma_- \varepsilon^{*\delta}(M). \end{aligned} \tag{6.9}$$

The propagator has been simplified by the gauge invariance of (8), or explicitly by $\varepsilon_{\alpha\beta\gamma\delta} P^\alpha_\rho P^\beta_\rho = 0$. In the last expression, we have inserted $P_\rho = P_+ + P_0$, $P_\omega = P_+ + P_0 + P_-$, and applied the antisymmetry of $\varepsilon_{\alpha\beta\gamma\delta}$. For comparison with (4), we must add the matrix elements of $\omega \to \rho^+\pi^-$, $\omega \to \rho^0\pi^0$ and $\omega \to \rho^-\pi^+$. From the Clebsch-Gordan coefficients of the state $\boxed{1\,|\,2}$ $I = 0$, we find

$$G_{\omega\rho\pi} = G_{\omega\rho^+\pi^-} = G_{\omega\rho^-\pi^+} = -G_{\omega\rho^0\pi^0}. \tag{6.10}$$

Observing also all other sign factors, we get agreement with (4) by putting

$$G_{\omega\pi^3} = -G_1 G_{\omega\rho\pi} \left(\frac{1}{m^2 - s_{+0} - im\Gamma} + \frac{1}{m^2 - s_{+-} - im\Gamma} + \frac{1}{m^2 - s_{-0} - im\Gamma} \right). \tag{6.11}$$

The relative signs should be correct since the expression must be totally symmetric. If G_1 and $G_{\omega\rho\pi}$ are taken as constants, then the ω decay width may be calculated from (11), (5), (6) and definition (2-3.3). One integration must be performed numerically, since even the simpler $\int \mathrm{d}\,\mathrm{Lips}(m^2, P_+P_0P_-)$ cannot be evaluated analytically. A rough evaluation gives $G^2_{\omega\rho\pi}/4\pi = 25/\mathrm{GeV}^2$, for a partial width of 10 MeV.

The K* resonance was discovered by ALSTON *et al.* [1961] in the reaction $K^-p \to \overline{K}^0\pi^-p$. Strictly speaking, this is the $\overline{K}^*$: the K* itself has $Y = 1$. Examples of K* production are $K^+p \to K^{*+}p$ and $K^+p \to K^{*0}N^{*++}$. The K* has $I = \frac{1}{2}$ like the kaon. From (4-2.9) we find

$$\Gamma(K^* \to K\pi^\pm) = 2\Gamma(K^* \to K\pi^0), \tag{6.12}$$

both for the charged and the neutral K*. In the reaction $K^+p \to K^*p$ at 3 GeV/c, the K* decay distribution is of the form $\sin^2 \vartheta(A - B\cos 2\varphi)$ which is again described by (3-2.12), this time with a mixture of $M = +1$ and $M = -1$. This indicates that the K* is a P-wave resonance like the ρ. Due to its non-vanishing hypercharge, K* is not an eigenstate of G or C.

Taking the matrix element for $K^* \to K\pi^0$ in the form

$$T(K^*_M \to K\pi^0) = -GP_K \cdot \varepsilon(M), \tag{6.13}$$

we again get a partial width of this decay mode of the form (3). By (12), this is one-third of the total K* width. The result is $G^2/4\pi = 3.3$.

Finally, the ϕ resonance has been found in the $\overline{K}K$ effective mass distributions of $K^-p \to \Lambda K^+K^-$ and $K^-p \to \Lambda K^0\overline{K}^0$. In the latter reaction, the observed decay pattern is $\Lambda K_1^0 K_2^0$. The decay mode $\phi \to K_1^0 K_2^0$ allows the conclusion that ϕ has negative parity. From (4-7.15), we see that any system consisting of a meson and its antimeson has $CP = +1$. Since K_1 and K_2 are eigenstates of CP, with eigenvalues $+1$ and -1, it follows that the $\overline{K}K$ system in $\phi \to \overline{K}K$ has negative orbital parity.

From the absence of charged ϕ states, we infer $I = 0$. In that case, we might expect $\Gamma(\phi \to K^+K^-) = \Gamma(\phi \to K^0\overline{K}^0)$. However, the energy release of this decay is so small that one cannot neglect the $K^+ - K^0$ mass difference. For a resonance in the Lth partial wave, we expect (see the discussion following (1.9))

$$\frac{\Gamma(\phi \to K^+K^-)}{\Gamma(\phi \to K^0\overline{K}^0)} = \frac{p_+ v_L(p_+ R)}{p_0 v_L(p_0 R)} \approx \left(\frac{p_+}{p_0}\right)^{2L+1}. \tag{6.14}$$

For $L = 1$ and according to table 5-6, this yields $(126/109)^3 = 1.5$, which is slightly larger than the observed ratio. Already $L = 3$ would give a much too large branching ratio of (14). Together with the parity argument, this shows that the ϕ is also a 1^- resonance. With $I = 0$, the ϕ has $G = C = -1$. In summary: all discrete quantum numbers of ϕ are identical with those of ω.

With $T(\phi_M \to K^+K^-) = -GP_+ \cdot \varepsilon(M)$, the partial width for $\phi \to \overline{K}K$ is

$$\Gamma(\phi \to \overline{K}K) = \frac{G^2}{4\pi}\frac{1}{6m_\phi^2}(p_+^3 + p_0^3). \tag{6.15}$$

Taking this width as 4 MeV, we find $G^2/4\pi = 7.6$. Like the ω, the ϕ also decays into $\pi^+\pi^-\pi^0$. Since $m_\phi > m_\rho + m_\pi$, the ρ-resonance should be more distinct in the Dalitz plot of the ϕ decay than in that of the ω decay. Unfortunately, the partial width $\Gamma(\phi \to \pi^+\pi^-\pi^0)$ is surprisingly small.

Finally, we mention the electromagnetic decay $\omega \to \pi^0\gamma$, the matrix element of which is of the same form as (8). With both spins quantized along the decay momentum, we have

$$T(M,M') = G_{\omega\gamma\pi}\mathrm{i}\, M m_\omega p \delta_{MM'}, \quad \Gamma = p^3 G^2_{\omega\gamma\pi}/8\pi. \qquad (6.16)$$

5-7. SU$_3$ classification of the vector mesons

The nine 1^- resonances may be accommodated in one SU$_3$ octet and one SU$_3$ singlet. The assignment is similar to that of the 0^- mesons; for π, K and η we substitute ρ, K* and ϕ_0 (see fig. 5-7). This ϕ_0 could be either ϕ or ω. In fact, the symmetry-breaking interaction may cause a mixing of

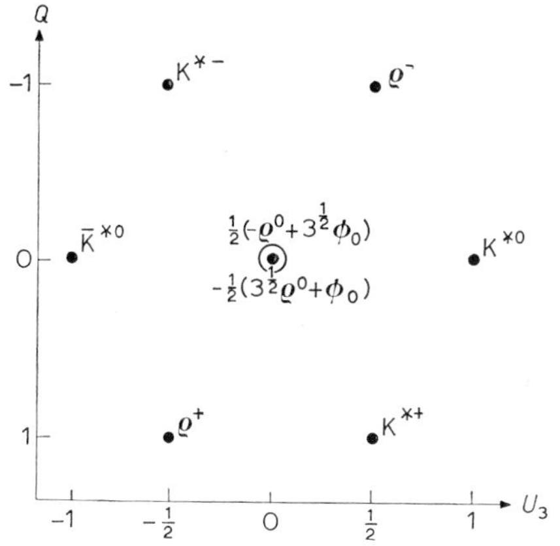

Fig. 5-7. Plot of the electric charge versus the third component of U-spin for the vector mesons ($\phi_0 = \phi \cos\vartheta - \omega \sin\vartheta$).

different SU$_3$ multiplets, and the ϕ_0 may be a linear superposition of ϕ and ω. The orthogonal combination is denoted by ω_0:

$$|\text{octet}, I = 0\rangle \equiv \phi_0 = \phi \cos\vartheta - \omega \sin\vartheta, \qquad (7.1)$$

$$|\text{singlet}, I = 0\rangle \equiv \omega_0 = \phi \sin\vartheta + \omega \cos\vartheta. \qquad (7.2)$$

The first indication of such mixing comes from the mass formula analogous to (5.11)

$$4m_{K^*}^2 = m_\rho^2 + 3m_{\phi_0}^2 . \tag{7.3}$$

This formula gives $m_{\phi_0}^2 = 0.86$, which lies between the squares of the ω and ϕ masses. If we assume that (3) should hold exactly, then we can determine the mixing parameters from the masses m_ω, m_ϕ and m_{ϕ_0} in the following way. The most general Hermitean mass matrix between the ϕ_0, ω_0 states may be written as

$$\begin{pmatrix} m_0+\delta & \mu \\ \mu^* & m_0-\delta \end{pmatrix}, \tag{7.4}$$

where the first (second) row and column refer to the ϕ_0 (ω_0). Thus $m_0+\delta$ is m_{ϕ_0} as given by (3). The relative phase between ϕ_0 and ω_0 may be chosen such that μ becomes real. The eigenvalues of (4) are

$$\left.\begin{matrix} m_\phi \\ m_\omega \end{matrix}\right\} = m_0 \pm \sqrt{\delta^2+\mu^2}. \tag{7.5}$$

After determination of m_0, δ and μ, the angle ϑ may be found by insertion of (1) or (2) into the eigenvalue equation,

$$\begin{pmatrix} m_0+\delta & \mu \\ \mu & m_0-\delta \end{pmatrix}\begin{pmatrix} \sin\vartheta \\ \cos\vartheta \end{pmatrix} = (m_0-\sqrt{\delta^2+\mu^2})\begin{pmatrix} \sin\vartheta \\ \cos\vartheta \end{pmatrix}. \tag{7.6}$$

The result is (DASHEN and SHARP [1964])

$$\cos\vartheta = 0.78, \qquad \sin\vartheta = 0.62, \qquad \vartheta = 38°. \tag{7.7}$$

Thus ϕ_0 is 61% ϕ and 39% ω. However, these numbers may be quite inaccurate because of the theoretical uncertainties in the mass formula (3).

We now relate the coupling constants for $\rho \to \pi\pi$, $K^* \to K\pi$ and $\phi \to \bar{K}K$ by means of U-spin invariance. The states K^{*0} and $\frac{1}{2}(-\rho^0+\sqrt{3}\phi_0)$ are members of a U-spin triplet. Among the decay products, K^+, π^+ as well as K^-, π^- form U-spin doublets. Insertion of the appropriate Clebsch-Gordan coefficients gives

$$\begin{aligned} 2^{-\frac{1}{2}}G(K^* \to K^+\pi^-) &= -\tfrac{1}{2}G(\rho \to \pi^+\pi^-) = \\ &= -\tfrac{1}{2}G(\rho \to K^+K^-) + \tfrac{1}{2}\sqrt{3}G(\phi_0 \to K^+K^-). \end{aligned} \tag{7.8}$$

In the second term, we have already used $G(\phi_0 \to \pi^+\pi^-) = 0$, due to conservation of G-parity. With $G^2(K^* \to K^+\pi^-) = 2\,G_{K^*}^2$, we obtain from (8)

$$G_{K^*}^2 : G_\rho^2 = 1 : 4, \tag{7.9}$$

which is a little smaller than the ratio 3.3/7.8 = 0.42 of table 5-6.

Next, we calculate the width for $\phi \to \overline{K}K$. We begin with the $K^0\overline{K}^0$ mode. Due to the extended Bose-Einstein symmetry, the $K^0\overline{K}^0$ state must be antisymmetric in U-spin space, which implies $U = 1$. (The I-spin analog would be the P-wave $\pi^+\pi^-$ state, which is allowed in ρ^0 decay but not in ω decay.) From the vanishing of the $U = 0$ combination,

$$\sqrt{3}G(\rho \to K^0\overline{K}^0)+G(\phi_0 \to K^0\overline{K}^0) = 0, \tag{7.10}$$

and the isospin symmetry $G(\rho \to K^0\overline{K}^0) = G(\rho \to K^+K^-)$, $G(\phi_0 \to K^0\overline{K}^0) = -G(\phi_0 \to K^+K^-) \equiv -G_{\phi_0}$, the second equation of (8) becomes

$$G(\rho \to \pi^+\pi^-) = G(\rho \to K^+K^-)-\sqrt{3}G_{\phi_0} = -\tfrac{2}{3}\sqrt{3}G_{\phi_0} = -\tfrac{2}{3}\sqrt{3}G_{\phi} \cos \vartheta. \tag{7.11}$$

This is in reasonable agreement with the ratio found from table 5-6.

Finally, we mention that $G^2_{\omega\rho\pi}/G^2_{\phi\rho\pi}$ is not restricted by SU_3 invariance. The experimental widths indicate a value of about 400 for this ratio. This would imply destructive interference of $\phi_0 \to \rho\pi$ and $\omega_0 \to \rho\pi$ in the $\rho\pi$ decay of the physical ϕ.

5-8. Other meson resonances

Of the other resonances of table 5-6, the η^* and the f occur only in the neutral charge state and thus have $I = 0$. The η^* was discovered in the reaction $K^-p \to \Lambda\eta^*$. It mainly decays into $\eta\pi\pi$. From isospin invariance, we expect $\Gamma(\eta^* \to \eta\pi^+\pi^-) = 2\Gamma(\eta^* \to \eta\pi^0\pi^0)$. From the isotropy of η^* decays, one concludes that $J = 0$. Together with $J^{PG} = 0^{-+}$ for the η, this implies 0^{-+} for the η^*. According to table 4-7, the η^* could decay strongly into 4-pions. However, there would be three P-wave barriers. In $\eta^* \to \eta\pi\pi$ on the other hand, the two $I = 0$ pions may be in an S-state, in which case the relative angular momentum between η and the pion pair vanishes.

The f was discovered in the $\pi^+\pi^-$ effective mass distribution of $\pi^-p \to \pi^+\pi^-n$. The spin 2 was concluded from the decay angular distribution. With the coupling

$$T(f_M \to \pi\pi) = G_f P_1^\mu P_1^\nu \varepsilon_{\mu\nu}(M) = 2G_f p^2(4\pi/30)^{\frac{1}{2}} Y_M^2 \tag{8.1}$$

(see 3-2.13), we get

$$\Gamma(f) = \frac{1}{15}\frac{G_f^2}{4\pi}\frac{p^5}{m^2}. \tag{8.2}$$

This gives $G_f^2/4\pi = 22/\text{GeV}^2$ for $\Gamma = 100$ MeV. Note that the pion charges are unspecified in (1). We have $G(\text{f} \to \pi^0\pi^0) = 3^{-\frac{1}{2}}G_f$.

The A_2 resonance was discovered as a peak in the three-pion effective mass distribution of the reactions $\pi^{\pm}p \to \pi^{\pm}\pi^{\pm}\pi^{\mp}p$ (GOLDHABER *et al.* [1964]). From the Dalitz plot of the pions, one finds that the decay $A_2 \to \pi\pi\pi$ proceeds via the $\pi\rho$ intermediate state. Since A_2 exists in charged states, its isospin must be at least 1. The $\bar{K}K$ decay modes of A_2 show that the isospin cannot be larger than 1. Also, the decay $A_2 \to K_S^0 K_S^0$ allows only the spin-parity combinations $2^+, 4^+$ etc. (0^+ is already excluded by the existence of the $\pi\pi\pi$ decay mode). Finally, the Dalitz plot of $A \to \pi\pi\pi$ favours 2^+ over 4^+.

There exist two more resonances which are probably 2^+ states, namely the f′ at 1.51 GeV, decaying mainly into $K\bar{K}$, and the K_V at 1.41 GeV, which decays mainly into $K\pi$ and $K^*\pi$. For a compilation of these and possible other resonances, see ROSENFELD *et al.* [1967]. Of course, not every bump in an effective mass distribution must be a resonance. For example, the reaction $\pi^{\pm}p \to \pi^{\pm}\pi^{\pm}\pi^{\mp}p$ has another peak at lower values of the $\rho-\pi$ effective mass distribution (at 1.08 GeV), which is called A_1. This peak could arise from a particular threshold behaviour of $\rho\pi$-production (DECK [1964]). More details about hadron resonances are found in the review by TENNER and WOLTERS [1965].

CHAPTER 6

S-MATRIX THEORY

6-1. Double scattering and iε-rule

So far, we have mainly exploited the symmetries of the S-matrix, such as Lorentz and isospin invariance. In this chapter, we investigate the analytic structure of the S-matrix, which forms the basis of most dynamical models of strong interactions.

To be more specific, we shall study the T matrix as a function of the complex variables s, t, u, etc., keeping the squares of the external momenta real and fixed at $P_i^2 = m_i^2$. This is necessary not only for the study of crossing symmetry, but also for the definition of the particle concept itself. Let us illustrate this last point by a simple example, namely the reaction $\text{pp} \to \text{nN}^*$. The observed final states will be $\text{np}\pi^+$ states. The matrix element may be written as the matrix element T_d of the unstable-particle approximation (2-3.15), plus a remainder:

$$\begin{aligned} T(\text{ab} \to 12\text{c}) &= T_\text{d}(\text{ab} \to 12\text{c}) + T'(\text{ab} \to 12\text{c}), \\ T_\text{d}(\text{ab} \to 12\text{c}) &= T(\text{ab} \to \text{cd}) \frac{1}{m^2 - s_\text{d} - im\Gamma} T(\text{d} \to 12). \end{aligned} \tag{1.1}$$

Here m and Γ are the mass and width of the N^*, and $s_\text{d} = (P_1 + P_2)^2$ is the square of the $\text{p}\pi^+$ effective mass. The rest T' contains a term similar to T_d from the reaction $\text{pp} \to \text{pN}^*$, which will show up in the $\text{n}\pi^+$ effective mass distribution of the same final states. In addition, T' contains the "background" which refers neither to N^{*++} nor to N^{*+}. The precise definition of T' is that it is finite at $s_\text{d} = m^2 - im\Gamma$. Then T_d may be isolated from T by

$$T(\text{ab} \to \text{cd}) T(\text{d} \to 12) = T(\text{ab} \to 12\text{c})(m^2 - s_\text{d} - im\Gamma) \text{ at } s_\text{d} = m^2 - im\Gamma. \tag{1.2}$$

However, this prescription requires that $T(\text{pp} \to \text{np}\pi^+)$ can be continued from real values of s_d to complex values, lying $m\Gamma$ below the real s_d-axis. To achieve this continuation, we must assume that $T(\text{ab} \to \text{cd})$, $T(\text{d} \to 12)$ and $T'(\text{ab} \to 12\text{c})$ are analytic functions of s_d. When the s_d dependence of Γ is neglected, the propagator $\Phi(s_\text{d})$ produces a pole in $T(\text{ab} \to 12\text{c})$, the residue of which is given by (2).

Qualitatively the same method *defines* the matrix elements for η, π^0 and Σ^0 production. The matrix element for $pp \rightarrow pp\eta$ for example is inferred from the matrix elements of $pp \rightarrow pp\pi^+\pi^0\pi^-$, $pp \rightarrow pp\gamma\gamma$, etc. In practice one may of course neglect the finite width of the η-meson. Formally, one puts $m\Gamma = \varepsilon$ and takes lim $(\varepsilon \rightarrow 0)$ in the final formulae. This is an example of the general "iε-rule", which we shall discuss in this and the following section.

When we defined the *S*-matrices for scattering and decay (sections 2-2 and 2-3), we omitted the necessary limiting procedures. In practice, the 4-momenta of hadrons are measured either from their decay products or from multiple collisions. The multiple collisions are of two types. First of all there are the ionization tracks of the charged hadrons, e.g. in a bubble chamber or in a counter. Secondly, the hadrons may collide with other hadrons. Collisions of this type are necessary e.g. for the production of meson beams. For the practical study of $\pi^{\pm}p$ collisions, it is of course irrelevant how the pions have been produced. The situation becomes more interesting if we consider collisions of neutral pions. In a bubble chamber, one might observe the reaction $\pi^- pp \rightarrow \pi^+ nn$, due to the double scattering $\pi^- p \rightarrow \pi^0 n$, $\pi^0 p \rightarrow \pi^+ n$. Clearly, the matrix element for double scattering is an approximation of a general matrix element for the scattering of three incident particles, which we shall consider later. Again, we shall find that particles correspond to poles in the scattering amplitudes of the overall process. By crossing symmetry, we shall then derive the existence of poles in the amplitude referring to two incident and four outgoing particles. Finally, we shall find poles in all places where particles may occur.

The method of starting with multiparticle amplitudes is mainly due to GUNSON [1965] and OLIVE [1964]. It is explained in some detail in the book of EDEN, LANDSHOFF, OLIVE and POLKINGHORNE [1966]. The derivation of the analytic structure is by no means rigorous. We shall adopt the method with some important modifications. Specifically, we shall not try to derive crossing symmetry, but introduce it as a postulate, as discussed in section 4-6. We believe that at least the *TCP* theorem is more fundamental than the many analyticity and factorization assumptions from which it may be derived in this approach.

The final analytic structure will be that of perturbation theory. Here we apologize for not reviewing perturbation theory itself. There are, however, a number of textbooks on that subject. Also, parts of the new approach, e.g. three-particle unitarity, are certainly more general than perturbation theory or any other local field theory.

For simplicity, we consider spinless, non-identical particles. The connection between spin and statistics of an exchanged particle will be derived in section 6-3. The reader who is only interested in the applications needs just the Born terms of section 6-4, and sections 6-5, 6-7 and 6-8.

The S-matrix for general three-particle processes is postulated to be of the form

$$\begin{aligned} S(123 \to 456) = {} & \langle 4|1\rangle \langle 5|2\rangle \langle 6|3\rangle \\ & + \mathrm{i}(2\pi)^4 \langle 4|1\rangle \delta(P_2+P_3-P_5-P_6)T(23 \to 56) + \text{permutations} \\ & + \mathrm{i}(2\pi)^4 \delta(P_1+P_2+P_3-P_4-P_5-P_6)T(123 \to 456). \qquad (1.3) \end{aligned}$$

The product $\langle 4|1\rangle$ is $(2\pi)^3 2E_1 \delta(\boldsymbol{P}_4-\boldsymbol{P}_1)$ according to (1-5.6). Equation (3) is a generalization of (2-2.10) for two incident particles. The term in the first row corresponds to no scattering. The term in the second row corresponds to scattering $23 \to 56$, with particle "1" going straight through, and its permutations correspond to $12 \to 45$ and $13 \to 46$ scattering, with the remaining particle going straight through. The term of the third row describes the simultaneous scattering of all three particles. It contains among other parts the matrix element T_d for double scattering. In analogy with (1), we try

$$T(123 \to 456) = T_\mathrm{d}(133 \to 456) + T'(123 \to 456), \qquad (1.4)$$

$$T_\mathrm{d}(123 \to 456) = T(12 \to 4\mathrm{d})T(\mathrm{d}3 \to 56)\frac{1}{m^2 - s_\mathrm{d} - \mathrm{i}\varepsilon}, \qquad (1.5)$$

$$s_\mathrm{d} \equiv (P_1+P_2-P_4)^2 = (P_5+P_6-P_3)^2, \qquad (1.6)$$

which is illustrated in fig. 6-1. For $1 = \pi^-$, $2 = \mathrm{p}$, $3 = \mathrm{p}$, $4 = \mathrm{n}$, $5 = \mathrm{n}$, $6 = \pi^+$, d has the quantum numbers of the π^0.

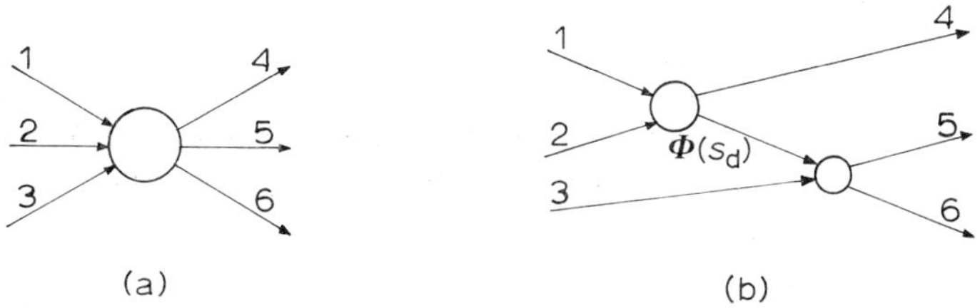

Fig. 6-1. The general matrix element for three-particle scattering and its double-scattering part.

In the next section, we shall show that in the limit $\varepsilon \to 0$, the existence of a term with the structure (5) in $T(123 \to 456)$ implies the existence of a stable particle d with the quantum numbers of the $12\bar{4}$-system. Here, we merely discuss the physical meaning of (5). The small positive number ε is given by

$$\varepsilon = m[\Gamma(\text{decay}) + \Gamma(\text{scattering})], \tag{1.7}$$

where Γ(decay) is the π^0 decay rate and Γ(scattering) its collision rate, given as the ratio of velocity and mean free path. The derivation of this expression is analogous to the derivation of (2-3.13) or rather (2-3.11). The physical motivation for the factorization (5) is of course the large distance between production and secondary scattering. For distances of the order of a nuclear radius, T' of (4) will also contribute, in which case the total $T(123 \to 456)$ does not factorize. As in (2), T' denotes the regular part of T at the "pole" $s_d = m^2 - i\varepsilon$:

$$T(12 \to 4\text{d})T(\text{d}3 \to 56) = T(123 \to 456)(m^2 - s_d - i\varepsilon) \text{ at } s_d = m^2 - i\varepsilon. \tag{1.8}$$

These considerations suggest that the iε rule is the correct limiting procedure for hadrons both in the initial and in the final state. The rule requires that the T-matrix elements are analytic functions of the effective masses in the neighbourhood of the physical effective mass region. This pertains also to expressions such as (6), which contain 4-momenta both of the initial and of the final state.

The decomposition (3) of the S-matrix for three incident and three outgoing particles is called the cluster decomposition or "connectedness structure". Similar decompositions exist for arbitrary numbers of particles. The idea is that the particles should interact (a) not at all, (b) in pairs, (c) two in and three out, (d) in triplets etc. This idea is motivated by the short range of strong interactions. The Coulomb interaction must be excluded from the beginning.

6-2. Three-particle unitarity

In this section we show that the pole term T_d in (1.4) requires the inclusion of a particle d in the three-particle unitarity (OLIVE [1964]). Below the four-particle threshold, we have

$$\int \mathrm{d\,Lips}\,(4,5,6)S(123 \to 456)S^*(1'2'3' \to 456) + \int \mathrm{d\,Lips}\,(\mathrm{a},\mathrm{b})S(123 \to \mathrm{ab})S^*(1'2'3' \to \mathrm{ab})$$
$$= \langle 1'|1\rangle\langle 2'|2\rangle\langle 3'|3\rangle = 8(2\pi)^9 E_1 E_2 E_3 \delta(\boldsymbol{p}_1 - \boldsymbol{p}_1')\delta(\boldsymbol{p}_2 - \boldsymbol{p}_2')\delta(\boldsymbol{p}_3 - \boldsymbol{p}_3'). \tag{2.1}$$

The S-matrix elements of the second integral refer to the rather unusual reaction 123 → ab, which has three incident particles but only two outgoing particles. However, by time-reversal invariance, this is identical with the matrix element for ab → 123. Later, we shall be mainly interested in the consequences of unitarity for ab → cd. Two-particle unitarity (2-4.1) and three-particle unitarity (1) will then be linked by $S(ab → 123)$.

Insertion of (1.3) into (1) leads to lengthy expressions. Here a symbolic bubble notation is appropriate, in which the decomposition of the two-particle → two-particle part of (2-2.10) and its Hermitean conjugate reads

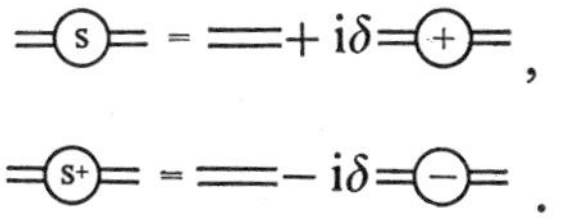

$$=\!\!\bigcirc\!\!\!_{S}\!\!= \; = \; =\!\!= + i\delta =\!\!\oplus\!\!= \; ,$$

$$=\!\!\bigcirc\!\!\!_{S^+}\!\!= \; = \; =\!\!= - i\delta =\!\!\ominus\!\!= \; . \tag{2.2}$$

The bubbles $=\!\oplus\!=$ and $=\!\ominus\!=$ thus stand for $T(12 → 1'2')$ and $T^*(1'2' → 12)$, respectively, and $\delta \equiv (2\pi)^4 \delta^4(P_i - P_f)$. Eq. (1.3) now is written similarly as

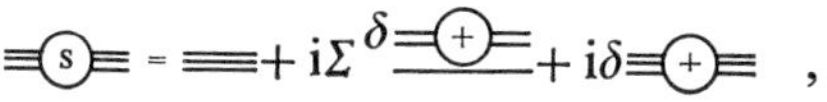

$$=\!\!\bigcirc\!\!\!_{S}\!\!= \; = \; =\!\!= + i\Sigma \overset{\delta}{=\!\!\oplus\!\!=} + i\delta =\!\!\oplus\!\!= \; , \tag{2.3}$$

where the sum in front of the second term goes over all three two-particle combinations. With (2), the two-particle unitarity below the three-particle threshold is

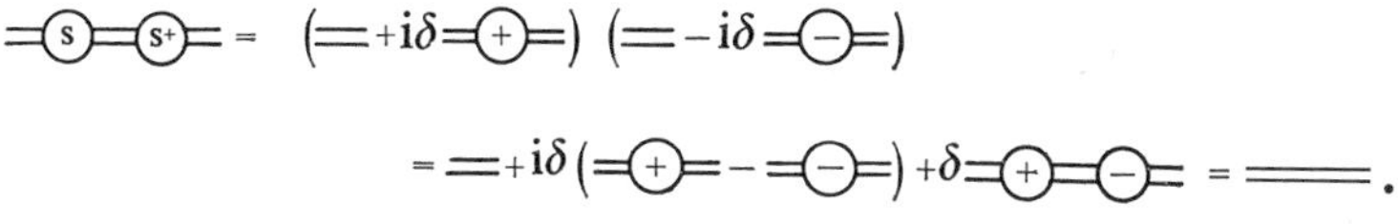

$$=\!\!\bigcirc\!\!\!_{S}\!\!=\!\!\bigcirc\!\!\!_{S^+}\!\!= \; = \; (=\!\!= + i\delta =\!\!\oplus\!\!=) \, (=\!\!= - i\delta =\!\!\ominus\!\!=)$$

$$= \; =\!\!= + i\delta \, (=\!\!\oplus\!\!= - =\!\!\ominus\!\!=) + \delta =\!\!\oplus\!\!=\!\!\ominus\!\!= \; = \; =\!\!= . \tag{2.4}$$

For lines joining $\oplus$ and $\ominus$, integration over the restricted phase space (1-5.9) of the corresponding particles is implied, whereas the unrestricted phase space (1-5.8) appears between S and S^+. After cancellation of a factor δ, (4) reduces to

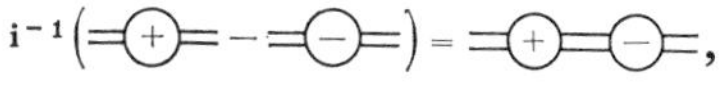

$$i^{-1} (=\!\!\oplus\!\!= - =\!\!\ominus\!\!=) = =\!\!\oplus\!\!=\!\!\ominus\!\!= , \tag{2.5}$$

which is the bubble notation of (2-4.1) in the absence of three-particle intermediate states. The bubble notation of (1) is

$$=\!\!\bigcirc\!\!\!_{S}\!\!=\!\!=\!\!\bigcirc\!\!\!_{S^+}\!\!= \; + =\!\!\bigcirc\!\!\!_{S}\!\!-\!\!\bigcirc\!\!\!_{S^+}\!\!= \; = \; =\!\!= . \tag{2.6}$$

Substitution of (3) into this equation gives

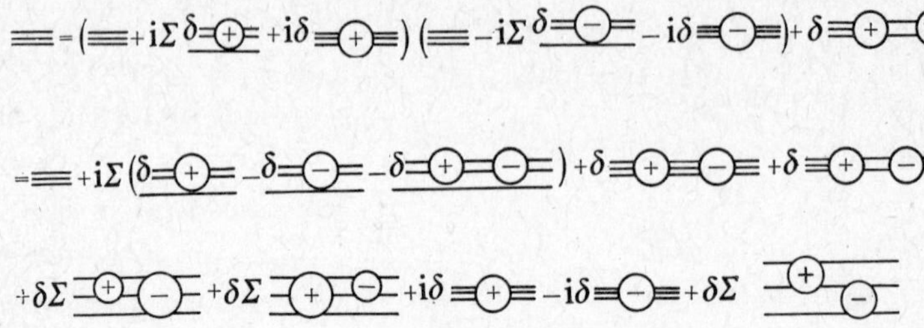

(2.7)

As expected, the terms  cancel out. In addition, the sum of all terms with one disconnected line (those in the bracket) vanishes because of (5). Dropping again a common factor $(2\pi)^4\delta^4(P_1+P_2+P_3-P_4-P_5-P_6)$, (7) is rewritten as

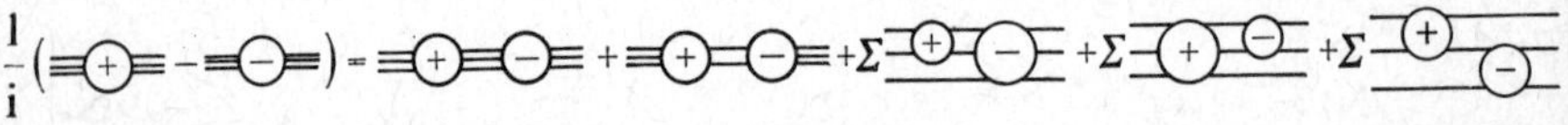

(2.8)

This is the three-particle unitarity. The explicit expression in terms of T-matrix elements, δ-functions and phase space integrals is still rather lengthy. Here we discuss only the last symbol in (7) and (8). The sum consists of $3\times 3 = 9$ terms, corresponding to which of the three incident particles misses the $\oplus$ bubble, and which of the three outgoing particles misses the $\ominus$ bubble. We discuss only one of these terms. For comparison with (1.5), let particles 3 and 4 be the "missing" particles. Then the last term in (7) and (8) contains $T(12 \to 4\text{d})\ T^*(3\text{d} \to 56)$ and the following δ-functions and one-particle phase space:

$$\int \mathrm{d\ Lips}\,(P_\mathrm{d})(2\pi)^8\delta^4(P_1+P_2-P_4-P_\mathrm{d})\delta^4(P_5+P_6-P_3-P_\mathrm{d})$$

$$= \frac{\delta(s_\mathrm{d}-m^2)}{(2\pi)^3}(2\pi)^8\delta^4(P_1+P_2-P_4-P_5-P_6+P_3) = 2\pi\delta(s_\mathrm{d}-m^2)\cdot\delta, \quad (2.9)$$

with s_d defined by (1.6). This result was anticipated in (7) by writing $\delta\Sigma$ instead of a sum over δ-functions for two-particle subsystems. Equation (9) expresses the fact that $2\pi\delta(s_\mathrm{d}-m^2)$ is the restricted one-particle phase space integral of particle d.

Now we demonstrate that the existence of a non-zero T_d (1.5) in 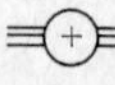

implies a non-zero contribution of the last term of (8), which proves the existence of a particle d with quantum numbers of the $12\bar{4}$ and $56\bar{3}$ systems (OLIVE [1964]). If we denote the propagator $\Phi(s_d)$ by an arrow, then (1.5) is associated with the symbol

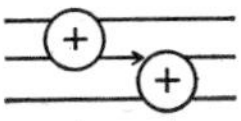

The complex conjugate $\Phi^*(s_d)$ is denoted by an arrow in the opposite direction. With this convention, the part of (8) which is singular at $s_d = m^2$ is

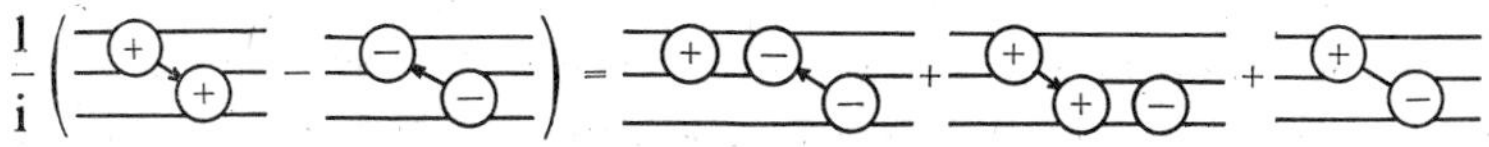 (2.10)

The last term is identical with the last term of (8), apart from the summation. The second and third last terms are obtained from the second and third last terms of (8) by the substitutions

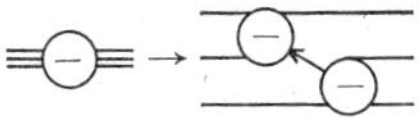 and 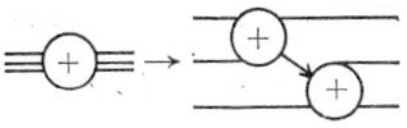

These substitutions transform the term

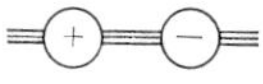 of (8) into 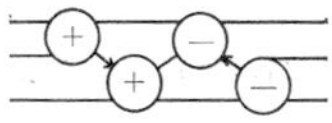

which therefore contains a singularity in two of the integration variables. However, the integral itself is regular at $(P_1+P_2-P_4)^2 = m^2$. Therefore, this term has been omitted from (10).

After elimination of 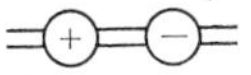 from (10) by the two-particle unitarity (5), a few terms cancel out, and the equation reduces to

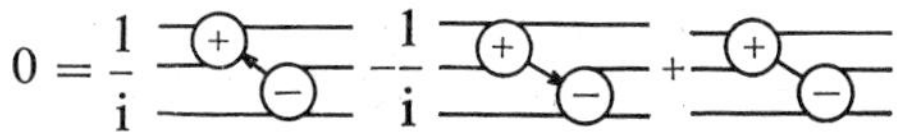 (2.11)

This equation is indeed satisfied, since

$$\frac{1}{i}\Phi^*(s)-\frac{1}{i}\Phi(s) = \frac{1}{i}\left(\frac{1}{m^2-s+i\varepsilon}-\frac{1}{m^2-s-i\varepsilon}\right) = -\frac{2\varepsilon}{(m^2-s)^2+\varepsilon^2} \tag{2.12}$$

approaches $-2\pi\delta(s-m^2)$ in the limit $\varepsilon \to 0$, according to (2-3.21). Therefore, three-particle unitarity is only possible if to each double-scattering pole T_d there corresponds a particle. With some caution, the inverse statement is also true. Some particles of the three-particle states need not produce double-scattering poles in certain reactions, because of selection rules. For example, π^0 and η^0 will produce poles in $\pi^- pp \to \pi^+ nn$, but K^0 will not.

Another point concerns the form of the propagator, which could be either $\Phi(E)/2m = [(m-E-i\varepsilon/2m)2m]^{-1}$ or $\Phi(s_d) = \Phi(E)/2m + \Phi(-E)/2m$ (cf. (2-3.11) and (2-3.13)). The first possibility arises from the fact that the function $\delta(s_d - m^2)$ in the one-particle phase space may be written as $\delta(m-E)/2E$ according to (1-5.4), since the remaining part $\delta(m+E)/2E$ is zero throughout the range of integration. To demonstrate this, we merely need the sign of E_d in a particular Lorentz frame, since at $P_d^2 = m^2 > 0$, this sign is Lorentz invariant. Clearly, in the rest system of particle 3 (lab system), $E_d = E_5 + E_6 - m_3$ is positive. Consequently the physical region singularities lead to

$$\frac{1}{i}\left(\frac{1}{m-E-i\varepsilon/2m} - \frac{1}{m-E+i\varepsilon/2m}\right) = -\frac{\varepsilon/2m}{(m-E)^2+\varepsilon^2/4m^2} \tag{2.13}$$

rather than to (12). As expected, the pole $\Phi(-E)$ is not required by three-particle unitarity alone. This pole follows instead from *TCP* invariance, which requires invariance under $P_i \to -P_i$, $i = 1, \ldots, 6$, and therefore under $E \to -E$. (Cf. the analogous remark at the end of section 4-6.)

6-3. The antiparticle pole. Spin and statistics

To investigate some more delicate consequences of crossing symmetry, we now consider reactions, for which not only the particle pole $\Phi(E)$, but also the antiparticle pole $\Phi(-E)$ may cause successive interactions. Requiring as before the external particles to be stable, we need at least one more outgoing particle at the upper bubble and one more incoming particle at the lower bubble of fig. 6-1.

To keep the notation as simple as possible, we abbreviate pairs of particles by a, b, c, d as indicated in fig. 6-3. We thus have $P_a = P_1 + P_2$,

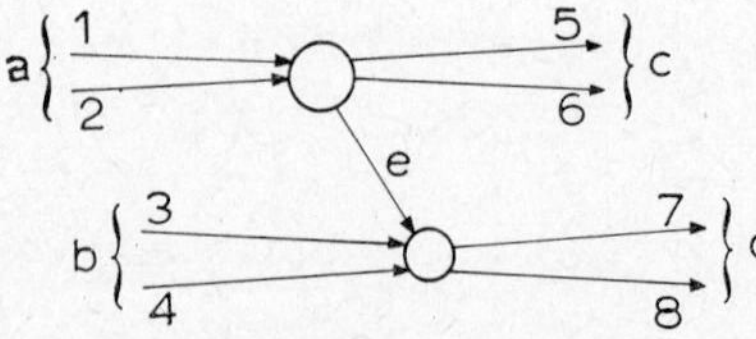

Fig. 6-3. The amplitude T_d for the sequence $12 \to 56e$, $e34 \to 78$ in the general process $1234 \to 5678$.

$P_b = P_3+P_4$, etc. This allows us formally to speak about the reaction ab → cd, with variable masses m_a, m_b, m_c and m_d. The exchanged particle in the two-step process is now called e,

$$P_e = P_a - P_c = P_d - P_b, \qquad P_e^2 = t. \tag{3.1}$$

As before, the matrix element T for the overall process 1234 → 5678 is separated into T_d and T',

$$T = T' + T_d, \qquad T_d = T(\mathrm{a} \to \mathrm{ce})T(\mathrm{eb} \to \mathrm{d})\Phi(t). \tag{3.2}$$

T_d describes, at $t = m^2$, the sequence a → ce, eb → d. There is a similar part $T'_d = T(\mathrm{a\bar{e}} \to \mathrm{c})\Phi_{\bar{e}}(t)T(b \to \mathrm{\bar{e}d})$ which describes, also at $t = m^2$, the sequence b → ēd, aē → c. In the remaining variables, the physical regions of the two sequences, which we shall call e and ē, are well separated by the restrictions on the external "masses",

$$\begin{aligned} &\mathrm{e)}\quad m_a > m_c + m, \qquad m_d > m_b + m,\\ &\mathrm{\bar{e})}\quad m_a < m_c - m, \qquad m_d < m_b - m. \end{aligned} \tag{3.3}$$

In bubble notation, the two sequences are

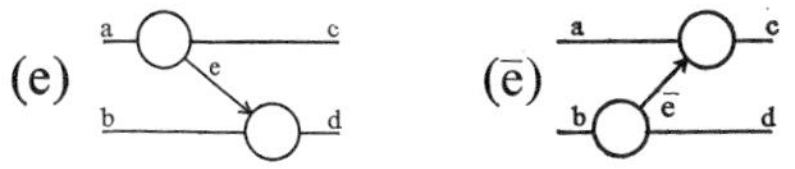

(3.4)

If the matrix element T for the overall process 1234 → 5678 is an analytic function of the "masses" $m_a, \ldots, m_d$ and of t, then the residues of T_d and T'_d (i.e. the products $T(\mathrm{a} \to \mathrm{ce})T(\mathrm{be} \to \mathrm{d})$ and $T(\mathrm{a\bar{e}} \to \mathrm{c})T(\mathrm{b} \to \mathrm{\bar{e}d})$, summed over the magnetic quantum numbers of the exchanged particle) are also analytic functions of $m_a, \ldots, m_d$, well-defined even outside the regions (e) and (ē). Moreover, unless T has a branchpoint for some $t < m^2$, the two residues are analytic continuations of each other, i.e.

$$T(\mathrm{a} \to \mathrm{ce})\Phi_e T(\mathrm{e} \to \mathrm{bd}) = T(\mathrm{a\bar{e}} \to \mathrm{c})\Phi_{\bar{e}} T(\mathrm{b} \to \mathrm{\bar{e}d}). \tag{3.5}$$

This relation could be used to derive crossing symmetry, if the branchpoint in t could be excluded (OLIVE [1964]). Of course, one cannot admit a branchpoint for T in the physical region of the overall process. However, not all of the region $t < m^2$ is physical. From section 1-3 we remember $t_{max} \to 0$ for $m_a \to m_c$ or $m_b \to m_d$. Since the regions $m_a = m_c$ and $m_b = m_d$ obviously lie between (e) and (ē) as defined by (3), there could be branchpoints in the unphysical region of the overall process, which could spoil (5). Instead, (5) follows trivially from our *postulate* of crossing symmetry as discussed in section 4-6, and single branchpoints for $t < m^2$ are thereby excluded.

Careful use of (5) leads to the connection between spin and statistics (LU and OLIVE [1966], TAYLOR [1966], FROISSART and TAYLOR [1967]). The proof starts from the equation

$$\Phi_e \equiv \sum_M \frac{|M_e\rangle\langle M_e|}{m^2-t-i\varepsilon} = (-1)^{2S_e}\Phi_{\bar{e}}, \tag{3.6}$$

where S_e is the spin of the exchanged particle. This equation is an identity for $S_e = 0$. We shall now derive it for $S_e = \frac{1}{2}$.

Using four-component spinors, the spin summation on the l.h.s. of (5), at $P_e = -P_{\bar{e}}$, is

$$\sum_M u(P_e, M)\bar{u}(P_e, M) = P_e \cdot \gamma + m. \tag{3.7}$$

The first factor u refers to the absorption of e in eb → d. It must be related to the emission of ē in b → ēd. For this crossed process, we could use the negative energy spinor $u(-P_e, M)$, or the adjoint charge conjugate spinor,

$$\bar{u}_c(P_e, M) = u_c^+(P_e, M)\gamma_0 = u_{tr}(-P_e, M)\gamma_0 C^+\gamma_0 = -u_{tr}(-P_e, M)C, \tag{3.8}$$

according to (4-7.3). In a symmetric description of particles and antiparticles, we must use u (u_c) for incoming particles (antiparticles) and $\bar{u}$ ($\bar{u}_c$) for outgoing particles (antiparticles). Therefore, the spin summation of ē is

$$\begin{aligned}(m^2-t-i\varepsilon)\Phi_{\bar{e}} &\equiv \sum_M u_c(P_e, M)\bar{u}_c(P_e, M)\\ &= -\sum_M C\bar{u}(-P_e, M)_{tr}u(-P_e, M)_{tr}C\\ &= -Cu(-P_e, M)\bar{u}(-P_e, M)C\\ &= -C(-P_e\cdot\gamma+m)C = -(P_e\cdot\gamma+m),\end{aligned} \tag{3.9}$$

which is the opposite of (7). This explains eq. (6). Insertion into (5) gives (λ = helicity)

$$\sum_\lambda T(a \to ce_\lambda)T(e_\lambda b \to d) = (-1)^{2S_e}\sum_\lambda T(a\bar{e}_\lambda \to c)T(b \to \bar{e}_\lambda d). \tag{3.10}$$

At fixed $T(a \to ce)$, we may now vary the energies m_b and m_d at the lower vertex, thereby getting a number of equations of the type (10). From these, we conclude that (10) must hold for each component separately,

$$T(a \to ce_\lambda) = T(a\bar{e}_\lambda \to c) \tag{3.11}$$

(which is of course trivial if crossing symmetry is postulated), apart from a possible phase factor $\phi_{e\lambda}$, which would be cancelled by the inverse phase factor in the crossing of $T(e_\lambda b \to d)$. The sign factor $(-1)^{2S_e}$ cannot cancel, however. Therefore, with the crossing phase of the upper vertex fixed by (11), we get for the lower vertex

$$T(e_\lambda b \to d) = (-1)^{2S_e} T(b \to \bar{e}_\lambda d). \tag{3.12}$$

To prove the connection between spin and statistics, one must observe the ordering of particles in the various states. In this section, we have used the same order of particles for initial, intermediate and final states. This is necessary in view of the connection with three-particle unitarity. Taking upper lines first, we have for the sequence e the combinations ab, ceb and cd for initial, intermediate and final states. For the sequence $\bar{e}$ of (4), the corresponding combinations are ab, a$\bar{e}$d and cd. The difference between (11) and (12) is the position of the crossed particle: in (11) e and $\bar{e}$ are the last particles in the state, whereas in (12) they are the first. Replacing in (12) e by $\bar{e}$, b by a and d by c, we get

$$T(\bar{e}_\lambda a \to c) = (-1)^{2S_e} T(a \to ec). \tag{3.13}$$

The exchange of a and $\bar{e}$ on the l.h.s. and of e and c on the r.h.s. must transform this equation into (11). If S_e is half-integer (fermion), this simultaneous exchange must produce a factor -1. By the conservation modulo two of fermion number, the sum of the fermion numbers in a and c is odd. Thus the exchange produces a minus sign, if and only if the states are antisymmetric under the exchange of fermions. Similarly, it must be symmetric under the exchange of bosons. For the exchange of bosons with fermions, both symmetry and antisymmetry are allowed.

One should note here that the symmetry or antisymmetry of a two-particle state has observable consequences only if the exchanged particles are identical. For a state consisting of a π^0 of 4-momentum P_1 and a K^0 of 4-momentum P_2, the symmetry

$$|\pi^0, P_1; K^0, P_2\rangle = |K^0, P_2; \pi^0, P_1\rangle \tag{3.14}$$

does not exclude states of odd angular momentum. When both particles are π^0, the symmetry

$$|\pi^0, P_1; \pi^0, P_2\rangle = |\pi^0, P_2; \pi^0, P_1\rangle \tag{3.15}$$

does in fact exclude antisymmetric states.

6-4. Poles in the *S*-matrix for two incident particles. Born terms

By crossing symmetry, the matrix element $T(123 \to 456)$ for three-particle scattering is related to various processes with two particles in the initial state, such as $12 \to 456\bar{3}$ or $\bar{4}3 \to \bar{1}\bar{2}56$. In these crossed reactions, the double scattering pole (1.5) is represented by the diagrams of fig. 6-4.1. The point $s_d = m^2$ is now remote from the physical region, $s_d \geqq (m_5+m_6+m_3)^2$ in $12 \to 456\bar{3}$. In the reactions $\bar{4}3 \to \bar{1}\bar{2}56$, s_d is a momentum transfer t. In the physical region of this reaction, we have $s_d \leqq t_{max} < 0$, where t_{max} is obtained from (1-3.12) by replacing $m_a \to m_4$, $m_b \to m_3$, $m_c^2 \to (P_{\bar{1}}+P_{\bar{2}})^2$, $m_d^2 \to (P_5+P_6)^2$.

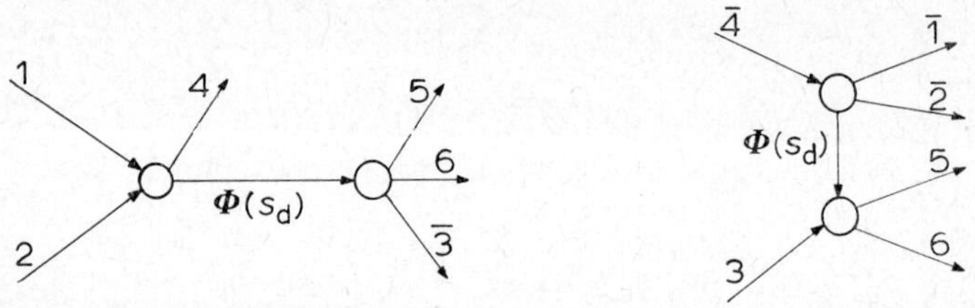

Fig. 6-4.1. Two graphs obtained from crossing of the double-scattering part of fig. 6-1.

It is convenient to call poles in effective mass variables and momentum transfers "direct" and "crossed" poles, respectively. We begin by discussing the crossed pole, which forms the basis of most high-energy models. Because of $s_d < 0$, we have $\Phi(s_d) < 1/m^2$ in the physical region, which is negligible with respect to the possible values of $\Phi(s_d)$ in the double scattering region of $123 \to 456$. In that region, T' of (1.4) was negligible, too. We conclude that T_d and T' may be of the same order of magnitude in $\bar{4}3 \to \bar{1}\bar{2}56$.

The actual size of T_d depends not only on the propagator, but also on the amplitudes $T(12 \to 4d)$ and $T(d3 \to 56)$, extrapolated to negative s_d. Without further restrictions, this extrapolation could in principle give any value of T_d, e.g. $T_d = 0$ for all $s_d < 0$. We now require that the extrapolation must be made with analytic functions of s_d. At present, we only need the fact that an analytic function which is zero in some interval is zero everywhere. Since we assume $T(12 \to 4d)\, T(d3 \to 56) \neq 0$ around $s_d = m^2$, we cannot have $T_d = 0$ for all $s_d < 0$. To show that $T(\bar{4}3 \to \bar{1}\bar{2}56)$ really has a pole at $s_d = m^2$, we should of course exclude the possibility that T_d is cancelled by a similar pole in T'. The original T' was defined as that part of $T(123 \to 456)$ which is finite at $s_d = m^2$. Then, if T' is an analytic function in the remaining variables, it cannot develop a pole at $s_d = m^2$ when the remaining variables are changed. The dynamical models which we consider later will explicitly satisfy all analyticity requirements. For example, the s_d-dependence of $T(\mathrm{d}3 \to 56)$ will be taken essentially as $\lambda^n(s_{56}, m_3^2, s_d)$, $n = 0, \frac{1}{2}, 1, \ldots$, and T' will be calculated as an analytic integral. In the one-particle exchange model, we shall put $T' = 0$. The models could also contain non-analytic functions as approximations to more complicated analytic expressions.

Once the existence of the poles of fig. 6-4.1 is established, it is easily shown that reactions with smaller numbers of particles must also have poles. Consider for example the pion-exchange pole in the reaction $\mathrm{K^+p \to K^{*0}N^{*++} \to K^0\pi^0p\pi^+}$. The unstable-particle approximation T_d^{**} of T_d for this reaction is defined as (fig. 6-4.2)

$$T_d(\mathrm{K^+p \to K^0\pi^0pn^+}) = T_d'(\mathrm{K^+p \to K^0\pi^0p\pi^+}) + T_d^{**}, \tag{4.1}$$

$$T_d^{**} = T_d(\mathrm{K^+p \to K^{*0}N^{*++}})\Phi(s_{\mathrm{K}^*})T(\mathrm{K^* \to K^0\pi^0})\Phi(s_{\mathrm{N}^*})T(\mathrm{N^* \to p\pi^+}). \tag{4.2}$$

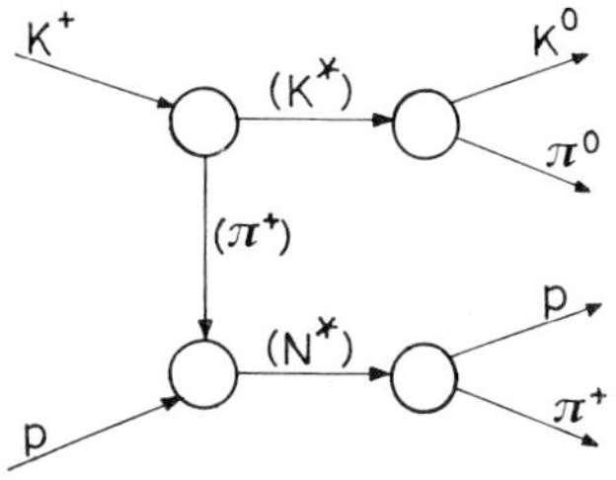

Fig. 6-4.2. The unstable-particle part T_d^{**} of the reaction $\mathrm{K^+p \to K^0\pi^0p\pi^+}$.

In addition to the pole of

$$t \equiv (P_{\mathrm{K}^+} - P_{\mathrm{K}^0} - P_{\pi^0})^2 \tag{4.3}$$

at $m_{\pi^+}^2$, T_d^{**} has poles at $s_{\mathrm{K}^0\pi^0} = m_{\mathrm{K}^*}^2 - \mathrm{i}m_{\mathrm{K}^*}\Gamma_{\mathrm{K}^*}$ and $s_{\mathrm{p}\pi^+} = m_{\mathrm{N}^*}^2 - \mathrm{i}m_{\mathrm{N}^*}\Gamma_{\mathrm{N}^*}$. The remaining part T_d' includes those terms which have at most one of the two effective mass poles in addition to the crossed pole. Clearly, $T_d(\mathrm{K^*p \to K^*N^*})$ is the crossed pole term in the production of unstable particles. It does not contain the resonance widths explicitly. Therefore, qualitatively the same argument works e.g. for K exchange in $\mathrm{\bar{p}p \to \bar{\Lambda}\Lambda \to \bar{p}\pi^+p\pi^-}$, although the decay of Λ into p and a *real* $\mathrm{K^-}$ is forbidden by the conservation of energy and momentum. Finally, we approximate the unstable particles by stable ones, thereby getting poles in reactions ab → cd, irrespective of the masses of particles a, b, c and d. By crossing symmetry, direct poles must also be possible in such reactions (see fig. 6-4.3). Alternatively, we may infer the direct pole in ab → cd from the direct pole 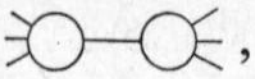, using a similar chain of arguments.

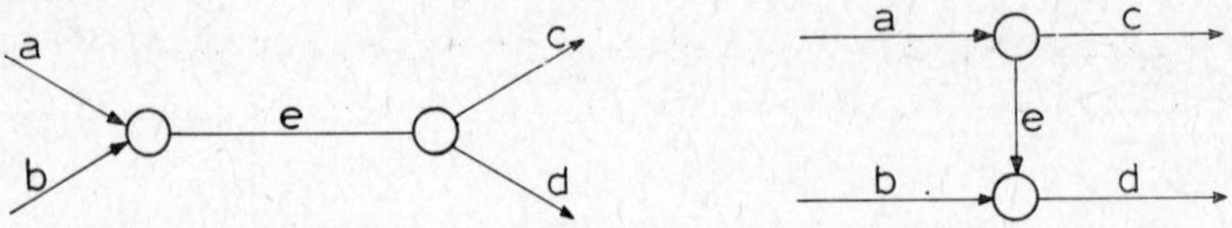

Fig. 6-4.3. Direct and crossed poles in the reaction ab → cd.

The direct and crossed poles in elastic scattering are to some extent known in potential theory. Consider for example pn scattering in the triplet S-state at low energies. It contains a bound state, the deuteron. This bound state produces a pole at s = (deuteron mass)^2. In this case, the pole must be present due to the analyticity properties of the radial wave function $u_L(r)$, which follow from the Schrödinger equation (2-5.3). This differential equation contains q^2 as a parameter. According to a theorem by Poincaré, solutions of differential equations are analytic functions of such parameters, provided the boundary condition does not explicitly involve the parameter. Instead of the boundary condition at $r = \infty$, one may use the condition $u_L(r) = r^{L+1}$ for $r \to 0$, which is independent of q^2. Therefore, $u_L(r)$ is an analytic function of q^2. Similarly, crossed poles determine the main features of "direct" nuclear reactions (SHAPIRO [1963]).

Historically, the occurrence of particle poles in two-particle reactions irrespective of the bound state interpretation was discovered in the perturbation theory of local field theory. The matrix elements of the lowest non-vanishing order are called Born terms, T^{Born}. Depending on the nature of the pole which they contain, we shall speak about direct and crossed Born terms. The direct Born term of ab → cd is of the form

$$\begin{aligned} T^{\text{Born}}(\text{ab} \to \text{cd}) &= B(\text{e} \to \text{cd})\Phi(\text{s})B(\text{ab} \to \text{e}) \\ &= \sum_M B(\text{e}_M \to \text{cd})B(\text{ab} \to \text{e}_M)\frac{1}{m^2 - s}, \qquad (4.4) \end{aligned}$$

where the functions $B(\text{e}_M \to \text{cd})$ are identical with the previously discussed decay matrix elements $T(\text{d}_M \to 1, 2)$, provided the coupling constants G are taken as proper constants, independent of s. The Born term is the simplest possible matrix element which has a pole at $s = m^2$ (after putting $\varepsilon = 0$), the residue of which factorizes. When all particles have spin zero,

T^{Born} consists only of this pole:

$$T^{\text{Born}} = G_{\text{ecd}} G_{\text{abe}} \frac{1}{m^2 - s} . \tag{4.5}$$

When the "virtual" particle e carries spin, the spin summation is performed by means of the matrix propagator Φ_{ij} as in (3-2.14). The Born terms for the exchange of vector mesons and baryons are of the form

$$T_{\text{v}}^{\text{Born}} = B^{\mu}(\text{e} \to \text{cd}) \frac{-g_{\mu\nu} + P_{\mu} P_{\nu}/m^2}{m^2 - s} B^{\nu}(\text{ab} \to \text{e}), \tag{4.6}$$

$$T_{\text{b}}^{\text{Born}} = B_i(\text{e} \to \text{cd}) \frac{P_{\mu}(\gamma^{\mu})_{ij} + m\delta_{ij}}{m^2 - s} B_j(\text{ab} \to \text{e}), \tag{4.7}$$

where B^{μ} is a 4-vector and B_i a 4-component spinor. Note that the spin summation in the propagator was defined so far only for $P^2 = m^2$. In (6) and (7), we have $P^2 = s \neq m^2$. Therefore, (6) and (7) *define* the propagators of virtual spin-1 and -$\frac{1}{2}$ particles. Other definitions are clearly possible. One could for example replace m by $s^{\frac{1}{2}}$ in the numerators. This does not change the residue of the pole, which by definition is the value of the numerator at $s = m^2$. The same problem exists in principle also for resonances, where $P_{\text{d}}^2 = s_{\text{d}}$ varies around its mean value m^2. There, however, $|s_{\text{d}} - m^2|$ was of the order of $m\Gamma$, whereas now it may be much larger than m^2 itself.

An important property of Born terms is that they are real. This is due to the reality of the coupling constants. If time-reversal invariance does not hold, the matrix of Born terms is a Hermitean matrix. Let us see how this property arises in perturbation theory. Writing $1 + \text{i}T = S = \text{e}^{\text{i}H}$, we find $T = H$ to lowest order in H. If S is to be unitary, H must be Hermitean.

This simple argument indicates that the Born term may be a good approximation to the complete matrix element in electromagnetic and weak interactions, where H is small (due to the smallness of the coupling constant). In strong interactions, the role of the Born term is very doubtful. We only know that there are poles corresponding to stable particles, and that the residue of the pole factorizes. The nucleon pole for example plays an important role in the theory of low-energy πN scattering. However, the discussion usually starts from the full Born term. Sometimes the non-pole terms are dropped afterwards, but more frequently, the Born terms are only modified (by "form factors" or "Regge poles"). This is the case e.g. in the models of high-energy interactions, to be discussed in chapter 11. Such a procedure is motivated by the correct threshold behaviour of Born terms (see sections 7-4 and 7-5 below). However, the detailed form of the modification is uncertain, both theoretically and experimentally.

In the following, we shall need the Born terms of πN scattering. In view of possible generalizations to other meson-baryon systems, we examine a Born term in which all 5 masses are different, namely that of $K^-p \to \Lambda \to \pi\Sigma$. The matrix element (3-5.18) for $\Lambda \to \pi p$ contained the combination $G + G'\gamma_5$. For $\Lambda \to \pi\Sigma$ and $K^-p \to \Lambda$, parity conservation requires $G = 0$, due to the mesons' negative eigenparity. We therefore take

$$B(\Lambda \to \pi\Sigma) = G_{\Lambda\pi\Sigma}\bar{u}(\Sigma)\gamma_5 u(\Lambda), \qquad B(K^-p \to \Lambda) = -G_{\Lambda K p}\bar{u}(\Lambda)\gamma_5 u(p). \quad (4.8)$$

The minus sign in $B(K^-p \to \Lambda)$ comes from $B(K^-p \to \Lambda) = B^*(\Lambda \to K^-p)$ and the fact that γ_0 and γ_5 anticommute. Inserting (8) into (7), we find

$$\begin{aligned} T^{\text{Born}} &= -G_{\Lambda\pi\Sigma}G_{\Lambda K p}\bar{u}(\Sigma)\gamma_5(P_\mu\gamma^\mu + m_\Lambda)\gamma_5 u(p)\frac{1}{m_\Lambda^2 - s} \\ &= G_{\Lambda\pi\Sigma}G_{\Lambda K p}\bar{u}(\Sigma)(P_\mu\gamma^\mu - m_\Lambda)u(p)\frac{1}{m_\Lambda^2 - s}, \end{aligned} \quad (4.9)$$

where $P = P_K + P_p = P_\pi + P_\Sigma$ is the total 4-momentum. It is convenient to split off the functions $\bar{u}$ and u and to consider instead the scalar functions A and B defined by (3-9.14):

$$T^{\text{Born}} = \bar{u}(\Sigma)[A^{\text{Born}} + \tfrac{1}{2}(P_K + P_\pi)\cdot\gamma B^{\text{Born}}]u(p). \quad (4.10)$$

For this purpose, we write P as $\frac{1}{2}(P_p + P_\Sigma) + \frac{1}{2}(P_K + P_\pi)$. The Dirac equation enables us to replace the first bracket by $\frac{1}{2}(m_p + m_\Sigma)$. Then comparison between (9) and (10) gives

$$\begin{aligned} A^{\text{Born}} &= G_{\Lambda\pi\Sigma}G_{\Lambda K p}\left(\frac{m_p + m_\Sigma}{2} - m_\Lambda\right)\frac{1}{m_\Lambda^2 - s}, \\ B^{\text{Born}} &= G_{\Lambda\pi\Sigma}G_{\Lambda K p}\frac{1}{m_\Lambda^2 - s}. \end{aligned} \quad (4.11)$$

For historical reasons, one often uses instead of (8) the pseudovector "coupling",

$$B(\Lambda \to \pi\Sigma) = \sqrt{4\pi}\,\frac{f}{m_\pi}\,\bar{u}(\Sigma)\gamma_5\gamma_\nu P_\pi^\nu u(\Lambda). \quad (4.12)$$

To find the connection between (8) and (12), we write P_π as $P_\Lambda - P_\Sigma$ and apply the Dirac equations for $\bar{u}(\Sigma)$ and $u(\Lambda)$. For $\bar{u}(\Sigma)$, we replace

$-\gamma_5\gamma\cdot P_\Sigma = \gamma\cdot P_\Sigma\gamma_5$ by $m_\Sigma\gamma_5$. Comparing the result with (8), we find that the two couplings are equal for

$$G_{\Lambda\pi\Sigma} = \sqrt{4\pi} f \frac{m_\Lambda + m_\Sigma}{m_\pi}. \tag{4.13}$$

In general, however, the pseudoscalar and pseudovector Born terms are different. Using pseudovector coupling for $\Lambda\to\pi\Sigma$, we get instead of (9)

$$T^{\text{Born}}_{\text{pv}} = -\sqrt{4\pi}\frac{f}{m_\pi}\bar{u}(\Sigma)\gamma_5\gamma\cdot P_\pi\frac{P\cdot\gamma+m_\Lambda}{m_\Lambda^2-s}\dots \tag{4.14}$$

The points indicate the unchanged part of the Born term, which is irrelevant at present. As before we may replace $\gamma P_\pi = \gamma(P-P_\Sigma)$ by $\gamma P+m_\Sigma =$ $= \gamma P - m_\Lambda + (m_\Sigma + m_\Lambda)$. We obtain

$$T^{\text{Born}}_{\text{pv}} = -\sqrt{4\pi} f\frac{m_\Sigma+m_\Lambda}{m_\pi}\bar{u}(\Sigma)\gamma_5\frac{P\cdot\gamma+m_\Lambda}{m_\Lambda^2-s}\dots$$

$$-\sqrt{4\pi}\frac{f}{m_\pi}\bar{u}(\Sigma)\gamma_5(P\cdot\gamma-m_\Lambda)(P\cdot\gamma+m_\Lambda)\frac{1}{m_\Lambda^2-s}\dots \tag{4.15}$$

In view of (13), the first term is identical with (9). The second term is

$$T^{\text{Born}}_{\text{pv}} - T^{\text{Born}} = \sqrt{4\pi}\frac{f}{m_\pi}\bar{u}(\Sigma)\gamma_5\dots, \tag{4.16}$$

which has no pole at $s = m_\Lambda^2$. Therefore, if the Born term is only used for getting the residue at the pole, pseudoscalar and pseudovector coupling are equally good. This will be the case in the theory of low-energy πN scattering. On the other hand, in the peripheral model (section 11-3), one sometimes includes the full Born term of "baryon exchange", in which case pseudoscalar and pseudovector Born terms will lead to different scattering amplitudes.

The historical motivation of the pseudovector coupling comes from the static approximation, in which one neglects the baryon 3-momenta. For the Dirac spinors, this implies neglecting the small components. The pseudovector matrix element between big components is

$$(\gamma_5\gamma\cdot P_\pi)_{\text{bb}} = \boldsymbol{\sigma}\cdot\boldsymbol{p}_\pi, \tag{4.17}$$

whereas the corresponding pseudoscalar matrix element $(\gamma_5)_{\text{bb}}$ is zero. Of course, this merely shows that in general one cannot neglect the baryon momentum unless one also puts $\boldsymbol{p}_\pi = 0$, because of $\boldsymbol{p}_\pi = \boldsymbol{p}_\Lambda - \boldsymbol{p}_\Sigma$. The correct limit of the pseudoscalar coupling is in fact proportional to $\boldsymbol{\sigma} \cdot \boldsymbol{p}_\pi$, as may be seen from (3-4.14).

6-5. Threshold branchpoints

In potential theory, $\tan \delta_L / q^{2L+1}$ is an analytic function of s, regular at threshold, $s_0 \equiv (m_a + m_b)^2$. This follows from (2-6.2) and the fact that the logarithmic derivative g_L of the radial wave function is regular at $q = 0$. The corresponding T_L (2-6.5) has a square root branch point at s_0. We assume that only S-waves contribute for $q \to 0$,

$$T = \frac{A}{1 - \mathrm{i}qA} = \frac{A(1 + \mathrm{i}qA)}{1 + q^2 A^2}. \tag{5.1}$$

The denominator of the second form is regular at $s = s_0$. The numerator has a branch point at $q = 0$, which follows from the definitions $q = (\lambda/4s)^{\frac{1}{2}}$,

$$\lambda = [s - (m_a + m_b)^2][s - (m_a - m_b)^2] \equiv (s - s_0)(s - \bar{s}_0). \tag{5.2}$$

The question therefore arises whether for $\lambda < 0$, we should take $q = \mathrm{i}(-\lambda/4s)^{\frac{1}{2}}$ or $q = -\mathrm{i}(-\lambda/4s)^{\frac{1}{2}}$ in the analytic continuation of T. This question is easily decided if we remember that possible bound states must appear as poles in the analytic continuation of T. In the scattering length approximation, a pole occurs at $1 - \mathrm{i}qA = 0$. For bound states we have

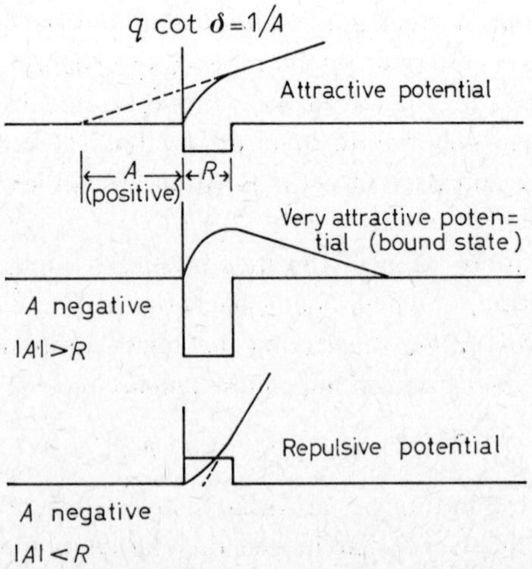

Fig. 6-5.1. Illustration of the scattering length in potential theory (after TRIPP [1965, 1966]).

$-A > R$ (see fig. 6-5.1). Therefore,

$$q = \mathrm{i}(-\lambda/4s)^{\frac{1}{2}} \text{ for } \lambda < 0 \tag{5.3}$$

must be used in (1).

It is convenient to make the function T single-valued in the complex s-plane by introducing two cuts along the real s-axis, one from $-\infty$ to $\bar{s}_0$ and the other from s_0 to ∞ (see fig. 6-5.2). For arbitrary complex s, we may write

$$\frac{\lambda}{4s} = r\mathrm{e}^{\mathrm{i}\phi}, \qquad q = r^{\frac{1}{2}}\mathrm{e}^{\frac{1}{2}\mathrm{i}\phi}, \qquad 0 \leqq \phi < 2\pi, \tag{5.4}$$

where r is the absolute value of $\lambda/4s$. The points (3) correspond to real negative λ, i.e. $\phi = \pi$. In the physical region $s > s_0$, we get q positive for $\phi \to 0$ and negative for $\phi \to 2\pi$. This shows, that the physical scattering amplitude $T(s > s_0)$ is located at the upper edge of the cut, $\lim_{\varepsilon \to 0} (s + \mathrm{i}\varepsilon)$.

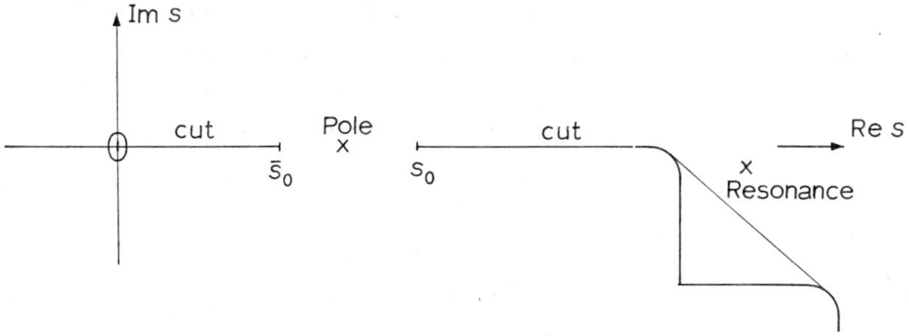

Fig. 6-5.2. The two cuts of $q = (\lambda/4s)^{\frac{1}{2}}$, $\lambda = (s-s_0)(s-\bar{s}_0)$.

The Riemann sheet defined by the cut $s_0 < s \leqq \infty$ is called the "physical sheet". This name is somewhat misleading, since the most important singularities of the scattering amplitude, namely the resonances, are on the second sheet, at distance $m\Gamma$ below the real s-axis. To illustrate this, we have in fig. 6-5.2 lifted the right corner of the lower half plane, thereby getting a glimpse of that part of the second sheet which is close to the physical region.

For $\lambda < 0$, the matrix element (1) is real. This suggests that the discontinuity of T across the cut is related to Im T. In fact, for any analytic function $T(z)$, we may put

$$T(z) = h(z) + g(z), \qquad h^*(z) = h(z^*), \qquad g^*(z) = -g(z^*), \tag{5.5}$$

where h and g are analytic, too.

If T is real on a part of the real axis $z = x$, then $T^*(x) = T(x)$ implies

$g(x) = 0$ and therefore $g(z) = 0$ everywhere. As a result, we get

$$T^*(z) = T(z^*), \quad \Delta T \equiv T(s+\mathrm{i}\varepsilon)-T(s-\mathrm{i}\varepsilon) = 2\mathrm{i}\,\mathrm{Im}\,T(s+\mathrm{i}\varepsilon). \tag{5.6}$$

Next, we study the behaviour of T at the thresholds s_f, $f = 1, 2, 3, \ldots$ for various inelastic processes. The elastic amplitude T_{ii} as well as those inelastic $T_{ii'}$ which refer to processes already open below a given s_n must be singular at s_n. This follows from the unitarity equation (2-4.1), which for $s < s_n$ reads

$$-\mathrm{i}(T_{ii'} - T^*_{i'i}) = \sum_{f=0}^{n-1} \int \mathrm{d}\,\mathrm{Lips}(s;f) T_{if} T^*_{i'f}. \tag{5.7}$$

If the integrand were regular at $s = s_n$, then the analytic continuation of $T_{ii'}$ and $T^*_{i'i}$ from $s < s_n$ to $s > s_n$ would also satisfy (7). Since (7) is not true for $s > s_n$, s_n is a singular point. For the production amplitudes, the singularity appears also in the various effective mass variables, and the situation may be quite complicated. For two-particle amplitudes, a new cut in s begins at each threshold. Therefore, already for two-particle scattering, the complete analytic structure extends over infinitely many sheets.

For two-particle amplitudes $T_{ii'}$, (6) may be extended as follows:

$$\begin{aligned} T^*_{ii'}(z) &= T_{i'i}(z^*), \\ \Delta T_{ii'} &\equiv T_{ii'}(s+\mathrm{i}\varepsilon) - T_{i'i}(s-\mathrm{i}\varepsilon) \\ &= T_{ii'}(s+\mathrm{i}\varepsilon) - T^*_{i'i}(s+\mathrm{i}\varepsilon) \end{aligned} \tag{5.8}$$

in matrix form $T^+(z) = T(z^*)$, $\Delta T = T - T^+$.

This is called Hermitean analyticity. In multichannel potential scattering, it follows from the fact that the Hamiltonian is a Hermitean matrix in the space of channels. In the S-matrix framework, the derivation of Hermitean analyticity is relatively complicated (EDEN, LANDSHOFF, OLIVE and POLKINGHORNE [1966], section 4-6). Essentially one needs a physical unitarity condition, in which $T_{ii'}$ enters for $s < s_i$ or $s < s_{i'}$. This is possible in four-particle unitarity. The connected part of the 4-particle scattering amplitude

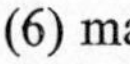

contains a double pole

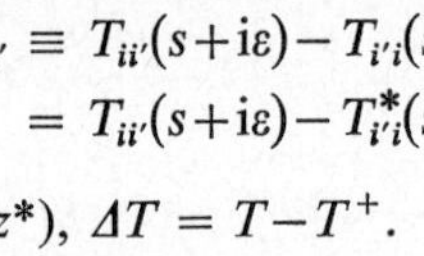

which corresponds to triple scattering. For the second scattering, $s_{d3} = s_{6e}$

may be below threshold without leaving the physical region of the over-all process $1234 \to 5678$. By analytic continuation of $T(1234 \to 5678)$ and by using the 4-particle unitarity, one finds that the combination

(5.9)

does not contain the double pole. Splitting off the external matrix elements, one is left with

(5.10)

The reversal of the two arrows implies $s+\mathrm{i}\varepsilon \to s-\mathrm{i}\varepsilon$, and the substitution $\oplus \to \ominus$ implies $T \to T^+$. The result is therefore exactly (8).

A much simpler derivation of Hermitean analyticity is possible if we allow ourselves to extend the unitarity condition (7) below the thresholds of the "external" states i and i'. Then we may write the unitarity condition in matrix form,

$$-\mathrm{i}(T-T^+) = \int T \,\mathrm{d}\,\mathrm{Lips}(s) T^+, \tag{5.11}$$

where d Lips (s) is a diagonal matrix of the form

$$(\mathrm{d}\,\mathrm{Lips}(s))_{ff'} = \mathrm{d}\,\mathrm{Lips}(s;f)\delta_{ff'}. \tag{5.12}$$

Here we understand as usual

$$\mathrm{d}\,\mathrm{Lips}(s;f) = 0 \qquad \text{for} \quad s < s_f. \tag{5.13}$$

For $s < s_0$, all intermediate channels f are closed, and we get $-\mathrm{i}(T-T^+) = 0$, i.e. T is a Hermitean matrix below the lowest threshold. For the diagonal elements, the real analyticity (6) follows again. For time-reversal invariant interactions, the partial-wave T-matrix is symmetric, in which case the whole matrix T is in fact real below threshold.

From (11), the existence of bound state poles follows, too. At $s = m^2$, we insert d Lips $(s; P) = 2\pi\delta(P^2-m^2)$. The rest of the argument is quite analogous to the derivation of the double-scattering pole (2.12). The matrix elements

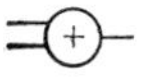 and 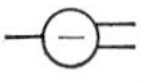

on the r.h.s. of (11) at $s = m^2$ are the coupling constants.

Unfortunately, extended unitarity is not a general principle. In the presence of anomalous thresholds (see the next section), extended unitarity is not true. In that case, the conclusions of this section will be modified.

Before we leave this section, we mention one application of extended unitarity which is needed in the theory of low-energy πN scattering. By crossing symmetry, the amplitude $T(\pi\bar{\pi} \to N\bar{N})$ enters, for values of $s_{\pi\bar{\pi}}$ much below the N$\bar{\text{N}}$ threshold. As a first approximation, only the elastic $\pi\bar{\pi}$ intermediate state is included in the extended unitarity (11). Assuming time-reversal invariance for the matrix element between the only open (o) and all the closed (c) channels, the partial wave version (2-4.8) of (11) is

$$\operatorname{Im} T_{oc} = q_o T_{oo} T_{oc}^* . \tag{5.14}$$

Since Im T_{oc} is a real function, the r.h.s. must be real, too, which is only possible if T_{oo} and T_{oc} have identical phases. Therefore, in a time-reversal invariant theory, extended unitarity requires the phases of all closed channels to be identical with that of the open channel.

6-6. Triangle singularity and anomalous thresholds

The singularities of the S-matrix may be calculated from the rules of LANDAU [1959] and CUTKOSKY [1960]. These rules were found in the perturbation treatment of local field theory, but it appears that they are more general. In fact, it has been shown recently that the physical-region singularities obtained from the Landau-Cutkosky rules correspond to interactions of the particles over macroscopic space-time intervals (COLEMAN and NORTON [1965], PHAM [1966], IAGOLNITZER [1967]). The remaining singularities follow from crossing.

The properties needed in the derivation of the Landau-Cutkosky rules are the "cluster decomposition" of the S-matrix analogous to (1.3), and the unitarity equation for multiparticle systems. We shall not derive these rules for the general case. Instead, we discuss the normal threshold and the triangle singularity. The single-particle pole need not be discussed any more. There, the fact that two successive interactions of a particle occur at large spatial separation led to the factorization (1.5) of T_d.

Consider now, from this point of view, a two-particle threshold s_0. We have two free particles of 4-momenta P_1 and P_2, which are both at the origin $\boldsymbol{x} = 0$ of a coordinate system. What is the classical condition that they remain together? After a time interval t, the first particle is at (τ = proper time)

$$\boldsymbol{x}_1 = \boldsymbol{v}_1 t = (\boldsymbol{p}_1/m_1)\tau_1 = \alpha_1 \boldsymbol{p}_1, \qquad \alpha \equiv (\tau/m), \tag{6.1}$$

and the second particle is at $\boldsymbol{x}_2 = \alpha_2 \boldsymbol{p}_2$. Requiring $\boldsymbol{x}_1 = \boldsymbol{x}_2$ for all times, we get $\alpha_1 \boldsymbol{p}_1 = \alpha_2 \boldsymbol{p}_2$, $\tau_1 = \tau_2$. These equations can be summarized in the 4-component equation

$$\alpha_1 P_1 = \alpha_2 P_2, \qquad \alpha_1, \alpha_2 > 0, \tag{6.2}$$

which says that the 4-vectors P_1 and P_2 must be parallel, $P_1 \cdot P_2 = = (P_1^2)^{\frac{1}{2}}(P_2^2)^{\frac{1}{2}} = m_1 m_2$. Therefore the location of the singularity in $s = (P_1+P_2)^2$ is $s_0 = (m_1+m_2)^2$. The point $\bar{s}_0 = (m_1-m_2)^2$ is not a singular point, since $P_1 \cdot P_2 = -m_1 m_2$ would require one of the α_i to be negative, in contradiction with (2). However, the analytic continuation of $T(s, t)$ on the second Riemann sheet will be singular at $\bar{s}_0$.

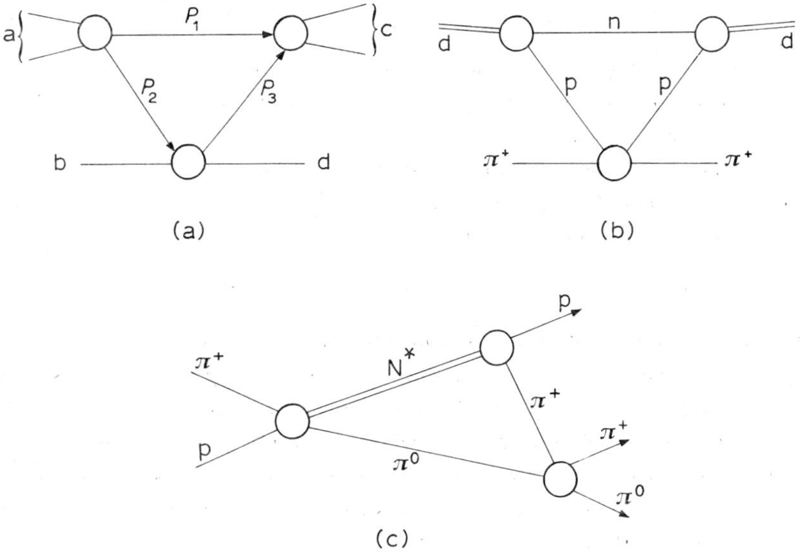

Fig. 6-6.1. Graphs containing the triangle singularity. In (c), the N* is treated as an unstable particle.

The triangle singularity arises from the possibility of rescattering after double scattering, illustrated by the graph (a) of fig. 6-6.1. Again, we require that the three interactions have a macroscopic separation. Processes of this type might be observed in billiards, but not in a bubble chamber. However, if such a process causes a singularity, the singularity persists in the analytic continuation of P_a^2 and P_c^2 below threshold, where bound states may exist at $P_a^2 = m_a^2$, $P_c^2 = m_c^2$. We then expect the same type of singularity also in reactions like elastic πd scattering (fig. 6-6.1b), where it will be outside the physical region, but still very close to it. A similar process may occur in resonance production, when one of the resonance decay products collides with another particle of the final state (fig. 6-6.1c).

First, it should be noted that the three "internal momenta" P_1, P_2, P_3 are not fixed by the values of the external momenta. Therefore, unless one of the internal particles actually produces a short ionization track, the matrix-element of the overall process is the coherent sum over all possible processes leading to the same final state,

$$T_3(\mathrm{ab} \to \mathrm{cd}) = \int \frac{\mathrm{d}^4 P_1}{(2\pi)^4} \frac{T(\mathrm{a} \to 12)}{m_1^2 - P_1^2 - \mathrm{i}\varepsilon} \frac{T(2\mathrm{b} \to 3\mathrm{d})}{m_2^2 - P_2^2 - \mathrm{i}\varepsilon} \frac{T(13 \to \mathrm{c})}{m_3^2 - P_3^2 - \mathrm{i}\varepsilon}, \tag{6.3}$$

$$P_2 = P_a - P_1, \qquad P_3 = P_b + P_2 - P_d = P_c - P_1. \tag{6.4}$$

Similarly, one must sum coherently over the possible charges of the re-scattered particle (p and n in fig. 6-6.1b, π^+ and π^0 in fig. 6-6.1c), and over a possible magnetic quantum number.

The index "3" on T_3 indicates that part of T which has three poles coupled as in (3). As usual, there is also a remainder, $T = T_3 + T'$. The new singularity of T_3 comes from the point

$$P_i^2 = m_i^2, \qquad i = 1, 2, 3; \qquad \alpha_1 P_1 = \alpha_2 P_2 + \alpha_3 P_3, \qquad \alpha_i > 0. \tag{6.5}$$

This may of course be verified from the integral (3), but here we want to derive it instead from the kinematics of the macroscopic process, following the method of Coleman and Norton. Then the requirement $P_i^2 = m_i^2$ is trivial. The linear relation (5) between the P_i follows from the requirement that particles 1 and 3 arrive at the same space-point $\boldsymbol{x}_1$ at the same time t_1. Let the emission of particles 1 and 2 occur at $\boldsymbol{x} = t = 0$. Then, after proper times τ_1 and τ_2, these particles will be at

$$(t_1, \boldsymbol{x}_1) = \frac{\tau_1}{m_1} P_1, \qquad (t_2, \boldsymbol{x}_2) = \frac{\tau_2}{m_2} P_2. \tag{6.6}$$

At the point $(t_2, \boldsymbol{x}_2)$, particle 3 is emitted. The condition that it hits the first particle at some later time t_1 is

$$\frac{\tau_2}{m_2} P_2 + \frac{\tau_3}{m_3} P_3 = \frac{\tau_1}{m_1} P_1, \tag{6.7}$$

which is the same as (5), with $\alpha_i = \tau_i / m_i$.

The existence of T_3 is also made plausible by "solving" the three-particle unitarity (2.8) by iteration. The method is to replace the ⊖ bubbles on the r.h.s. of the unitarity equation by expressions for them in terms of the unitarity equations themselves,

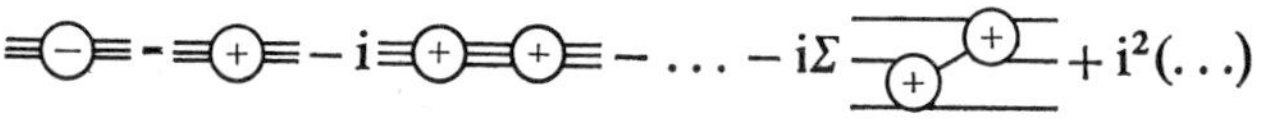

(6.8)

Inserting this into ⊖ on the r.h.s. of (2.8), we get

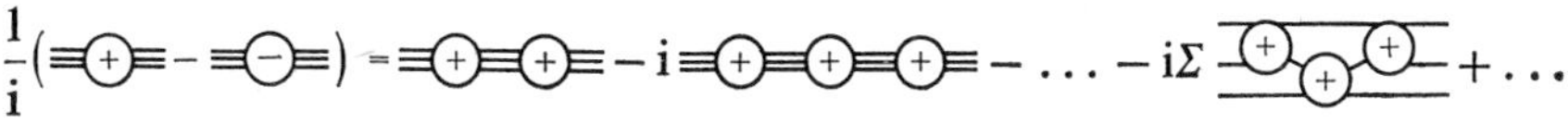

(6.9)

The last term in (9) is contained in the insertion of the last term of (8) into the last term of (2.8). The full sum in the first iteration contains many more combinations. The question is of course whether the unitarity equation can be solved by iteration.

Let us now localize the triangle singularity in the external variables

$$P_a^2 = m_a^2, \qquad P_c^2 = m_c^2, \qquad (P_b - P_d)^2 = t. \tag{6.10}$$

The condition (5) $\alpha_1 P_1 = \alpha_2 P_2 + \alpha_3 P_3$ says that the 4-momenta P_1, P_2 and P_3 are coplanar. By the conservation laws (4), the external momenta lie also in this plane. These relations are summarized in fig. 6-6.2a, which is

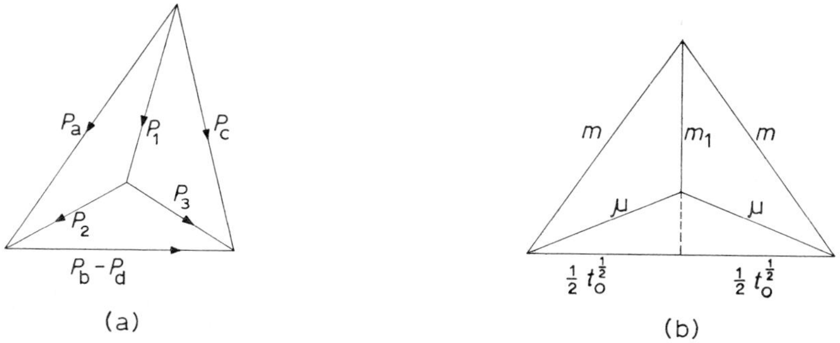

Fig. 6-6.2. The dual diagram of fig. 6-6.1. The triangle singularity occurs when the 4-component vectors P_1, P_2, P_3 form a 2-dimensional plane; (a) general case, (b) $m_a = m_c$, $m_2 = m_3$.

called the "dual diagram" of fig. 6-6.1a. This diagram reproduces (4). Therefore, it is correct not only in the three-dimensional space of p_x, p_y

and p_z, but also in the four-dimensional P_μ-space, where the length of each 4-vector is given by its mass. The singular point t_0 is determined by the requirement that the area of the whole triangle equals the sum of the areas of the three triangles contained in it. In view of the geometrical interpretation of the triangle function λ mentioned below (1-2.11), this requirement is

$$\tfrac{1}{4}\sqrt{-\lambda(t_0, m_a^2, m_c^2)} = \tfrac{1}{4}\sqrt{-\lambda(t_0, m_2^2, m_3^2)} + \tfrac{1}{4}\sqrt{-\lambda(m_a^2, m_1^2, m_2^2)} + \tfrac{1}{4}\sqrt{-\lambda(m_c^2, m_1^2, m_3^2)}. \quad (6.11)$$

Here we have assumed that the common point of the lines P_1, P_2, P_3 lies inside the triangle. If it lies outside, at least one of the α_i is negative, and no singularity arises on the physical sheet. However, it is not necessary that the triangles really exist. The eqs. (5) may be solved by algebraic methods, and (11) is true in general. In the following, we only consider the special case

$$m_a = m_c = m, \qquad m_2 = m_3 = \mu. \quad (6.12)$$

Then $P_1 \cdot P_2 > 0$ ensures $\alpha_i > 0$. By (4), we have quite generally $2P_1 \cdot P_2 = m_a^2 - m_1^2 - m_2^2$ and similar equations for $P_1 \cdot P_2$ and $P_2 \cdot P_3$. For (12), the condition $\alpha_i > 0$ therefore reduces to

$$m^2 - m_1^2 - \mu^2 > 0. \quad (6.13)$$

The area of the triangle with sides m, m_1 and μ is $\frac{1}{4}m_1 t_0^{\frac{1}{2}}$ (see fig. 6-6.2b), which determines t_0 as

$$t_0 = \frac{-1}{m_1^2}\lambda(m^2, m_1^2, \mu^2) = 4\mu^2 - \frac{1}{m_1^2}(m^2 - m_1^2 - \mu^2)^2. \quad (6.14)$$

It may be shown that t_0 is a branchpoint, similar to the normal branchpoint. In the crossed channel $\mathrm{b\bar{d}} \to \mathrm{\bar{a}c}$, $t^{\frac{1}{2}}$ is the cms energy. There, t_0 produces an "anomalous threshold". When $4\mu^2$ is the lowest normal threshold of that reaction, then the scattering amplitude has a cut even below $4\mu^2$, down to t_0. An example of such a reaction is $\pi^+\pi^- \to \Sigma^+\bar{\Sigma}^-$, with

$$\mu = m_\pi, \qquad m = m_\Sigma, \qquad m_1 = m_\Lambda. \quad (6.15)$$

In such cases, extended unitarity is not valid even immediately below threshold.

6-7. Crossed cuts and poles

In addition to the elastic cut $s > (m_a + m_b)^2$ and a possible pole, the amplitude $T(\mathrm{ab} \to \mathrm{cd})$ contains cuts and poles from the crossed reactions

$a\bar{c} \to \bar{b}d$ and $\bar{c}b \to \bar{a}d$. It is convenient to introduce the following "channel" names:

$$\begin{aligned} &s\text{-channel:} \quad ab \to cd, && \text{example:} \quad \pi^+ p \to \pi^+ p, \\ &t\text{-channel:} \quad a\bar{c} \to \bar{b}d, && \text{example:} \quad \pi^+\pi^- \to \bar{p}p, \\ &u\text{-channel:} \quad \bar{c}b \to \bar{a}d, && \text{example:} \quad \pi^- p \to \pi^- p. \end{aligned} \tag{7.1}$$

According to the definitions (1-3.2) to (1-3.4) of the Mandelstam variables and the crossing prescription $P_{\bar{a}} = -P_a$ etc., the same analytic function $T(s, t, u)$ describes all three reactions if we identify $t^{\frac{1}{2}}$ and $u^{\frac{1}{2}}$ with the cms energies in the t and u channels, respectively. In fig. 6-7.1, the variables s, t and u are plotted in a symmetrical fashion, using the relation $s+t+u = \Sigma m^2$.

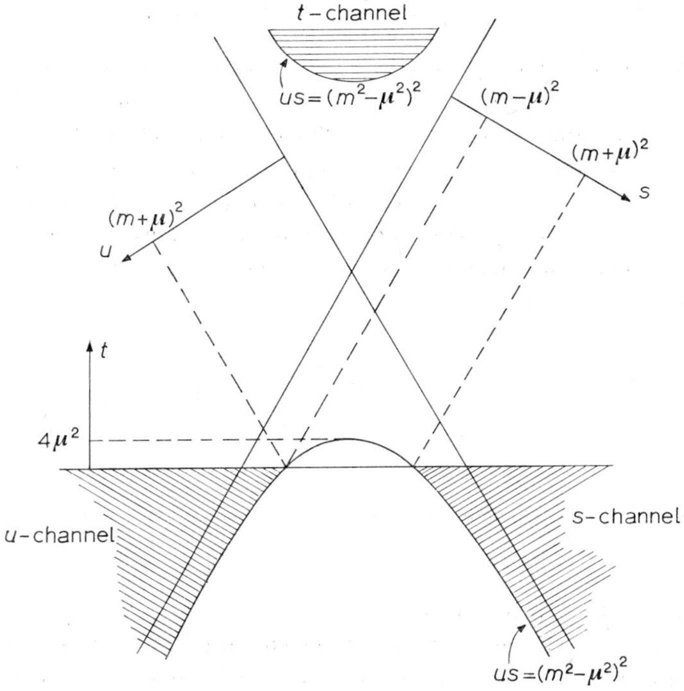

Fig. 6-7.1. The physical regions of the s, t and u channels, for $m_b = m_d = 4m_a = 4m_c$ (after TRUEMAN and WICK [1964]).

The shaded areas denote the physical regions of the three processes (1). In principle, there are 12 different reactions, namely the three time-reversed reactions of (1), cd → ab etc., and the six TCP-conjugate reactions. For example, by crossing b and d from ab → cd, one obtains $a\bar{d} \to \bar{b}c$, which is the TCP conjugate of the u-channel. Such reactions will not be considered explicitly.

The physical regions are limited by the thresholds in the initial and final states and by $\cos\theta = \pm 1$. These limits are summarized by putting $sq^2q'^2 \sin^2\theta = 0$. Thus the limits for all three channels are given by the zeros of (1-4.11). For $m_a = m_c = \mu$, $m_b = m_d = m$, the solutions are

$$t = 0 \quad \text{and} \quad us = (m^2 - \mu^2)^2. \tag{7.2}$$

Consider now the cuts of $T(s, t, u)$ in s, for fixed t. In addition to the cut $s > (m+\mu)^2$, we also have (in the equal-mass case) the cut $u > (m+\mu)^2$ from the u-channel. This latter cut may be written as

$$s+t-2m^2-2\mu^2 = -u < -(m+\mu)^2 \quad \text{or} \quad s < (m-\mu)^2 - t. \tag{7.3}$$

The physical u-channel amplitude is located at the *lower* edge of this cut, since $\lim_{\varepsilon\to 0}(u+i\varepsilon)$ implies $\lim_{\varepsilon\to 0}(s-i\varepsilon)$ for real t, according to (3). The path of analytic continuation from the s-channel amplitude to the u-channel amplitude therefore passes from the upper half plane to the lower half plane (fig. 6-7.2). For $-t > 2m\mu$, the two cuts overlap, and a continuation at fixed t is no longer possible. One may of course always continue in the upper half plane, in which case one arrives at $T^*(\bar{a}d \to \bar{c}b)$, by Hermitean analyticity.

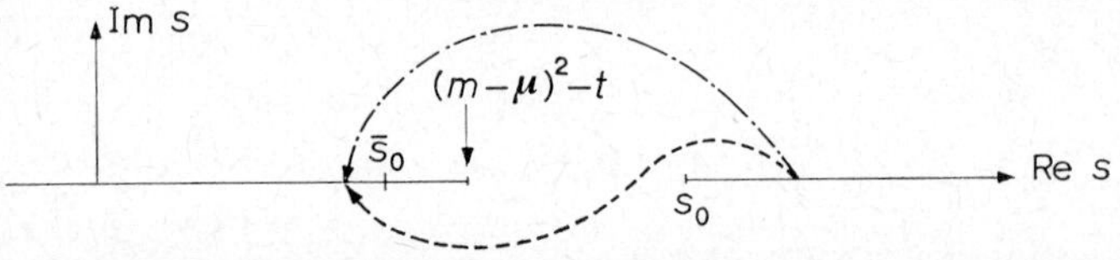

Fig. 6-7.2. The analytic continuation of $T(s, t)$ from the s-channel to the u-channel (– – –), and to $T^*(s, t)$ for the time-reversed u-channel (—·—·—·).

So far we have really considered the scattering of spinless particles. In meson-nucleon scattering, additional "kinematical" singularities arise from the factors $(E \pm m)^{-\frac{1}{2}}$ in the spinors $\bar{u}$ and u. To avoid these factors, one considers the scalar amplitudes $A(s, t)$ and $B(s, t)$ of (3-9.14). Here, some care with the sign of B is necessary. Let a and c denote the spinless mesons and b and d the baryons. Also, let us define the matrix Q in the same form

$$Q_\pm(s, t) = A_\pm(s, t) + \tfrac{1}{2}(P+P')\gamma B_\pm(s, t) \tag{7.4}$$

for the s-channel (+) and the u-channel (−). Then crossing symmetry reads

$$A_+(s, t) = A_-(u, t), \qquad B_+(s, t) = -B_-(u, t). \tag{7.5}$$

The minus sign in the second relation comes from the reversal of the meson momenta P and P' under crossing. Note the difference to the treatment of the t-channel, 4-6.7. There we did not fix a priori the form of $T(\bar{p}p \to \pi^-\pi^+)$, but we deduced this form from crossing. Here, it is advantageous to take the same from for π^+p and π^-p scattering, to retain the formulation of the isospin symmetry.

In the antimeson-baryon scattering (u-channel), baryon poles occur, e.g. the Λ pole in $K^-p \to \pi^-\Sigma^+$ scattering. The corresponding Born terms are given in (4.11). By (5), this produces the crossed Born terms (fig. 6-4.3) in the s-channel $\pi^+p \to K^+\Sigma^+$, A_+^{Born} and B_+^{Born}, with s replaced by u, and a minus sign in front of B_+:

$$\begin{aligned} A_+^{\text{Born}} &= G_{\Lambda\pi\Sigma}G_{\Lambda Kp}\left(\frac{m_p+m_\Sigma}{2}-m_\Lambda\right)\frac{1}{m_\Lambda^2-u}, \\ B_+^{\text{Born}} &= -G_{\Lambda\pi\Sigma}G_{\Lambda Kp}\frac{1}{m_\Lambda^2-u}. \end{aligned} \tag{7.6}$$

6-8. Dispersion relations

The starting point of dispersion relations is the Cauchy integral formula,

$$T(z) = \frac{1}{2\pi i}\oint \frac{dz'}{z'-z}\,T(z'), \tag{8.1}$$

where the integration extends anticlockwise over a closed contour, the point z lies inside this contour and $T(z')$ is regular inside and on the contour. The contour may be expanded until it winds around the singularities of T. Thereby poles are encircled clockwise, giving a contribution $-2\pi i R/(m^2-z)$, where m^2 in the location of the pole and R its residue. Consider now the elastic scattering amplitude $T(z, t)$, $z = \text{Re } s + i \text{ Im } s$, for fixed t. If T has only two cuts and a pole on the real axis $z = s$ (see fig. 6-8), the integration contour can be expanded infinitely, giving

$$T(z) = \frac{-R}{m^2-z} + \frac{1}{2\pi i}\left(\int_{-\infty}^{\bar{s}_0} + \int_{s_0}^{\infty}\right)\frac{ds'}{s'-z}\,\Delta T(s') + \frac{1}{2\pi i}\int_C \frac{dz'}{z'-z}\,T(z'), \tag{8.2}$$

where ΔT is the discontinuity of T across the cut, and C in the last integral denotes the circle at infinity. Suppose now that $|(T(z')|$ decreases as $|z'|^{-\alpha}$, $\alpha > 0$, for $|z'| \to 0$ (this requirement will be relaxed below). Then the contribution of the circle tends to zero for $|z'| \to \infty$. In the remaining two integrals, ΔT may be replaced by 2i Im T, if the theory is time-reversal invariant:

$$T(z) = -\frac{R}{m^2-z} + \frac{1}{\pi}\left(\int_{-\infty}^{\bar{s}_0} + \int_{s_0}^{\infty}\right)\frac{ds'}{s'-z}\,\mathrm{Im}\,T(s'). \tag{8.3}$$

Now we put $z = s+i\varepsilon$, in which case $T(s+i\varepsilon)$ on the l.h.s. of (3) is the physical scattering amplitude, if $s > s_0$. In that case, the integrand must be handled carefully at $s' = s$. In the limit $\varepsilon \to 0$, we have

$$\frac{1}{s'-s-i\varepsilon} = \frac{s'-s+i\varepsilon}{(s'-s)^2+\varepsilon^2} = \mathrm{P}\,\frac{1}{s'-s} + i\pi\delta(s'-s). \tag{8.4}$$

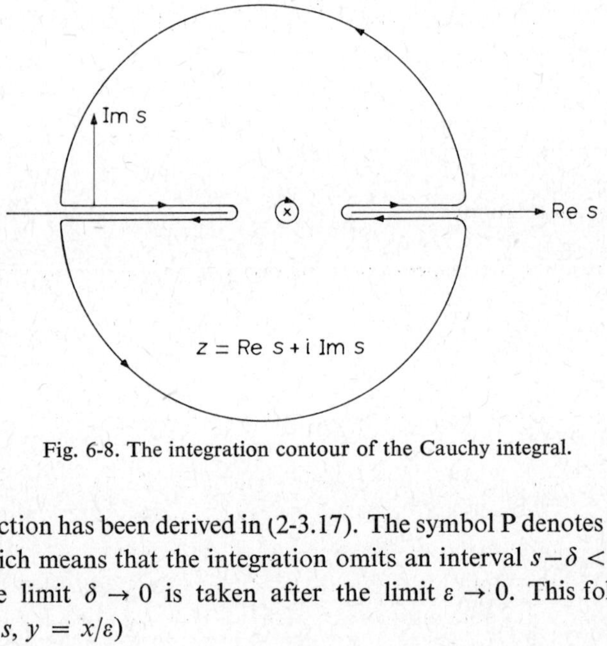

Fig. 6-8. The integration contour of the Cauchy integral.

The δ-function has been derived in (2-3.17). The symbol P denotes a principle value, which means that the integration omits an interval $s-\delta < s' < s+\delta$, where the limit $\delta \to 0$ is taken after the limit $\varepsilon \to 0$. This follows from ($x = s'-s$, $y = x/\varepsilon$)

$$\int_a^b dx\,\frac{xf(x+s)}{x^2+\varepsilon^2} = \left(\int_a^{-\delta} + \int_\delta^b\right)\frac{dx}{x}f(x+s) + \int_{-\delta/\varepsilon}^{\delta/\varepsilon}\frac{y\,dy}{1+y^2}f(\varepsilon y+s). \tag{8.5}$$

Inserting (4) into (3), we see that the imaginary part of this equation is an identity. The real part is the desired dispersion relation

$$\mathrm{Re}\,T(s) = -\frac{R}{m^2-s} + \frac{1}{\pi}\mathrm{P}\left(\int_{-\infty}^{\bar{s}_0} + \int_{s_0}^{\infty}\right)\frac{ds'}{s'-s}\,\mathrm{Im}\,T(s'). \tag{8.6}$$

In general, $|T(s')|$ will not decrease for $|s'| \to \infty$. If $T(s')$ is polynomial-bounded, i.e. if

$$|T(z' \to \infty)| \leqq \text{const.}\, |z'|^{n-\alpha}, \qquad 0 < \alpha < 1, \qquad n = 1, 2, 3, \ldots, \tag{8.7}$$

then a dispersion relation with n "subtractions" is possible. For a finite contour, we subtract from (1) the Cauchy integral for $T(z_1)$, at a fixed point z_1:

$$T(z) - T(z_1) = \frac{1}{2\pi i} \oint dz'\, T(z') \left(\frac{1}{z'-z} - \frac{1}{z'-z_1} \right) = \frac{z+z_1}{2\pi i} \oint \frac{dz'\, T(z')}{(z'-z)(z'-z_1)}. \tag{8.8}$$

The new integral converges better by one power of z'. Therefore, for $n = 1$, it will give no contribution to the circle at infinity. For $n = 2$, a second subtraction leads to

$$\begin{aligned} T(z) - T(z_1) - \frac{z-z_1}{z-z_2} (T(z) - T(z_2)) \\ = \frac{z-z_1}{2\pi i} \oint \frac{dz'\, T(z')}{z'-z} \left(\frac{1}{z'-z_1} - \frac{1}{z'-z_2} \right), \end{aligned} \tag{8.9}$$

and so on. For $z = z_1$, (8) vanishes. This shows that each subtraction introduces one unknown constant in the dispersion relation. Sometimes it is possible to improve the convergence of the integral by means of general principles, without introducing new parameters (see chapter 7).

The requirement that n is finite in (7) must be considered as an extra assumption. Otherwise, dispersion relations would be impossible. Note that (7) is required not only for $z = s = \pm\infty$, but also for $z \to \infty$ in any direction of the complex plane.

$T(z)$ could also have singularities at complex z. However, the singularities deduced from unitarity and crossing all appear at real values of the variables s and t apart from $i\varepsilon$ terms. The postulate that the S-matrix should have no other singularities is called the principle of *maximal analyticity*. (See e.g. JACOB and CHEW [1964], CHEW [1966].) It applies to the physical Riemann sheet only. On the second sheet, resonance poles and other singularities appear at complex z. For a derivation of dispersion relations in quantum field theory, see e.g., MARTIN [1966], and the reviews of GASIOROWICZ [1960, 1966], KÄLLÉN [1964].

To exploit the dispersion relation (6), the discontinuity across the left hand cut is related to the imaginary part of the crossed reaction. Writing

T_+ instead of T in (6), the crossing symmetry

$$T_+(s'+i\varepsilon, t) = T_-(u'-i\varepsilon, t), \qquad u' = \sum m^2 - s' - t, \tag{8.10}$$

implies

$$\int_{-\infty}^{\bar{s}_0} \frac{ds'}{s'-s} \operatorname{Im} T_+(s') \equiv \frac{1}{2i}\int_{-\infty}^{\bar{s}_0} \frac{ds'}{s'-s} [T_+(s'+i\varepsilon) - T_+(s'-i\varepsilon)]$$

$$= \frac{1}{2i}\int_{\bar{s}_0}^{-\infty} \frac{ds'}{s'-s} [T_-(u'+i\varepsilon) - T_-(u'-i\varepsilon)]$$

$$= \int_{\bar{s}_0}^{-\infty} \frac{ds' \operatorname{Im} T_-(u')}{\Sigma m^2 - t - u' - s} = \int_{u_0}^{\infty} \frac{du' \operatorname{Im} T_-(u')}{u'+s+t-\Sigma m^2}. \tag{8.11}$$

Finally, changing the name of the integration variable in (11) from u' to s', we gain the form

$$\operatorname{Re} T_+(s, t) = \frac{-R}{m^2 - s} + \frac{1}{\pi} \mathrm{P}\int_{s_0}^{\infty} ds' \left(\frac{\operatorname{Im} T_+(s', t)}{s'-s} + \frac{\operatorname{Im} T_-(s', t)}{s'+s+t-\Sigma m^2} \right) \tag{8.12}$$

for the dispersion relation (6). At first sight, it seems that (12) involves the amplitudes T_+ and T_- only at physical values of the arguments, provided t is in the physical region. However, for $t \neq 0$ this is not the case. From fig. 6-7.1, we see that the minimum possible value of s is greater than $s_0 = (m+\mu)^2$ for $t \neq 0$. The general expression for s_{min} may be obtained from (1-3.12). Therefore, dispersion relations for $t \neq 0$ require an extrapolation of Im $T(s', t)$ below the physical region.

For elastic forward scattering, Im $T(s, 0)$ may be expressed in terms of the total cross-section (optical theorem), in which case (12) becomes an integral relation between the real part of the forward scattering amplitude and the total cross-section. This relation will be applied in section 7-2.

6-9. Partial wave dispersion relations and Mandelstam representation

In the dispersion relations of the last section, the momentum transfer was kept fixed. This is an unpleasant restriction, since the unitarity relation involves an integration over t. Only at $t = 0$ may unitarity be included, in the form of the optical theorem (2-4.2). To make full use of unitarity, one assumes dispersion relations for the partial wave amplitudes $T_L(s)$ defined by (2-4.10) (in this section, we consider spinless particles only). This is possible in potential theory. The analytic properties of the radial wave function $u_L(r)$ and of $\tan \delta_L/q^{2L+1}$ have been mentioned in sections 6-4 and 6-5. In the relativistic theory, certain complications arise from crossing symmetry. Consider for simplicity elastic scattering, with

$$\cos\theta = x = 1+t/2q^2 \tag{9.1}$$

according to (1-3.11). The partial wave projection $T_L(s)$ is defined by

$$T_L(s) = \frac{1}{16\pi s^{\frac{1}{2}}}\int_{-1}^{1} T(s,t)P_L(x)\mathrm{d}x = \frac{1}{32\pi q^2 s^{\frac{1}{2}}}\int \mathrm{d}t\, T(s,t)P_L\left(1+\frac{t}{2q^2}\right) \tag{9.2}$$

for all (complex) values of s. In pion-nucleon scattering, $T(s, t)$ has the t-channel cut along $t > 4\mu^2$. For negative q^2, the integration in (2) may involve a part of this cut. For imaginary q^2, t will be imaginary, too, if the path of the x-integration is kept along the real axis. The resulting analytic structure will be discussed in section 7-3.

An important conjecture about the analytic structure of $T(s, t)$ as a function of complex s and t has been made by MANDELSTAM [1958]. Apart from possible subtractions, T is assumed to satisfy the double dispersion relation

$$\begin{aligned} T(s,t,u) &= \frac{1}{\pi^2}\iint \frac{\mathrm{d}s'\mathrm{d}t'}{(s'-s)(t'-t)}\rho_{st}(s't') \\ &+ \frac{1}{\pi^2}\iint \frac{\mathrm{d}s'\mathrm{d}u'}{(s'-s)(u'-u)}\rho_{su}(s'u') \\ &+ \frac{1}{\pi^2}\iint \frac{\mathrm{d}u'\mathrm{d}t'}{(u'-u)(t'-t)}\rho_{tu}(t'u') \\ &+ \frac{1}{\pi}\int \frac{\mathrm{d}s'}{s'-s}\rho_s(s') + \frac{1}{\pi}\int \frac{\mathrm{d}u'}{u'-u}\rho_u(u') + \frac{1}{\pi}\int \frac{\mathrm{d}t'}{t'-t}\rho_t(t'). \end{aligned} \tag{9.3}$$

The "single-spectral functions" ρ_s, ρ_u and ρ_t as well as the "double-spectral functions" ρ_{st}, ρ_{su} and ρ_{tu} are real. They are non-zero only in a certain region of positive values of their arguments. The exact limits are found e.g. in the book of CHEW [1962]. The missing variable in the double-spectral functions is defined by $s'+t'+u' = \sum m^2$. Expression (3) is symmetric in all three channels. From it, single dispersion relations at fixed t, s and u may be derived. The discontinuity of T across the real axis is contained in those integrands, the denominator of which vanishes. For $s' > s_0$, the discontinuity is

$$A_s(s, t, u) = \rho_s(s) + \frac{1}{\pi}\int \frac{dt'}{t'-t}\,\rho_{st}(s, t') + \frac{1}{\pi}\int \frac{du'}{u'-u}\,\rho_{su}(s, u'). \tag{9.4}$$

The denominators of the remaining three integrals cannot vanish for $s' > s_0$. A_s is called the absorptive part in the s-channel. Analogous absorptive parts $A_u(s, t, u)$ and $A_t(s, t, u)$ are defined for the u and t channels. With these, three different single dispersion relations for $T(s, t, u)$ are formulated. One of these is

$$T(s, t, u) = \frac{1}{\pi}\int \frac{dt'}{t'-t}\,\rho_t(t') + \frac{1}{\pi}\int \frac{ds'}{s'-s}\,A_s(s', t, \textstyle\sum m^2 - s' - t)$$
$$+ \frac{1}{\pi}\int \frac{du'}{u'-u}\,A_u(\textstyle\sum m^2 - t - u', t, u'), \tag{9.5}$$

where each integration extends from the appropriate (positive) threshold to infinity. Apart from the first integral, (5) has the form of a fixed-t dispersion relation (8.3). The first integral is a constant, independent of s.

Further, partial wave dispersion relations follow from the Mandelstam representation. In the case of anomalous thresholds, the Mandelstam representation must be modified. Despite its great influence on the development of dispersion relations and other theoretical methods, the Mandelstam representation has so far been of little use in practical calculations.

CHAPTER 7

THEORY OF LOW-ENERGY πN SCATTERING

7-1. Isospin in πN-scattering

Below the $\pi\pi$N threshold,

$$s_1^{\frac{1}{2}} = m_{\pi^+} + m_{\pi^0} + m_p = 1213 \text{ MeV}, \tag{1.1}$$

π^+p scattering is purely elastic, whereas π^-p has the elastic and the charge exchange ($\pi^-\text{p} \to \pi^0\text{n}$) channels open. Neglecting Coulomb scattering and the $\pi^\pm - \pi^0$ mass difference for the time being, we can express the amplitudes of these three reactions in terms of the isospin amplitudes $T^{\frac{3}{2}}$ and $T^{\frac{1}{2}}$ by (5-3.1), (5-3.4) and (5-3.5). Denoting for brevity the amplitudes for $\pi^+\text{p} \to \pi^+\text{p}$, $\pi^-\text{p} \to \pi^-\text{p}$ and $\pi^-\text{p} \to \pi^0\text{n}$ by T_+, T_- and T_0, we have

$$T_+ = T^{\frac{3}{2}}, \qquad T_- = \tfrac{1}{3}(T^{\frac{3}{2}} + 2T^{\frac{1}{2}}), \qquad T_0 = \tfrac{1}{3}\sqrt{2}(T^{\frac{3}{2}} - T^{\frac{1}{2}}), \tag{1.2}$$

which are related by

$$2^{\frac{1}{2}} T_0 = T_+ - T_- . \tag{1.3}$$

Both T_- and T_0 contain the neutron pole in the direct channel. The corresponding Born terms are of the general form (6-4.9) to (6-4.11). Neglecting the mass differences, we put

$$m_p = m_n \equiv m, \qquad m_{\pi^+} = m_{\pi^0} \equiv \mu, \tag{1.4}$$

in which case (6-4.11) simplifies to

$$A^{\text{Born}}_{\substack{\pm\\0}} = 0, \qquad B^{\text{Born}}_+ = 0, \qquad B^{\text{Born}}_- = \frac{G^2(\text{n} \to \pi^-\text{p})}{m^2 - s},$$

$$B^{\text{Born}}_0 = \frac{G(\text{n} \to \pi^-\text{p})G(\text{n} \to \pi^0\text{n})}{m^2 - s}. \tag{1.5}$$

Because of their importance for the theory of low-energy $\pi - \text{N}$ scattering, we investigate these terms in some detail. In general, there are four different coupling constants, namely $G(\text{p} \to \pi^0\text{p})$, $G(\text{p} \to \pi^+\text{n})$, $G(\text{n} \to \pi^0\text{n})$ and $G(\text{n} \to \pi^-\text{p})$. By isospin invariance (4-2.9), these four constants are expressed in terms of one constant G which, by definition, is taken equal to

$G(\mathrm{p} \to \pi^0\mathrm{p})$:

$$G \equiv G(\mathrm{p} \to \pi^0\mathrm{p}) = -G(\mathrm{n} \to \pi^0\mathrm{n}), \tag{1.6}$$

$$\sqrt{2}G = G(\mathrm{n} \to \pi^-\mathrm{p}) = -G(\mathrm{p} \to \pi^+\mathrm{n}). \tag{1.7}$$

Thus the NNπ coupling of charged pions is a factor $2^{\frac{1}{2}}$ stronger than that of neutral pions. The coupling constants of the inverse processes $\pi\mathrm{N} \to \mathrm{N}$ are equal to those of $\mathrm{N} \to \pi\mathrm{N}$, e.g. $G(\pi^+\mathrm{n} \to \mathrm{p}) = G(\mathrm{p} \to \pi^+\mathrm{n})$. This conforms with the expression obtained from crossing the π^- in $G(\mathrm{n} \to \pi^-\mathrm{p})$. Due to the negative charge parity (4-7.10) of π^-, we have

$$G(\pi^+\mathrm{n} \to \mathrm{p}) = -G(\mathrm{n} \to \pi^-\mathrm{p}). \tag{1.8}$$

Inserting (7) into (5), we get

$$B_+^{\mathrm{Born}} = 0, \qquad B_-^{\mathrm{Born}} = \frac{2G^2}{m^2 - s}. \tag{1.9}$$

The crossed Born terms are obtained by application of the crossing symmetry (6-7.6) to (9):

$$B_+^{\mathrm{Born}}(\text{crossed}) = -\frac{2G^2}{m^2 - u}, \qquad B_-^{\mathrm{Born}}(\text{crossed}) = 0. \tag{1.10}$$

The direct and crossed Born terms for $I = \frac{3}{2}$ and $I = \frac{1}{2}$ follow from insertion of (9) and (10) into the first two equations of (2):

$$B^{\frac{1}{2}}(\text{Born}) = \frac{3G^2}{m^2 - s} + \frac{G^2}{m^2 - u}, \qquad B^{\frac{3}{2}}(\text{Born}) = -\frac{2G^2}{m^2 - u}. \tag{1.11}$$

Quite generally, the crossing relation $B_+(s, t) = -B_-(u, t)$ may be transformed into a crossing relation between the isospin amplitudes B^I, $I = \frac{1}{2}$ and $\frac{3}{2}$:

$$B^I(u, t) = \sum_{I'} C_{II'} B^{I'}(s, t), \tag{1.12}$$

$$\begin{aligned} C_{\frac{1}{2}\frac{1}{2}} &= \tfrac{1}{3}, & C_{\frac{1}{2}\frac{3}{2}} &= -\tfrac{4}{3}, \\ C_{\frac{3}{2}\frac{1}{2}} &= -\tfrac{2}{3}, & C_{\frac{3}{2}\frac{3}{2}} &= -\tfrac{1}{3}. \end{aligned} \tag{1.13}$$

The coefficients $C_{\frac{1}{2}\frac{1}{2}}$ and $C_{\frac{3}{2}\frac{1}{2}}$ are read off directly from (11). The decisive point here is not the explicit form (9) of B_-^{Born}, but the fact that $B_+^{\mathrm{Born}} = 0$. Similarly, the coefficients $C_{\frac{1}{2}\frac{3}{2}}$ and $C_{\frac{3}{2}\frac{3}{2}}$ follow from the crossing of a matrix element which has a direct pole in the $I = \frac{3}{2}$ state only, e.g. the N_{33} resonance. According to (2), this contributes to B_+ and B_- with relative amplitudes 1 and $\frac{1}{3}$, respectively. By crossing, it then contributes to $B_-(u)$ and

$B_+(u)$ with relative amplitudes -1 and $-\frac{1}{3}$. Relating the crossed amplitudes to $B^{\frac{1}{2}}(u)$ and $B^{\frac{3}{2}}(u)$ again by (2), we gain the crossing coefficients $C_{\frac{1}{2}\frac{3}{2}}$ and $C_{\frac{3}{2}\frac{3}{2}}$ of (13). The matrix C is called the isospin crossing matrix.

7-2. Determination of the coupling constant and S-wave scattering lengths

The coupling constant G and the S-wave scattering lengths of πN scattering are suitably determined from dispersion relations for forward scattering. For this purpose, it is necessary to study the fixed-t dispersion relations in more detail. We introduce the energy

$$\nu = \frac{1}{2m}(s - m^2 - \mu^2 + \tfrac{1}{2}t), \tag{2.1}$$

for which the crossing $s \leftrightarrow u$ means $\nu \to -\nu$. Denoting the scalar amplitudes A and B for $\pi^\pm$p scattering by $A_\pm$ and $B_\pm$, crossing reads

$$A_\pm(\nu, t) = A_\mp(-\nu, t), \qquad B_\pm(\nu, t) = -B_\mp(-\nu, t). \tag{2.2}$$

The dispersion relation (6-8.12) is now applied to A and B,

$$\operatorname{Re} A_\pm(\nu, t) = \frac{1}{\pi} \mathrm{P} \int_{\mu + t/4m}^{\infty} d\nu' \left[\frac{\operatorname{Im} A_\pm(\nu', t)}{\nu' - \nu} + \frac{\operatorname{Im} A_\mp(\nu', t)}{\nu' + \nu} \right], \tag{2.3}$$

$$\operatorname{Re} B_\pm(\nu, t) = \frac{2G^2}{-2m\nu \pm \mu^2 \mp \frac{1}{2}t} + \frac{1}{\pi} \mathrm{P} \int_{\mu + t/4m}^{\infty} d\nu' \left[\frac{\operatorname{Im} B_\pm(\nu', t)}{\nu' - \nu} - \frac{\operatorname{Im} B_\mp(\nu', t)}{\nu' + \nu} \right]. \tag{2.4}$$

The first term in Re $B_\pm$ is the Born term, $2G^2/(m^2 - s)$ for B_- and $-2G^2/(m^2 - u)$ for B_+. Relation (3) actually needs a subtraction, as we shall see later. We now specialize to forward scattering, i.e. $t = 0$. In this case, the integrals extend over physical ν' only. Comparing (1) with (1-2.3), we see that ν is identical with the pion lab energy, for $t = 0$.

Next, we eliminate Im $A_\pm(\nu', 0)$ and Im $B_\pm(\nu', 0)$ by means of the optical theorem (3-8.16). For forward scattering, we have

$$T_\pm(\nu, 0) = \bar{u}(A_\pm + P_a \cdot \gamma B_\pm)u = 2m(A_\pm + \nu B_\pm). \tag{2.5}$$

Magnetic quantum numbers are unnecessary, since the helicity-flip amplitudes are zero for $\theta = 0$, and the non-flip amplitudes are equal by parity conservation. Instead of (3) and (4), we now consider a dispersion relation for (5). In this new dispersion relation, we replace Im $T_\pm$ by $2qs^{\frac{1}{2}}\sigma_\pm$

according to the optical theorem. Remembering moreover $qs^{\frac{1}{2}} = mp^{\text{lab}} = m(\nu^2-\mu^2)^{\frac{1}{2}}$, we obtain

$$\frac{1}{2m}\operatorname{Re} T_{\pm}(\nu) = \frac{2\nu G^2}{-2m\nu \pm \mu^2} + \frac{1}{\pi}\mathrm{P}\int_{\mu}^{\infty} \mathrm{d}\nu'(\nu'^2-\mu^2)^{\frac{1}{2}} \left[\frac{\sigma_{\pm}(\nu')}{\nu'-\nu} + \frac{\sigma_{\mp}(\nu')}{\nu'+\nu}\right]. \tag{2.6}$$

Actually, this dispersion relation needs two subtractions, since experiments indicate that the total $\pi^{\pm}$p cross-sections $\sigma_{\pm}$ tend to constants for $\nu' \to \infty$.

In general, two subtractions for each reaction would introduce quite a number of undetermined parameters. In the present case, we can reduce this number to two, if we make use of isospin invariance and crossing symmetry. For π^+p scattering, we use the S-wave scattering length a_3. The index 3 refers to the isospin $\frac{3}{2}$. From (3-8.3) at $\theta = \phi = 0$ and at threshold, we have

$$T_+(\nu = \mu) = 8\pi(m+\mu)(f_1+f_2) = 8\pi(m+\mu)a_3. \tag{2.7}$$

The identification of a_3 with the S-wave scattering length follows from the expansions (3-9.8) and (3-9.9) and the fact that the scattering length approximation (2-6.5) applies to the $f_{L\pm}$. For our present purpose, we merely need the reality property of a_3 in (7).

The corresponding scattering length of π^-p scattering is complex, due to the π^0n channel which extends below threshold. We imagine that we have already separated the Coulomb effects, including π^-p bound states (π-mesic atoms). Then we may apply isospin invariance (1.2), getting

$$T_-(\nu = \mu) = 8\pi(m+\mu)\cdot\tfrac{1}{3}(2a_1+a_3), \tag{2.8}$$

where a_1 is the scattering length of the $I = \frac{1}{2}$ state. Next, the second subtraction is made at the unphysical point $\nu = -\mu$ which, by crossing symmetry, yields

$$\begin{aligned} T_+(-\mu) &= 8\pi(m-\mu)\cdot\tfrac{1}{3}(2a_1+a_3);\\ T_-(-\mu) &= 8\pi(m-\mu)a_3. \end{aligned} \tag{2.9}$$

The twice-subtracted dispersion relation is

$$\begin{aligned} \operatorname{Re} T_{\pm}(\nu) = {} & \frac{1}{2}\left(1+\frac{\nu}{m}\right) T_{\pm}(\mu) + \frac{1}{2}\left(1-\frac{\nu}{m}\right) T_{\mp}(\mu)\\ & \pm \frac{2G^2(\nu^2-\mu^2)}{2m\nu \mp \mu^2}\,\frac{1}{1-\mu^2/4m^2}\\ & + 2m(\nu^2-\mu^2)\frac{1}{\pi}\mathrm{P}\int_{\mu}^{\infty}\frac{\mathrm{d}\nu'}{(\nu'^2-\mu^2)^{\frac{1}{2}}}\left(\frac{\sigma_{\pm}(\nu')}{\nu'-\nu} + \frac{\sigma_{\mp}(\nu')}{\nu'+\nu}\right). \end{aligned} \tag{2.10}$$

Remember that ν and μ denote the $\pi^{\pm}$ lab energy and mass, respectively. Insertion of the experimental functions $\sigma_{\pm}(\nu)$ and $\mathrm{Re}\,T_{\pm}(\nu)$ gives $G^2/4\pi$ and the scattering lengths a_3 and a_1. A recent analysis by SAMARANAYAKE and WOOLCOCK [1965] gives

$$f^2 = 0.082 \pm 0.002 \quad \text{or} \quad G^2/4\pi = 14.9. \tag{2.11}$$

Of course, $\mathrm{Re}\,T_{\pm}(\nu)$ and $\sigma_{\pm}(\nu)$ must be parametrized by some smooth functions. Also, the integral in (10) requires extrapolation of $\sigma_{\pm}$ to infinite lab energy.

In the actual calculation, the dispersion relation of GOLDBERGER, MIYAZAWA and OEHME [1955],

$$\frac{1}{8\pi m}(\mathrm{Re}\,T_{-}(\nu) - \mathrm{Re}\,T_{+}(\nu)) = \frac{4f^2\nu}{\nu^2 - (\mu^2/2m)^2} + \frac{\nu}{2\pi^2}\,\mathrm{P}\int_{\mu}^{\infty} \frac{\mathrm{d}\nu'\,p^{\mathrm{lab}}(\nu')}{\nu'^2 - \nu^2}[\sigma_{-}(\nu') - \sigma_{+}(\nu')] \tag{2.12}$$

is used instead of (10). It is obtained directly from (6). It exploits the fact that the difference between the total π^-p and π^+p cross-sections becomes small at high energies (see fig. 11-1.1). For the integral (12) to converge, it is necessary that $[\sigma_{-}(\nu') - \sigma_{+}(\nu')]\log(\nu'/\nu)$ tends to zero for $\nu' \to \infty$, and that the derivative of $\sigma_{-} - \sigma_{+}$ remains finite. Samaranayake and Woolcock used $0.85/(p^{\mathrm{lab}})^{\frac{1}{2}}$ for $\sigma_{-} - \sigma_{+}$ in the region $\nu' > 10$ GeV. This is in units of μ. Combination of (12) and (10) then leads to the scattering lengths

$$a_1 - a_3 = 0.29, \qquad a_1 + 2a_3 = -0.035, \tag{2.13}$$

in units of $1/\mu$. For a critical discussion of the errors, see HAMILTON [1966].

7-3. Singularities of the partial wave amplitudes

Our aim is to calculate the complete amplitude $T(\lambda\lambda', stu)$ for elastic πN scattering. This might be accomplished for example by means of the Mandelstam representation, but so far it has not been done. Another possibility is to solve dispersion relations for the partial-wave amplitudes $T_J(\lambda\lambda')$ (3-8.5) or $f_{L\pm}$ (3-9.4), (3-9.10). This latter problem has been solved to some extent (see e.g. HAMILTON [1967]). More explicitly, low-energy πN scattering is accurately described by very few parameters. This is a remarkable success of partial-wave dispersion relations. Of course it does not prove that our general assumptions about maximal analyticity are correct. Instead, it may be a consequence of the low-energy approximations, of the choice of parameters, or of the threshold behaviour of partial wave amplitudes. In any case, the success is encouraging, and essential parts of the calculation must be approximately correct.

In this section, we find the locations of the singularities of partial-wave amplitudes.

We recall the singularities of the amplitude $T(s, t, u)$ for elastic π^+p scattering (MacDowell [1960], Hamilton and Spearman [1961]).

1) A cut for $s > (m+\mu)^2$. This is called the physical cut. Strictly, it consists of several cuts. The first inelastic cut starts at $s_1 = (m+2\mu)^2$. In the following, all such higher cuts are disregarded.
2) A cut for $u > (m+\mu)^2$. This is the cut from the crossed channel, π^-p $\to$ π^-p, shortly called the crossed cut.
3) A cut for $t > 4\mu^2$, which comes from the reaction $\pi^+\pi^- \to$ p$\bar{\text{p}}$. Its lower part is unphysical, since the threshold value for this reaction is $4m^2$.
4) A pole at $u = m^2$, which corresponds to the crossed Born term. If we had chosen π^-p scattering as the direct channel, then this pole would of course appear in the direct channel, and the crossed channel would have no pole.

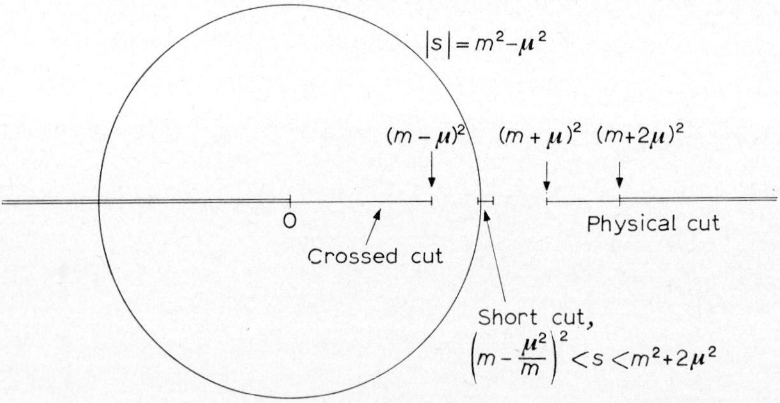

Fig. 7-3. The singularities of partial wave amplitudes $f_{L\pm}$ for πN-scattering.

The corresponding cuts of $f_{l\pm}(s)$ are shown in fig. 7-3. Except for the physical cut, they are not easily recognized. The reason is that f_l is obtained from $T(s, t, u)$ by integrating over x, the cms scattering angle, which is related to t by

$$t = -2q^2(1-x) = -\frac{1}{2s}\lambda(s, m^2, \mu^2)(1-x). \tag{3.1}$$

Therefore any variation in x, with t or u fixed at some singular point, produces a whole range of s-values. A pole in t or u becomes a cut in $f_l(s)$.

The situation is relatively simple for the crossed cut. By virtue of the Mandelstam relation $s+t+u = 2m^2+2\mu^2$, the cut goes along

$$2m^2+2\mu^2-s-t > (m+\mu)^2, \tag{3.2}$$

which, using (1), is transformed into

$$s-2q^2(1-x) < (m-\mu)^2. \tag{3.3}$$

Let us investigate which range of s fulfills the inequality (3), for any x in the interval $-1 < x < 1$. For $x = 1$, the second term in (3) vanishes, and the result is $s < (m-\mu)^2$. This is in fact the whole crossed cut, because any value $x < 1$ gives a shorter cut. In order to show this, we first try to satisfy (3) with some s in the interval $(m-\mu)^2 < s < (m+\mu)^2$. In this interval, q^2 is negative according to (6-5.2), whereas $s > (m-\mu)^2$ could satisfy (3) only for $q^2 > 0$. Next, we try $s > (m+\mu)^2$. Now q^2 is positive, but s is already so large that (3) cannot be satisfied any more, not even for $x = -1$. This follows immediately if we insert for q^2 the expression

$$q^2 = \frac{1}{4s}[s^2-2s(m^2+\mu^2)+(m^2-\mu^2)^2]. \tag{3.4}$$

With $x = -1$, the terms linear in s cancel, and (3) becomes

$$2(m^2+\mu^2)-\frac{1}{s}(m^2-\mu^2)^2 < (m-\mu)^2,$$

which is incompatible with $s > (m+\mu)^2$.

For the third cut, $t > 4\mu^2$, we use a slightly different method. Because of $q^2 = -t/2(1-x)$, $t > 4\mu^2$ requires

$$q^2 < \frac{-4\mu^2}{2(1-x)} < -\mu^2. \tag{3.5}$$

From this equation, the possible values of s are obtained by using

$$s = (\sqrt{m^2+q^2}+\sqrt{\mu^2+q^2})^2 = m^2+\mu^2+2q^2+2\sqrt{(m^2+q^2)(\mu^2+q^2)}. \tag{3.6}$$

Because of the factors of the square root, we treat the intervals $q^2 < -m^2$

and $-m^2 < q^2 < -\mu^2$ separately. Let us begin with the first interval, with $q^2 = -\infty$. Here (6) gives us $s = -\infty$ if we take the root as negative, and $s = 0$ if we take it as positive. As q^2 increases, the two solutions of (6) approach each other, and finally, for $q^2 = -m^2$, they join together in the point $s = \mu^2 - m^2$. In the second interval, the square root is imaginary, so s becomes complex. By writing $s^{\frac{1}{2}} = (m^2+q^2)^{\frac{1}{2}} \pm i(-\mu^2-q^2)^{\frac{1}{2}}$, one finds $|s| = m^2-\mu^2$ independent of q^2, i.e. s describes a circle in the complex plane, with radius $m^2-\mu^2$. The minimum of t, $t = 4\mu^2$, corresponds to the point $s = m^2-\mu^2$.

Finally, we find the singularities generated by the crossed Born term, $u = m^2$. In terms of s and t, $u = m^2$ means

$$s+t = m^2+2\mu^2. \tag{3.7}$$

Here we eliminate t by (1) and (4) and obtain finally the quadratic equation for s,

$$s_\pm(x) = \frac{1}{1+x}\,[m^2x+\mu^2(1+x) \pm \sqrt{(m^2x+\mu^2(1+x))^2+(m^2-\mu^2)^2(1-x^2)}]. \tag{3.8}$$

The limiting values for s occur for $x = \pm 1$,

$$\begin{aligned} s_+(1) &= m^2+2\mu^2, & s_+(-1) &= (m-\mu^2/m)^2, \\ s_-(1) &= 0, & s_-(-1) &= -\infty. \end{aligned} \tag{3.9}$$

Thus the solution $s_+(x)$ gives the short cut in fig. 7-3, whereas $s_-(x)$ gives the distant cut $s < 0$. Note that a straightforward calculation of $s_+(-1)$ gives the value 0/0. Before we derive the definite expression for $s_+(-1)$, we introduce the abbreviation

$$\varepsilon \equiv \mu^2/m^2, \tag{3.10}$$

which we shall also need later. Then we rewrite the square root of (8) as

$$\begin{aligned} \sqrt{\ldots} &= m^2\sqrt{(x+\varepsilon(1+x))^2+(1-\varepsilon)^2(1-x^2)} \\ &= m^2\sqrt{1+2(1+x)\varepsilon(2x-1+\varepsilon)} \\ &\approx m^2[1+(1+x)\varepsilon(2x-1+\varepsilon)], \end{aligned} \tag{3.11}$$

which gives us

$$s_+(x) \approx m^2(1+2x\varepsilon+\varepsilon^2). \tag{3.12}$$

In the limit of $x \to -1$, (11) becomes an equality, and $s_+(-1)$ is given exactly by (12).

7-4. Partial wave dispersion relations of πN scattering

For any regular point in the complex s-plane, we can express $f_L(s)$ by means of Cauchy's formula:

$$f(s) = \frac{1}{2\pi i}\left(\int_{c_1} + \int_{c_2} + \int_{c_3}\right)\frac{f(s')}{s'-s}\,ds'. \tag{4.1}$$

The integration contours are indicated in fig. 7-4. The circle at $|s| = \infty$ is neglected. For s outside the circle $|s| = m^2-\mu^2$, the integral over c_3 gives zero. The reason for including c_3 is the following: The sum of the three integrals over $f(s)$ equals the integrated discontinuity of $f(s)$ across the cuts.

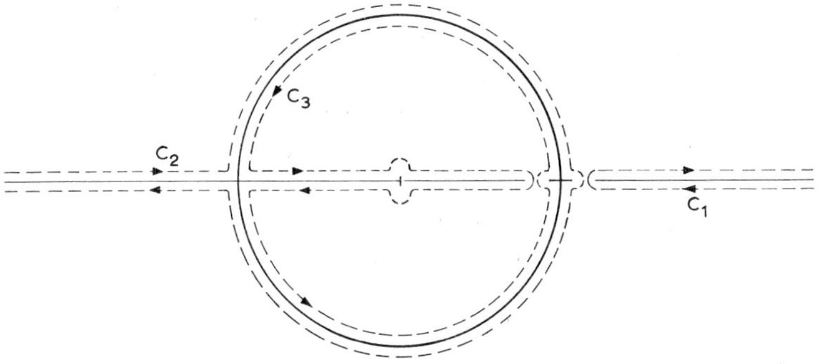

Fig. 7-4. The paths of the three integrals of (1).

For the cuts along the real axis, the discontinuity is of course 2i times the imaginary part of f. The discontinuity across the circle is in general complex. We thus have the dispersion relation

$$\operatorname{Re} f(s) = \frac{1}{\pi}\,\mathrm{P}\left(\int_{(m+\mu)^2}^{\infty} + \int_{(m-\mu^2/m)^2}^{m^2+2\mu^2} + \int_{-\infty}^{(m-\mu)^2}\right) ds' \,\frac{\operatorname{Im} f(s')}{s'-s}$$

$$+ \operatorname{Re}\oint \frac{ds'}{2\pi i}\,\frac{\mathrm{disc.}\, f(s')}{s'-s}. \tag{4.2}$$

In this form, the circular cut is no unsurmountable obstacle. As a zeroth order approximation, we can neglect the discontinuity across the circle. We shall see later that this corresponds to neglecting $\pi\pi$-scattering. The Chew-Low model [1956] for example makes this approximation.

Some important features of low-energy πN scattering can be understood in terms of the nucleon Born terms alone. Spezialization of (3-9.18) to elastic scattering gives

$$\begin{aligned} f_1 &= \frac{1}{8\pi s^{\frac{1}{2}}}(E+m)(A+B(s^{\frac{1}{2}}-m)), \\ f_2 &= \frac{1}{8\pi s^{\frac{1}{2}}}(E-m)(-A+B(s^{\frac{1}{2}}+m)). \end{aligned} \tag{4.3}$$

Since the Born terms (1.11) contribute only to B, the contributions $f_{B,L\pm}$ to the partial wave amplitudes $f_{L\pm}$ are, by (3) and (3-9.10),

$$f^I_{B,L\pm} = \frac{1}{16\pi s^{\frac{1}{2}}}\int_{-1}^{1} \mathrm{d}x[P_L(x)(E+m)(s^{\frac{1}{2}}-m) + P_{L\pm 1}(x)(E-m)(s^{\frac{1}{2}}+m)]B^I(\text{Born}). \tag{4.4}$$

Unfortunately, this formula is rather useless. It predicts large S-wave amplitudes, whereas experimentally low-energy N-scattering occurs mainly in the P-waves. We shall discuss the reason of this failure later. Here we merely show the dominance of S-waves in (4). The direct Born term is proportional to $(m^2-s)^{-1}$ and independent of t, or u, which means independent of x. The only nonvanishing integrals are those containing $P_0(x)$. Therefore, the direct Born term contributes only to f_{0+} and f_{1-}:

$$f^{\frac{1}{2}}_{B,0+} = \frac{1}{16\pi s}[(s^{\frac{1}{2}}+m)^2-\mu^2](s^{\frac{1}{2}}-m)\frac{-3G^2}{s-m^2}, \tag{4.5}$$

$$f^{\frac{1}{2}}_{B,1-} = \frac{1}{16\pi s}[(s^{\frac{1}{2}}-m)^2-\mu^2](s^{\frac{1}{2}}+m)\frac{-3G^2}{s-m^2}. \tag{4.6}$$

The f_{1-} amplitude is smaller because of the angular momentum barrier. Next, we consider the crossed Born term which is proportional to $(u-m^2)^{-1}$. This again gives mainly S-waves. The argument is the same as that following (2-6.8). We write

$$\begin{aligned} u-m^2 &= m^2+2\mu^2-s+2q^2(1-x) \equiv 2q^2(z-x); \\ z &= 1-\frac{s-m^2-2\mu^2}{2q^2}. \end{aligned} \tag{4.7}$$

Since z becomes very large as $q^2 \to 0$, the Legendre function Q_0 dominates. Intuitively, it is clear that such a dominance of S-waves cannot be correct. Since the intrinsic parity of the pion is negative, a nucleon should absorb and emit single pions in P-waves. This of course is a non-relativistic argument. In the relativistic coupling, we must remember that big and small components of a Dirac spinor have opposite parities.

7-5. Nearby singularities and peripheral method

Our explicit calculation of $f_{L\pm}(s)$ will be restricted to the "elastic region", where $\operatorname{Im} f_{L\pm}$ may be replaced by $qf^*_{L\pm}f_{L\pm}$. From this region of s, we can classify the singularities into nearby and distant ones. Apart from the physical cut, only the short cut, the pole at $s = m^2$, and the "front" part of the circle are nearby singularities. The crossed cut for example is more remote from the low-energy elastic region than the inelastic region, where various inelastic channels yield important contributions to $\operatorname{Im} f_{L\pm}$.

The short cut and the pole at $s = m^2$ depend on a single parameter, namely the coupling constant G. The discontinuity across the front part of the circle will be parametrized in terms of low-energy $\pi\pi$-scattering, on which some information exists from the final state interaction of $\pi N \to \pi\pi N$ (see section 5-6). Our hope is then that these few parameters will suffice for a calculation of low-energy πN scattering. Originally, this hope was motivated as follows: In the dispersion relation

$$\operatorname{Re} f(s) = \frac{1}{\pi}\int \frac{ds'}{s'-s} \operatorname{Im} f(s'), \tag{5.1}$$

the contribution of distant singularities is damped by the factor $(s'-s)^{-1}$. However, this damping turns out to be much too weak. As a rule, integral (1) needs several subtractions, before the distant singularities can be neglected.

There is another way of looking at the different singularities. The contributions of the distant singularities to the integral will change relatively slowly as one goes from one value of s to another. Therefore, rapid variations in $f(s)$ such as resonances should be due to nearby singularities. We therefore expect strong relations between e.g. the N_{33} and its nearby singularities.

There are several methods of suppressing the influence of the unknown distant singularities. In the following, we present the "peripheral method" of DONNACHIE, HAMILTON and LEA [1964], which has been successfully applied to low-energy πN scattering. It consists of solving dispersion relations for

$$F_L(s) = f_L(s)/q^{2L}. \tag{5.2}$$

From the threshold behaviour $A_L q^{2L}$ of $f_L(s)$, it follows that $F_L(s)$ has no extra singularity at threshold. It does have a new singularity at $s = \bar{s}_0$, where q is again zero. However, the contribution of this singularity to the dispersion integral appears to be small for $L < 3$.

To examine the suppression of distant singularities, we look at the function $1/q^2$. In the region of the short cut, i.e. for $s \approx m^2$, $1/q^2$ is of the order of $-1/\mu^2$. In the region of the distant cut, $s < 0$, $1/|q^2|$ is largest at $-(m^2-\mu^2)$, where it has the value $1/m^2$. Therefore, the contributions of the distant cut are suppressed by a factor $(\mu^2/m^2)^2 \approx (1/45)^2$ relative to those of the short cut. Distant singularities are now easily approximated by a few poles. A suitably chosen pole on the distant cut, for example, is taken to represent the joint contributions of the distant Born cut and the distant parts both of the crossed cut and of the circle.

We shall see below that the contribution of the short cut alone is more complicated than that of the whole Born term. Specifically, we shall not obtain the functions $Q_L(z)$ which gave the threshold behaviour for $f_L(s)$. Therefore, the omission of the distant cut is possible only in the peripheral method, in which the correct threshold behaviour is *assumed* from the outset (2).

Let us now calculate the nearby singularities of $F_{L\pm}$. The partial wave projections $f^{\frac{1}{2}}_{B,\,L\pm}$ of the direct Born term $f^{\frac{1}{2}}_{B}$ are given by (4.5) and (4.6). For $L = 0$, F_L is identical with (4.5). Writing $s-m^2 = (s^{\frac{1}{2}}-m)(s^{\frac{1}{2}}+m)$, we may cancel $s^{\frac{1}{2}}-m$ in the numerator and denominator, which shows that $F^{\frac{1}{2}}_{B,\,0+}$ has no pole at $s = m^2$. There is a pole at $s = 0$ from the factor $1/s$, and a cut along $s < 0$, coming from the requirement that $s^{\frac{1}{2}}$ should be a single-valued function in the complex s-plane. However, these singularities are "distant" ones, and may be neglected. For $L = 1$, we have

$$F^{\frac{1}{2}}_{B,\,1-} = f^{\frac{1}{2}}_{B,\,1-}/q^2 = \frac{(s^{\frac{1}{2}}-m)^2-\mu^2}{\lambda(s,\,m^2,\,\mu^2)}\,(s^{\frac{1}{2}}+m)\,\frac{3G^2/4\pi}{m^2-s}\,, \tag{5.3}$$

$$\lambda(s,\,m^2,\,\mu^2) = ((s^{\frac{1}{2}}-m)^2-\mu^2)(s^{\frac{1}{2}}+m)^2-\mu^2). \tag{5.4}$$

A factor $(s^{\frac{1}{2}}-m)^2-\mu^2$ cancels as expected (otherwise F would have an extra singularity at threshold). There remains a pole at $s = m^2$, with residue $3G^2/8\pi m$ (to lowest order in $\mu^2/4m^2$). In summary: the direct Born term produces a nearby singularity only in $F^{\frac{1}{2}}_{1-}$. This singularity is a pole, which we denote by dB (for direct Born term):

$$F^{\frac{1}{2}}_{1-}(\mathrm{dB}) = \frac{3G^2}{8\pi m}\,\frac{1}{m^2-s}\,. \tag{5.5}$$

Next, we separate the crossed Born term into the distant cut and the short cut. By (3.8), we write

$$\frac{1}{m^2-u} = \frac{2s}{(1+x)(s-s_+(x))(s-s_-(x))}$$

$$= \frac{2s}{(1+x)(s_+(x)-s_-(x))}\left(\frac{1}{s-s_+(x)} - \frac{1}{s-s_-(x)}\right). \tag{5.6}$$

The second term in the last bracket represents the distant cut. We neglect it and get

$$\frac{1}{m^2-u} \approx \frac{s}{\sqrt{\ldots}\,(s-s_+(x))}, \tag{5.7}$$

with the square root and $s_+(x)$ given by (3.11) and (3.12), respectively. Now we may calculate $F_{L\pm}$ (cB), the contribution of the short cut (cB = crossed Born term). This time we choose $I = \frac{3}{2}$ and insert $B^{\frac{3}{2}}$ (Born) $= -2G^2/(m^2-\mu)$ into (4.4). With (7), we get the integrals

$$F^{\frac{3}{2}}_{L\pm}(\mathrm{cB}) = \frac{-2G^2}{32\pi}\int \mathrm{d}x \left(\frac{4s}{\lambda(s, m^2, \mu^2)}\right)^L \frac{P_L(x)C_+ + P_{L\pm 1}(x)C_-}{\sqrt{\ldots}\,(s-s_+(x))}, \tag{5.8}$$

$$C_\pm \equiv (s\pm m)(s-m^2)-\mu^2(s\mp m). \tag{5.9}$$

For fixed x, the integrand has a pole at $s = s_+(x)$, the residue of which is given by

$$\left(\frac{4s_+(x)}{\lambda(s_+(x), m^2, \mu^2)}\right)^L \frac{P_L(x)C_+(s_+(x))+P_{L\pm 1}(x)C_-(s_+(x))}{m^2\sqrt{1+2(1+x)\varepsilon(2x-1+\varepsilon)}}, \quad \varepsilon \equiv \frac{\mu^2}{m^2}. \tag{5.10}$$

This is quite a complicated function of x. To be able to perform the final integration, we now calculate to lowest order in ε. From (3.12) we have $s_+(x) = m^2(1+2x\varepsilon)$ to first order in ε. From (10) and (9), we find that we may use $s_+ = m^2$ anywhere except in C_+, where the zeroth order terms cancel. With this approximation, (10) simplifies to

$$\frac{4P_L(x)m\mu^2x+P_{L\pm 1}(x)(-2m\mu^2)}{(-\mu^2)^Lm^2} = \frac{-2P_L(x)x+P_{L\pm 1}(x)}{\frac{1}{2}(-\mu^2)^{L-1}m}. \tag{5.11}$$

Now the integration over the poles is trivial,

$$F^{\frac{3}{2}}_{L\pm}(\mathrm{cB}) = \frac{G^2}{4\pi}\int \mathrm{d}x\, \frac{P_L(x)x-\frac{1}{2}P_{L\pm 1}(x)}{(-\mu^2)^{L-1}m(s-m^2)}. \tag{5.12}$$

This integral is zero except for $L = 1$. For $L > 1$, (12) does not apply, since the presence of the factor $(-\mu^2)^{L-1}$ in the denominator requires the numerator to be calculated to L^{th} order in ε. For $L = 0$, (12) demonstrates the absence of the short cut from S-wave amplitudes. Since the contribution of the direct Born term to F_{0+} is zero, too, we conclude that the S-wave πN scattering is essentially independent of the πNN coupling constant.

For P-waves, (12) gives the poles

$$F^{\frac{3}{2}}_{1+}(\text{cB}) = \frac{\frac{2}{3}}{m(s-m^2)}\frac{G^2}{4\pi}, \qquad F^{\frac{3}{2}}_{1-}(\text{cB}) = \frac{-\frac{1}{3}}{m(s-m^2)}\frac{G^2}{4\pi}. \tag{5.13}$$

According to (1.11), the crossed Born terms of $I = \frac{1}{2}$ are $-\frac{1}{2}$ of the corresponding $I = \frac{3}{2}$ Born terms. Adding to $F^{\frac{1}{2}}_{1-}$ the direct Born term (5), we obtain the following poles from the Born terms:

$$F^{\frac{1}{2}}_{1+}(\text{Born}) = -\frac{G^2}{4\pi}\frac{\frac{1}{3}}{m(s-m^2)}, \qquad F^{\frac{1}{2}}_{1-}(\text{Born}) = -\frac{G^2}{4\pi}\frac{\frac{4}{3}}{m(s-m^2)}. \tag{5.14}$$

In potential theory, these poles (and the front of the circle) would produce the long-range forces. A positive (negative) sign of F(Born) produces attraction (repulsion). Since a resonance requires attraction, the only candidate for a P-wave resonance is the P_{33} amplitude $F^{\frac{3}{2}}_{1+}$.

7-6. The Chew-Low model

The first successful dynamical model of πN-scattering is due to Chew and Low (Low [1955], Chew and Low [1956]). In this model, the nucleon recoil is neglected, i.e. one sets

$$E = m, \qquad s^{\frac{1}{2}} = E_\pi + m = (\mu^2+q^2)^{\frac{1}{2}} + m. \tag{6.1}$$

This approximation is good near $s = s_0$. For a non-relativistic nucleon, we have $E = m + q^2/2m$. As discussed in the last section, $|q^2|$ is of the order of μ^2 in the region of the short cut. Therefore, the "static approximation" $E = m$ is identical with the calculation to lowest order in $\varepsilon = q^2/m^2$ of the previous section. This will be demonstrated explicitly below. However, for other parts of the s-axis, the static approximation breaks down. The great danger of assuming (1) from the beginning is that one does not know beforehand which values of s will be important in the dispersion integrals. For the N^*_{33} resonance, one cannot hope that (1) is a good approximation. The mass of the N^*_{33} is 1240 MeV, which is larger than the inelastic threshold $s_1^{\frac{1}{2}}$ (1.1). Therefore, singularities up to $s = 2m^2$ are closer to the N* peak than the poles at $s = m^2$. As a result, the Chew-Low model needs a cut-off for the integral along the physical cut.

Let us now re-derive the poles (5.13) and (5.14) in the static approximation. First we note that the direct Born term can only contribute to the P_{11} state, due to conservation of spin and parity. Since the pion has negative intrinsic parity, a static nucleon can absorb a pion only in a P-state. (The S-wave pole in the relativistic treatment involves a parity-changing matrix element between small and big spinor components.)

The remaining Born term singularities of the partial wave amplitudes follow from crossing. In general, crossing symmetry between partial wave amplitudes is complicated. Under the crossing $s' = u$, $u' = s$, we have $t' = t$, which implies $q^2(1-x) = q'^2(1-x')$ or

$$\frac{\lambda(s, m^2, \mu^2)}{4s}(1-x) = \frac{\lambda(u, m^2, \mu^2)}{4u}(1-x'),$$
$$u = \sum m^2 - s + 2q^2(1-x). \tag{6.2}$$

This shows that the relation between x and x' under $s \leftrightarrow u$ crossing is nonlinear. Consequently, a partial wave in the direct channel contributes to all partial waves in the crossed channel. In the static approximation, however, the substitution $P_\pi \to -P_\pi$ under crossing simply implies $E'_\pi = -E_\pi$ and consequently $q'^2 = q^2$. Then (2) requires $x' = x$, i.e. the cms scattering angle remains invariant under crossing. With this approximation, S-waves cross into S-waves, P-waves into P-waves etc.

Now the singularities of the crossed Born term follow trivially. The pole at $u = m^2$ is equivalent to a pole at $s = m^2$, due to the relation $s+u = 2m^2$. The crossing coefficients from $J = \frac{1}{2}$ to $J = \frac{1}{2}$ and $\frac{3}{2}$ may be taken over from the isospin case (1.13). In fact, in the static model spin and isospin appear symmetrically. The nucleon has $I = J = \frac{1}{2}$ and the pion has $I = L = 1$. Consequently, the scattering amplitude is also symmetric under the exchange $I \leftrightarrow J$. This explains the equality of $F^{\frac{3}{2}}_{1-}$ (cB) and $F^{\frac{1}{2}}_{1+}$ (Born) in (5.13) and (5.14).

To derive (5.13) from (5.5), $F^{\frac{1}{2}}_{1-} = 3G^2/8\pi m(m^2-s)$, one first multiplies $F^{\frac{1}{2}}_{1-}$ by $-\frac{2}{3}$, which is the crossing coefficient (1.13) from the $I = \frac{1}{2}$ to the $I = \frac{3}{2}$ state. Then one obtains the $F^{\frac{3}{2}}_{1+}$ ($F^{\frac{3}{2}}_{1-}$) state by multiplying by $\frac{2}{3}$ ($-\frac{1}{3}$), which is the crossing coefficient $C_{\frac{3}{2}\frac{1}{2}}(C_{\frac{1}{2}\frac{1}{2}})$, multiplied by -1. The extra minus sign is necessary in order to include the minus sign from the crossing $B_+(s, t) = -B_-(u, t)$ only once. The complete crossing matrix in the static approximation is defined by

$$B^I_J(u, t) = -\sum_{I'}\sum_{J'} C_{II'}\, C_{JJ'}\, B^{I'}_{J'}(s, t), \tag{6.3}$$

where both $C_{II'}$ and $C_{JJ'}$ are given by (1.13).

The original Chew-Low model is explained e.g. in the books of SCHWEBER [1961] and KÄLLÉN [1964]. Here we reproduce a treatment of the main feature, namely the N^*_{33} resonance, which is due to HAMILTON [1967]. Of all the lefthand singularities, we only retain the pole at $s = m^2$, which we abbreviate as

$$F^{\frac{3}{2}}_{1+}(\text{Born}) = \frac{c}{s-m^2}, \qquad c = \frac{2}{3m}\frac{G^2}{4\pi}. \tag{6.4}$$

For the complete function $F^{\frac{3}{2}}_{1+}(s) \equiv F(s)$, we make the ansatz

$$F = \frac{c}{s-m^2}\frac{1}{D(s)}, \tag{6.5}$$

where $D(s)$ is regular at $s = m^2$, namely $D(m^2) = 1$. The knowledge of $D(m^2)$ is used to write a once-subtracted dispersion relation,

$$\text{Re}\, D(s) = 1+(s-m^2)\frac{1}{\pi}\,\text{P}\int_{s_0}^{\infty}\frac{\mathrm{d}s'\,\text{Im}\, D(s')}{(s'-m^2)(s'-s)}. \tag{6.6}$$

Next, we try to eliminate $\text{Im}\, D(s')$ by the partial wave optical theorem (2-7.9). Dividing (2-7.9) by $|T_L|^2 = \sigma_L\,(\text{elastic})/4\pi(2L+1)$, we get

$$-\text{Im}\left(\frac{1}{T_L}\right) = \frac{\text{Im}\, T_L}{|T_L|^2} = \frac{q\sigma_L(\text{total})}{\sigma_L(\text{elastic})} \equiv qR. \tag{6.7}$$

By (5), we now get, with $1/F = q^2/T_L$,

$$\text{Im}\, D(s) = \frac{c}{s-m^2}\,\text{Im}\left(\frac{1}{F}\right) = -\frac{cR(s)}{s-m^2}\,q^3(s), \tag{6.8}$$

$$\text{Re}\, D(s) = 1-(s-m^2)cI(s), \qquad I(s) = \frac{1}{\pi}\,\text{P}\int_{s_0}^{\infty}\frac{\mathrm{d}s'\,q^3(s')R(s')}{(s'-m^2)^2(s'-s)}. \tag{6.9}$$

Suppose now that we know the integral $I(s)$. Then we may calculate directly the cotangent of the phase shift δ. By (2-4.12) we have

$$q^3 \cot\delta = \frac{1}{F} + iq^3 = (s-m^2)\frac{D(s)}{c} + iq^3 = (s-m^2)\frac{\text{Re}\, D(s)}{c}. \tag{6.10}$$

Here the imaginary parts have cancelled by (8). We must of course assume $R(s) = 1$, if we use (2-4.12).

We now estimate the integral (9), following HAMILTON [1967]. The ratio R of total to elastic partial wave cross-section is a slowly rising function of energy. It cannot become larger than 2, which corresponds to $\eta_L = 0$ (see

2-7.5 and 2-7.7). For a crude estimate, we put $R = 1$. Then we may compute $I(s_0)$. With $q^2(s') = (s'-s_0)(s'-\bar{s}_0)/4s'$, we get

$$I(s_0) = \frac{1}{\pi}\int_{s_0}^{\infty} \frac{q(s')\mathrm{d}s'}{4s'(s'-m^2)^2}(s'-\bar{s}_0). \tag{6.11}$$

The principal value symbol is omitted, since the point $s' = m^2$ lies outside the range of integration. The integral (11) is finite, but it gets large contributions from large values of s'. Thus, although we have avoided the cut-off of the original Chew-Low model, we cannot expect any precision. As s increases above s_0, $I(s)$ decreases slowly. Neglecting this variation, we get the "effective range" formula

$$\frac{q^3 \cot \delta}{s-m^2} = \frac{1}{c} - (s-m^2)I(s_0), \tag{6.12}$$

where δ is the P_{33} phase shift. A plot of $q^3 \cot \delta/(s-m^2)$ versus $s-m^2$ should give a straight line according to (12). Experimentally, this is in fact the case, at least up to 1240 MeV, where cot δ passes through zero. However, the experimental values of c and $I(s_0)$ do not quite agree with the theoretical ones. The constant c comes out about 20 % larger than the theoretical value (4). This need not surprise us, since we have neglected the discontinuities both across the circle and across the crossed cut.

7-7. *N/D* method and bootstrap

An important tool of solving dispersion relations is the so-called *N/D* method of CHEW and MANDELSTAM [1960], which is a special case of the Wiener-Hopf method of solving integral equations (see also the books of DIU [1965], BARTON [1965]). Solving the dispersion relation for F by the ansatz (6.5), (6.6) of the previous section actually was a special case of the *N/D* method.

Consider a general partial wave amplitude $T_L(s)$, which is real-analytic and which satisfies a dispersion relation. For simplicity, we assume that T has two cuts along the real axis, $s < s_l$ (the left-hand cut) and $s > s_0$ (the right-hand cut), with $s_l < s_0$, and that no subtractions are necessary:

$$T_L(s) = \frac{1}{\pi}\int_{-\infty}^{s_l} \frac{\mathrm{d}s'}{s'-s} \operatorname{Im} T_L(s') + \frac{1}{\pi}\int_{s_0}^{\infty} \frac{\mathrm{d}s'}{s'-s} \operatorname{Im} T_L(s'). \tag{7.1}$$

We make the ansatz

$$T_L(s) = N(s)/D(s), \tag{7.2}$$

where both N and D are real-analytic functions. $N(s)$ contains the left-hand singularities of T_L, but is regular on the right-hand cut. Similarly, D has only the right-hand cut and is regular for $s < s_0$. We thus have

$$\operatorname{Im} N(s) = D(s) \operatorname{Im} T(s) \quad \text{for} \quad s < s_l, \quad \operatorname{Im} N(s) = 0 \quad \text{for} \quad s > s_l, \tag{7.3}$$

$$\operatorname{Im} D(s) = -qR(s)\, N(s) \quad \text{for} \quad s > s_0, \quad \operatorname{Im} D(s) = 0 \quad \text{for} \quad s < s_0. \tag{7.4}$$

In (4), we have expressed Im (T_L^{-1}) by (6.7). Poles may be included in the left-hand cut, (s_l need not coincide with the u-channel threshold), but they may also appear as zeros of $D(s)$. In the N/D method, the left-hand singularities of $T_L(s)$ are assumed to be known. Therefore, if a pole is fixed from the beginning, it is included in the left-hand cut. This was the case in (6.5), where the entire function N consisted of a single pole, $c/(s-m^2)$. The other possibility is that one wants to calculate the mass m_B of a "bound state", in which case the pole appears at the end of the calculation as $D(m_B^2) = 0$.

N and D satisfy the following dispersion relations:

$$N(s) = \frac{1}{\pi} \int_{-\infty}^{s_l} \frac{ds'}{s'-s} D(s') \operatorname{Im} T_L(s'), \tag{7.5}$$

$$D(s) = 1 - \frac{s-s_1}{\pi} \int_{s_0}^{\infty} \frac{ds'\, q'R(s')N(s')}{(s'-s_1)(s'-s)}. \tag{7.6}$$

In (6), s_1 is the subtraction point. Since only the quotient N/D is of interest, one may always normalize $D(s_1) = 1$. Substituting (5) into (6) and changing the order of integration, we get

$$D(s) = 1 - \frac{s-s_1}{\pi^2} \int_{-\infty}^{s_l} ds''\, K(s, s'')D(s''), \tag{7.7}$$

$$K(s, s'') \equiv \operatorname{Im} T_L(s'') \int_{s_0}^{\infty} \frac{ds'\, q'R(s')}{(s''-s')(s'-s_1)(s'-s)}. \tag{7.8}$$

This is a Fredholm equation. The kernel (8) is known, since s'' is restricted by (7) to the left-hand cut. In practice, (5) and (6) are frequently "solved" by iteration, starting from $D(s) = 1$.

Usually, a calculation of $T_L(s)$ requires additional assumptions. The "bootstrap" idea was suggested by CHEW and MANDELSTAM [1961] as a method of solving these equations by self-consistency requirements. It was used to calculate the mass and width of the ρ-meson resonance in $\pi\pi$-

scattering. In this system, no stable particle pole exists, and the crossed channel is again $\pi\pi$ scattering, although of a different isospin composition. It turns out that the crossing matrix has a large component from the $I = J = 1$ state to itself. In a very crude model, we may therefore say that this state transforms into itself under crossing. Suppose now that the crossed channel has a resonance, namely the ρ. Inserting this resonance as the only left-hand singularity in an N/D calculation, it turns out that the solution $D(s)$ given by (7) develops a resonance in the direct channel. By postulating identical masses and widths for the input and output resonances, one is able to express both parameters in terms of the pion mass.

There is a large literature on the theory of $\pi\pi$ scattering (see e.g. CHEW [1962], DIU [1965]). The weak point of bootstraps is that self-consistency is only necessary to the extent that the system under consideration really crosses into itself. This makes numerical calculations quite unreliable.

A similar model is the "reciprocal bootstrap" of the N and N*. We saw in the last section that a crude description of the N* is possible in terms of the nucleon pole alone. The original idea was that the nucleon pole itself would appear as a bound state in the N/D solution of the P_{11} partial wave, with the main singularity of N given by the N* in the crossed cut. Actually, the situation is rather different from this simple picture. There is however one feature worth mentioning. As a first improvement over the calculation of the preceding section, we include the N* resonance as the most important singularity of the crossed cut. We approximate it by a pole on the real s-axis at $u = m_{N^*}^2$, neglecting the N* width. In the static approximation, the crossing of the $J = I = \frac{3}{2}$ channel is given by (6.3),

$$B_J^I(u, t) = -C_{I\frac{3}{2}} C_{J\frac{3}{2}} B_{\frac{3}{2}}^{\frac{3}{2}}(s, t). \tag{7.9}$$

For $I = J = \frac{3}{2}$, we get $(C_{\frac{3}{2}\frac{3}{2}})^2 = \frac{1}{9}$, which is relatively small. This justifies to some extent our neglect of the crossed cut for the calculation of the resonance. For the partial wave containing the direct nucleon pole, however, $I = J = \frac{1}{2}$, we get the large value $(C_{\frac{1}{2}\frac{3}{2}})^2 = 16/9$. Therefore, the N_{33}^* pole is expected to be of some importance for the calculation of the P_{11} amplitude.

7-8. The contribution of the circle

The singularities of the circle $|s| = m^2 - \mu^2$ come from the t-channel, $\pi\bar{\pi} \rightarrow N\bar{N}$. However, only the cut $4\mu^2 < t < 4m^2$ below the physical threshold of this reaction contributes. In fact, writing

$$s = (m^2 - \mu^2)\,\mathrm{e}^{\mathrm{i}\alpha}, \qquad -\pi < \alpha \leqq \pi \tag{8.1}$$

for s on the circle, we get from (3.6)

$$q^2 = -\mu^2 \cos^2 \tfrac{1}{2}\alpha - m^2 \sin^2 \tfrac{1}{2}\alpha = -\frac{t}{2(1-x)}, \tag{8.2}$$

which gives the maximal value of t as a function of α,

$$t_{\max}(\alpha) = 4(\mu^2 \cos^2 \tfrac{1}{2}\alpha + m^2 \sin^2 \tfrac{1}{2}\alpha). \tag{8.3}$$

For $\alpha = 0$ and $\alpha = \pi$, we get $t_{\max} = 4\mu^2$ and $4m^2$, respectively. The front part of the circle corresponds to small $|\alpha|$ and therefore to small t. (The inverse is not true: the smallest t-value contributes to the whole circle and to the cut $s < 0$.)

For $4\mu^2 < t < 16\mu^2$, only the $\pi\pi$ channel is open. The three-pion channel is closed, since $\pi\pi \to \pi\pi\pi$ is forbidden by G-parity. Above $16\mu^2$, 4-pion states are possible. However, it is likely that they contribute very little to the unitarity condition. Above $t = (m_\omega + m_\pi)^2$, the $\omega\pi$ state begins to contribute to the $I = 1$ amplitude. The corresponding α is 58.7°. This shows that, for the front part of the circle, the only important state in the t-channel unitarity is the $\pi\pi$ state. By extended unitarity (6-5.14), we conclude that the partial wave amplitudes of $\pi\pi \to \mathrm{N\bar{N}}$ have the phases of the corresponding partial wave amplitudes of elastic $\pi\pi$-scattering.

Since the phase shifts of $\pi\pi$ scattering are largely unknown, the procedure in the past has been to evaluate $\pi\pi$ scattering from the discontinuity across the circle. The starting point is (4.2) for S-waves, which is rewritten in the form

$$\mathrm{Re}\, f_{0+}(s) = \frac{1}{\pi}\,\mathrm{P}\int_{(m+\mu)^2}^{\infty} \frac{\mathrm{d}s'}{s'-s}\,\mathrm{Im}\, f_{0+}(s') + \frac{1}{\pi}\int_0^{(m-\mu)^2} \frac{\mathrm{d}s'}{s'-s}\,\mathrm{Im}\, f_{0+}(s') + \Delta_0(s). \tag{8.4}$$

The integral along the short cut has been omitted according to our result of section 7-5 (see the discussion following (5.12)). The function $\Delta_0(s)$ is called the "discrepancy". It comprises the contribution of the cut $-\infty < s' < 0$ and that of the circle. It can be determined by inserting the experimental values of $\mathrm{Re}\, f_{0+}(s)$ and $\mathrm{Im}\, f_{0+}(s')$ into (4). In practice, $\Delta_0(s)$ is parametrized by three poles (HAMILTON, MENOTTI, SPEARMAN and WOOLCOCK [1961]). One of these poles lies on the negative real s-axis. The other two poles lie on the front part of the circle. They are complex conjugate of each other, since $\Delta_0(s)$ must be real for real s:

$$\Delta_0^{(\pm)}(s) = \frac{b_\pm}{s_b - s} + \frac{c_\pm}{s_c - s} + \frac{c_\pm^*}{s_c^* - s}. \tag{8.5}$$

Before continuing, we explain the meaning of the index $\pm$. We define

$$f^{(\pm)} = \tfrac{1}{2}(f_- \pm f_+), \tag{8.6}$$

where f_- and f_+ are the amplitudes of π^-p and π^+p elastic scattering. It is clear that $f_{0+}^{(+)}$ and $f_{0+}^{(-)}$ satisfy dispersion relations of the type (4). The corresponding discrepancies are $\Delta_0^{(\pm)}$. By (1.3), $f^{(-)} = -2^{-\frac{1}{2}} f_0$, where f_0 is the corresponding charge exchange amplitude. The charge exchange reaction $\pi^-\text{p} \to \pi^0\text{n}$ crosses into $\pi^-\pi^0 \to \bar{\text{p}}\text{n}$, which has $I_3 = -1$ in the final state and therefore $I_{\pi\pi} = 1$. Since the amplitude $f^{(+)}$ refers to an orthogonal state, it must describe the $I_{\pi\pi} = 0$ scattering in the crossed channel. The $I_{\pi\pi} = 2$ scattering is decoupled because $I_{\text{N}\bar{\text{N}}}$ cannot be larger than 1.

For the pions, $I_{\pi\pi} = 0$ (1) allows only even (odd) values of the angular momentum. Neglecting higher partial waves, we can therefore say that $c_+(c_-)$ comes from the $I = J = 0$ ($I = J = 1$) amplitude of the reaction $\pi^+\pi^- \to \text{N}\bar{\text{N}}$. The general partial wave decomposition of this reaction will be given in section 9-4. The $J = 0$ amplitude can be read off directly from (4-6.9) and (4-6.10) for $\text{p}\bar{\text{p}} \to \pi\bar{\pi}$. With $E_{\bar{\pi}} = E_{\pi'}$, we get $Q_{\text{bb}} = Q_{\text{ss}} = A$ in (4-6.10). In (4-6.9), we put $m' = m$, $\bar{E} = E$, and obtain

$$T(\text{p}\bar{\text{p}}, M\bar{M}) = \text{i}p\chi_0^+(-\bar{M})\left[A(1-4M\bar{M}) - B\boldsymbol{p}_{\pi'}\cdot\boldsymbol{\sigma}\left(\frac{2Mp}{E+m} - \frac{2\bar{M}p}{-E+m}\right)\right]\chi_0(M), \tag{8.7}$$

$$\begin{aligned} T(\text{p}\bar{\text{p}}, \tfrac{1}{2}\tfrac{1}{2}) &= -\text{i}p_\pi \sin\theta_t \cdot 2EB = -T(\text{p}\bar{\text{p}}, -\tfrac{1}{2}, -\tfrac{1}{2}),\\ T(\text{p}\bar{\text{p}}, \tfrac{1}{2}, -\tfrac{1}{2}) &= \text{i}(2Ap + 2mBp_\pi\cos\theta_t). \end{aligned} \tag{8.8}$$

Here θ_t is the scattering angle between the incident p and outgoing π^+. For $p_\pi = 0$, only the term $2Ap$ remains in (8). Therefore, the S-wave amplitude must be proportional to the average of A over $\cos\theta_t$. For $J > 0$, two partial wave amplitudes exist. In the notation of FRAZER and FULCO [1960], these are called f_+^J and f_-^J. Apart from a factor, they are identical with the helicity amplitudes $T_J(\frac{1}{2}, \pm\frac{1}{2})$ which we shall introduce in section 9-4. Here we merely mention that the amplitudes $T(\lambda, \lambda', \theta)$ of (9-4.12) are identical with (7), for $M = \lambda$, $\bar{M} = -\lambda'$. Insertion of (8) into (9-4.12) leads to

$$T_J(\tfrac{1}{2}, \tfrac{1}{2}) = \frac{\mathrm{i}}{8\pi}\int \mathrm{d}\cos\theta_t P_J(\cos\theta_t)[Ap + mp_\pi B\cos\theta_t] \equiv \mathrm{i}f_+^J(pp_\pi)^J/p,$$

$$T_J(\tfrac{1}{2}, -\tfrac{1}{2}) = -\frac{\mathrm{i}p_\pi E}{8\pi}\frac{\sqrt{J(J+1)}}{2J+1}\int \mathrm{d}\cos\theta_t(P_{J-1}-P_{J+1})B \equiv \mathrm{i}f_-^J(pp_\pi)^J E/p. \tag{8.9}$$

Neglecting $J = 2, 4, 6\ldots$ in $A^{(+)}$, $B^{(+)}$ and $J = 3, 5, 7\ldots$ in $A^{(-)}$, $B^{(-)}$, we find from (9)

$$A^{(+)} = \frac{4\pi}{p^2}f_+^0, \qquad B^{(+)} = 0, \tag{8.10}$$

$$B^{(-)} = \frac{12\pi}{2^{\frac{1}{2}}}f_-^1, \qquad A^{(-)} = \cos\theta_t\frac{p_\pi}{p}(12\pi f_+^1 - mB^{(-)}). \tag{8.11}$$

Now we are in a position to express the discontinuity of $f_{0+}^{(\pm)}$ across the front part of the circle in terms of the partial wave amplitudes f_+^0, f_+^1 and f_-^1 for $\pi\bar{\pi}\to \mathrm{N\bar{N}}$. From (3-9.10), we have $f_{0+}^{(\pm)} = \frac{1}{2}\int \mathrm{d}x\,(f_1^{(\pm)}+xf_2^{(\pm)})$. The functions $f_1^{(\pm)}$ and $f_2^{(\pm)}$ are expressed in terms of $A^{(\pm)}$ and $B^{(\pm)}$ by (4.3). Finally, $A^{(\pm)}$ and $B^{(\pm)}$ are given by (10) and (11). By

$$\tfrac{1}{4}t = \mu^2 + p_\pi^2 = m^2 + p^2, \tag{8.12}$$

p_π is real and p is imaginary on the circle $|s| = m^2-\mu^2$, according to (3). Similarly, $\cos\theta_t$ is imaginary because of

$$s = (P_\mathrm{p}-P_{\bar{\pi}})^2 = -(\boldsymbol{p}+\boldsymbol{p}_{\pi'})^2 = -p^2-p_\pi^2-2pp_\pi\cos\theta_t. \tag{8.13}$$

Therefore, the coefficient $\cos\theta_t/p$ in (11) is real, and Im $A^{(\pm)}$, Im $B^{(\pm)}$ are related to Im $f_\pm^J$ by (10) and (11).

The phase shift of $\pi\pi$ scattering may be calculated by the method of Omnès [1958] and Mushkelishvili [1946, 1953]. See also the article of Jackson (Screaton [1961]). We omit this part of the problem (see e.g. Hamilton [1967]), and merely quote the main result. The low-energy $\pi\pi$-scattering is strong and attractive, both for $I = J = 0$ and $I = J = 1$. In the latter case, this conforms with the evidence on the ρ-resonance as a resonance in $\pi\pi$ scattering. Also, in connection with (5-6.1), we mentioned the existence of a large S-wave $\pi\pi$ scattering amplitude in the ρ resonance region. From the analysis of S-wave πN scattering, it appears that this amplitude has a large positive scattering length but no resonance. However, the analysis of other reactions, mainly of πp backward scattering (Lovelace, Heinz and Donnachie [1966]) indicates that also this partial wave may have a resonance. This resonance is denoted by the letter σ. Presumably it occurs below the ρ resonance, with a broad width.

The rather abstract argumentation of this section may be illustrated by a simple picture (fig. 7-8). In pion-nucleon scattering, the nucleon and the

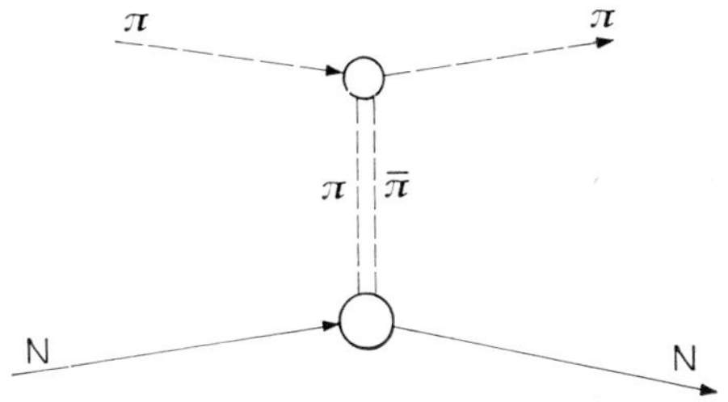

Fig. 7-8. Exchange of a pion pair in πN-scattering.

pion may exchange a $\pi\bar{\pi}$ pair. If $\bar{\pi}\pi$ scattering were negligible except for a narrow resonance, then the effect would be approximated by a Born term, the resonance being the exchanged particle. Models of this type will be considered in chapter 11.

7-9. The inelastic channels

The lowest inelastic final states in πN collisions are $\pi\pi$N and ηN ($\pi\pi\pi$N states are negligible). By their dynamical structure and threshold behaviour, these states will prefer certain partial wave amplitudes.

We first discuss the ηN final state. Since both η and π are pseudoscalar, the lowest possible angular momentum state is an S-state. By the partial wave threshold behaviour, we therefore expect ηN production $\pi^- p \rightarrow \eta n$ in the vicinity of the threshold $m_n + m_\eta = 1488$ MeV to occur in S-waves. Because η carries no isospin, the total isospin is $\frac{1}{2}$. In summary: the quantum numbers $L_{2I,2J}$ of low-energy η-production are S_{11}. A calculation of the coupled πN, ηN system has been performed by TUAN [1965] by means of the K-matrix (see chapter 8).

The three-particle system $\pi\pi$N is more complicated. At threshold, we expect zero angular momentum between the two pions, and also zero angular momentum of the pion pair relative to the nucleon. This requires $J = \frac{1}{2}$, but this time the change in intrinsic parity requires $L = 1$ for the initial state, i.e. $P_{2I,1}$. The isospin could be both $\frac{1}{2}$ and $\frac{3}{2}$, corresponding to $I_{\pi\pi} = 0$ and 2, respectively. ($I_{\pi\pi} = 1$ is forbidden for $L_{\pi\pi} = 0$.) However, the P_{11} state is preferred, due to the large $\pi\pi$ interaction in the $I = L = 0$

state (σ-resonance). The inelasticity of the P_{11} amplitude in elastic scattering may be read off from fig. 2-7. For comparison, the P_{31} amplitude remains almost purely elastic up to 600 MeV pion lab kinetic energy. This is an indication that the low-energy $I = 2$ $\pi\pi$-interaction is weak.

In addition to the P_{11}, only the D_{13} and D_{33} partial waves show appreciable inelasticity below 600 MeV (cf. HAMILTON [1967]). This can also be understood qualitatively, in terms of πN^*_{33} final states. We have $m_\pi + m_{N^*} = 1379$ MeV, which is more than 100 MeV lower than the ηN threshold. Due to the broad width of the N*, there is of course no sharp threshold for πN*. Also, the two-particle approximation $\pi N \to \pi N^*$ may break down when the relative momentum of the second pion becomes very small. What we really need is that the nucleon forms a P_{33} state with one of the pions. If the total cms energy is small, the second pion will be in an S-state relative to these two particles. Conservation of spin and parities then restricts the initial πN states to $D_{2I,3}$. This time both values of I are possible. From table 5-3, we remember that the amplitude D_{13} of elastic πN scattering has a resonance at 1518 MeV. The relatively large fraction of $\pi\pi$N "decays" of this resonance manifests the above πN* configuration. For a general analysis of the $\pi\pi$N final states, see ARNOLD and URETSKY [1967].

CHAPTER 8

$\overline{\mathrm{K}}$N INTERACTIONS AND MULTI-CHANNEL FORMALISM

8-1. Isospin in K^-p interactions

The characteristic feature of $\overline{\mathrm{K}}$N interactions is the presence of several two-particle channels. Even at zero kaon kinetic energy, the $\Lambda\pi$ and $\Sigma\pi$ channels are open, in addition to the elastic channel. As far as spin and parity are concerned, these reactions are like πN scattering, and we can again apply the results of sections 3-8 and 3-9. The amplitudes f_{L+} and f_{L-} however are no longer of the form $e^{i\delta}$, since unitarity is now a matrix equation.

There are of course also three-body final states. The $\Lambda\pi\pi$ channel for example is open already at the $\overline{\mathrm{K}}$N threshold. Such states are more difficult to incorporate in the formalism. Fortunately, they can be neglected at low energies.

Isospin states for the neutral $\overline{\mathrm{K}}$N system have been given in (5-4.1) and (5-4.2). By table 4-3, the isotopic states of Σ^+, Σ^0 and Σ^- are identical with those of π^+, π^0 and π^-, respectively. Therefore, $\Sigma\pi$ total isospin eigenstates are given by table 4-2, with the first π replaced by Σ. This time we do not enumerate the matrix elements for all possible charge combinations as we did for πN interactions in section 5-3. The initial state is usually K^-p. The matrix elements for final states of various charges are expressed in terms of the matrix elements T^I between states of total isospin I as follows:

$$\langle \mathrm{K}^-\mathrm{p}|T|\mathrm{K}^-\mathrm{p}\rangle = \tfrac{1}{2}(T^1+T^0), \qquad \langle \overline{\mathrm{K}}{}^0\mathrm{n}|T|\mathrm{K}^-\mathrm{p}\rangle = \tfrac{1}{2}(T^1-T^0), \tag{1.1}$$

$$\langle \Sigma^{\pm}\pi^{\mp}|T|\mathrm{K}^-\mathrm{p}\rangle = 6^{-\frac{1}{2}}T^0_{\Sigma}\pm\tfrac{1}{2}T^1_{\Sigma}, \qquad \langle \Sigma^0\pi^0|T|\mathrm{K}^-\mathrm{p}\rangle = -6^{-\frac{1}{2}}T^0_{\Sigma}, \tag{1.2}$$

$$\langle \Lambda\pi^0|T|\mathrm{K}^-\mathrm{p}\rangle = 2^{-\frac{1}{2}}T^1_{\Lambda}. \tag{1.3}$$

Since Λ has zero isospin, the index 1 on T^1_{Λ} is unnecessary. On the other hand, each amplitude should really have two lower indices, one for the initial channel and one for the final channel. Here we have suppressed the index for the $\overline{\mathrm{K}}$N channel. Later we shall be more careful. We can also express the cross-sections of $I = 0$ and $I = 1$ reactions in terms of the cross-sections of K^-p reactions. From (2) and (3), we find

$$\sigma^1(\pi\Sigma) = 2[\sigma(\pi^+\Sigma^-)+\sigma(\pi^-\Sigma^+)-2\sigma(\pi^0\Sigma^0)], \tag{1.4}$$

$$\sigma^1(\pi\Lambda) = 2\sigma(\pi^0\Lambda), \qquad \sigma^0(\pi\Sigma) = 6\sigma(\pi^0\Sigma^0), \tag{1.5}$$

where $\sigma^1(\pi\Sigma)$ and $\sigma(\pi^+\Sigma^-)$ are shorthand notations for $\sigma(\overline{\text{K}}\text{N} \to \pi\Sigma,\ I=1)$ and $\sigma(\text{K}^-\text{p} \to \pi^+\Sigma^-)$, etc. The $I = 0$ and $I = 1$ cross-sections for elastic $\overline{\text{K}}$N scattering cannot be expressed in terms of the K^-p elastic and charge-exchange cross-sections. However, the $I = 1$ cross-section may be obtained from elastic K^-n scattering. Since the K^-n state has $I_3 = -1$, it must have $I = 1$:

$$\sigma^1(\overline{\text{K}}\text{N}) = \sigma(\text{K}^-\text{n}), \tag{1.6}$$

$$\sigma^0(\overline{\text{K}}\text{N}) = 2\sigma(\text{K}^-\text{p})+2\sigma(\overline{\text{K}}{}^0\text{n})-\sigma(\text{K}^-\text{n}). \tag{1.7}$$

The last equation follows from the combination of (6) and (1). In practice, K^-n scattering must be extracted from an analysis of K^-d interactions.

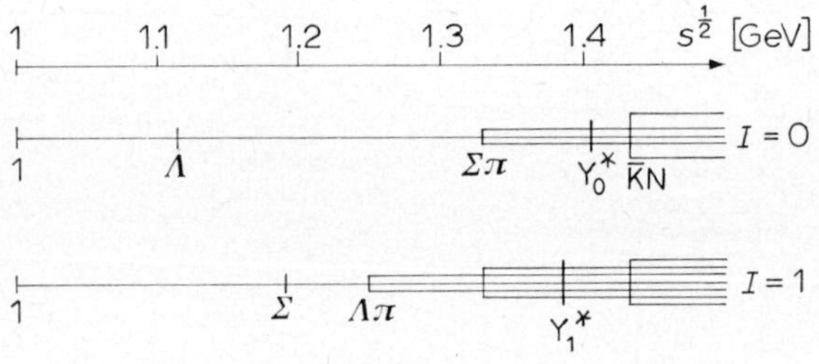

Fig. 8-1. The poles, cuts and resonances of amplitudes connecting meson-baryon states of zero hypercharge.

The positions of the poles, thresholds and resonances of the $I = 0$ and $I = 1$ $\overline{\text{K}}$N interactions are shown in fig. 8-1. We now consider the consequences of isospin invariance for the Born terms associated with the Λ and Σ poles. When written in the form (6-4.7), (6-4.8), these functions contain the $\overline{\text{K}}\text{N}\Lambda$ or $\overline{\text{K}}\text{N}\Sigma$ coupling constant for the initial $\overline{\text{K}}$N state and the $\Lambda\pi\Sigma$ or $\Sigma\pi\Sigma$ coupling constant for the final pion-hyperon state.

Let us begin with those coupling constants which involve a Λ. The coupling constants for $\Lambda \to \pi\Lambda$ are zero, since the transition would have $I = 0$ in the initial state and $I = 1$ in the final state. The coupling constants for $\pi^+\Lambda \to \Sigma^+$, $\pi^0\Lambda \to \Sigma^0$, $\pi^-\Lambda \to \Sigma^-$ must be equal, since the Clebsch-Gordan coefficients of $I+0 \to I$ are all 1. The same argument applies to $\text{K}\Lambda \to \text{N}$. The coupling constants for $\Lambda \to \pi\Sigma$ and $\Lambda \to \overline{\text{K}}\text{N}$ are now easily obtained from the charge conjugation of the mesons. Remembering the negative charge parity of the charged pions and kaons, we find altogether

$$\begin{aligned} G_{\Lambda\pi\Sigma} &\equiv G(\pi^+\Lambda \to \Sigma^+) = G(\pi^0\Lambda \to \Sigma^0) = G(\pi^-\Lambda \to \Sigma^-) \\ &= -G(\Lambda \to \pi^-\Sigma^+) = G(\Lambda \to \pi^0\Sigma^0) = -G(\Lambda \to \pi^+\Sigma^-). \end{aligned} \tag{1.8}$$

$$\begin{aligned} G_{\mathrm{NK}\Lambda} &\equiv G(\mathrm{K}^+\Lambda \to \mathrm{p}) = G(\mathrm{K}^0\Lambda \to \mathrm{n}) \\ &= -G(\Lambda \to \mathrm{K}^-\mathrm{p}) = G(\Lambda \to \overline{\mathrm{K}}^0\mathrm{n}). \end{aligned} \tag{1.9}$$

Alternatively, the relative signs in the second rows of (8) and (9) may be derived from the $I = 0$ two-pion $\left(\boxed{1|2}\text{ of table 4-2}\right)$ and two-nucleon (4-2.4) states, after the substitutions $\Sigma \to \pi$ and $\mathrm{K} \to \mathrm{N}$.

For the $\Sigma \to \pi\Sigma$ vertices, we find from the three

$$\begin{array}{|c|}\hline 1 \\ \hline 2 \\ \hline \end{array}$$

states of table 4-2,

$$\begin{aligned} G_{\Sigma\pi\Sigma} &\equiv G(\Sigma^0 \to \pi^+\Sigma^-) = -G(\Sigma^0 \to \pi^-\Sigma^+) = G(\Sigma^+ \to \pi^+\Sigma^0) \\ &= -G(\Sigma^+ \to \pi^0\Sigma^+) = -G(\Sigma^- \to \pi^-\Sigma^0) = G(\Sigma^- \to \pi^0\Sigma^-), \\ &\qquad G(\Sigma^0 \to \pi^0\Sigma^0) = 0. \end{aligned} \tag{1.10}$$

The coupling constants of $\mathrm{N} \to \Sigma\mathrm{K}$ finally are defined in analogy with (7-1.6), (7-1.7) for $\mathrm{N} \to \pi\mathrm{N}$,

$$\begin{aligned} G_{\mathrm{NK}\Sigma} &\equiv G(\mathrm{p} \to \Sigma^0\mathrm{K}^+) = -G(\mathrm{n} \to \Sigma^0\mathrm{K}^0) = -G(\mathrm{K}^-\mathrm{p} \to \Sigma^0) \\ &= -G(\overline{\mathrm{K}}^0\mathrm{n} \to \Sigma^0), \end{aligned} \tag{1.11}$$

$$\begin{aligned} 2^{\frac{1}{2}}G_{\mathrm{NK}\Sigma} &= G(\mathrm{n} \to \Sigma^-\mathrm{K}^+) = -G(\mathrm{p} \to \Sigma^+\mathrm{K}^0) = -G(\mathrm{K}^-\mathrm{n} \to \Sigma^-) \\ &= -G(\overline{\mathrm{K}}^0\mathrm{p} \to \Sigma^+). \end{aligned} \tag{1.12}$$

The two last coupling constants in each row follow also from (4-2.4).

In section 8-7, we shall relate the various coupling constants by SU_3 symmetry.

8-2. The *K*-matrix

As explained in appendix B-1, the *S*-matrix is unitary if it is calculated from the Hermitean matrices *H* or *K*. Usually, *K* is preferred for mathematical convenience. In potential theory, *K* is sometimes called the Wigner *R*-matrix. It corresponds to an interaction formalism with standing waves in all channels, instead of the usual incoming wave in one channel and outgoing waves in all channels. In the theory of elementary particles, the K-matrix was first used by HEITLER [1941, 1944] in his theory of radiation damping. DALITZ and TUAN [1959, 1960] introduced the K-matrix for the K^-p interactions. The role of the K-matrix in potential theory has been reviewed by DALITZ [1961, 1962].

For low-energy K^-p interactions, unitarity connects the $\overline{\text{K}}$N, $\pi\Lambda$ and $\pi\Sigma$ channels. As explained in the last sections, isospin invariance reduces the number of independent channels to three for $I = 1$ and to two for $I = 0$. For each partial wave and parity, the S-matrix is therefore a 3×3 matrix for $I = 1$ and a 2×2 matrix for $I = 0$. Let us consider the $I = 1$ matrix in more detail. By time-reversal invariance, it is symmetric. Its six different amplitudes refer to the $I = 1$ parts of the reactions $\pi\Lambda \to \pi\Lambda$, $\pi\Lambda \leftrightarrow \pi\Sigma$, $\pi\Lambda \leftrightarrow \overline{\text{K}}\text{N}$, $\pi\Sigma \to \pi\Sigma$, $\pi\Sigma \leftrightarrow \overline{\text{K}}\text{N}$ and $\overline{\text{K}}\text{N} \to \overline{\text{K}}\text{N}$. Unitarity enables us to express these six *complex* amplitudes in terms of the six *real* amplitudes of the K-matrix.

The connection between the partial wave S and T-matrices is given by (2-4.13), or in matrix notation

$$S = 1+2iq^{\frac{1}{2}}Tq^{\frac{1}{2}}, \qquad q \equiv \begin{pmatrix} q_{\pi\Lambda} & 0 & 0 \\ 0 & q_{\pi\Sigma} & 0 \\ 0 & 0 & q_{\overline{\text{K}}\text{N}} \end{pmatrix}. \tag{2.1}$$

Here we have ordered the channels according to increasing thresholds (for $I = 0$, the $\pi\Lambda$ channel would be absent). The matrix $q^{\frac{1}{2}}$ is a diagonal matrix, with diagonal elements $q^{\frac{1}{2}}_{\pi\Lambda}$, etc. Its inclusion in the definition of S is necessary if one wants the unitarity equation (2-4.8) for T to lead to $S^+S = 1$, without additional kinematical factors.

Before continuing, we should mention the treatment of spin. We considered multichannel meson-baryon scattering at the end of section 3-8. In section 3-9, we considered parity conservation without explicit reference to the multichannel case. However, formulae (3-9.1) through (3-9.6) clearly remain valid for the multichannel case if the amplitudes $f_1, \ldots, f_4$, $T_J(\lambda, \lambda'), f_{L+}$ and f_{L-} as well as the momentum q are replaced by the corresponding matrices. In particular, (3-9.7) tells us that the matrix T of (1) must be identified with the matrix $f^I_{L\pm}$ of orbital angular momentum L, total angular momentum $J = L\pm\frac{1}{2}$ and isospin I.

In view of (1), we now define the K-matrix not by (B-1.5) but by

$$S = (1+iq^{\frac{1}{2}}Kq^{\frac{1}{2}})(1-iq^{\frac{1}{2}}Kq^{\frac{1}{2}})^{-1}. \tag{2.2}$$

The connection between T and K is given by

$$T = K(1-\mathrm{i}qK)^{-1} \quad \text{or} \quad T-\mathrm{i}TqK = K. \tag{2.3}$$

The second equation is called Heitler's integral equation. (It becomes a proper integral equation when the $\pi\pi\Lambda$ states are included.) It is checked by combining definitions (1) and (2) into

$$1+2\mathrm{i}q^{\frac{1}{2}}Tq^{\frac{1}{2}} = 1+2\mathrm{i}q^{\frac{1}{2}}Kq^{\frac{1}{2}}(1-\mathrm{i}q^{\frac{1}{2}}Kq^{\frac{1}{2}})^{-1}. \tag{2.4}$$

Comparing (3) with (2-4.12), we see that K is the matrix generalization of $\tan\delta_L/q$. We may hope that the approximation

$$K_L = q^L A_L q^L \tag{2.5}$$

with a constant matrix A_L is as good as the scattering length approximation (2-6.3) in the one-dimensional case. In fact, ROSS and SHAW [1961] have extended (5) to a multichannel effective range theory of the inverse K-matrix,

$$K^{-1} = T^{-1}+\mathrm{i}q, \tag{2.6}$$

analogous to (2-6.4). It is difficult to say how good these approximations are in a relativistic theory.

Like $\tan\delta_L/q$, K is free from normal thresholds singularities. Intuitively this is obvious, since the discontinuity across the cut is given by the imaginary part of the matrix and since K is real. However, to exclude a threshold singularity, we must convince ourselves that K remains real below the threshold. For that purpose, we need the extended unitarity (6-5.11). For our partial-wave matrix T, extended unitarity reads

$$\operatorname{Im} T = T^{+}\theta(q^2)qT, \tag{2.7}$$

where $\theta(q^2)$ is a diagonal matrix of step functions which ensures that the phase space factor is zero below threshold. Since a particular q^2, e.g. $q^2_{\pi\Sigma}$, is negative only in an interval $\bar{s}_0 < s < s_0$, (7) applies only to the right of all left-hand cuts. We now rewrite $\operatorname{Im} T$ as $(T-T^{+})/2\mathrm{i}$ and multiply (7) by $(T^{+})^{-1}$ from the left and by T^{-1} from the right, getting

$$\operatorname{Im}(T^{-1}) = -\theta(q^2)q. \tag{2.8}$$

From (6) we obtain

$$\operatorname{Im}(K^{-1}) = \operatorname{Im}(T^{-1})+\operatorname{Re} q. \tag{2.9}$$

Since q becomes purely imaginary below threshold, we have $\operatorname{Re} q = \theta(q^2)q$ for $s > \bar{s}_0$. This shows that K^{-1} is in fact real both above and below the normal threshold s_0, analogous to $q \cot \delta_L$ (as discussed at the end of section 7-6).

8-3. The reduced *K*-matrix

Let us return to the $I = 1$ 3×3 K-matrix of the last section. We must investigate in more detail what happens when the total cms energy decreases below the $\overline{\mathrm{K}}$N threshold $s_0^{\frac{1}{2}} = m_{\mathrm{K}}+m_{\mathrm{N}}$. For this purpose, we introduce the common index o (for "open") for the $\pi\Lambda$ and $\pi\Sigma$ channels and the index c (for "closed") for the $\overline{\mathrm{K}}$N channel:

$$T \equiv \begin{pmatrix} T_{\mathrm{oo}} & T_{\mathrm{oc}} \\ T_{\mathrm{co}} & T_{\mathrm{cc}} \end{pmatrix}, \qquad K \equiv \begin{pmatrix} K_{\mathrm{oo}} & K_{\mathrm{oc}} \\ K_{\mathrm{co}} & K_{\mathrm{cc}} \end{pmatrix}, \qquad q \equiv \begin{pmatrix} q_{\mathrm{o}} & 0 \\ 0 & q_{\mathrm{c}} \end{pmatrix}. \tag{3.1}$$

Thus T_{oo} is a symmetric 2×2 matrix, $T_{\mathrm{co}} = (T_{\mathrm{oc}})_{\mathrm{tr}}$ is a two-component row vector and T_{cc} is a single number. The formalism may be extended to include several closed channels.

In the unitarity equation $S^+S = 1$, only open channels are allowed. Therefore, this S is a 2×2 matrix S_{oo} below the $\overline{\mathrm{K}}$N threshold and a 3×3 matrix S above. Repeating our arguments of the previous section for S_{oo}, we conclude the existence of a symmetric 2×2 matrix K_{r}, defined by

$$T_{\mathrm{oo}} = K_{\mathrm{r}}(1-\mathrm{i}q_{\mathrm{o}}K_{\mathrm{r}})^{-1}, \tag{3.2}$$

such that K_{r} is real below the $\overline{\mathrm{K}}$N threshold. This matrix is called the reduced K-matrix. The advantage of using K_{r} instead of K is that one need not consider closed channels explicitly. However, one may also use the definitions (1) and (2) above the $\overline{\mathrm{K}}$N threshold. There, K_{r} will of course be complex. The explicit relation between K_{r} and K is

$$K_{\mathrm{r}} = K_{\mathrm{oo}} + \frac{\mathrm{i}q_{\mathrm{c}}K_{\mathrm{oc}}^2}{1-\mathrm{i}q_{\mathrm{c}}K_{\mathrm{cc}}}. \tag{3.3}$$

To derive it, we consider that part of Heitler's equation (2.3) for which the first index is o:

$$\begin{aligned} T_{\mathrm{oo}}(1-\mathrm{i}q_{\mathrm{o}}K_{\mathrm{oo}}) &= K_{\mathrm{oo}}+\mathrm{i}T_{\mathrm{oc}}q_{\mathrm{c}}K_{\mathrm{co}}, \\ T_{\mathrm{oc}}(1-\mathrm{i}q_{\mathrm{c}}K_{\mathrm{cc}}) &= K_{\mathrm{oc}}+\mathrm{i}T_{\mathrm{oo}}q_{\mathrm{o}}K_{\mathrm{oc}}. \end{aligned} \tag{3.4}$$

Elimination of T_{oc} from these equations leads to (2), with K_{r} given by (3).

A corresponding expression for T_{cc},

$$\begin{aligned} T_{\mathrm{cc}} &= \frac{A_{\mathrm{cc}}}{1-\mathrm{i}q_{\mathrm{c}}A_{\mathrm{cc}}}, \\ A_{\mathrm{cc}} &= K_{\mathrm{cc}}+\mathrm{i}K_{\mathrm{co}}(1-\mathrm{i}q_{\mathrm{o}}K_{\mathrm{oo}})^{-1}q_{\mathrm{o}}K_{\mathrm{oc}}, \end{aligned} \tag{3.5}$$

follows from the remaining parts of Heitler's equation,

$$T_{cc}(1-iq_c K_{cc}) = K_{cc}+iT_{co}q_o K_{oc},$$
$$T_{co}(1-iq_o K_{oo}) = K_{co}+iT_{cc}q_c K_{co}. \tag{3.6}$$

Obviously, the formalism is symmetric in c and o. The vector T_{co} may be expressed in two different ways. From the second eq. (6), we get

$$T_{co} = \frac{A_{co}}{1-iq_c A_{cc}}, \qquad A_{co} = K_{co}(1-iq_o K_{oo})^{-1}. \tag{3.7}$$

This expression is particularly useful for $\overline{K}p \to \pi\Lambda$ and $\overline{K}p \to \pi\Sigma$, since it contains the same denominator as the elastic $\overline{K}N$ scattering matrix element (5). The unitarity condition which connects T_{cc} and T_{co} may be expressed as

$$\text{Im}\, A_{cc} = A_{co}^{+}\, q_0\, A_{co}. \tag{3.8}$$

It is automatically satisfied by the expressions (5) and (7) for A_{cc} and A_{co}.

8-4. Parameters of the low-energy K^-p interactions

The isotropy of K^-p cross-sections up to 300 MeV/c kaon lab momentum indicates a dominance of S-wave amplitudes. The first thing we may try to do is to parametrize these amplitudes by scattering lengths. As explained in section 8-2, this corresponds to an energy-independent K-matrix. Unfortunately, even this first step meets with difficulties. Only the absolute squares of the six matrix elements (1.1) to (1.3) have been measured so far. A reconstruction of the K-matrix requires three real parameters for $I = 0$ and six for $I = 1$, which shows that three parameters are still missing.

Instead, we can parametrize the amplitudes T^I, T_Σ^I and T_Λ^I by the complex functions A of (3.5) and (3.7):

$$T^I = \frac{A^I}{1-iqA^I}, \qquad T_\Sigma^I = \frac{A_\Sigma^I}{1-iqA^I}, \qquad T_\Lambda^1 = \frac{A_\Lambda^1}{1-iqA^1}. \tag{4.1}$$

Here $q = q_c$ means $q_{\overline{K}N}$, A^I stands for A_{cc}^I, and A_Σ^I, A_Λ^I are the components of the vector A_{co}^I. As a first approximation, we assume the functions A to be energy-independent "scattering lengths". By the definitions (3.5) and (3.7) of the A's, this contradicts our assumption of an energy-independent K-matrix. In fact, (3.8) shows that some components are necessarily energy-dependent. Explicitly, (3.8) reads

$$\begin{aligned} \text{Im}\, A^0 &= q_{\pi\Sigma}|A^0_\Sigma|^2, \\ \text{Im}\, A^1 &= q_{\pi\Lambda}|A^1_\Lambda|^2 + q_{\pi\Sigma}|A^1_\Sigma|^2. \end{aligned} \tag{4.2}$$

However, the A's do not depend explicitly on $q = q_c$, which is the critical momentum near the $\overline{\text{K}}$N threshold.

The cross-sections for $\text{K}^-\text{p} \to \text{K}^-\text{p}$, $\to \overline{\text{K}}{}^0\text{n}$, $\to \pi^0\Lambda$, and $\text{K}^-\text{p} \to \pi^0\Sigma^0$ are now expressed as

$$\left.\begin{matrix} \sigma(\text{K}^-\text{p}) \\ \sigma(\overline{\text{K}}{}^0\text{n}) \end{matrix}\right\} = \pi \left| \frac{A^1}{1 - \text{i}qA_1} \pm \frac{A^0}{1 - \text{i}qA^0} \right|^2, \tag{4.3}$$

$$\sigma(\pi^0\Sigma^0) = \tfrac{2}{3}\pi \frac{q_{\pi\Sigma}}{q} \frac{|A^0_\Sigma|^2}{1 + q^2|A^0|^2} = \frac{2\pi}{3q} \frac{\text{Im}\, A^0}{1 + q^2|A^0|^2}, \tag{4.4}$$

$$\sigma(\pi^0\Lambda) = 2\pi \frac{q_{\pi\Lambda}}{q} \frac{|A^1_\Lambda|^2}{1 + q^2|A^1|^2} = \frac{2\pi}{q} \frac{\varepsilon\, \text{Im}\, A^1}{1 + q^2|A^1|^2}. \tag{4.5}$$

In (4) we have applied (2), and in (5) we have introduced the fraction

$$\varepsilon \equiv q_{\pi\Lambda} \frac{|A^1_\Lambda|^2}{\text{Im}\, A^1} = \frac{\sigma^1(\pi\Lambda)}{\sigma^1(\pi\Lambda) + \sigma^1(\pi\Sigma)}. \tag{4.6}$$

The cross-sections $\sigma^1(\pi\Sigma)$ and $\sigma^1(\pi\Lambda)$ are given by (1.4) and (1.5). Finally, the cross-sections for $\text{K}^-\text{p} \to \Sigma^\pm\pi^\mp$ follow from (1.2) in the form

$$\sigma(\Sigma^\pm\pi^\mp) = \pi \frac{q_{\pi\Sigma}}{q} \left(|T^1_\Sigma|^2 + \tfrac{2}{3}|T^0_\Sigma|^2 \pm 2(\tfrac{2}{3})^{\frac{1}{2}} |T^1_\Sigma||T^0_\Sigma| \cos\phi\right), \tag{4.7}$$

where ϕ is the relative phase between T^1_Σ and T^0_Σ. Applying again (2), we obtain

$$q_{\pi\Sigma}|T^1_\Sigma|^2 = \frac{(1-\varepsilon)\, \text{Im}\, A^1}{1 + q^2|A^1|^2}, \qquad q_{\pi\Sigma}|T^0_\Sigma|^2 = \frac{\text{Im}\, A^0}{1 + q^2|A^0|^2}. \tag{4.8}$$

For comparison with experiment, one must include both the Coulomb interaction (section 10-1) and the $\text{K}^- - \text{K}^0$ mass difference (JACKSON and WYLD [1959], DALITZ and TUAN [1960]). The values of ε and ϕ are (KIM [1965])

$$\varepsilon = 0.32, \qquad \phi = 53.8°. \tag{4.9}$$

A recent determination of the complex parameters A^I (KITTEL, OTTER and WACEK [1966]) gives

$$\begin{aligned} A^0 &= (-1.57 + \text{i}\, 0.54)\text{fm} = (-8.0 + \text{i}\, 2.7)/\text{GeV}, \\ A^1 &= (-0.24 + \text{i}\, 0.43)\text{fm} = (-1.2 + \text{i}\, 2.2)/\text{GeV}. \end{aligned} \tag{4.10}$$

For many years, experiments allowed a second set of parameters, which was rejected mainly on the basis of theoretical considerations. For example, the real part of A^0 in this latter set is as small as -0.4 fm. This would be in disagreement with the model of the $Y_0^*(1405)$ resonance to be discussed in the next section.

8-5. The $Y_0^*(1405)$ as a virtual $\overline{\mathrm{K}}\mathrm{N}$ bound state

A striking feature of the parameters A of (4.10) is the large negative value of Re A^0. If the $\pi\Sigma$ channels were decoupled, the $I = 0$ $\overline{\mathrm{K}}\mathrm{N}$ scattering would be a one-channel problem close to threshold. In that case, A^0 would be real, and T^0 as given by (4.1) would have a pole at $1 - \mathrm{i}qA^0 = 0$, provided $-A$ is much larger than the effective range (see section 6-5). This pole would correspond to a $\overline{\mathrm{K}}\mathrm{N}$ bound state. When the $\pi\Sigma$ channel is included, the state may decay into $\pi\Sigma$. Clearly, the Y_0^* (1405) resonance, which was mentioned in section 5-4 (see eq. (5-4.10)), is a candidate for such a state. Being unstable against decay by strong interactions, it is called a "virtual bound state". If this interpretation is correct, the Y_0^* (1405) must be a $\frac{1}{2}^-$ state.

The position of the resonance may be calculated if the K-matrix element K_{oo} for elastic $\pi\Sigma$ scattering for $I = 0$ can be neglected (DALITZ [1961]). We then have ($q_{\mathrm{o}} = q_{\pi\Sigma}$)

$$A^0 = K_{\mathrm{cc}} + \mathrm{i}K_{\mathrm{co}}^2 q_{\mathrm{o}}, \tag{5.1}$$

according to (3.5). The reduced K-matrix of $\pi\Sigma$ scattering is given by (3.3). Remembering that K_{cc} and K_{co} are real, (1) implies

$$K_{\mathrm{r}} = \frac{\mathrm{i}q_{\mathrm{c}} K_{\mathrm{oc}}^2}{1 - \mathrm{i}q_{\mathrm{c}} K_{\mathrm{cc}}} = \mathrm{i}\frac{q_{\mathrm{c}}}{q_{\mathrm{o}}} \frac{\mathrm{Im}\, A^0}{1 - \mathrm{i}q_{\mathrm{c}}\, \mathrm{Re}\, A^0}. \tag{5.2}$$

This expression is real below the $\overline{\mathrm{K}}\mathrm{N}$ threshold. It becomes infinite at $1 = \mathrm{i}q_{\mathrm{c}}$ Re A^0, which corresponds to the position of the $\pi\Sigma$ resonance (remember that $q_0 K_{\mathrm{r}} = \tan \delta^0(\pi\Sigma \to \pi\Sigma)$). In terms of the "binding energy" E_{B} and the reduced mass μ of the $\overline{\mathrm{K}}\mathrm{N}$ bound state, the non-relativistic approximation gives

$$-2\mu E_{\mathrm{B}} = q_{\mathrm{c}}^2(\mathrm{res.}) = -(\mathrm{Re}\, A^0)^{-2}. \tag{5.3}$$

Inserting Re A^0 from (4.10), we obtain 24 MeV binding energy, which corresponds to a Y_0^* mass of

$$494 \text{ MeV} + 938 \text{ MeV} - 24 \text{ MeV} = 1408 \text{ MeV}, \tag{5.4}$$

in rough agreement with the experimental mass of 1405 MeV.

The width of the Y_0^* may be calculated in the same approximation. Remembering the definition of mass and width of a narrow resonance, we have

$$\frac{\frac{1}{2}\Gamma}{m-E} = \tan\delta = q_0 K_r = \frac{iq_c \operatorname{Im} A^0}{1-iq_c \operatorname{Re} A^0} = \frac{\operatorname{Im} A^0}{\dfrac{1}{iq_c} - \operatorname{Re} A^0}. \tag{5.5}$$

Since we have assumed constant A^0, we need only the variation of $(iq_c)^{-1}$ in the neighbourhood of $E = m$,

$$(iq_c)^{-1} = \operatorname{Re} A^0 + (E-m)\frac{d}{dE}\left(\frac{1}{iq_c}\right)_{E=m}. \tag{5.6}$$

From (3), we find the value $(2\mu E_B)^{-\frac{1}{2}}/\mu$ for the derivative, which implies

$$\tfrac{1}{2}\Gamma = \frac{1}{\mu}\operatorname{Im} A^0 (2\mu E_B)^{\frac{1}{2}} = -\frac{1}{\mu}\operatorname{Im} A^0/(\operatorname{Re} A^0)^3. \tag{5.7}$$

The last expression gives a width of 34 MeV. If we use the experimental value of E_B instead of Re A^0, we get a somewhat larger value. In any case, the agreement with the experimental width of 35 MeV is satisfactory.

These results give some confidence in the correctness of the model. We therefore conclude that (i) the Y_0^* (1405) is an S-wave resonance and (ii) that it is strongly coupled to the $\overline{\mathrm{K}}$N system.

8-6. The Y_0^*(1520) and the Σ parity

There are a number of resonances above the $\overline{\mathrm{K}}$N threshold. The first two of these, namely the Y_0^* (1520) and the Y_1^* (1660), were already mentioned in section 5-4 (see table 5-3). The Y_0^* (1520) corresponds to an incident K^- momentum of 393 MeV/c. It was found by FERRO-LUZZI, WATSON and TRIPP [1962, 1963] in a study of K^-p interactions between 250 and 500 MeV/c. The reaction $K^-p \to \Lambda\pi^+\pi^-$, the cross-section of which is much smaller than 1 mb below 350 MeV/c, exhibits a peak of about 3 mb at resonance energy. The $\Sigma^+\pi^-$, $\Sigma^-\pi^+$ and $\Sigma^0\pi^0$ final states also have peaks of about 3 mb each. These peaks are less pronounced, since they are superimposed on non-resonant scattering of about 10, 6 and 4 mb, respectively. The elastic scattering, which is of the order of 40 mb at 400 MeV/c, shows hardly any peak. In the charge exchange, the peak is again visible, being roughly 5 mb on a background of 5 mb. The reaction $K^-p \to \Lambda\pi^0$ finally has a cross-section of about 4 mb and shows no peak.

The absence of a peak in the $\Lambda\pi^0$ state and the equal heights of the peaks in the three $\Sigma\pi$ states indicate $I = 0$ for the resonance.

Spin and parity of the resonance may be determined from the angular distribution of elastic and charge exchange scattering. Below the resonance energy, the scattering is isotropic, i.e. S-wave scattering. As the energy increases, the isotropic part decreases and a large $\cos^2\theta$ term appears, without appreciable $\cos\theta$ or $\cos^3\theta$ terms. The relation between these terms and the partial wave amplitudes $f_{L\pm}$ was given in (5-1.6). The smallness of the $\cos\theta$ term excludes f_{1+} and f_{1-} as resonating partial wave amplitudes. The only remaining amplitude is f_{2-}. This in fact produces a large $\cos^2\theta$ term, mainly by interference with the S-wave amplitude. With $f_{1+} = f_{1-} = 0$, we may rewrite (5-1.4) and (5-1.6) in the form

$$\frac{d\sigma}{d\Omega} = |f_{0+} + 2f_{2-}|^2 \cos^2\theta + |f_{0+} - f_{2-}|^2 \sin^2\theta. \tag{6.1}$$

At resonance energy, the resonating amplitude is imaginary. Since f_{0+} has a large imaginary part, we get constructive interference in the $\cos^2\theta$ term. We thus have succeeded in determining the spin and parity of the resonance from the differential cross-section, although the integrated elastic cross-section shows hardly any bump.

The inelasticity $x = \Gamma_e/\Gamma$ of the resonance is obtained by inspection of the $\overline{K}n$ peak. According to (1.1), the $I = 0$ amplitude occurs in the amplitude for $K^-p \to \overline{K}^0 n$ with a coefficient $\frac{1}{2}$. Therefore, the height of the peak should be $\frac{1}{4}$ of (5-3.11), which leads to $x = 0.3$.

We now study the reactions $K^-p \to \Sigma\pi$ in the resonance region. Knowing the spin and parity of the resonance, we can determine the intrinsic parity of the Σ-hyperon from these reactions. As mentioned in section 4-4, the intrinsic parity of K is known to be negative from the analysis of K-mesic atoms. Therefore, if Σ and p have equal parities, the final state in $K^-p \to \Sigma\pi$ will be a mixture of $S_{\frac{1}{2}}$ and $D_{\frac{3}{2}}$ waves. If they have opposite parities, it will be a mixture of $P_{\frac{1}{2}}$ and $P_{\frac{3}{2}}$ waves instead.

Because of the Minami ambiguity (section 5-1), the $\cos\theta$ dependence of the cross-section is the same in both cases. Also, we cannot apply arguments about threshold behaviour, since $K^-p \to \Sigma\pi$ is exothermic. However, the Minami ambiguity is resolved by the Σ polarization. The polarization is measured by the angular distributions of the parity-nonconserving decays $\Sigma \to \pi N$. This will be discussed in section 9-3 below. As will be derived in (9-3.11), the polarization P_y is proportional to $-2\,\mathrm{Im}\,T(\frac{1}{2},\frac{1}{2})T^*(\frac{1}{2},-\frac{1}{2})$. The partial wave decompositions of $T(\frac{1}{2},\frac{1}{2})$ and $T(\frac{1}{2},-\frac{1}{2})$ are given by the two sums in (5-1.2), apart from an uninteresting factor $16\pi s^{\frac{1}{2}}$. The $J = \frac{1}{2}$ and $J = \frac{3}{2}$ terms of these expansions are given in (5-1.3). Including a normalization factor, we find

$$P_y \frac{\mathrm{d}\sigma}{\mathrm{d}\Omega} = -8 \operatorname{Im} \{\cos \tfrac{1}{2}\theta[f_{0+} + f_{1-} + (1-3\sin^2 \tfrac{1}{2}\theta)(f_{1+} + f_{2-})] \times \sin \tfrac{1}{2}\theta[f_{0+}^* - f_{1-}^* + (3\cos^2 \tfrac{1}{2}\theta - 1)(f_{1+} - f_{2-})]\}. \quad (6.2)$$

Evaluation of this expression gives a form similar to (5-1.4), (5-1.6),

$$P_y \frac{\mathrm{d}\sigma}{\mathrm{d}\Omega} = \sin\theta(B_0 + B_1 \cos\theta + B_2 \cos^2\theta), \quad (6.3)$$

$$B_0 = 2 \operatorname{Im} (f_{0+} - f_{2-})(f_{1-}^* - f_{1+}^*),$$
$$B_1 = 6 \operatorname{Im} (f_{0+} f_{2-}^* - f_{1-} f_{1+}^*),$$
$$B_2 = 18 \operatorname{Im} f_{1+} f_{2-}^* . \quad (6.4)$$

Obviously, the polarization changes sign under the Minami transformation $f_{L+} \leftrightarrow f_{(L+1)-}$. Therefore, positive and negative Σ parities lead to opposite polarization. However, the polarization is invariant under the exchange $f_{L+} \leftrightarrow f_{(L+1)-}^*$. Therefore, one needs a separate argument to exclude complex conjugation. Here we use the fact, discussed in sections 2-8 and 2-9, that a resonating amplitude describes a circle counter-clockwise.

In the present case, B_0 and B_2 are small, and B_1 is approximately, for $\eta_\Sigma = +1$,

$$B_1 = 6 \operatorname{Im} f_{0+} f_{2-}^* = 6 \operatorname{Im} f_{0+} \operatorname{Re} f_{2-} - 6 \operatorname{Re} f_{0+} \operatorname{Im} f_{2-} . \quad (6.5)$$

For $\eta_\Sigma = -1$, the term $-6 \operatorname{Im} f_{1-} f_{1+}^*$ gives the main contribution. Next, we look at the energy variation of B_1. The non-resonating amplitude and the imaginary part of the resonating amplitude vary comparatively slowly in the resonance region. On the other hand, the real part of the resonating amplitude varies rapidly, going from positive to negative values as one passes the resonance energy. Since the imaginary part of the non-resonating amplitude is positive, the rapidly varying part of B_1 will be positive below resonance energy for $\eta_\Sigma = +1$ and negative for $\eta_\Sigma = -1$. In other words, $\eta_\Sigma = +1$ requires a bump below resonance energy, and a dip above. For $\eta_\Sigma = -1$, the dip must come first. By this method η_Σ is determined to be $+1$.

8-7. The meson-baryon coupling constants in SU_3 symmetry

In section 8-1, we defined the meson-baryon coupling constants $G_{\Lambda\pi\Sigma}$, $G_{\text{NK}\Lambda}$, $G_{\Sigma\pi\Sigma}$ and $G_{\text{NK}\Sigma}$. None of these constants is known with an accuracy comparable with that of the pion-nucleon coupling constant G. Relatively well known is $G_{\Lambda\pi\Sigma}$, mainly from the analysis of Λp scattering. A rough value is $G^2_{\Lambda\pi\Sigma}/4\pi = 10$ (see e.g. MARTIN [1965]). By SU_3 symmetry, the remaining coupling constants may be expressed in terms of G and $G_{\Lambda\pi\Sigma}$.

The occurrence of two independent SU_3-invariant couplings for baryon → (meson, baryon) reflects the fact that the irreducible representation $\underline{8}$ is contained twice in the direct product $8 \otimes 8$:

$$8 \otimes 8 = 1+8+8+10+\overline{10}+27. \tag{7.1}$$

We shall not discuss the reduction of $8 \otimes 8$. Instead, we derive the desired relations by means of U-spin invariance, as we did for the decays vector meson → (meson, meson). The situation is analogous, since vector mesons, mesons and baryons all belong to octets. In fact, we may use (5-7.8), if we replace the vector meson and one of the final mesons by the corresponding baryons. The correspondence is found from the (Q, U)-plots of figs. 5-5 and 5-7,

$$K^{*0} \to n, \qquad \rho^0 \to \Sigma^0, \qquad \phi_0 \to \Lambda, \qquad \pi^+ \to \Sigma^+, \quad K^+ \to p. \tag{7.2}$$

Applying this substitution in (5-7.8), we obtain

$$\begin{aligned} 2^{-\frac{1}{2}}G(n \to p\pi^-) &= -\tfrac{1}{2}G(\Sigma^0 \to \Sigma^+\pi^-)+\tfrac{1}{2}\sqrt{3}G(\Lambda \to \Sigma^+\pi^-) \\ &= -\tfrac{1}{2}G(\Sigma^0 \to pK^-)+\tfrac{1}{2}\sqrt{3}G(\Lambda \to pK^-). \end{aligned} \tag{7.3}$$

There is one difference between this equation and (5-7.8): the coupling constant $G(\phi_0 \to \pi^+\pi^-)$ is zero due to G-parity, whereas the corresponding $G(\Lambda \to \Sigma^+\pi^-)$ need not be zero. Following GELL-MANN [1961], we define

$$-\tfrac{1}{2}\sqrt{3}G_{\Lambda\pi\Sigma} = \alpha G. \tag{7.4}$$

Then, from eqs. (7-1.7), (1.10), (1.8), (1.11) and (1.9) for G, $G_{\Sigma\pi\Sigma}$, $G_{\Lambda\pi\Sigma}$, $G_{NK\Sigma}$ and $G_{NK\Lambda}$, we obtain (3) in the form

$$G = \tfrac{1}{2}G_{\Sigma\pi\Sigma}-\tfrac{1}{2}\sqrt{3}G_{\Lambda\pi\Sigma} = \tfrac{1}{2}G_{NK\Sigma}-\tfrac{1}{2}\sqrt{3}G_{NK\Lambda}. \tag{7.5}$$

The first equality reads, in terms of α,

$$G_{\Sigma\pi\Sigma} = 2G(1-\alpha). \tag{7.6}$$

The parameter α is called the "fraction of D-type coupling", and $1-\alpha$ is called the "fraction of F-type coupling". In the case of vector meson decay, the D-type coupling was excluded by G-parity.

Next, we calculate the coupling constants $G_{NK\Sigma}$ and $G_{NK\Lambda}$ of the r.h.s. of

(5). We obtain a second independent equation from (5-7.8) if we substitute

$$K^{*0} \to n, \qquad \rho^0 \to \Sigma^0, \qquad \phi_0 \to \Lambda, \qquad \pi^- \to \Sigma^-, \qquad K^- \to \Xi^-. \quad (7.7)$$

Here we have substituted the negative meson according to fig. 5-5, instead of the positive meson as in (7). The resulting equation is

$$\begin{aligned} 2^{-\frac{1}{2}}G(n \to K^+\Sigma^-) &= -\tfrac{1}{2}G(\Sigma^0 \to \pi^+\Sigma^-)+\tfrac{1}{2}\sqrt{3}G(\Lambda \to \pi^+\Sigma^-) \\ &= -\tfrac{1}{2}G(\Sigma^0 \to K^+\Xi^-)+\tfrac{1}{2}\sqrt{3}G(\Lambda \to K^+\Xi^-). \quad (7.8) \end{aligned}$$

By (1.12), (1.10) and (1.8), the first equality becomes

$$G_{NK\Sigma} = -\tfrac{1}{2}G_{\Sigma\pi\Sigma}-\tfrac{1}{2}\sqrt{3}G_{\Lambda\pi\Sigma} = -G(1-2\alpha). \quad (7.9)$$

Inserting this into the second equality of (5), we find

$$3^{\frac{1}{2}}G_{NK\Lambda} = G_{NK\Sigma}-2G = -G(3-2\alpha). \quad (7.10)$$

This completes our task. The "orthodox" way, namely the reduction of $8 \otimes 8$ as indicated by (1), is more laborious (DESWART [1963]). There is one point which we have not discussed, namely the phase between π^- and K^-. Here we draw profit from our phase conventions in charge conjugation and in antiparticle isospin multiplets, as discussed in section 4-7. In particular, if we had not used positive charge parity for n and Λ and negative charge parity for p, some extra minus signs would have been necessary in the SU_3 multiplets.

At present, the meagre evidence on $G_{\Sigma\pi\Sigma}$, $G_{NK\Sigma}$ and $G_{NK\Lambda}$ allows no exact test of eqs. (6), (9) and (10). $G^2_{NK\Lambda}$ appears to be much larger than $G^2_{NK\Sigma}$ (JARLSKOG and PILKUHN [1966], ZOVKO [1966]). This agrees with

$$\alpha^2 = \frac{3}{4}\frac{G^2_{\Lambda\pi\Sigma}}{G^2} \approx \frac{1}{2} \quad (7.11)$$

and shows that α must be positive, $\alpha \approx 0.71$. The absolute values of $G^2_{NK\Lambda}/4\pi$ and $G^2_{NK\Sigma}/4\pi$ are 7 ± 3 and 2 ± 1, according to dispersion relations of $K^\pm$p-scattering (ZOVKO [1966]).

Another coupling constant which might be of interest is that of $N \to \eta N$,

$$G_\eta \equiv G(n \to \eta n) = G(p \to \eta p). \quad (7.12)$$

From the fact that n and $\frac{1}{2}(-\Sigma^0+3^{\frac{1}{2}}\Lambda)$ are in one U-spin triplet and K^0 and $\frac{1}{2}(-\pi^0+3^{\frac{1}{2}}\eta)$ are in another U-spin triplet, we obtain

$$-G(n \to \pi^0 n)+3^{\frac{1}{2}}G(n \to \eta n) = G(n \to K^0\Sigma^0)-3^{\frac{1}{2}}G(n \to K^0\Lambda). \quad (7.13)$$

Here the corresponding terms on both sides have opposite signs, due to the antisymmetry of the Clebsch-Gordan coefficients for the coupling $1 \rightarrow 1+1$. In terms of G and α, (13) reads

$$G_\eta = 3^{-\frac{1}{2}} G(3-4\alpha). \tag{7.14}$$

For $\alpha = 0.71$, G_η is about 10% of G.

Finally, we may reverse the signs of U_3 in (3), (8), and (13), thereby replacing

$$\mathrm{n} \leftrightarrow \Xi^0, \quad \mathrm{p} \leftrightarrow \Sigma^+, \quad \Sigma^- \leftrightarrow \Xi^-, \quad \pi^- \leftrightarrow \mathrm{K}^-, \quad \mathrm{K}^0 \leftrightarrow \overline{\mathrm{K}}^0, \quad \pi^+ \leftrightarrow \mathrm{K}^+. \tag{7.15}$$

We then arrive at the following relations between coupling constants (DESWART [1963]):

$$G_{\Sigma\mathrm{K}\Xi} = -G, \qquad G_{\Lambda\mathrm{K}\Xi} = G_\eta, \tag{7.16}$$

$$G_{\Sigma\eta\Sigma} = -G_{\Lambda\eta\Lambda} = G_{\Lambda\pi\Sigma}, \tag{7.17}$$

$$G_{\Xi\pi\Xi} = -G_{\mathrm{NK}\Sigma}, \qquad G_{\Xi\eta\Xi} = G_{\mathrm{NK}\Lambda}. \tag{7.18}$$

Of course, the signs in front of the new coupling constants are a matter of definition. For example, the signs of (16) imply

$$G_{\Sigma\mathrm{K}\Xi} \equiv G(\Sigma^0 \rightarrow \mathrm{K}^+\Xi^-), \qquad G_{\Lambda\mathrm{K}\Xi} \equiv -G(\Lambda \rightarrow \mathrm{K}^+\Xi^-), \tag{7.19}$$

which may be verified from (8). At present, none of these coupling constants is known.

CHAPTER 9

HELICITY AND POLARIZATION

9-1. One- and two-particle helicity states

In chapter 3, we discussed a number of special cases of the relativistic spin problem. We constructed states for particles of spin $\frac{1}{2}$, 1, $\frac{3}{2}$ and 2. We also discussed in detail the partial wave decomposition of meson-baryon scattering. In section 4-8, we considered the decays $\pi^0 \to \gamma\gamma$ and $\Sigma^0 \to \gamma\Lambda$. In this chapter, we shall study decays d → 12 and reactions ab → cd, allowing all particles to have arbitrary spins. Our aim is to obtain as much information as possible about the matrix elements, without using explicit expressions for the spin states.

The helicity formalism of JACOB and WICK [1959] is particularly elegant for this purpose. Reviews on the subject have been given by JACOB [1961], DURAND [1961], GOLDBERGER and WATSON [1964] and WERLE [1966]. We shall adopt the phase conventions of Jacob and Wick. Otherwise, we shall deviate considerably from the original presentation. By treating the decay problem first, we can avoid the use of abstract rotation operators for spinning particles in flight.

We begin with the spin states $|M\rangle$ of a particle at rest. We assume that the particle has a non-zero mass, although many results will apply also to the massless case. States of momentum $\boldsymbol{p}$ are obtained by acting with a boost operator $A(\boldsymbol{p})$ on the rest states. For spin $\frac{1}{2}$, $A(\boldsymbol{p})$ is given by (3-4.9) or (3-4.10). The boosts for higher spins will not be considered explicitly. Instead, we investigate the commutation relations of $A(\boldsymbol{p}) = \exp(\boldsymbol{p} \cdot \boldsymbol{J})$ with the generators $\boldsymbol{J}$ of rotations. Since these commutation relations are independent of the representation, they may be found from the operators of section 3-4, with $\boldsymbol{J} = \frac{1}{2}\boldsymbol{\sigma}$.

We first observe that $A(\boldsymbol{p})$ does not commute with J_z. Therefore, states $|\boldsymbol{p}, M\rangle$ which are simultaneous eigenstates of the momentum operator and of J_z do not exist (unless $p_x = p_y = 0$). In this respect, our notation $u(\boldsymbol{p}, M)$ for Dirac spinors was misleading. That M was the eigenvalue of a more complicated operator, which reduces to J_z for particles at rest.

Next, we observe that $A(\boldsymbol{p})$ does commute with the helicity operator

$$\Lambda = \boldsymbol{J} \cdot \boldsymbol{p}/p = \boldsymbol{J} \cdot \hat{\boldsymbol{p}}, \tag{1.1}$$

which is the component of the spin operator along the momentum. Its eigenvalues are denoted by λ. The simultaneous eigenstates of Λ and the momentum operator are denoted by $|\boldsymbol{p}, \lambda\rangle$ or $|p, \lambda, \vartheta, \varphi\rangle$, where ϑ and φ are the polar and azimuthal angles of $\boldsymbol{p}$. By the boost $A(\boldsymbol{p})$, we have

$$|\boldsymbol{p}, \lambda\rangle = |p, \lambda, \vartheta, \varphi\rangle = A(\boldsymbol{p})|M = \lambda, \vartheta, \varphi\rangle = \sum_{M'} A(\boldsymbol{p}) D_{M'M}(\varphi, \vartheta, -\varphi)|M'\rangle. \tag{1.2}$$

In the last equation, we have inserted (3-1.1). A minor complication is that $\hat{\boldsymbol{p}}$ cannot be defined as $\boldsymbol{p}/p$ for $p = 0$. However, we may say that in the limit $p \to 0$, the eigenstates of Λ coincide with the rotated spin states $|M, \vartheta, \varphi\rangle$.

Next, we consider two particles of helicities λ_1 and λ_2 in their cms. Because of $\boldsymbol{p}_1 = -\boldsymbol{p}_2 \equiv \boldsymbol{p}$, the total helicity operator is

$$\Lambda = \Lambda_1 + \Lambda_2 = (\boldsymbol{J}_1 - \boldsymbol{J}_2) \cdot \boldsymbol{p}/p. \tag{1.3}$$

Stated inversely, two particles of helicities λ_1 and λ_2 in their cms have magnetic quantum number $\lambda_1 - \lambda_2$ along $\boldsymbol{p}_1$. This circumstance was already noted for the decay $\pi^0 \to \gamma\gamma$ of section 4-8. In general, $|p, \lambda_1 \lambda_2, \vartheta\varphi\rangle$ will denote a cms two-particle state with angles ϑ and φ for $\boldsymbol{p}_1$ ($\pi - \vartheta$ and $\varphi + \pi$ for $\boldsymbol{p}_2$):

$$|p, \lambda_1 \lambda_2, \vartheta\varphi\rangle = |\boldsymbol{p}, \lambda_1\rangle|-\boldsymbol{p}, \lambda_2\rangle\phi, \tag{1.4}$$

$$\boldsymbol{J} \cdot \boldsymbol{p}|p, \lambda_1 \lambda_2, \vartheta\varphi\rangle = (\lambda_1 - \lambda_2)|p, \lambda_1 \lambda_2, \vartheta, \varphi\rangle \equiv \lambda|p, \lambda_1 \lambda_2, \vartheta, \varphi\rangle. \tag{1.5}$$

Note that $\lambda = \lambda_1 - \lambda_2$ is the eigenvalue of $\boldsymbol{J} \cdot \hat{\boldsymbol{p}}$, but not of Λ. The factor ϕ in the definition of $|p, \lambda_1 \lambda_2, \vartheta\varphi\rangle$ is a phase. Following Jacob and Wick [1959], we adjust ϕ such that $|-\boldsymbol{p}, \lambda_2\rangle$ reduces to $|-\lambda_2, \vartheta, \varphi\rangle$ for $p = 0$. For $\boldsymbol{p}$ in the xz-plane, we have $\varphi = 0$, and

$$\begin{aligned} |-\boldsymbol{p}, \lambda_2\rangle &= A_2(-\boldsymbol{p})|M_2 = \lambda_2, \pi - \vartheta, \pi\rangle, \\ |\lambda_2, \pi - \vartheta, \pi\rangle &= (\mathrm{e}^{-i\pi J_y})_{M'\lambda_2}|M', \vartheta, 0\rangle = (-1)^{S_2 - \lambda_2}|-\lambda_2, \vartheta, 0\rangle, \end{aligned} \tag{1.6}$$

according to (C-2.8). Therefore ϕ in (4) should be taken as

$$\phi = (-1)^{S_2 - \lambda_2} \qquad \text{for} \quad \varphi = 0. \tag{1.7}$$

For the rest of this section, we discuss the behaviour of helicity states under parity conjugation, $\mathscr{P}$. For the spin states $|M, \vartheta, 0\rangle$ at rest, we have

$$\mathscr{P}|M, \vartheta, 0\rangle = \eta|M, \vartheta, 0\rangle, \tag{1.8}$$

where η is the intrinsic parity of the particle under consideration. For the helicity states $|\boldsymbol{p}, \lambda\rangle$ on the other hand, λ is reversed even in the limit $\boldsymbol{p} \to 0$. Thus the limit of the parity-transformed state is not the parity transformed state (8) of the limit. Jacob and Wick solve this problem by considering instead of $\mathscr{P}$ a reflection in the (x, z)-plane (inversion of the y-axis)

$$\mathscr{Y} = e^{-i\pi J_y}\mathscr{P}. \tag{1.9}$$

This operator does not affect p_x or p_z and therefore commutes with all boosts $A(\boldsymbol{p})$ for which $p_y = 0$. Therefore, $|\boldsymbol{p}, \lambda\rangle$ and $|M = \lambda, \vartheta, 0\rangle$ transform in the same way under $\mathscr{Y}$:

$$\mathscr{Y}|M = \lambda, \vartheta, 0\rangle = e^{-i\pi J_y}\eta|M = \lambda, \vartheta, 0\rangle = \eta(-1)^{S-\eta}|-\lambda, \vartheta, 0\rangle, \tag{1.10}$$

$$\mathscr{Y}|p, \lambda, \vartheta, 0\rangle = \eta(-1)^{S-\lambda}|p, -\lambda, \vartheta, 0\rangle. \tag{1.11}$$

In the following, we shall derive consequences of parity conservation by means of the operator $\mathscr{Y}$. For reactions ab → cd, $\mathscr{Y}$ will represent the inversion of the normal to the production plane, leaving all particle momenta unchanged.

For the two-particle helicity states, $\mathscr{Y}$ gives

$$\mathscr{Y}|p, \lambda_1\lambda_2, \vartheta, 0\rangle = \eta_1\eta_2(-1)^{S_1+S_2-\lambda_1+\lambda_2}|p, -\lambda_1, -\lambda_2, \vartheta, 0\rangle. \tag{1.12}$$

Here $+\lambda_2$ appears in the exponent instead of $-\lambda_2$, since $|-\boldsymbol{p}, \lambda_2\rangle\phi$ reduces to $|-\lambda_2, \vartheta, 0\rangle$ for $-\boldsymbol{p} \to 0$, according to (6).

9-2. Decay into two spinning particles

Consider the matrix elements $\langle p, \lambda_1, \lambda_2, \vartheta, \varphi|T|M\rangle$ for the decay $d_M \to 1, 2$ in the decay rest frame. The angles ϑ and φ are the polar and azimuthal angles of $\boldsymbol{p}_1$, and the states $|M\rangle$ are quantized along the z-axis. By inversion of (3-1.1), we have

$$|M\rangle = \sum_{M'} D^{-1}_{M'M}(\varphi, \vartheta, -\varphi)|M', \vartheta, \varphi\rangle = \sum_{M'} D^{*}_{MM'}(\varphi, \vartheta, -\varphi)|M', \vartheta, \varphi\rangle. \tag{2.1}$$

Now invariance of $\langle p, \lambda_1, \lambda_2, \vartheta, \varphi|T|M', \vartheta, \varphi\rangle$ against rotations of the coordinate system requires

$$\langle p_1, \lambda_1, \lambda_2, \vartheta, \varphi|T|M', \vartheta, \varphi\rangle = \langle p, \lambda_1, \lambda_2, 0, 0|T|M', 0, 0\rangle$$
$$= \sqrt{\frac{2S+1}{4\pi}}\, \delta_{\lambda M'}\, T(p, \lambda_1, \lambda_2). \qquad (2.2)$$

In deriving the last equation, we have applied the fact that $|p, \lambda_1 \lambda_2, 00\rangle$ is an eigenstate of J_z with eigenvalue $\lambda = \lambda_1 - \lambda_2$. The factor $\delta_{\lambda M'}$ expresses conservation of J_z. Note that $T(p, \lambda_1, \lambda_2)$ does depend on λ through $\lambda = \lambda_1 - \lambda_2$. Finally, the symbol S under the square root is the spin of particle d. The square root is a convenient normalization factor for the decay density matrix, as we shall see below. Inserting (2) into (1), we obtain the final result

$$\langle p, \lambda_1, \lambda_2, \vartheta, \varphi|T|M\rangle = \sqrt{\frac{2S+1}{4\pi}}\, D^{S*}_{M\lambda}(\varphi, \vartheta, -\varphi) T(p, \lambda_1, \lambda_2). \qquad (2.3)$$

With $D^*_{M\lambda}(\varphi, \vartheta, -\varphi) = e^{i\varphi(M-\lambda)} d_{M\lambda}(\vartheta)$ and the orthogonality relation (C-4.1) of the d-functions, we have

$$\frac{2S+1}{4\pi} \int d\varphi\, d\cos\vartheta\, D^{S*}_{M\lambda}(\varphi, \vartheta, -\varphi) D^{S}_{M'\lambda}(\varphi, \vartheta, -\varphi) = \delta_{MM'}. \qquad (2.4)$$

The R-matrix (3-1.7) for the decay $d_M \rightarrow 1, 2$ is defined by

$$R(\vartheta, \varphi, \lambda_1 \lambda_2)_{MM'} \equiv \langle p, \lambda_1\lambda_2, \vartheta, \varphi|T|M\rangle \langle p, \lambda_1\lambda_2, \vartheta\varphi|T|M'\rangle^*$$
$$= \frac{2S+1}{4\pi} |T(p, \lambda_1, \lambda_2)|^2 D^{S*}_{M\lambda}(\varphi, \vartheta, -\varphi) D^{S}_{M'\lambda}(\varphi, \vartheta, -\varphi). \quad (2.5)$$

It satisfies the orthogonality relation (3-1.11), with

$$C(\lambda_1, \lambda_2) = |T(p, \lambda_1, \lambda_2)|^2. \qquad (2.6)$$

In many cases, one measures only the decay distribution $W(\vartheta, \varphi)$ or $W(s, t, \vartheta, \varphi)$, summing over the remaining variables of the decay. In our case, these remaining variables are the helicities λ_1 and λ_2 of the decay products. We therefore introduce the following decay density matrix (by "density matrix" we mean any normalized Hermitean matrix acting in spin space)

$$A_{MM'}(\vartheta, \varphi) = \frac{\sum_{\lambda_1, \lambda_2} R(\vartheta, \varphi, \lambda_1, \lambda_2)_{MM'}}{\sum_{\lambda_1, \lambda_2} |T(p, \lambda_1, \lambda_2)|^2}. \qquad (2.7)$$

Similarly, if the helicities or magnetic quantum numbers of particles a, b, and c in the reaction $ab \to cd_M$ are not measured, we need the production density matrix analogous to (3-1.10),

$$\rho(s,t)_{MM'} = \frac{\sum\limits_{M_a M_b M_c} T(ab \to cd_M) T^*(ab \to cd_{M'})}{\sum\limits_{M_a M_b M_c M_d} |T(ab \to cd)|^2}. \tag{2.8}$$

Then the decay distribution $W(s, t, \vartheta, \varphi)$ analogous to (3-1.12) is

$$W(s,t,\vartheta,\varphi) = \sum_{MM'} \rho(s,t)_{MM'} A(\vartheta,\varphi)_{MM'} = \text{trace}\,[\rho(s,t)A^*(\vartheta,\varphi)]. \tag{2.9}$$

We now calculate A for a few simple examples. When both particles 1 and 2 are spinless, insertion of

$$D^{S*}_{M0} = \sqrt{\frac{4\pi}{2S+1}}\, Y^S_M$$

into (5) and (7) gives

$$A_{MM'}(\vartheta,\varphi) = Y^S_M(\vartheta,\varphi) Y^{S*}_{M'}(\vartheta,\varphi). \tag{2.10}$$

This agrees with the expression obtained from (3-2.13) for $T(d^L_M \to 1, 2)$. Next, we consider decays of the type $\Lambda \to p\pi$ or $N^* \to p\pi$, where particles 1 and 2 have $S = \frac{1}{2}$ and 0, respectively. For brevity, we write $T(\lambda_1)$ instead of $T(p, \lambda_1, 0)$. Now (5) and (7) lead to

$$A_{MM'}(\vartheta,\varphi) = \frac{2S+1}{4\pi} e^{i\varphi(M-M')} \frac{|T(\frac{1}{2})|^2 d^S_{M\frac{1}{2}} d^S_{M'\frac{1}{2}} + |T(-\frac{1}{2})|^2 d^S_{M,-\frac{1}{2}} d^S_{M',-\frac{1}{2}}}{|T(\frac{1}{2})|^2 + |T(-\frac{1}{2})|^2}$$

$$= \frac{2S+1}{8\pi} e^{i\varphi(M-M')} [d^S_{M\frac{1}{2}} d^S_{M'\frac{1}{2}} + d^S_{M,-\frac{1}{2}} d^S_{M',-\frac{1}{2}} + \alpha(d^S_{M\frac{1}{2}} d^S_{M'\frac{1}{2}} - d^S_{M,-\frac{1}{2}} d^S_{M',-\frac{1}{2}})]. \tag{2.11}$$

In the last expression, we have introduced the asymmetry parameter,

$$\alpha = \frac{|T(\frac{1}{2})|^2 - |T(-\frac{1}{2})|^2}{|T(\frac{1}{2})|^2 + |T(-\frac{1}{2})|^2}. \tag{2.12}$$

From table C-3, we find for $S = \frac{1}{2}$ (hyperon decay)

$$A_{\frac{1}{2}\frac{1}{2}} = \frac{1}{4\pi}(1+\alpha\cos\vartheta), \qquad A_{-\frac{1}{2}-\frac{1}{2}} = \frac{1}{4\pi}(1-\alpha\cos\vartheta),$$

$$A_{\frac{1}{2},-\frac{1}{2}} = \frac{\alpha}{4\pi} e^{i\varphi}\sin\vartheta = A^*_{-\frac{1}{2},\frac{1}{2}}. \tag{2.13}$$

For parity-conserving decays, α is zero. This was remarked already in the derivation of (5-4.8). In the general case when both decay particles carry spin, parity invariance requires

$$T(p, -\lambda_1, -\lambda_2) = \eta_d \eta_1 \eta_2 (-1)^{S_1+S_2-S} T(p, \lambda_1, \lambda_2). \qquad (2.14)$$

This follows from invariance of (2) against $\mathscr{Y}$-reflections,

$$\langle p, \lambda_1 \lambda_2, 0, 0 | \mathscr{Y}^+ T \mathscr{Y} | \lambda, 0, 0 \rangle = \langle p, \lambda_1 \lambda_2, 0, 0 | T | \lambda, 0, 0 \rangle. \qquad (2.15)$$

The effect of $\mathscr{Y}$ on the initial and final states is given by (1.10) and (1.12), respectively. The sign factor for the initial state may be written as $\eta_d(-1)^{\lambda-S}$. Multiplying this by the sign factor $\eta_1\eta_2(-1)^{S_1+S_2-\lambda}$ of (1.12) for the final state, λ drops out, and the phase of (14) results.

From (14), the symmetry

$$A_{-M,\,-M'} = (-1)^{M-M'} A^*_{MM'} \qquad (2.16)$$

follows. Namely, with $|T(p, -\lambda_1 - \lambda_2)^2 = |T(p, \lambda_1 \lambda_2)|^2$, the terms in the sum (7) may be arranged pairwise as

$$|T(p, \lambda_1, \lambda_2)|^2 (D^*_{M\lambda} D_{M'\lambda} + D^*_{M,\,-\lambda} D_{M',\,-\lambda}). \qquad (2.17)$$

(For $\lambda = 0$, a factor $\frac{1}{2}$ is necessary.) The corresponding pair in $A_{-M,\,-M'}$ contains

$$|T(p, \lambda_1, \lambda_2)|^2 (D^*_{-M\lambda} D_{-M'\lambda} + D^*_{-M,\,-\lambda} D_{-M',\,-\lambda}). \qquad (2.18)$$

In view of the symmetry (C-2.10) of the D-functions, the two brackets are just related by (16).

As a final example, we consider the decay $N^*_{33} \to p\pi$. Putting $\alpha = 0$ and $S = \frac{3}{2}$ in (11), we obtain from table C-3,

$$A_{33} = A_{-3-3} = \frac{3}{8\pi} \sin^2 \vartheta,$$

$$A_{11} = A_{-1-1} = \frac{1}{8\pi}(1 + 3\cos^2 \vartheta),$$

$$A_{31} = -A^*_{-3-1} = -\frac{1}{8\pi}\sqrt{3}\, e^{i\varphi} \sin 2\vartheta,$$

$$A_{3-1} = A^*_{-31} = -\frac{1}{8\pi}\sqrt{3}\, e^{2i\varphi} \sin^2 \vartheta,$$

$$A_{3-3} = A_{-33} = A_{1-1} = A_{-11} = 0. \qquad (2.19)$$

Here we have written $A_{2M,\,2M'}$ to avoid half-integer indices.

9-3. Decay distribution and polarization

In this section we examine the decay distribution (2.9) in more detail. We assume parity conservation for the production process ab → cd. This will entail a symmetry property for the density matrix ρ defined in (2.8). Let the spin states $|M_a\rangle, \ldots, |M_d\rangle$ refer to the rest systems of particles a, . . ., d, with quantization axis in the production plane, and let the y-axis be the normal to the production plane. Then the operator $\mathscr{Y} = e^{-i\pi J_y}\mathscr{P}$ represents a reflection in the production plane. Invariance of the T-matrix against this reflection requires

$$T(M_a, \ldots, M_d, \theta) = \eta(-1)^{S_a - M_a \ldots + S_d - M_d} T(-M_a, \ldots, -M_d, \theta), \qquad (3.1)$$

$$\eta \equiv \eta_a \eta_b \eta_c \eta_d. \qquad (3.2)$$

This follows from the fact that $\mathscr{Y}$ leaves the momenta $\boldsymbol{p}_a, \ldots, \boldsymbol{p}_d$ unchanged. Therefore, one merely needs (1.10) for the spin states. Inserting (1) and (2) into (2.8), we get

$$\rho_{-M, -M'} = (-1)^{M-M'} \rho_{M, M'}. \qquad (3.3)$$

The simplest way to see this is to write the phase factor of $T^*(M_a, \ldots, M_d', \theta)$ as $\eta^{-1}(-1)^{M_a - S_a \ldots M_d' - S_d}$. Note also the similarity with (2.16), where for $\varphi = 0$, A^* may be replaced by A. For $S = \frac{1}{2}$, 1 and $\frac{3}{2}$, (3) requires the density matrix $\rho(S)$ to be of the form

$$\rho(\tfrac{1}{2}) = \begin{pmatrix} \rho_{\frac{1}{2}\frac{1}{2}} & \rho_{\frac{1}{2}-\frac{1}{2}} \\ -\rho_{\frac{1}{2}-\frac{1}{2}} & \rho_{\frac{1}{2}\frac{1}{2}} \end{pmatrix}, \qquad \rho(1) = \begin{pmatrix} \rho_{11} & \rho_{10} & \rho_{1-1} \\ \rho_{10}^* & \rho_{00} & -\rho_{10}^* \\ \rho_{1-1} & -\rho_{10} & \rho_{11} \end{pmatrix},$$

$$\rho(\tfrac{3}{2}) = \begin{pmatrix} \rho_{33} & \rho_{31} & \rho_{3-1} & \rho_{3-3} \\ \rho_{31}^* & \rho_{11} & \rho_{1-1} & \rho_{3-1}^* \\ \rho_{3-1}^* & -\rho_{1-1} & \rho_{11} & -\rho_{31}^* \\ -\rho_{3-3} & \rho_{3-1} & -\rho_{31} & \rho_{33} \end{pmatrix}, \qquad (3.4)$$

when the z-axis is in the production plane. The indices in $\rho(\frac{3}{2})$ are again $2M$ and $2M'$. By definition (2.8), ρ is a Hermitean matrix. Therefore, all diagonal elements ρ_{MM} are real. In addition, $\rho_{\frac{1}{2}-\frac{1}{2}}$ of $\rho(\frac{1}{2})$ and ρ_{3-3}, ρ_{1-1} of $\rho(\frac{3}{2})$ are purely imaginary, while ρ_{1-1} of $\rho(1)$ is real. The normalization of the trace finally gives

$$\rho_{\frac{1}{2}\frac{1}{2}} = \tfrac{1}{2}, \qquad 2\rho_{11} + \rho_{00} = 1, \qquad 2(\rho_{33} + \rho_{11}) = 1 \qquad (3.5)$$

for $S = \frac{1}{2}$, 1 and $\frac{3}{2}$, respectively. As examples, we now calculate the decay distribution of $\Lambda \to p\pi^-$, $\rho^0 \to \pi^+\pi^-$ and $N^* \to p\pi$ from (2.9). The corresponding decay matrices are given by (2.13), (2.10) and (2.19). The results are

$$W_\Lambda(\vartheta, \varphi) = \frac{1}{4\pi}(1 - 2\alpha \sin\vartheta \sin\varphi \operatorname{Im} \rho_{\frac{1}{2}-\frac{1}{2}}), \tag{3.6}$$

$$W_\rho(\vartheta, \varphi) = \frac{1}{4\pi}[1 + (1 - 3\cos^2\vartheta)(\rho_{11} - \rho_{00}) \\ - 3\sqrt{2}\sin 2\vartheta \cos\varphi \operatorname{Re}\rho_{10} - 3\sin^2\vartheta \cos 2\varphi\rho_{1-1}], \tag{3.7}$$

$$W_{N^*}(\vartheta, \varphi) = \frac{3}{4\pi}\Big[\rho_{33}\sin^2\vartheta + \rho_{11}(1 + \tfrac{1}{3}\cos^2\vartheta) \\ - \frac{2}{\sqrt{3}}\operatorname{Re}\rho_{3-1}\sin^2\vartheta\cos 2\varphi - \frac{2}{\sqrt{3}}\operatorname{Re}\rho_{31}\sin 2\vartheta\cos\varphi\Big]. \tag{3.8}$$

Here, ϑ and φ are the angles of emission of particle nr. 1 (p in $\Lambda \to p\pi^-$ and $N^* \to p\pi$, π^+ in $\rho \to \pi^+\pi^-$) in the decay rest frame, with the y-axis normal to the production plane. Specifically, $\varphi = 0$ and $\varphi = \pi$ correspond to decays in the production plane.

For spin-$\frac{1}{2}$ particles, one frequently expresses the density matrix in terms of the polarization vector $\boldsymbol{P}$, defined by

$$\rho(\tfrac{1}{2}) \equiv \tfrac{1}{2}(1 + \boldsymbol{P}\cdot\boldsymbol{\sigma}) = \frac{1}{2}\begin{pmatrix} 1+P_z & P_x - iP_y \\ P_x + iP_y & 1 - P_z \end{pmatrix}. \tag{3.9}$$

Obviously this matrix is Hermitean and of unit trace. For parity-conserving interactions, (4) requires

$$P_x = P_z = 0, \qquad \tfrac{1}{2}P_y = -\operatorname{Im}\rho_{\frac{1}{2}-\frac{1}{2}} = i\rho_{\frac{1}{2}-\frac{1}{2}}, \tag{3.10}$$

which means that the particle is "polarized along the normal to the production plane". For meson-baryon scattering, we have

$$\tfrac{1}{2}P_y = i\rho_{\frac{1}{2},-\frac{1}{2}} = \frac{-\operatorname{Im} T(\frac{1}{2},\frac{1}{2})T^*(\frac{1}{2},-\frac{1}{2})}{|T(\frac{1}{2},\frac{1}{2})|^2 + |T(\frac{1}{2},-\frac{1}{2})|^2}, \tag{3.11}$$

according to the definition (2.8) and the symmetry (1). The first of the two magnetic quantum numbers of T refers to the initial proton. Note that (11) applies also to helicity states. In fact, the initial and final spin-$\frac{1}{2}$ states may be quantized along two arbitrary directions in the (x, z)-plane.

Similarly, for spin-1, the density matrix $\rho(1)$ may be expressed in terms of a polarization vector $\boldsymbol{P}$ and a symmetrical traceless polarization tensor P_{ij},

$$\rho = \tfrac{1}{3}[1+\boldsymbol{P}\cdot\boldsymbol{J}+\sum_{ik} P_{ik}\cdot\tfrac{3}{2}(J_i J_k + J_k J_i - \tfrac{4}{3}\delta_{ik})]. \tag{3.12}$$

The matrices $\boldsymbol{J}$ are the spin matrices of C-1 for $j = 1$,

$$J_x = \frac{1}{\sqrt{2}}\begin{pmatrix}0 & 1 & 0\\ 1 & 0 & 1\\ 0 & 1 & 0\end{pmatrix}, \quad J_y = \frac{1}{\sqrt{2}}\begin{pmatrix}0 & -\mathrm{i} & 0\\ \mathrm{i} & 0 & -\mathrm{i}\\ 0 & \mathrm{i} & 0\end{pmatrix}, \quad J_z = \begin{pmatrix}1 & 0 & 0\\ 0 & 0 & 0\\ 0 & 0 & -1\end{pmatrix}. \tag{3.13}$$

The general decomposition of ρ into irreducible tensor matrices is given e.g. by GOLDFARB [1958].

9-4. Partial wave expansion of helicity amplitudes

In this section, we consider the partial wave expansion of the helicity matrix element for a reaction ab → cd,

$$T(\lambda_a, \ldots, \lambda_d, \Omega) \equiv T(\lambda_a, \lambda_b, \lambda_c, \lambda_d, s, \theta, \phi). \tag{4.1}$$

As usual, we work in the cms and let $\boldsymbol{p}_a = -\boldsymbol{p}_b$ point along the z-axis. The direction of $\boldsymbol{p}_c = -\boldsymbol{p}_d$ is fixed by the angles θ and ϕ.

In (5-2.2), we deduced the angular dependence of the decay matrix element of a meson-nucleon resonance from the partial wave expansion (3-8.5) of meson-nucleon scattering. Now we invert the argument to find the general form of the partial wave expansion of (1). According to (9.3), the decay of a resonance of spin J into particles c and d is described by $D^{J*}_{M,\,\lambda_c-\lambda_d}(\varphi_c, \vartheta_c, -\varphi_c)T^{cd}_J(\lambda_c, \lambda_d)$. The same resonance will contribute to the reaction ab → cd a term proportional to

$$\sum_M D^J_{M\lambda}(\Omega_a)D^{J*}_{M\lambda'}(\varphi_c, \vartheta_c, -\varphi_c)T^{ab*}_J(\lambda_a, \lambda_b)T^{cd}_J(\lambda_c, \lambda_d)$$
$$= D^{J*}_{\lambda\lambda'}(\phi, \theta, -\phi)T^{ab*}_J(\lambda_a, \lambda_b)T^{cd}_J(\lambda_c, \lambda_d). \tag{4.2}$$

Here we have introduced the abbreviations

$$\lambda = \lambda_a - \lambda_b, \qquad \lambda' = \lambda_c - \lambda_d. \tag{4.3}$$

In general, a partial wave amplitude $T_J(\lambda_a, \lambda_b, \lambda_c, \lambda_d)$ replaces the product of production and decay matrix elements in (2). This does not affect our conclusion about the angular dependence of (2), since $T_J(\lambda_a, \ldots, \lambda_d)$ can always be written, at fixed s, as a sum of several factorizing matrix elements. Finally, summing (2) over all possible spins J, we obtain

$$T(\lambda_a, \ldots, \lambda_d, \Omega) = 8\pi s^{\frac{1}{2}} \sum_J (2J+1) D^{J*}_{\lambda\lambda'}(\Omega) T_J(\lambda_a, \ldots, \lambda_d). \tag{4.4}$$

Here we have introduced the same normalization factor in the definition of T_J as in (3-8.5). Except for the larger number of helicities in T_J and the generalization (3) of λ and λ', (4) is identical with the partial wave expansion (3-8.5). Therefore, the derivation of the partial wave unitarity (3-8.13) goes as before. Only the number of summation indices increases:

$$-\mathrm{i}[T_{\mathrm{if},J}(\lambda_a\lambda_b\lambda_c\lambda_d) - T^*_{\mathrm{fi},J}(\lambda_c\lambda_d\lambda_a\lambda_b)]$$
$$= 2\sum_c q_c \sum_{\lambda_1\lambda_2} T_{\mathrm{ic},J}(\lambda_a\lambda_b\lambda_1\lambda_2) T^*_{\mathrm{fc},J}(\lambda_c\lambda_d\lambda_1\lambda_2). \tag{4.5}$$

For time-reversal invariant interactions, the l.h.s. may be replaced by $2\,\mathrm{Im}\, T_{\mathrm{if},J}(\lambda_a\lambda_b\lambda_c\lambda_d)$. The derivation is analogous to that of section 4-5. We merely have to interpret the indices λ and λ' in (4-5.2), (4-5.3) and (4-5.4) as representing the index pairs λ_a, λ_b and λ_c, λ_d. In the angular functions, λ and λ' are of course defined by (3).

Next, we consider the restrictions on $T_J(\lambda_a, \ldots, \lambda_d)$ due to parity conservation. For that purpose, we use (2.14) for the decay $\mathrm{d}' \to \mathrm{cd}$ of a resonance and the corresponding formula for the production $\mathrm{ab} \to \mathrm{d}'$. The resulting phase for the product $T_J^{\mathrm{ab}*}(\lambda_a\lambda_b) T_J^{\mathrm{cd}}(\lambda_c\lambda_d)$ is

$$\eta_c\eta_d(-1)^{S_c+S_d-J} \cdot \eta_a\eta_b(-1)^{S_a+S_b-J} = \eta(-1)^{S_a+S_b-S_c-S_d},$$
$$\eta \equiv \eta_a\eta_b\eta_c\eta_d. \tag{4.6}$$

Replacing the product by the general amplitude $T_J(\lambda_a\lambda_b\lambda_c\lambda_d)$, we obtain

$$T_J(-\lambda_a - \lambda_b - \lambda_c - \lambda_d) = \eta(-1)^{S_a+S_b-S_c-S_d} T_J(\lambda_a\lambda_b\lambda_c\lambda_d). \tag{4.7}$$

The construction of matrix elements between parity eigenstates is analogous to that of section 3-9. One introduces the combinations

$$T_J^{\pm} = T_J(\lambda_a\lambda_b\lambda_c\lambda_d) \pm T_J(\lambda_a\lambda_b - \lambda_c - \lambda_d) \tag{4.8}$$

and shows that the partial wave unitarity (5) decouples into two separate matrix equations, one for T_J^+ and one for T_J^-. The elements of T_J^+ and T_J^- are labelled by the absolute values of $\lambda_a, \ldots, \lambda_d$ and by the signs of $\lambda_a\lambda_b$ and $\lambda_c\lambda_d$.

As a first application, we calculate the partial-wave expansion of $T(\lambda_N, \lambda_{\bar{N}}, \theta\phi)$ for the reaction $\pi\bar{\pi} \to \mathrm{N\bar{N}}$. Here we have $\lambda_a = \lambda_b = 0$ and therefore $\lambda = 0$, while λ' may assume the values 0, +1 and −1. Explicitly, (4) becomes

$$T(\tfrac{1}{2}, \tfrac{1}{2}, \theta\phi) = 8\pi \sum_J (2J+1) D^{J*}_{00}(\phi, \theta, -\phi) T_J(\tfrac{1}{2}, \tfrac{1}{2})$$

$$= 8\pi \sum_J (2J+1) P_J(\cos\theta) T_J(\tfrac{1}{2}, \tfrac{1}{2}), \tag{4.9}$$

$$T(\tfrac{1}{2}, -\tfrac{1}{2}, \theta\phi) = 8\pi \sum_J (2J+1) D^{J*}_{01}(\phi, \theta, -\phi)$$

$$= 8\pi e^{-i\phi} \sum_J \frac{2J+1}{\sqrt{J(J+1)}} \sin\theta P_J'(\cos\theta) T_J(\tfrac{1}{2}, -\tfrac{1}{2}). \tag{4.10}$$

Here we have applied the results of appendix C-4, especially (C-4.7) in the last expression (10). Similar equations apply to $T(-\frac{1}{2}, -\frac{1}{2}, \theta, \phi)$ and $T(-\frac{1}{2}, \frac{1}{2}, \theta, \phi)$. Conservation of parity requires

$$T_J(\tfrac{1}{2}, \tfrac{1}{2}) = T_J(-\tfrac{1}{2}, -\tfrac{1}{2}), \qquad T_J(\tfrac{1}{2}, -\tfrac{1}{2}) = T_J(-\tfrac{1}{2}, \tfrac{1}{2}). \tag{4.11}$$

This follows from (7), for $S_c + S_d = 1$ and $\eta = -1$. Recall that fermions and antifermions have opposite intrinsic parities, $\eta_{\bar{N}} = -\eta_N$. By (A-1.1) and (A-1.10), the inversion of (9) and (10) is, for $\phi = 0$,

$$T_J(\tfrac{1}{2}, \tfrac{1}{2}) = \frac{1}{16\pi} \int_{-1}^{1} d\cos\theta P_J(\cos\theta) T(\tfrac{1}{2}, \tfrac{1}{2}, \theta),$$

$$T_J(\tfrac{1}{2}, -\tfrac{1}{2}) = \frac{1}{16\pi} \frac{\sqrt{J(J+1)}}{2J+1} \int_{-1}^{1} d\cos\theta (P_{J-1} - P_{J+1}) \frac{T(\tfrac{1}{2}, -\tfrac{1}{2}, \theta)}{\sin\theta}. \tag{4.12}$$

As a second example, we consider nucleon-nucleon scattering. From (7) we conclude that T_J is symmetric under the helicity reversal $\lambda_i \to -\lambda_i$. Then $T_J^{\pm}$ as defined by (8) may be written as

$$T_J^{\pm} = {}_{\pm}\langle \lambda_c \lambda_d J | T | J \lambda_a \lambda_b \rangle_{\pm},$$

$$|J \lambda_a \lambda_b\rangle_{\pm} \equiv 2^{-\frac{1}{2}} |J \lambda_a \lambda_b\rangle \pm 2^{-\frac{1}{2}} |J, -\lambda_a - \lambda_b\rangle. \tag{4.13}$$

The states $|J\lambda_a \lambda_b\rangle_{\pm}$ are eigenstates of the total angular momentum, symmetric and antisymmetric under helicity reversal. For low energies, states $|JLS\rangle$ of orbital angular momentum L and total spin S are more convenient, since the matrix elements $\langle L'S'J|T|JLS\rangle$ behave like $q^L (q')^{L'}$ near threshold. The transformation from $|J\lambda_a \lambda_b\rangle$ to $|JLS\rangle$ is given by (JACOB and WICK [1959])

$$|J\lambda_a \lambda_b\rangle = \sum_{L,S} \sqrt{\frac{2L+1}{2J+1}} C^{S_a \; S_b S}_{\lambda_a - \lambda_b \lambda} C^{LSJ}_{0\lambda\lambda} |JLS\rangle. \tag{4.14}$$

The first Clebsch-Gordan coefficient couples the spins S_a and S_b to a total spin S, while the second couples L and S to J. Since the orbital angular momentum $\boldsymbol{L}$ has no component in the production plane, the corresponding magnetic quantum number is zero. The normalization constant $[(2L+1)/(2J+1)]^{\frac{1}{2}}$ is justified below.

From the symmetry properties of the Clebsch-Gordan coefficients

$$C_{-\lambda_a\lambda_b-\lambda}^{S_aS_b\ S} = (-1)^{S_a+S_b-S} C_{\lambda_a-\lambda_b\lambda}^{S_a\ S_bS}, \quad C_{0-\lambda-\lambda}^{L\ S\ J} = (-1)^{L+S-J} C_{0\lambda\lambda}^{LSJ}, \tag{4.15}$$

it follows that the expansion of $|J\lambda_a\lambda_b\rangle_+$ ($|J\lambda_a\lambda_b\rangle_-$) contains only even (odd) values of S_a+S_b+L-J. This result holds true in general. Specifying $S_a = S_b = \frac{1}{2}$, we find $L = J\pm 1$, $S = 1$ for $|J\lambda_a\lambda_b\rangle_+$ and $L = J$, $S = 0$ or 1 for $|J\lambda_a\lambda_b\rangle_-$ as the only possible values of L and S. The case $L = J$ is particularly simple, since

$$C_{000}^{J0J} = 1, \qquad C_{000}^{J1J} = 0, \qquad C_{011}^{J1J} = -2^{-\frac{1}{2}}. \tag{4.16}$$

The spin addition coefficient is $2^{-\frac{1}{2}}$ except for $\lambda = 1$, when it is unity. Finally, a factor $2^{\frac{1}{2}}$ comes from the sum in (13). The net result is

$$|J\tfrac{1}{2}\tfrac{1}{2}\rangle_- = |JJ0\rangle, \qquad |J\tfrac{1}{2}-\tfrac{1}{2}\rangle_- = -|JJ1\rangle, \tag{4.17}$$

i.e. these states are identical with the states ${}^1S_0$, ${}^1P_1$, ${}^1D_2$ . . . and $-{}^3P_1$, $-{}^3D_2$, $-{}^3F_3$, . . ., respectively. For the $|J\lambda_a\lambda_b\rangle_+$ states, insertion of the coefficients $C_{0\lambda\lambda}^{L1J}$ into (14) gives

$$\begin{aligned} |J\tfrac{1}{2}\tfrac{1}{2}\rangle_+ &= \sqrt{\frac{J}{2J+1}}\,|J, J-1, 1\rangle - \sqrt{\frac{J+1}{2J+1}}\,|J, J+1, 1\rangle, \\ |J\tfrac{1}{2}-\tfrac{1}{2}\rangle_- &= \sqrt{\frac{J+1}{2J+1}}\,|J, J-1, 1\rangle + \sqrt{\frac{J}{2J+1}}\,|J, J+1, 1\rangle. \end{aligned} \tag{4.18}$$

TABLE 9-4

Symmetric and antisymmetric helicity states (13), expressed in terms of orbital angular momentum states

J	$\lvert J\,\frac{1}{2}\,\frac{1}{2}\rangle_+$	$\lvert J\,\frac{1}{2}\,-\frac{1}{2}\rangle_+$	$\lvert J\,\frac{1}{2}\,\frac{1}{2}\rangle_-$	$\lvert J\,\frac{1}{2}\,-\frac{1}{2}\rangle_-$
0	$-{}^3P_0$		${}^1S_0$	
1	$\sqrt{\frac{1}{3}}\,{}^3S_1-\sqrt{\frac{2}{3}}\,{}^3D_1$	$\sqrt{\frac{2}{3}}\,{}^3S_1+\sqrt{\frac{1}{3}}\,{}^3D_1$	${}^1P_1$	$-{}^3P_1$
2	$\sqrt{\frac{2}{5}}\,{}^3P_2-\sqrt{\frac{3}{5}}\,{}^3F_2$	$\sqrt{\frac{3}{5}}\,{}^3P_2+\sqrt{\frac{2}{5}}\,{}^3F_2$	${}^1D_2$	$-{}^3D_2$
3	$\sqrt{\frac{3}{7}}\,{}^3D_3-\sqrt{\frac{4}{7}}\,{}^3G_3$	$\sqrt{\frac{4}{7}}\,{}^3D_3+\sqrt{\frac{3}{7}}\,{}^3G_3$	${}^1F_3$	$-{}^3F_3$

For $J = 0$, the states $|J\frac{1}{2}-\frac{1}{2}\rangle$ and $|J, J-1, 1\rangle$ are of course absent (see table 9-4). Also, for pp scattering, the Pauli principle requires odd L for $S = 1$ and even L for $S = 0$. From (18), we see that the normalization constant $[(2L+1)/(2J+1)]^{\frac{1}{2}}$ is necessary to make (14) an orthogonal transformation.

9-5. Scattering of polarized particles

So far, we have assumed that the particles a and b in the initial state are unpolarized. One might think that the most general cross-section for the scattering of polarized particles is given by

$$\mathrm{d}\sigma(\mathrm{ab} \to \mathrm{cd}) = \frac{\pi\,\mathrm{d}t}{4q^2 s} \sum_{M_\mathrm{a}\ldots M_\mathrm{d}} P(M_\mathrm{a})P(M_\mathrm{b}) \left| \frac{T(s, t, M_\mathrm{a}, \ldots, M_\mathrm{d})}{4\pi} \right|^2, \tag{5.1}$$

where $P(M_i)$ is the probability of finding particle i in the spin state of magnetic quantum number M_i. It is true that (1) reduces to the scattering cross-section (3-1.14) when a and b are unpolarized. Nevertheless, (1) is not correct in general.

As an example of the general formalism, we discuss double scattering. Consider for example the elastic scattering of hyperons in a bubble chamber. The hyperon is produced in a primary collision, which provides a certain amount of polarization. To fix the notation, let us discuss the sequence of reactions $\mathrm{K}^-\mathrm{p} \to \pi^0\Lambda$, $\Lambda\mathrm{p} \to \Sigma^+\mathrm{n}$. The matrix element of the overall process is

$$T(\mathrm{K}^-\mathrm{pp} \to \pi\Sigma\mathrm{n}) = \sum_M T(\mathrm{K}^-\mathrm{p} \to \pi\Lambda_M)T(\Lambda_M\mathrm{p} \to \Sigma\mathrm{n}) \frac{1}{m_\Lambda^2 - s_\mathrm{d} - \mathrm{i}\varepsilon}. \tag{5.2}$$

It has the same structure as the matrix element (3-1.5) for the more common sequence production → decay. Consequently, the cross-section for the secondary reaction must have a structure analogous to that of the decay distribution (2.9),

$$\mathrm{d}\sigma(\Lambda\mathrm{p} \to \Sigma\mathrm{n}) = \frac{\pi\,\mathrm{d}t}{4q^2 s} \sum_{MM'} \rho(s't'\phi)_{MM'} \sum T(\Lambda_M\mathrm{p} \to \sum \mathrm{n})T^*(\Lambda_{M'}\mathrm{p} \to \Sigma\mathrm{n})/16\pi^2. \tag{5.3}$$

The Σ following $\rho_{MM'}$ indicates summation over the magnetic quantum numbers of the remaining particles p, Σ and n. We assume that the protons are unpolarized. The density matrix ρ refers to the productions of the hyperon. Apart from a different normalization factor, it is given by (2.8).

Thus s' and t' are the Mandelstam variables of the primary reaction $K^-p \to \pi^0\Lambda$. Finally, the angle ϕ is the angle between the normals to the scattering planes of the first and second reaction. It is measured in the Λ rest frame.

The ϕ-dependence is typical of polarization experiments. Usually, we have defined our coordinate system such that $p_y = 0$ for all particle momenta. In the Λ-rest frame, we may do this for the momenta of p, Σ and n, but then the momenta of K, p and π^0 of the first reaction will have $p_y \neq 0$, unless the two reaction planes coincide.

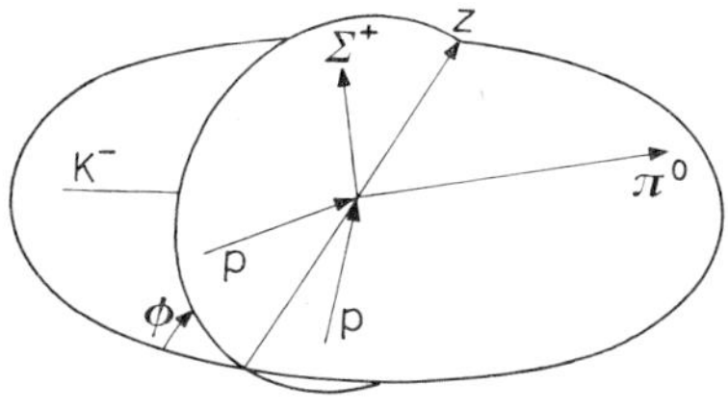

Fig. 9-5. The two reactions $K^-p \to \pi^0\Lambda$, $p\Lambda \to \Sigma^+n$, as seen in the rest frame of Λ. The neutron momentum lies in the lower half of the inclined plane.

To compute the ϕ-dependence of $\rho_{MM'}$ we take the spin quantization axis of Λ (z-axis) along the intersection of the two planes (see fig. 9-5). Then the only ϕ-dependence of $T(K^-p \to \pi\Lambda_M)$ is a factor $e^{iM\phi}$. This factor comes from rotating the spin states of Λ from one scattering plane to the other. We therefore have

$$\rho(s', t', \phi)_{MM'} = \rho(s't')_{MM'} e^{i\phi(M-M')}. \tag{5.4}$$

T and T^* of (3) are independent of ϕ. Of course, if we had taken $p_y = 0$ for the momenta of the primary collision, then ρ would have been independent of ϕ and T would contain the factor $e^{iM\phi}$. The product (3) is the same in both cases.

Averaging (3) over ϕ, we find

$$\int \frac{d\phi}{2\pi} d\sigma(\Lambda p \to \Sigma n) = \frac{\pi dt}{4q^2 s} \sum_M \rho(s', t')_{MM} \sum |T(\Lambda_M p \to \sum n)|^2/16\pi^2. \tag{5.5}$$

This shows that (1) applies to the differential cross-section of polarized particles, if an average over the orientation of the scattering plane is taken. The probability $P(M)$ is the diagonal element of the density matrix.

In our example, M and M' assume only the values $\pm\frac{1}{2}$, and the only term which contributes to (3) but not to (5) is

$$2\,\mathrm{Re}\,[\rho(s't')_{\frac{1}{2}-\frac{1}{2}}\mathrm{e}^{\mathrm{i}\phi}\sum T(\Lambda_{\frac{1}{2}}\mathrm{p}\to\Sigma\mathrm{n})T^*(\Lambda_{-\frac{1}{2}}\mathrm{p}\to\Sigma\mathrm{n})]. \tag{5.6}$$

Actually, these expressions are simplified by parity conservation, as discussed in section 9-3. In particular, if the z-axis is taken *normal* to the production plane instead of *in* the production plane, then the density matrix for spin-$\frac{1}{2}$ is diagonal, $P_{x'} = P_{y'} = 0$, $P_{z'} = P_y$, according to (3.10).

9-6. Joint decay distributions

In reactions such as $\pi\mathrm{N}\to\rho\mathrm{N}^*$ or $\mathrm{K}^-\mathrm{p}\to\omega\Lambda$, the final state contains two unstable particles of nonzero spins. In such cases, measuring the joint decay distribution may yield more information about the production matrix elements than measuring each decay distribution separately. For the sake of notation, we consider $\mathrm{K}^-\mathrm{p}\to\omega\Lambda$. The distribution $W_\Lambda(\vartheta_\mathrm{p}\varphi_\mathrm{p})$ of Λ-decay has been given in (3.6). The distribution $W_\omega(\vartheta_\omega, \varphi_\omega)$ of ω is given by (3.7), if ϑ_ω and φ_ω are taken as the angles of the normal to the decay plane of the decay $\omega\to\pi^+\pi^0\pi^-$ (see 5-6.6). The joint decay distribution $W(\vartheta_\mathrm{p}\varphi_\mathrm{p}\vartheta_\omega\varphi_\omega)$ describes the probability of finding the orientation $(\vartheta_\omega, \varphi_\omega)$ of the normal to the ω-decay plane in the ω-rest frame, when the decay proton from $\Lambda\to\pi\mathrm{p}$ moves in the direction $(\vartheta_\mathrm{p}, \varphi_\mathrm{p})$ in the Λ-rest frame.

In the absence of any correlations, the joint decay distribution would be given by

$$W(\vartheta_\mathrm{p}\varphi_\mathrm{p}, \vartheta_\omega\varphi_\omega) = W_\Lambda(\vartheta_\mathrm{p}\varphi_\mathrm{p})W_\omega(\vartheta_\omega\varphi_\omega). \tag{6.1}$$

The matrix element of the over-all process $\mathrm{K}^-\mathrm{p}\to\pi^+\pi^0\pi^-\mathrm{p}\pi^-$ is proportional to

$$\sum_{M,N} T(\mathrm{K}^-\mathrm{p}\to\omega_M\Lambda_N)T(\omega_M\to\pi^+\pi^0\pi^-)T(\Lambda_N\to\mathrm{p}\pi^-). \tag{6.2}$$

Obviously, the absolute square of (2) contains four summation indices M, N, M' and N'. In addition, the absolute square must be summed over the magnetic quantum number M_a of the initial proton and the helicity λ_1 of the final proton. Defining the joint decay density matrix

$$\rho_{NN'}^{MM'} = \frac{\sum_{M_\mathrm{a}M_\mathrm{b}} T(\mathrm{ab}\to\mathrm{c}_M\mathrm{d}_N)T^*(\mathrm{ab}\to c_{M'}\mathrm{d}_{N'})}{\sum_{M_\mathrm{a}M_\mathrm{b}MN}|T(\mathrm{ab}\to\mathrm{cd})|^2}, \tag{6.3}$$

we may repeat the argument of section 3-1 which led to the single decay distribution. The result is

$$W(\vartheta_\omega \varphi_\omega \vartheta_\mathrm{p} \varphi_\mathrm{p}) = \sum_{MM'} \sum_{NN'} A_{MM'}(\vartheta_\omega \varphi_\omega) A_{NN'}(\vartheta_\mathrm{p} \varphi_\mathrm{p}) \rho_{NN'}^{MM'} . \tag{6.4}$$

A few general properties of the joint density matrix are worth mentioning: Normalization and Hermiticity are

$$\sum_{M,N} \rho_{NN}^{MM} = 1, \qquad \rho_{NN'}^{MM'} = \rho_{N'N}^{M'M*} . \tag{6.5}$$

Parity conservation (3.3) now reads

$$\rho_{-N-N'}^{-M-M'} = (-1)^{M-M'+N-N'} \rho_{NN'}^{MM'} , \tag{6.6}$$

which implies that ρ_{N-N}^{M-M} is real (imaginary) if $2(N-M)$ is even (odd). With the A-matrices of ω- and Λ-decay given by (2.10) and (2.13), we find

$$W(\vartheta_\omega \varphi_\omega, \vartheta_\mathrm{p} \varphi_\mathrm{p}) = \frac{1}{16\pi^2} [1 + B(\vartheta_\omega) + B(\vartheta_\omega, \varphi_\omega) + B(\vartheta_\mathrm{p}, \varphi_\mathrm{p})$$
$$+ B(\vartheta_\omega \varphi_\omega \vartheta_\mathrm{p}) + B(\vartheta_\omega \varphi_\omega \varphi_\mathrm{p}) + B(\vartheta_\omega \varphi_\omega, \vartheta_\mathrm{p} \varphi_\mathrm{p})]. \tag{6.7}$$

$$B(\vartheta_\omega) = (1 - 3\cos^2 \vartheta_\omega)(\rho_{11} - \rho_{00}),$$
$$B(\vartheta_\omega, \varphi_\omega) = -3\sqrt{2} \sin 2\vartheta_\omega \cos \varphi_\omega \operatorname{Re} \rho_{10} - 3 \sin^2 \vartheta_\omega \cos 2\varphi_\omega \rho_{1-1},$$
$$B(\vartheta_\mathrm{p} \varphi_\mathrm{p}) = -2\alpha \sin \vartheta_\mathrm{p} \sin \varphi_\mathrm{p} \operatorname{Im} \rho_{\frac{1}{2}-\frac{1}{2}},$$
$$B(\vartheta_\omega \varphi_\omega, \vartheta_\mathrm{p}) = 3\alpha \cos \vartheta_\mathrm{p} [2^{\frac{1}{2}} \sin 2\vartheta_\omega \sin \varphi_\omega \operatorname{Im} \rho_{\overline{10}}$$
$$+ \sin^2 \vartheta_\omega \sin 2\varphi_\omega \operatorname{Im} \rho_{\overline{1-1}}],$$
$$B(\vartheta_\omega, \vartheta_\mathrm{p} \varphi_\mathrm{p}) = -\alpha(1 - 3\cos \vartheta_\omega) \sin \vartheta_\mathrm{p} \sin \varphi_\mathrm{p} \operatorname{Im} \rho_{\overline{\frac{1}{2}-\frac{1}{2}}},$$
$$B(\vartheta_\omega \varphi_\omega, \vartheta_\mathrm{p} \varphi_\mathrm{p}) = 3\alpha \sin \vartheta_\mathrm{p} \sqrt{2} \sin 2\vartheta_\omega [\sin(\varphi_\omega + \varphi_\mathrm{p}) \operatorname{Im} \rho_{\frac{1}{2}-\frac{1}{2}}^{10}$$
$$+ \sin(\varphi_\omega - \varphi_\mathrm{p}) \operatorname{Im} \rho_{-\frac{1}{2}\frac{1}{2}}^{10}]$$
$$+ 3\alpha \sin \vartheta_\mathrm{p} \sin^2 \vartheta_\omega [\sin(2\varphi_\omega + \varphi_\mathrm{p}) \operatorname{Im} \rho_{\frac{1}{2}-\frac{1}{2}}^{1-1} + \sin(2\varphi_\omega - \varphi_\mathrm{p}) \operatorname{Im} \rho_{-\frac{1}{2}\frac{1}{2}}^{1-1}]. \tag{6.8}$$

Here we have used the single-particle density matrices

$$\rho_{MM'} = \sum_N \rho_{NN}^{MM'}, \qquad \rho_{NN'} = \sum_M \rho_{NN'}^{MM}, \tag{6.9}$$

and the abbreviations

$$\rho_{\overline{MM'}} \equiv \rho_{\frac{1}{2}\frac{1}{2}}^{MM'} - \rho_{-\frac{1}{2}-\frac{1}{2}}^{MM'}, \qquad \rho_{\overline{NN'}} = \rho_{NN'}^{11} + \rho_{NN'}^{-1-1} - 2\rho_{NN'}^{00}. \tag{6.10}$$

Also other joint angular distributions are governed by two-particle density matrices. For example, if particle a is polarized, one may calculate

$W(\vartheta_a\varphi_a, \vartheta, \varphi)$, where ϑ_a and φ_a specify the orientation of the polarization vector with respect to the production plane, while ϑ and φ are the decay angles of one of the final particles:

$$W(\vartheta_a\varphi_a, \vartheta\varphi) = \sum_{MM'} \sum_{NN'} \rho(\vartheta_a\varphi_a)_{MM'}\rho_{MM',NN'}A_{NN'}(\vartheta\varphi), \tag{6.11}$$

$$\rho_{MM',NN'} = T(a_M b \to cd_N)T^*(a_{M'} b \to cd_{N'})/\sum|T|^2. \tag{6.12}$$

The matrix $\rho(\vartheta_a\varphi_a)$ is the density matrix of the incident particle a, whereas $A(\vartheta\varphi)$ is the decay matrix (2.7) of particle d, and (12) is the joint density matrix of particles a and d. A distribution similar to (11) is discussed in the next section.

9-7. Pionic hyperon decays

As a simple application of decay correlations, we discuss the parameters of the pionic hyperon decays $\Xi \to \pi\Lambda$, $\Sigma \to \pi N$, and $\Lambda \to \pi N$. The matrix elements are of the form (3-5.18) $\bar{u}'(G+G'\gamma_5)u$, which leads to (3-4.17) in the decay rest frame. In view of the parity decomposition (3-9.4), we write

$$T(M, \lambda, \vartheta, \varphi) = D^*_{M\lambda}(\varphi.\,\vartheta, -\varphi)(T_S+2\lambda T_P), \tag{7.1}$$

where

$$T_S = G\sqrt{2m_d(E+m)}, \qquad T_P = -G'\sqrt{2m_d(E-m)} \tag{7.2}$$

are the S- and P-wave amplitudes, respectively. Clearly, there are at most three measurable parameters, e.g. $|T_S|^2$, $|T_P|^2$ and the relative phase between T_S and T_P. The first parameter is determined by the decay rate,

$$\Gamma = \frac{p}{4m_d^2}\sum_\lambda \int d\cos\vartheta \frac{d\varphi}{2\pi} \frac{|T(M, \lambda, \vartheta, \varphi)|^2}{4\pi}$$
$$= p\frac{|T_S|^2+|T_P|^2}{2m_d^2 \cdot 4\pi} = \frac{p}{m_d}\left[(E+m)\frac{|G|^2}{4\pi} + (E-m)\frac{|G'|^2}{4\pi}\right], \tag{7.3}$$

according to (2-3.4) and (3-4.18), where $p = (E^2-m^2)^{\frac{1}{2}}$ is the decay momentum. The second parameter is determined by the decay distribution (3.6): it is α as defined by (2.12). In terms of (1) and (2), we have

$$\alpha = \frac{2\,\mathrm{Re}\,(T_S^*T_P)}{|T_S|^2+|T_P|^2} = -\frac{2p\,\mathrm{Re}\,(G^*G')}{|G|^2(E+m)+|G'|^2(E-m)}. \tag{7.4}$$

The last parameter is determined by the polarization of the final baryon.

In the $\Xi \to \pi\Lambda$ decays, the Λ-polarization is easily measured from the angular distribution of the main decay mode $\Lambda \to \pi^- p$. In the $\Sigma \to \pi N$ and $\Lambda \to \pi N$ decays, the neutron polarization may be determined from the decay $n \to pe\bar{\nu}$ (see section 12-4), and the proton polarization is measured by nuclear scattering, usually on ^{12}C. It is customary to define two quadratically dependent parameters,

$$\beta = \frac{2\,\mathrm{Im}\,(T_S^* T_P)}{|T_S|^2 + |T_P|^2}, \qquad \gamma = \frac{|T_S|^2 - |T_P|^2}{|T_S|^2 + |T_P|^2}, \qquad \alpha^2 + \beta^2 + \gamma^2 = 1. \tag{7.5}$$

We now turn to the measurement of these quantities. For definiteness, we discuss Ξ-decay. The matrix element of $\Xi \to \pi\Lambda$, $\Lambda \to \pi^- p$ is

$$T(M, \lambda_p, \vartheta, \varphi) = \sum_{\lambda} T(\Xi_M \to \pi\Lambda_\lambda) T(\Lambda_\lambda \to \pi^- p_{\lambda_p}), \tag{7.6}$$

apart from factors which are independent of M, λ and λ_p. The distribution of the decay angles (ϑ_p, φ_p) of Λ-decay is given by a formula similar to (6.11),

$$W(\boldsymbol{P}, \vartheta_p, \varphi_p) = \sum_{MM'} \sum_{\lambda\lambda'} \rho_{MM'} T(\Xi_M \to \pi\Lambda_\lambda) T^*(\Xi_{M'} \to \pi\Lambda_{\lambda'}) A_{\lambda\lambda'}(\vartheta_p, \varphi_p), \tag{7.7}$$

where the density matrix ρ specifies the polarization of the cascade particle. This time, we choose the z-axis of our coordinate system along the polarization vector. By (3.9), this implies

$$\rho_{\frac{1}{2}-\frac{1}{2}} = P_x - iP_y = 0, \qquad \rho_{MM} = \tfrac{1}{2} + MP, \tag{7.8}$$

where $P = |\boldsymbol{P}|$ is the "degree" of polarization. We also choose the x axis such that the Λ-momentum in the Ξ-decay has $p_y = 0$ and $p_x > 0$, which corresponds to setting $\varphi = 0$ in (1). Then (7) becomes explicitly

$$\begin{aligned} W &= \tfrac{1}{2}(1+P) \sum_{\lambda\lambda'} d_{\frac{1}{2}\lambda}(\vartheta)(T_S + 2\lambda T_P) d_{\frac{1}{2}\lambda'}(\vartheta)(T_S^* + 2\lambda' T_P^*) A_{\lambda\lambda'} \\ &\quad + \tfrac{1}{2}(1-P) \sum_{\lambda\lambda'} d_{-\frac{1}{2}\lambda}(\vartheta)(T_S + 2\lambda T_P) d_{-\frac{1}{2}\lambda'}(\vartheta)(T_S^* + 2\lambda' T_P^*) A_{\lambda\lambda'} \\ &= \tfrac{1}{2}(|T_S|^2 + |T_P|^2)[A_{\frac{1}{2}\frac{1}{2}} + A_{-\frac{1}{2}-\frac{1}{2}} + P\cos\vartheta(A_{\frac{1}{2}\frac{1}{2}} - A_{-\frac{1}{2}-\frac{1}{2}})] \\ &\quad + \mathrm{Re}\,(T_S^* T_P)[A_{\frac{1}{2}\frac{1}{2}} - A_{-\frac{1}{2}-\frac{1}{2}} + P\cos\vartheta(A_{\frac{1}{2}\frac{1}{2}} + A_{-\frac{1}{2}-\frac{1}{2}})] \\ &\quad + iP\sin\vartheta\,\mathrm{Im}\,(T_S^* T_P)(A_{-\frac{1}{2}\frac{1}{2}} - A_{\frac{1}{2}-\frac{1}{2}}) \\ &\quad - \tfrac{1}{2}P\sin\vartheta(|T_S|^2 - |T_P|^2)(A_{-\frac{1}{2}\frac{1}{2}} + A_{\frac{1}{2}-\frac{1}{2}}). \end{aligned} \tag{7.9}$$

The matrix A has been calculated in (2.13); inserting in addition α, β, γ

and normalizing $\int d\Omega_p W = 1$, (9) takes the simpler form

$$4\pi W(\vartheta_p, \varphi_p) = 1 + P\cos\vartheta\, \alpha_p \cos\vartheta_p + \alpha(\alpha_p \cos\vartheta_p + P\cos\vartheta) + P\sin\vartheta\, \alpha_p \sin\vartheta_p(\beta\sin\varphi_p - \gamma\cos\varphi_p). \quad (7.10)$$

To determine β and γ, one must measure the distribution in φ_p, the azimuth of the proton momentum, with respect to the plane spanned by $\boldsymbol{P}$ and the Λ-momentum.

The experimental values of α, β and γ are collected in table 9-7. To date, reasonably accurate values for β and γ exist only for $\Xi^- \to \Lambda\pi^-$. However, many parameters are predicted by the $\Delta Y = \frac{1}{2}$ rule, mentioned in section 4-9. For the decays $\Lambda \to \pi N$ and $\Xi \to \pi\Lambda$, this rule requires

$$T(\Lambda \to \pi^- p) = 2^{\frac{1}{2}} T(\Lambda \to \pi^0 n), \quad T(\Xi^- \to \pi^-\Lambda) = 2^{\frac{1}{2}} T(\Xi^0 \to \pi^0\Lambda). \quad (7.11)$$

By the spurious-kaon rule, these decays have the isospin structure of $K^0\Lambda \to \pi N$ and $\Xi \to \pi\Lambda\bar{K}^0$, respectively. The Λ may be omitted since it has $I = 0$. Therefore, both equations (11) follow from (4-2.9), with $K^0 = |\frac{1}{2}, -\frac{1}{2}\rangle$ and $\bar{K}^0 = p$. Since (11) applies to all spin combinations, it applies to T_S and T_P separately. Consequently, $\Lambda \to \pi^- p$ and $\Lambda \to \pi^0 n$ ($\Xi^- \to \pi^-\Lambda$ and $\Xi^0 \to \pi^0\Lambda$) should have identical α, β, γ. This agrees with the available experimental information on α.

For the Σ-decays, the $\Delta I = \frac{1}{2}$ rule requires

$$T(\Sigma^- \to \pi^- n) = T(\Sigma^+ \to \pi^+ n) + 2^{\frac{1}{2}} T(\Sigma^+ \to \pi^0 p). \quad (7.12)$$

This rule follows from the isospin decomposition of $\Sigma K^0 \to \pi N$, which is identical with that of $\pi n \to \pi N$, if Σ is replaced by π and K^0 by n. The πN-scattering relation corresponding to (12) is

$$\langle \pi^- n|T|\pi^- n\rangle = \langle \pi^+ n|T|\pi^+ n\rangle + \sqrt{2}\langle \pi^0 p|T|\pi^+ n\rangle, \quad (7.13)$$

which is obtained from (7-1.3) by charge symmetry ($\pi^+ \leftrightarrow \pi^-$, $p \leftrightarrow n$). Experimentally, (12) is satisfied in a very peculiar way. The decay $\Sigma^+ \to p\pi^0$ has $\alpha \approx -1$, which implies

$$T_S(\Sigma^+ \to p\pi^0) \approx -T_P(\Sigma^+ \to p\pi^0), \quad (7.14)$$

and $\beta = \gamma = 0$. The decays $\Sigma^+ \to \pi^+ n$ and $\Sigma^- \to \pi^- n$ are both isotropic ($\alpha = 0$), which by (12) and (14) implies that one of these decays must be pure S-wave ($\beta = 0, \gamma = 1$) and the other pure P-wave ($\beta = 0, \gamma = -1$). Measurements of the neutron polarization in $\Sigma^+ \to \pi^+ n$ (BERLEY *et al.* [1966] show that this decay contains the P-wave. Consequently, $\Sigma^- \to \pi^- n$ must contain the S-wave. This very special distribution of S- and P-waves implies nearly equal decay rates (3), or

$$\frac{\Gamma(\Sigma^- \to \pi^- n)}{0.193} = \frac{\Gamma(\Sigma^+ \to \pi^+ n)}{0.185} = \frac{\Gamma(\Sigma^+ \to \pi^0 p)}{0.189}, \tag{7.15}$$

in rough agreement with experiment (see table 9-7). The numbers in the denominators are the relevant decay momenta p of table 4-1.

TABLE 9-7

The parameters of pionic hyperon decays. (Errors range between 1 and 10 per cent.)

decay	partial width ($\times 10^{-6}$ eV)	α	β	γ	$10^7 G$	$10^7 G'$
$\Lambda \to p\pi^-$	1.725	0.69			3.37	−24.0
$\Lambda \to n\pi^0$	0.875					
$\Sigma^+ \to p\pi^0$	4.3	−0.96		a) > 0	3.38	25.4
				b) < 0	2.54	33.9
$\Sigma^+ \to n\pi^+$	3.8	0		−1	0	−41.4
$\Sigma^- \to n\pi^-$	4.0	0			4.04	0
$\Xi^0 \to \Lambda\pi^0$	2.2	−0.3				
$\Xi^- \to \Lambda\pi^-$	3.8	−0.38	0.10	0.92	4.39	14.4

Finally, if the weak interactions are time-reversal invariant (symmetric S-matrix), then T_S and T_P have the phases of the elastic scattering amplitudes for the final state. This is due to the fact that the unitarity equation for weakly coupled channels may be approximated by the unitarity condition (6-5.14) for closed channels. We shall return to this point in section 10-8 (Watson's theorem). Since the πN phase shifts are roughly known, a measurement of β in $\Lambda \to \pi N$ may check the time-reversal invariance of this decay. Table 9-7 contains values for G and G', assuming that G and G' are real ($\beta = 0$). In the literature, one frequently multiplies these coupling constants by $(m_{\pi^+})^{\frac{1}{2}}$ and expresses the result in units of $10^5/\text{sec}^{\frac{1}{2}}$. The corresponding conversion factor is 2.1715×10^{-7}.

9-8. Crossing relations for helicity amplitudes

The only crossing relations which we have considered so far were those between π^+N and π^-N scattering. There we took advantage of the identical spin formalism of π^+N and π^-N scattering amplitudes. We still need the connection with the partial wave decomposition in the t-channel, $\pi\bar{\pi} \to \bar{\mathrm{p}}\mathrm{p}$. For this and more complicated reactions, it is useful to derive crossing relations directly for helicity amplitudes, thereby avoiding the re-evaluation in terms of the scalar amplitudes $A(s, t)$ and $B(s, t)$. This has been done by TRUEMAN and WICK [1964] and by MUZINICH [1964].

Let $T_s(\lambda_a \lambda_b, \lambda_c \lambda_d)$ and $T_t(\lambda_a \lambda_{\bar{c}}, \lambda_{\bar{b}} \lambda_d)$ denote the helicity amplitudes for the s-channel ab → cd and the t-channel $\mathrm{a}\bar{\mathrm{c}} \to \bar{\mathrm{b}}\mathrm{d}$. At fixed s and t, crossing symmetry requires $P_{\bar{c}} = -P_c$, $M_{\bar{c}} = -M_c$, $\lambda_{\bar{c}} = \lambda_c$, and corresponding equalities for $P_{\bar{b}}$, $M_{\bar{b}}$ and $\lambda_{\bar{b}}$. However, an identification of T_s with the crossed T_t is possible only if both amplitudes are calculated in the same Lorentz frame, e.g. the s-channel cms, $\boldsymbol{p}_a = -\boldsymbol{p}_b = \boldsymbol{p}_{\bar{b}}$, $\boldsymbol{p}_d = -\boldsymbol{p}_c = \boldsymbol{p}_{\bar{c}}$. This requires a generalized helicity amplitude T_t', the states of which refer no longer to the t-channel cms. The new helicity states are related to the t-channel cms states simply by rotations. For a particle of momentum $\boldsymbol{p}$ and helicity λ, the Lorentz transformation from the system $\boldsymbol{p}_a + \boldsymbol{p}_{\bar{c}} = 0$,

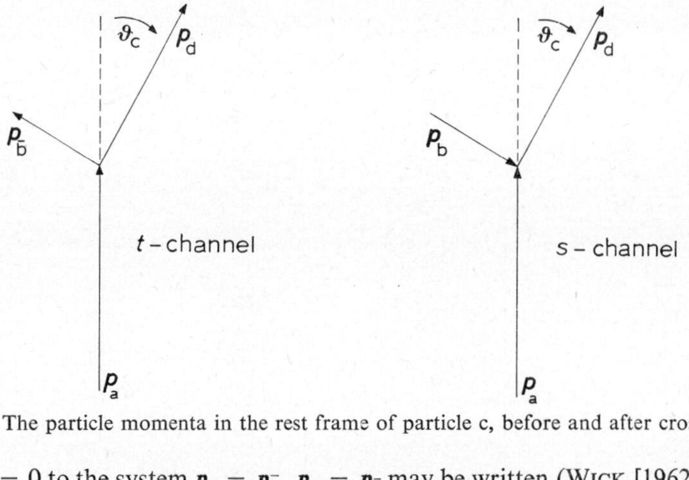

Fig. 9-8. The particle momenta in the rest frame of particle c, before and after crossing.

$\boldsymbol{p}_{\bar{b}} + \boldsymbol{p}_d = 0$ to the system $\boldsymbol{p}_a = \boldsymbol{p}_{\bar{b}}$, $\boldsymbol{p}_d = \boldsymbol{p}_{\bar{c}}$ may be written (WICK [1962]) as

$$L|\boldsymbol{p}, \lambda\rangle = \sum_{\lambda'\lambda} D^S_{\lambda'\lambda}(\vartheta)|\boldsymbol{p}', \lambda'\rangle, \tag{8.1}$$

where ϑ is the angle between $\boldsymbol{p}$ and $\boldsymbol{p}'$, in the particle's rest frame. This angle is illustrated in fig. 9-8 for the case of particle c. Let a and c be the particles of "type 2" in the s-channel, and let $\bar{\mathrm{b}}$ and $\bar{\mathrm{c}}$ be the particles of type "2" in the t-channel. Different choices differ by sign factors, which will be given below. For particle c, we thus have $\boldsymbol{p}_d$ as spin quantization axis in the s-channel and $\boldsymbol{p}_a$ as spin quantization axis in the t-channel. Before we can apply crossing symmetry, we must rotate the spin states of particle $\bar{c}$, in the c' rest frame, from $\boldsymbol{p}_a$ to $\boldsymbol{p}_d$. The corresponding angle is called ϑ_c (see fig. 9-8).

Similar considerations apply to the other particles. The spin states of particle a are rotated by ϑ_a, which is the angle between $\boldsymbol{p}_b$ and $\boldsymbol{p}_c$ in the a-rest frame. When the spin states of all four s-channel particles are rotated from the "t-channel positions" to the "s-channel positions", crossing symmetry implies equality of T_s and the transformed T_t:

$$T_s(\lambda_a\lambda_b\lambda_c\lambda_d) = \sum_{\lambda'_a\lambda_{\bar{b}}\lambda_{\bar{c}}\lambda'_d} \varepsilon d^{S_a}_{\lambda'_a\lambda_a}(\vartheta_a) d^{S_b}_{\lambda_{\bar{b}}\lambda_b}(\vartheta_b) d^{S_c}_{\lambda_{\bar{c}}\lambda_c}(\vartheta_c) d^{S_d}_{\lambda'_d\lambda_d}(\vartheta_d) T_t(\lambda'_a\lambda_{\bar{b}}\lambda_{\bar{c}}\lambda'_d). \quad (8.2)$$

Here ε is a phase factor, $\varepsilon = (-1)^{\lambda'_a - \lambda_{\bar{c}}}$ in our case. We assume that S_a and S_c are either both integer or both half-integer. If we had taken particle a instead of $\bar{c}$ as "particle 2" in the t-channel, we would have $\varepsilon = 1$. Similarly, taking d and a (d and $\bar{c}$) as "particles 2" implies $\varepsilon = (-1)^{\lambda_{\bar{b}} - \lambda'_d}$ $(\varepsilon = (-1)^{\lambda_{\bar{b}} - \lambda'_d} \times (-1)^{\lambda'_a - \lambda_{\bar{c}}})$. For a discussion of the phases, see TRUEMAN and WICK [1964].

Let us now calculate the rotation angle ϑ_c. This is conveniently done by the function κ defined by (1-4.10). From the discussion following (1-4.12), we understand that

$$\kappa = s^{\frac{1}{2}} q q' \sin\theta = t^{\frac{1}{2}} p p_\pi \sin\theta_t = m_c a_c d_c \sin\vartheta_c. \quad (8.3)$$

Here θ_t is the t-channel scattering angle, p_π and p are the initial and final cms momenta in the t-channel, and a_c and d_c are the magnitudes of $\boldsymbol{p}_a$ and $\boldsymbol{p}_d$ in the c-rest frame:

$$p_\pi = \sqrt{\lambda(t, m_a^2, m_c^2)/4t}, \qquad p = \sqrt{\lambda(t, m_b^2, m_d^2)/4t}, \quad (8.4)$$

$$a_c = \sqrt{\lambda(t, m_a^2, m_c^2)/4m_c^2}, \qquad d_c = \sqrt{\lambda(s, m_d^2, m_c^2)/4m_c^2}. \quad (8.5)$$

These expressions are self-evident in view of the property (1-2.13) of the triangle function. Inserting them into (3), we get

$$\sin\vartheta_c = \frac{\kappa}{m_c a_c d_c} = \sqrt{\frac{m_c^2\lambda(s, m_a^2, m_b^2)}{s\lambda(t, m_a^2, m_c^2)}} \sin\theta = \sqrt{\frac{m_c^2\lambda(t, m_b^2, m_d^2)}{t\lambda(s, m_c^2, m_d^2)}} \sin\theta_t. \quad (8.6)$$

For the remaining angles, the same method gives

$$\sin\vartheta_a = \frac{\kappa}{m_a b_a c_a}, \qquad \sin\vartheta_b = \frac{\kappa}{m_b a_b d_b}, \qquad \sin\vartheta_d = \frac{\kappa}{m_d c_d b_d}. \quad (8.7)$$

We also calculate the cosines of the rotation angles. For $\cos\vartheta_c$, we find from the definition $u = (P_a - P_d)^2$,

$$\tfrac{1}{2}(m_a^2 + m_d^2 - u) = P_a P_d = (E_a E_d)_c - a_c d_c \cos\vartheta_c. \quad (8.8)$$

The energies of particles a and d in the c-rest frame are

$$(E_a)_c = \sqrt{a_c^2+m_a^2} = -\frac{t-m_a^2-m_c^2}{2m_c}$$
$$(E_d)_c = \sqrt{d_c^2+m_d^2} = \frac{s-m_c^2-m_d^2}{2m_c}. \tag{8.9}$$

In the first expression, a minus sign is necessary to make $(E_a)_c$ positive. Inserting these expressions and $m_a^2+m_d^2-u = s+t-m_b^2-m_c^2$ into (8), we get

$$\cos \vartheta_c = \frac{(m_a^2+m_c^2-t)(s-m_d^2-m_c^2)+2m_c^2(m_b^2+m_c^2-s-t)}{\sqrt{\lambda(t, m_a^2, m_c^2)\lambda(s, m_d^2, m_c^2)}}$$
$$= \frac{-(t-m_a^2+m_c^2)(s-m_d^2+m_c^2)-2m_c^2 \Delta m^2}{\sqrt{\lambda(t, m_a^2, m_c^2)\lambda(s, m_d^2, m_c^2)}},$$
$$\Delta m^2 \equiv m_a^2-m_b^2-m_c^2+m_d^2. \tag{8.10}$$

For the other angles, we find similarly

$$\cos \vartheta_a = \frac{(t+m_a^2-m_c^2)(s+m_a^2-m_b^2)-2m_a^2 \Delta m^2}{\sqrt{\lambda(t, m_a^2, m_c^2)\lambda(s, m_a^2, m_b^2)}},$$
$$\cos \vartheta_b = \frac{-(t+m_b^2-m_d^2)(s+m_b^2-m_a^2)-2m_b^2 \Delta m^2}{\sqrt{\lambda(t, m_b^2, m_d^2)\lambda(s, m_a^2, m_b^2)}}, \tag{8.11}$$
$$\cos \vartheta_d = \frac{(t+m_d^2-m_b^2)(s+m_d^2-m_c^2)-2m_d^2 \Delta m^2}{\sqrt{\lambda(t, m_b^2, m_d^2)\lambda(s, m_c^2, m_d^2)}}.$$

For elastic scattering, we have $m_a = m_c = \mu$, $m_d = m_b = m$,

$$\cos \vartheta_b = -\cos \vartheta_d = \frac{-t(s+m^2-\mu^2)}{\sqrt{t(t-4m^2)\lambda(s, m^2, \mu^2)}}$$
$$= \sqrt{\frac{t}{\lambda(s, m^2, \mu^2)}}\,(p+p_\pi \cos \theta_t), \tag{8.12}$$

$$\sin \vartheta_b = \sin \vartheta_d = \frac{t^{\frac{1}{2}} p p_\pi \sin \theta_t}{m a_b d_b} = \frac{2m p_\pi \sin \theta_t}{\sqrt{\lambda(s, m^2, \mu^2)}}, \tag{8.13}$$

and corresponding expressions for $\cos \vartheta_a = -\cos \vartheta_c$, $\sin \vartheta_a = \sin \vartheta_c$. For elastic meson-nucleon scattering, $S_a = S_c = 0$, $S_b = S_d = \frac{1}{2}$, and (2) reduces to

$$T_s(\lambda\lambda') = \sum_{\lambda_{\bar{b}}\lambda'_d} d^{\frac{1}{2}}_{\lambda_{\bar{b}}\lambda}(\vartheta_b) d^{\frac{1}{2}}_{\lambda'_d\lambda'}(\pi-\vartheta_b) T_t(\lambda'_d\lambda_{\bar{b}}). \tag{8.14}$$

With $\sin\frac{1}{2}(\pi-\vartheta) = \cos\frac{1}{2}\vartheta$, $\cos\frac{1}{2}(\pi-\vartheta) = \sin\frac{1}{2}\vartheta$ and the parity invariance $T_t(\frac{1}{2},\frac{1}{2}) = T_t(-\frac{1}{2},-\frac{1}{2})$, $T_t(\frac{1}{2},-\frac{1}{2}) = -T_t(-\frac{1}{2},\frac{1}{2})$, (14) becomes

$$\begin{aligned} T_s(\tfrac{1}{2},\tfrac{1}{2}) &= \sin\vartheta_b\, T_t(\tfrac{1}{2},\tfrac{1}{2}) + \cos\vartheta_b\, T_t(\tfrac{1}{2},-\tfrac{1}{2}),\\ T_s(\tfrac{1}{2},-\tfrac{1}{2}) &= -\cos\vartheta_b\, T_t(\tfrac{1}{2},\tfrac{1}{2}) + \sin\vartheta_b\, T_t(\tfrac{1}{2},-\tfrac{1}{2}). \end{aligned} \tag{8.15}$$

We may check (15) by expressing T_s and T_t in terms of the invariant amplitudes A and B. For T_s, insertion of (7-4.3) into (3-8.3) gives

$$\begin{aligned} T_s(\tfrac{1}{2},\tfrac{1}{2}) &= 8\pi s^{\frac{1}{2}}\cos\tfrac{1}{2}\theta\,(f_1+f_2) = 2\cos\tfrac{1}{2}\theta\,[mA + B(Es^{\frac{1}{2}}-m^2)],\\ T_s(\tfrac{1}{2},-\tfrac{1}{2}) &= 8\pi s^{\frac{1}{2}}\sin\tfrac{1}{2}\theta\,(f_1-f_2) = -2\sin\tfrac{1}{2}\theta\,[EA + mB(s^{\frac{1}{2}}-E)]. \end{aligned} \tag{8.16}$$

The corresponding equations for $T_t(M = \lambda'_d, \overline{M} = -\lambda_{\bar{b}})$ have been given in (7-8.8), for the reaction $p\bar{p} \to \pi\bar{\pi}$. We now need the inverse reaction $\pi\bar{\pi} \to N\bar{N}$. By (4-5.3) and (4.9), (4.10), this makes only an extra minus sign for $\lambda_{\bar{b}} = -\lambda_d$:

$$T_t(\tfrac{1}{2},\tfrac{1}{2}) = 2i(Ap + mp_\pi B\cos\theta_t), \qquad T_t(\tfrac{1}{2},-\tfrac{1}{2}) = ip_\pi t^{\frac{1}{2}} B\sin\theta_t. \tag{8.17}$$

Comparing the coefficients of A on both sides of (15), we find that (15) is only valid for

$$-m\cos\tfrac{1}{2}\theta = ip\sin\vartheta_b, \qquad -E\sin\tfrac{1}{2}\theta = ip\cos\vartheta_b. \tag{8.18}$$

These equalities are in fact satisfied. From (1-3.11) we remember

$$\sin\tfrac{1}{2}\theta = \sqrt{-t/4q^2} = \sqrt{-st/\lambda(s, m^2, \mu^2)}. \tag{8.19}$$

Also, $E = (s+m^2-\mu^2)/2s^{\frac{1}{2}}$ is the proton energy in πp scattering. With $p = (t-\frac{1}{4}m^2)^{\frac{1}{2}}$, $p\cos\vartheta_b$ is found from the first expression of (12), and the second equality of (18) is verified. The first equality may be verified in several ways. We may start directly from (7),

$$\sin\vartheta_b = 4m\kappa[t(t-4m^2)\lambda(s, m^2, \mu^2)]^{-\frac{1}{2}}, \tag{8.20}$$

and then insert from (3) and (19)

$$\kappa = s^{\frac{1}{2}}q^2\sin\theta = 2s^{\frac{1}{2}}q^2\sin\tfrac{1}{2}\theta\cos\tfrac{1}{2}\theta = q(-st)^{\frac{1}{2}}\cos\tfrac{1}{2}\theta. \tag{8.21}$$

It should be noted that the signs of expressions such as (19) are not unique. We could have defined $\sin\frac{1}{2}\theta$ as $-(-t/4q^2)^{\frac{1}{2}}$, in which case both (19) and

(21) would change sign, and (18) would apply without minus signs. This would not affect (15), since we are free to include an additional minus sign in the definition of T_t. The question of signs is settled by analytic continuation of the square roots, taken as functions of complex s and t, such that $s+t$ remains real. From section 6-7 we remember that s must have a positive imaginary part in the physical region of the s-channel, while t must have a positive imaginary part in the physical region of the t-channel (upper shaded area of fig. 6-7.1). Therefore, if we could plot Im s out of the paper plane in fig. 6-7.1, the path of analytic continuation would lie above the paper plane in the physical s-channel region (lower right shaded area), then cross the paper at a point which is free from singularities ("white"), and continue below the paper plane to the physical t-channel region. Our signs correspond to traversing the paper within the small segment of the parabola $us = (m^2 - \mu^2)^2$ which lies above $t > 0$ (TRUEMAN and WICK [1964]).

Evidently, the crossing of cms helicity amplitudes is relatively complicated. For spin states quantized along the *normal* to the production plane, each amplitude essentially crosses into itself (KOTAŃSKI [1966]). This is due to the fact that the direction of the normal to the production plane changes at most its sign under crossing.

CHAPTER 10

ELECTROMAGNETIC INTERACTIONS OF HADRONS

10-1. Coulomb scattering

Electromagnetic interactions of hadrons occur in several places. Firstly, we have the electromagnetic decays of hadrons, some of which have already been discussed in section 4-8. Next, there is the one-photon exchange in the elastic scattering of charged particles. For small momentum transfer ($t \to 0$), this is called Coulomb scattering. Electron-proton and electron-neutron scattering are also due to one-photon exchange. Here, the scattering at large momentum transfers involves the electromagnetic form factors of the nucleons. Finally, in photoproduction such as $\gamma p \to$ hadrons, more complicated electromagnetic (and strong) interactions occur.

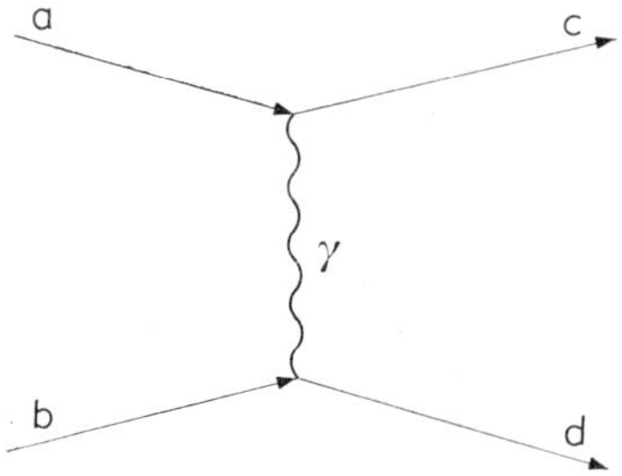

Fig. 10-1. The Born term of one-photon exchange.

The interaction between electrons and photons is described by quantum electrodynamics. This quantum field theory has been verified experimentally with a high degree of accuracy. There exists an extensive literature on this theory. (HEITLER [1954], JAUCH and ROHRLICH [1955], KÄLLÉN [1958], BJORKEN and DRELL [1964, 1965], to mention only a few books). The classical limit of quantum electrodynamics is given by the Maxwell equations, which provide the very basis of measurement in particle physics.

In principle, quantum electrodynamics may also describe the interactions of photons with hadrons. In practice, however, the precision is usually low, due to the presence of strong interactions.

We now turn to the study of Coulomb scattering. The matrix element T_γ of single photon exchange is illustrated in fig. 10-1. It is approximated by the crossed Born term of (6-4.6),

$$T_\gamma^{\text{Born}} = B^\mu(\text{a} \to \gamma\text{c}) \frac{g_{\mu\nu}}{t} B^\nu(\gamma\text{b} \to \text{d}) = \frac{1}{t} B^\mu(\text{a} \to \gamma\text{c}) B_\mu(\gamma\text{b} \to \text{d}). \quad (1.1)$$

Here we have put $m_\gamma = 0$ and omitted the term $P_\mu P_\nu / m_\gamma^2$ in the propagator, using gauge invariance (cf. (3-3.11)). For definiteness, we consider elastic meson-nucleon scattering,

$$m_\text{c} = m_\text{a}, \qquad m_\text{b} = m_\text{d} = m. \quad (1.2)$$

Assuming the same electric charge e for meson and nucleon, we have

$$B^\mu(\text{a} \to \gamma\text{c}) = e(P_\text{a} + P_\text{c})^\mu, \quad (1.3)$$

$$B_\nu(\gamma\text{b} \to \text{d}) = e\bar{u}'(M') \left[\gamma_\nu + \frac{\kappa}{2m} \sigma_{\mu\nu}(P_\text{b} - P_\text{d})^\mu \right] u(M). \quad (1.4)$$

From section 4-8, we remember that these couplings are gauge invariant when (2) is satisfied. The connection between (4) and the coupling constants of (4-8.6) is given by

$$G_\text{v} \equiv e, \qquad G_\text{t} \equiv e\kappa. \quad (1.5)$$

The constant κ is called the anomalous magnetic moment. For protons, κ is 1.7928. In the limit $t \to 0$, (4) reduces to

$$B_\nu(\gamma\text{b}_M \to \text{d}_{M'}) \approx e(P + P')_\nu \delta_{MM'}. \quad (1.6)$$

To see this, we observe that, between free-particle Dirac spinors, we may replace

$$\gamma_\nu \to \frac{(P+P')_\nu}{m+m'} + \frac{(P-P')^\mu \sigma_{\mu\nu}}{m+m'}. \quad (1.7)$$

This relation was already used in the derivation of (4-8.7) from (4-8.6). Since $t = 0$ requires $P_\text{b} = P_\text{d}$ (elastic forward scattering), we neglect terms proportional to $P_\text{b} - P_\text{d}$ and obtain (6) from $\bar{u}(M')u(M) = 2m\delta_{MM'}$. In fact, (6) is true for particles of any spin. It reflects the fact that spin-flip amplitudes vanish in the forward direction.

Inserting (3) and (6) into (1), we find the Coulomb scattering amplitude

$$T_\text{c} \approx \frac{e^2}{t} (P_\text{a} + P_\text{c})(P_\text{b} + P_\text{d}) \delta_{MM'} \approx 8\pi \frac{\alpha}{t} (s - m^2 - m_\text{a}^2) \delta_{MM'}. \quad (1.8)$$

Here we have introduced the fine-structure constant α of (4-1.1). For elastic scattering, inversion of (1-3.2) and (1-3.4) gives

$$P_a P_b = P_c P_d = \tfrac{1}{2}(s-m^2-m_a^2), \qquad P_c P_b = P_a P_d = \tfrac{1}{2}(m^2-m_a^2-u). \quad (1.9)$$

Inserting $u = 2(m^2+m_a^2)-s-t$ in the second expression, we find

$$(P_a+P_c)(P_b+P_d) = 2(s-m^2-m_a^2+\tfrac{1}{2}t). \quad (1.10)$$

Now (8) is obtained by neglecting the term $\frac{1}{2}t$.

For further discussion, the abbreviation

$$\frac{s-m^2-m_a^2}{s^{\frac{1}{2}}} \equiv 2\mu \quad (1.11)$$

is useful. For low energies, μ becomes the reduced mass.

The complete matrix elements are given by the sum of T_c and the matrix elements of the strong interaction. (For a detailed discussion, see e.g. SOLMITZ [1954].) For meson-nucleon scattering, the matrix elements $T(M, M', \theta)$ of (3-9.19), (3-9.20) are appropriate. Thus, for elastic π^+p or K^+p scattering, the cross-section becomes (apart from terms proportional to α or α^2/t)

$$\frac{d\sigma}{d\Omega} = \frac{1}{2}\sum_{MM'}\left|\frac{T_{\text{total}}(M, M')}{8\pi s^{\frac{1}{2}}}\right|^2 = \left|2\alpha\frac{\mu}{t} + f_1 + f_2\cos\theta\right|^2 + \sin^2\theta\,|f_2|^2. \quad (1.12)$$

The partial wave expansions of f_1 and f_2 are given by (3-9.8) and (3-9.9). Keeping only terms with $J < \frac{5}{2}$, we find explicitly

$$f_1(\cos\theta) = f_{0+} + 3\cos\theta\, f_{1+} - f_{2-}, \qquad f_2(\cos\theta) = f_{1-} - f_{1+} + 3\cos\theta\, f_{2-}. \quad (1.13)$$

A partial wave expansion of T_c is not appropriate. From (1-3.11), we remember $t = -4q^2\sin^2\frac{1}{2}\theta$. This shows that (12) diverges both for $\theta \to 0$ and for $q^2 \to 0$. Actually, the above treatment becomes inadequate for $q^2 \to 0$. When the particles move slowly, they may exchange more than one photon. This problem is solved by potential theory. Outside the range R of the strong interaction, the radial wave equation (2-5.3) applies, with

$$V(r) = \pm 2\mu\alpha/r = 2\eta q/r, \qquad \eta \equiv \pm\mu\alpha/q. \quad (1.14)$$

The minus sign for η applies for opposite charges of the scattering particles. Introducing the variable $y = qr$, (2-5.3) becomes

$$\left(\frac{d^2}{dy^2} + 1 - \frac{2\eta}{y} - \frac{L(L+1)}{y^2}\right) u_L(y) = 0. \quad (1.15)$$

The solutions of this equation are known as Coulomb wave functions. They are discussed e.g. by SCHIFF [1955] section 20, PRESTON [1962] appendix B, GOLDBERGER and WATSON [1964]. The asymptotic solution is of a form simular to (2-5.4)

$$u_L(y) = a_L \cdot \frac{1}{q} \sin\left(y - \tfrac{1}{2}\pi L - \eta \ln 2y + \sigma_L\right). \tag{1.16}$$

The necessity of the new term $-\eta \ln 2y$ in the sine function is verified by inserting (16) into (15) and neglecting the centrifugal potential $L(L+1)/y^2$. Because of the new term, a few changes in the general scattering formalism of section 2-5 are necessary. We only mention that for S-waves and for $y \to 0$, the regular solution of (15) is

$$u_0(y) = rC_0(1+\eta y + \ldots), \tag{1.17}$$

where the normalization constant C_0 is given by

$$\begin{aligned} C_0^2 &= |\Gamma(1+i\eta)|^2 e^{-\pi\eta} = \Gamma(1+i\eta)\Gamma(1-i\eta)e^{-\pi\eta} \\ &= \eta^2\Gamma(i\eta)\Gamma(-i\eta)e^{-\pi\eta} = \frac{2\pi\eta}{e^{2\pi\eta}-1}. \end{aligned} \tag{1.18}$$

Here we have applied the property $\Gamma(x)\Gamma(-x) = -\pi/x \sin \pi x$. C_0^2 measures the dependence of the wave function intensity, $|u_0|^2$ for $qr \ll 1$, on the Coulomb field. For $\eta = 0$, we have $C_0^2 = 1$. Expanding $e^x = 1 + x + \frac{1}{2}x^2$, we find

$$C_0^2 = \frac{1}{1+\pi\eta} \quad \text{for} \quad \pi\eta \ll 1, \tag{1.19}$$

which shows that the intensity increases for $\eta < 0$ (attraction) and decreases for $\eta > 0$ (repulsion). This result will be needed in the theory of β-decay (section 12-1).

10-2. Rosenbluth formula

Since the electron has no strong interaction, the full amplitude of electron-proton scattering is given by T_γ, the one-photon exchange amplitude. The exchange of two photons appears to be negligible.

The difference between T_γ and T_γ^{Born} comes from the proton vertex, where the constants e and κ are replaced by two functions of the momentum transfer. It is customary to introduce these functions in the form of the electric and magnetic form factors $F_1(t)$ and $F_2(t)$:

$$B_\nu(\gamma \mathrm{p} \to \mathrm{p}') = e\bar{u}'(M') \left[F_1(t)\gamma_\nu + \frac{\kappa}{2m} F_2(t)\sigma_{\mu\nu}(P-P')^\mu \right] u(M). \tag{2.1}$$

For $t = 0$, (1) must reduce to (1.4), which means

$$F_1(0) = F_2(0) = 1. \tag{2.2}$$

Terms such as $(P-P')_\nu F_3(t)$ are excluded by gauge invariance, $(P-P')^\nu B_\nu = 0$. For real photons, such terms cannot appear because of the Lorentz condition (3-3.1) $P_\gamma \cdot \varepsilon = 0$. The general form of the cross-section for the scattering of unpolarized electrons on unpolarized protons has been calculated by ROSENBLUTH [1950]. Before we derive it, we discuss a slightly more general problem, namely the form of the cross-section $\sigma_\mathrm{v}(\mathrm{ab} \to \mathrm{cd})$ due to vector exchange, when particles b and d are baryons. Particles a and c remain unspecified. We write the matrix element in the form (4-8.7),

$$T_\mathrm{v} = \bar{u}'(M') \left[(G_\mathrm{v} + G_\mathrm{t})\varepsilon^* \cdot \gamma - \frac{G_\mathrm{t}}{m+m'} (P+P') \cdot \varepsilon^* \right] u(M). \tag{2.3}$$

For the time being, ε^* is an arbitrary complex 4-vector satisfying $\varepsilon^* \cdot (P-P') = 0$, and G_v, G_t are arbitrary real functions. For $m \neq m'$, (3) will not be gauge invariant. Matrix elements of this type occur in the peripheral model.

The cross-section for unpolarized initial baryon, summed over the polarization of the final baryon, may be calculated by the trace method of section 3-6. From (3-6.10), we have

$$\begin{aligned} \tfrac{1}{2} \sum_{MM'} |T_\mathrm{v}|^2 &= \tfrac{1}{2}\,\mathrm{trace}\,(m' + P'\gamma) \left[(G_\mathrm{v} + G_\mathrm{t})\varepsilon^*\gamma - \frac{G_\mathrm{t}}{m+m'} (P+P')\varepsilon^* \right] \\ &\quad \times (m+P\gamma) \left[(G_\mathrm{v} + G_\mathrm{t})\varepsilon\gamma - \frac{G_\mathrm{t}}{m+m'} (P+P')\varepsilon \right] \\ &\equiv \tfrac{1}{2}(G_\mathrm{v} + G_\mathrm{t})^2 A - \tfrac{1}{2}(G_\mathrm{v} + G_\mathrm{t}) \frac{G_\mathrm{t}}{m+m'} B + \tfrac{1}{2} \frac{G_\mathrm{t}^2}{m+m'} C, \end{aligned} \tag{2.4}$$

where

$$\begin{aligned} A &= \mathrm{trace}\,(m' + P'\gamma)\varepsilon^*\gamma(m+P\gamma)\varepsilon\gamma \\ &= \mathrm{trace}\,(m' + P'\gamma)(m - P\gamma)\varepsilon^*\varepsilon + 2P \cdot \varepsilon^*\,\mathrm{trace}\,(m' + P'\gamma)\varepsilon \cdot \gamma \\ &= 4(m'm - P'P)\varepsilon^*\varepsilon + 8(P \cdot \varepsilon^*)(P \cdot \varepsilon). \end{aligned} \tag{2.5}$$

The traces of γ-matrices are explained in appendix E-1. Similarly, we find

$$B = (P+P')\cdot\varepsilon \,\text{trace}\,(m'+P'\gamma)\varepsilon^*\gamma(m+P\gamma) + (P+P')\cdot\varepsilon^* \,\text{trace}\,(m'+P'\gamma)(m+P\gamma)\varepsilon\gamma$$
$$= 16(m+m')(P\cdot\varepsilon^*)(P\cdot\varepsilon), \tag{2.6}$$

$$C = (P+P')\cdot\varepsilon^*(P+P')\cdot\varepsilon \,\text{trace}\,(m'+P'\gamma)(m+P\gamma)$$
$$= 16(P\cdot\varepsilon^*)(P\cdot\varepsilon)(mm'+PP'). \tag{2.7}$$

Here we have frequently applied the relation $P\cdot\varepsilon = P'\cdot\varepsilon$. From (1-3.3), we have

$$2(P'P\pm m'm) = (m\pm m')^2-t. \tag{2.8}$$

The final result is

$$\tfrac{1}{2}\sum_{MM'}|T_v|^2 = -(G_v+G_t)^2[(m-m')^2-t]\varepsilon^*\varepsilon+4(P\cdot\varepsilon^*)P\cdot\varepsilon\left(G_v^2-\frac{tG_t^2}{(m+m')^2}\right). \tag{2.9}$$

For our present purpose, we insert $m' = m$, $G_v = eF_1$, and $G_t = e\kappa F_2$. According to (1.1), the 4-vector ε is replaced by B/t, where B is the (real) vertex factor of the electrons. Then (9) reads

$$\tfrac{1}{2}\sum_{MM'}|T_v|^2 = \frac{e^2}{t}(F_1+\kappa F_2)^2B^2+\left(2\frac{e}{t}B\cdot P\right)^2\left(F_1^2-\frac{t\kappa^2}{4m^2}F_2^2\right). \tag{2.10}$$

Also this formula is relatively general; it applies to electrons and muons, polarized or unpolarized. To obtain the Rosenbluth formula, we specify B as $-e\bar{u}'\gamma u$. The minus sign comes from the electron's negative charge. The spinors $\bar{u}'$ and u now refer to the electron in the final and initial state. The anomalous magnetic moment of the electron, κ_e, is so small that it may be neglected. Averaging over the initial and summing over the final spin states of the electron, we get (μ = electron mass)

$$\frac{1}{2e^2}\sum B^2 = \tfrac{1}{2}\,\text{trace}\,(\mu+P_c\gamma)\gamma^\nu(\mu+P_a\gamma)\gamma_\nu = 4\mu^2+2t, \tag{2.11}$$

$$\frac{1}{2e^2}\sum(B\cdot P)^2 = \tfrac{1}{2}\,\text{trace}\,(\mu+P_c\gamma)P_b\gamma(\mu+P_a\gamma)P_b\gamma$$
$$= 4(P_aP_b)(P_cP_d)-2P_aP_c(m^2-\mu^2)$$
$$= (s-m^2-\mu^2)^2+ts-2\mu^2(m^2+t). \tag{2.12}$$

For high-energy electrons, μ^2 can be neglected, and (10) assumes the final form

$$\tfrac{1}{4}\sum_{\text{all spins}} |T_v|^2 = 4\frac{e^4}{t^2}\left[\tfrac{1}{2}t^2(F_1+\kappa F_2)^2 + \left(F_1^2 - \frac{t\kappa^2}{4m^2}F_2^2\right)((s-m^2)^2+ts)\right]. \quad (2.13)$$

The differential cross-section is obtained by dividing (13) by $16\pi\lambda(s, m^2, \mu^2)$:

$$\frac{d\sigma}{dt} = 4\pi\left(\frac{\alpha}{t(s-m^2)}\right)^2\left[\tfrac{1}{2}t^2(F_1+\kappa F_2)^2 + \left(F_1^2 - \frac{t\kappa^2}{4m^2}F_2^2\right)((s-m^2)^2+ts)\right]. \quad (2.14)$$

This is the Rosenbluth formula. Usually approximate expressions for s and t in terms of the lab energy and scattering angle are inserted in the final form. Specifically, one uses

$$-t = 4(q \sin \tfrac{1}{2}\theta)^2 \approx 4(p^{\text{lab}} \sin \tfrac{1}{2}\theta^{\text{lab}})^2. \quad (2.15)$$

10-3. Electromagnetic form factors of nucleons

The electromagnetic form factors of proton and neutron have received considerable attention (see e.g. DRELL [1963]). Here we mention only a few basic considerations.

Although the electromagnetic interactions do not conserve isospin, it is useful to split the nucleon form factors into isoscalar and isovector parts. We define

$$\begin{aligned} F_i(\text{proton}) &= F_i^s + F_i^v, \qquad i = 1, 2 \\ F_i(\text{neutron}) &= F_i^s - F_i^v, \qquad F_1^s(0) = F_1^v(0) = \tfrac{1}{2}. \end{aligned} \quad (3.1)$$

This splitting makes no assumptions whatsoever about the isospin properties of electromagnetic interactions, since we may always write two functions as the sum and difference of two other functions. However, from the point of view of the nucleons, the F^s coupling is that of an $I = 0$ meson and the F^v coupling that of an $I = 1$ meson (cf. the two signs of F_i in (1) with the opposite signs of $G(p \to \pi^0 p)$ and $G(n \to \pi^0 n)$ in (7-1.6)). In particular, F^v will have a pole at $t = m_\rho^2$, corresponding to the coupling γ~~•----ρ, and F^s will have poles at $t = m_\omega^2$ and $t = m_\phi^2$.

For comparison with experiment, the "electric" and "magnetic" form factors

$$\begin{aligned} G_E(t) &= F_1(t) + \frac{t\kappa}{4m^2}F_2(t), \\ G_M(t) &= F_1(t) + \kappa F_2(t), \end{aligned} \quad (3.2)$$

are more convenient than F_1 and F_2. This follows from the form of the Rosenbluth formula. Usually $t\kappa/4m^2$ is negligible, i.e. $G_E \approx F_1$. Numerically, we have

$$\kappa_p = 1.79276, \qquad \kappa_n = -1.9157, \tag{3.3}$$

$$G_M^s(0) = 0.5 + \tfrac{1}{2}(\kappa_p + \kappa_n) = 0.440, \qquad G_M^v(0) = 0.5 + \tfrac{1}{2}(\kappa_p - \kappa_n) = 2.353. \tag{3.4}$$

A rough fit to the experimental isovector form factors is (DUNNING *et al.* [1964])

$$G_E^v = \frac{2.01}{1-t/m_\rho^2} - \frac{1.51}{1-t/m_{\rho'}^2}, \qquad G_M^v = \frac{6.23}{1-t/m_\rho^2} - \frac{3.87}{1-t/m_{\rho'}^2},$$
$$m_{\rho'} = 940 \text{ MeV}. \tag{3.5}$$

One of the two poles has been fixed at the mass of the ρ-meson, while the position $m_{\rho'}^2$ of the other pole is a variable. In both cases, the residue of the ρ-pole is the larger one, which substantiates the theoretical considerations. Similarly, the isoscalar form factors may be described in terms of poles at the masses of the ω- and ϕ-mesons,

$$G_E^s = \frac{1.24}{1-t/m_\omega^2} - \frac{0.74}{1-t/m_\phi^2}, \qquad G_M^s = \frac{1.12}{1-t/m_\omega^2} - \frac{0.68}{1-t/m_\phi^2}. \tag{3.6}$$

If our theoretical considerations are correct, then the ratio of the residues of a pole in G_M and G_E should be $1 + G_t/G_v$, where G_v and G_t are the coupling constants of the corresponding resonance to the nucleon (cf. (2.3)). Numerically, we find

$$G_t/G_v \approx 2.1 \quad \text{for} \quad \rho, \qquad G_t/G_v \approx 0 \quad \text{for} \quad \omega \quad \text{and} \quad \phi. \tag{3.7}$$

However, for the ω- and ϕ-mesons such an interpretation is rather uncertain. We notice that there is destructive interference between the two poles in all four form factors. Consequently, the form factors are always steeper than the first pole term alone. We shall see later that steep form factors are a general feature of high-energy interactions. It is therefore quite unlikely that this steepness is caused by destructive interference of smoother functions. For the proton form factors, an accurate fit is given by the simpler formula (CHAN *et al.* [1966])

$$G_E = \frac{G_M}{1+\kappa} = (1 - t/0.70 \text{ GeV}^2)^{-2}. \tag{3.8}$$

10-4. Gauge invariance and charge conservation

The conservation of electric charge follows from gauge invariance. We demonstrate this by a simple example, namely the reaction $\pi^- K^+ \to \gamma\pi^0 K^0$. We assume that π^0 and K^0 have zero electric charge. Then we can show that the sum of the electric charges of π^- and K^+ must be zero, i.e. the total electric charge must be conserved in the process.

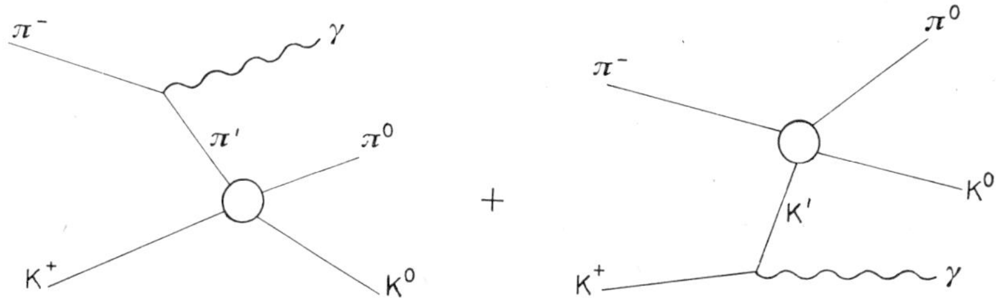

Fig. 10-4. The two Born terms of $\pi^- K^+ \to \pi^0 K^0 \gamma$.

The emission of the photon is calculated in the Born approximation. There are two Born terms, illustrated in fig. 10-4. We are only interested in the region of small momentum transfer to the photon, where we may approximate

$$P_\pi'^2 = m_\pi^2, \qquad P_K'^2 = m_K^2 \tag{4.1}$$

in the matrix elements $T'(\pi' K^+ \to \pi^0 K^0)$ and $T'(\pi^- K' \to \pi^0 K^0)$. We then have

$$T = T'(\pi^- K^+ \to \pi^0 K^0)\left[\frac{e_\pi}{m_\pi^2 - P_\pi'^2}\,\varepsilon^*(\lambda)\cdot(P_\pi + P_\pi') + \frac{e_K}{m_K^2 - P_K'^2}\,\varepsilon^*(\lambda)\cdot(P_K + P_K')\right]. \tag{4.2}$$

Gauge invariance requires the square bracket to become zero when $\varepsilon^*(\lambda)$ is replaced by P_γ. For the first term, we have

$$P_\gamma(P_\pi + P_\pi') = (P_\pi - P_\pi')(P_\pi + P_\pi') = m_\pi^2 - P_\pi'^2, \tag{4.3}$$

which just cancels the denominator. The same thing happens with the second term, where P_γ is $P_K - P_K'$. Consequently, neither of the two terms is gauge invariant, and (2) is only gauge invariant for

$$e_\pi + e_K = 0. \tag{4.4}$$

This argument is incomplete for the following reason: For $P_\pi'^2 \neq m_\pi^2$, $P_K'^2 \neq m_K^2$, (2) is only approximate valid. Even if we neglect the dependence of $T'(\pi^- K^+ \to \pi^0 K^0)$ on the new variables, there are still the electric form factors of π^-, K^- and K^0 (the electric form factor of π^0 is identically zero because of C invariance). In the limit (1), however, the denominators of (2) vanish, which shows that (2) cannot be complete, in any case. This is connected with the problem of "infrared divergence". Note that (1) implies $P_\gamma = 0$. Photons of zero momentum are undetectable. However, the classical electromagnetic field should correspond to a limiting case of infinitely many zero-energy photons, such that the total energy of the field remains finite. We leave this problem to the textbooks of quantum electrodynamics.

10-5. Isospin and SU_3 properties of electromagnetic interactions

In section 10-4, we saw that a photon may be decomposed into an isoscalar and an isovector part, as far as the nucleon form factors are concerned. This was a trivial consequence of the fact that the two nucleons form an isospin doublet. However, one expects that also in more general reactions such as photo-production, the photon may change the isospin of the hadron states by at most one unit.

Consider for example the destruction of an α-particle by a photon, $\gamma\alpha \to$ ppnn. The final four-nucleon states could have $I = 0$, 1 or 2. (As usual, the "stretched" configuration $I = 2$ corresponds to total symmetry 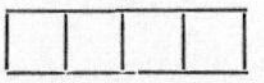 in isospace and therefore to total antisymmetry in momentum-spin space.) However, if the photon is absorbed by a single nucleon in the α-particle, the isospin may change in the reaction by at most one unit. Because α is an isospin singlet, this excludes the $I = 2$ state from the final nucleon configurations.

Next, we consider the electric form factors of pions (since the pions are spinless, each pion has only one form factor). To find the isospin properties, it is convenient to consider the crossed vertex $\gamma \to \pi\bar{\pi}$ instead of $\pi \to \gamma\pi$. The $\pi\bar{\pi}$ pair must have $J = 1$ in order to preserve the photon spin. On the other hand, we know that a P-wave pion pair has $I = 1$. Therefore, the photon carries exactly one unit of isospin in the electromagnetic interactions of pions. The electric form factors of π^+ and π^- are equal apart from sign, while that of π^0 is zero, for all values of the momentum transfer. (In fact, all spinless mesons which are their own antiparticles cannot absorb a photon, since P-states of two identical particles are excluded by the Bose-Einstein symmetry.)

Consider now the photoproduction of pions, $\gamma p \to \pi N$, $\gamma p \to \pi\pi N$, $\gamma p \to \pi\pi\pi N$, etc. from this point of view. Let us assume that the photon is always absorbed by a single nucleon or pion. In that case, only three independent isospin amplitudes exist, which we denote by

$$T^0, T^{\frac{1}{2}} \quad \text{and} \quad T^{\frac{3}{2}}.$$

T^0 corresponds to that part where the photon carries no isospin (absorption by a nucleon), while $T^{\frac{1}{2}}$ and $T^{\frac{3}{2}}$ correspond to that part where it carries one unit of isospin. The upper indices $\frac{1}{2}$ and $\frac{3}{2}$ denote the two possible values of the total isospin in this case. Of course, T^0 contributes only to $I = \frac{1}{2}$ states, since the initial nucleon has $I = \frac{1}{2}$. Explicitly, we find

$$\begin{aligned} T(\gamma p \to \pi^+ n) &= 2^{\frac{1}{2}}(T^{\frac{3}{2}} - T^{\frac{1}{2}} - T^0), \\ T(\gamma p \to \pi^0 p) &= 2T^{\frac{3}{2}} + T^{\frac{1}{2}} + T^0, \\ T(\gamma n \to \pi^- p) &= 2^{\frac{1}{2}}(T^{\frac{3}{2}} - T^{\frac{1}{2}} + T^0), \\ T(\gamma n \to \pi^0 n) &= 2T^{\frac{3}{2}} + T^{\frac{1}{2}} - T^0. \end{aligned} \tag{5.1}$$

The coefficients of T^0 are given by (7-1.6), (7-1.7) for $G = T^0$, $G(p \to \pi^0 p) = T(\gamma p \to \pi^0 p)$, etc., while those of $T^{\frac{3}{2}}$ and $T^{\frac{1}{2}}$ are calculated from the isospin decomposition (5-3.1 to 5-3.3) of $\pi N \to \pi N$, except for a normalization factor $\frac{1}{3}$. Notice in particular the agreement between (5-3.5) and $T(\gamma n \to \pi^- p)$.

For particles of non-zero spin and $I = 1$, e.g. Σ-hyperon or ρ-mesons, the photon could have an $I = 2$ component. Consider for example the electromagnetic scattering of hyperons, which is described by the method of section 10-2. The Σ^+, Σ^0 and Σ^- hyperons may have different form factors, except for

$$F_1(\Sigma^+, t = 0) = -F_1(\Sigma^-, t = 0) = 1, \qquad F_1(\Sigma^0, t = 0) = 0, \tag{5.2}$$

which says that Σ^+, Σ^- and Σ^0 have electric charges $+e$, $-e$ and 0, respectively. The form factors $F^{\pm}$ and F^0 may be expressed in terms of three other form factors, F^s, F^v, F^t, which correspond to $\bar{\Sigma}\Sigma$ states of $I = 0$, 1 and 2, respectively. Therefore, the absorption of a photon by Σ or ρ could change the isospin by two units. This would partly spoil our previous conclusions, since such particles could be virtually present in the process $\gamma\alpha \to ppnn$ or in pion photoproduction (quite apart from reactions such as $\gamma p \to \rho N$ or $\gamma p \to K\Sigma$, where the ρ or Σ appears as a real particle).

At this point, one may invoke (WATSON [1952]) the "principle of minimal electromagnetic interaction". Loosely speaking, this principle states that the "basic" electromagnetic interaction of each particle is given by its electric charge Q. An exact formulation of this principle seems to require a Lagrangian field theory. Without this principle, the anomalous magnetic moment of electron and muon could not be calculated from the electric charge.

For hadrons, the minimal electromagnetic interaction has less spectacular consequences. One may say that the form factors $F_1(t)$ and $F_2(t)$ as well as κ are determined by the properties of strong interactions alone (neglecting higher-order electromagnetic effects). Since these interactions conserve isospin, they should not change the isospin properties of the basic interaction. Writing the charge operator Q as $I_3+\frac{1}{2}Y$ (4-3.6), we may determine the isospin properties of Q. Under isospin rotations, I_3 transforms as the third component of a vector operator, while the hypercharge Y is invariant. This implies that for any hadron or system of hadrons, the photon behaves like the neutral component of an isotriplet (I_3 operator) or like an isoscalar (Y operator).

For the Σ form factors F_i, the principle of minimal electromagnetic interaction requires

$$F_i(\Sigma^\pm) = F_i^s \pm F_i^v, \qquad F_i(\Sigma^0) = F_i^s, \qquad i = 1, 2. \tag{5.3}$$

The coefficients of F_i^v, ± 1 for $\Sigma^\pm$ and 0 for Σ^0, follow from (8-1.10). From (2), we find $F_1^s(t=0) = 0$. It should be noted that the zero hypercharge of hyperons does not require $F_i^s = 0$. For example, F_i^s will contain an anomalous threshold from the diagram of fig. 10-5.

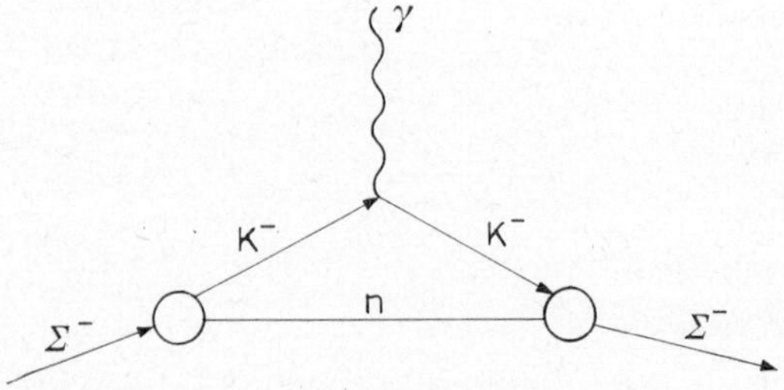

Fig. 10-5. A graph contributing to the isoscalar Σ form factors.

At present, a measurement of hyperon electromagnetic form factors is beyond experimental possibility. In addition to the electric charge, only the anomalous magnetic moment is known in some cases. Experimental values are given in table 10-5. For historical reasons, the magnetic moment,

$$\mu = e(\kappa + Q)/2m \tag{5.4}$$

is usually quoted, in units of nuclear magnetons ($e/2m_p = 1$). Q is the particle's electric charge in units of e, and m is its mass. For neutral particles, κ is given by $m\mu$, provided m is expressed in units of the proton mass (second column in table 10-5). In (3), we may replace $F_i(\Sigma)$ by the anomalous magnetic moment $\kappa(\Sigma)$, getting the relation

$$\kappa(\Sigma^+) + \kappa(\Sigma^-) = 2\kappa(\Sigma^0). \tag{5.5}$$

This relation also cannot be tested at present.

TABLE 10-5

Experimental magnetic moments μ of baryons (in units of nuclear magnetons), and SU_3-predictions for the anomalous magnetic moments κ (dimensionless)

particle	mass $[m_p]$	$\mu\left[\dfrac{e}{2m_p}\right]$	κ
p	1	2.7928	1.7928
n	1.00137	-1.9131	-1.9157
Λ	1.1888	-0.7	$\frac{1}{2}\kappa_n$
Σ^+	1.2677	2	κ_p
Σ^0	1.2709		$-\frac{1}{2}\kappa_n$
Σ^-	1.2760		$-\kappa_n - \kappa_p$

The last column of table 10-5 contains the SU_3-predictions for $\kappa(\Lambda)$ and $\kappa(\Sigma)$ (COLEMAN and GLASHOW [1961]). To derive these predictions, we remember that the charge Q is constant within each U-spin multiplet (see the discussion before (5-5.1)). Then, to the extent to which the strong interactions are U-spin invariant, the principle of minimal electromagnetic interaction requires the photon to behave like a U-spin singlet. Consequently, baryons within the same U-spin multiplet have identical κ. From fig. 5-5 we find

$$\kappa(\Sigma^+) = \kappa_p, \qquad \kappa(\Xi^-) = \kappa(\Sigma^-), \qquad \kappa(\Xi^0) = \kappa_n. \tag{5.6}$$

There are three more anomalous magnetic moments, namely $\kappa(\Sigma^0)$, $\kappa(\Lambda)$ and $\kappa(\Sigma\Lambda)$. The moment $\kappa(\Sigma\Lambda)$ induces the decay $\Sigma^0 \to \gamma\Lambda$. In the notation of (4-8.6), $e\kappa(\Sigma\Lambda)$ is the coupling constant G_t. In the U-spin classification, linear combinations of $\kappa(\Sigma^0)$, $\kappa(\Lambda)$ and $\kappa(\Sigma\Lambda)$ appear, which we denote by κ_{11}, κ_{10} and κ_{00}. The two indices refer to the U-spin of the initial and final baryons. Inserting $\frac{1}{2}(-\Sigma^0+3^{\frac{1}{2}}\Lambda)$ for the $U=1$ state and $-\frac{1}{2}(3^{\frac{1}{2}}\Sigma^0+\Lambda)$ for the $U=0$ state, we get

$$\begin{aligned} \kappa_{11} &= \tfrac{1}{4}[\kappa(\Sigma^0)+3\kappa(\Lambda)-2\sqrt{3}\,\kappa(\Sigma\Lambda)], \\ \kappa_{10} &= \tfrac{1}{4}[3^{\frac{1}{2}}\kappa(\Sigma^0)-3^{\frac{1}{2}}\kappa(\Lambda)-2\kappa(\Sigma\Lambda)], \\ \kappa_{00} &= \tfrac{1}{4}[3\kappa(\Sigma^0)-\kappa(\Lambda)+2\sqrt{3}\,\kappa(\Sigma\Lambda)]. \end{aligned} \tag{5.7}$$

For these three moments, U-spin invariance of the electromagnetic interaction requires

$$\kappa_{11} = \kappa_{\mathrm{n}}, \qquad \kappa_{10} = 0, \qquad \kappa_{00} = 2\kappa(\Lambda). \tag{5.8}$$

The first equation is of the type (6), and the second comes from conservation of U-spin. To derive the third, one exploits the fact that the I-spin singlet transforms into the U-spin singlet under that SU_3-transformation which transforms I-spin into U-spin. In the I-spin case, we have $Q = I_3+\frac{1}{2}Y$, but the operator I_3 does not contribute to $\kappa(\Lambda)$ since it corresponds to an isovector photon. The operator Y is transformed into $-Q$ under the named SU_3 transformation (cf the ordinates in figs. 4-3 and 5-5.)

With (5), (6), and (7), we now have 7 equations for the 9 moments κ. This allows one to express all of them in terms of κ_{p} and κ_{n}. In addition to (6) and the expressions given in table 10-5, we also have

$$\kappa(\Sigma\Lambda) = -\tfrac{1}{2}\sqrt{3}\,\kappa(\mathrm{n}) = 1.66, \tag{5.9}$$

which may be used for calculating the Σ^0 decay rate.

The physical importance of U-spin lies in the fact that any electromagnetic operator is a U-spin scalar. For example, instead of κ we may insert in (6) the electromagnetic mass splitting operator. Subtracting the last equation of (6) from the sum of the first two, we find

$$m_{\Sigma^+}-m_{\Sigma^-}+m_{\Xi^-}-m_{\Xi^0} = m_{\mathrm{p}}-m_{\mathrm{n}}. \tag{5.10}$$

This is the mass formula of COLEMAN and GLASHOW [1961], which is well satisfied experimentally.

Similar considerations apply also to reactions with two photons. Consider e.g. the decays $\pi^0 \to \gamma\gamma$ and $\eta \to \gamma\gamma$. The combination $\frac{1}{2}(-\pi^0+3^{\frac{1}{2}}\eta)$ has $U=1$, therefore it cannot decay into photons. This gives immediately

$$T(\pi^0 \to \gamma\gamma) = 3^{\frac{1}{2}}T(\eta \to \gamma\gamma). \tag{5.11}$$

However, this relation is vitiated by the large $\pi-\eta$ mass difference. In view of (4-8.5), it might be better to assume that the corresponding coupling constants g differ by a factor $3^{\frac{1}{2}}$, which would imply

$$\Gamma(\eta \to \gamma\gamma) = \frac{1}{3}\left(\frac{m_\eta}{m_\pi}\right)^3 \Gamma(\pi^0) = 22.4\,\Gamma(\pi^0). \tag{5.12}$$

10-6. The invariant amplitudes of photoproduction

In this and the next section, we discuss the general structure of reactions ab → cd, in which particle a is a photon. First we consider the case of spinless particles b, c and d, e.g. $\gamma\pi^+ \to \eta\pi^+$. In this reaction, all four particles have negative intrinsic parities. The most general parity conserving matrix element for this case is of the form

$$T(\lambda) = A(s, t)\varepsilon_{\alpha\beta\gamma\delta} P_{\rm a}^{\alpha} \varepsilon^{\beta}(\lambda) P_{\rm c}^{\gamma} P_{\rm d}^{\delta}. \tag{6.1}$$

In reactions where the total intrinsic parity changes, $\varepsilon(\lambda)$ is multiplied by a proper vector. Here the only gauge invariant combination is of the form

$$T'(\lambda) = A'(s, t)\varepsilon(\lambda)[P_{\rm c}(P_{\rm a} \cdot P_{\rm d}) - P_{\rm d}(P_{\rm a} \cdot P_{\rm c})]. \tag{6.2}$$

Note the similarity with (4-8.2) and (4-8.3). Matrix elements of $\rho\pi^+ \to \eta\pi^+$ or $\omega\pi^+ \to \pi^0\pi^+$ are also of the form (1). Let us now calculate (1) in the cms. We have

$$T(\lambda) = A(s, t)|P_{\rm a}\varepsilon(\lambda)P_{\rm c}P_{\rm d}| = A(s, t)|P_{\rm a}P_{\rm b}\varepsilon(\lambda)P_{\rm c}|, \tag{6.3}$$

by $P_{\rm d} = P_{\rm a} + P_{\rm b} - P_{\rm c}$. The determinant has been calculated in (1-4.10). We merely have to insert $\varepsilon_y(\lambda) = -\mathrm{i}2^{-\frac{1}{2}}$ for $P_{1,y}$:

$$T(\lambda) = -\mathrm{i}2^{-\frac{1}{2}} s^{\frac{1}{2}} qq' \sin\theta\, A(s, t). \tag{6.4}$$

Note that (4) is independent of λ. By (9-4.4), the partial wave expansion of $T(\lambda)$ is, for $\phi = 0$,

$$T(\lambda, \theta) = 8\pi s^{\frac{1}{2}} \sum_L (2L+1) d^L_{\lambda 0}(\theta)\, T_L(\lambda), \tag{6.5}$$

where $L = J$ is the total angular momentum. Inserting (C-4.7), we get

$$\mathrm{i}2^{-\frac{1}{2}} qq' A(s, t) = 8\pi \sum_L \frac{2L+1}{\sqrt{L(L+1)}} P_L'(\cos\theta) T_L(1), \quad T_L(-1) = -T_L(1). \tag{6.6}$$

The last relation is in agreement with the general formula (9-4.7).

We now turn to the photoproduction of mesons on nucleons, e.g. γp → πN or γp → KΛ. With two spin states for the photon, initial and final baryon each, we have 8 invariant amplitudes. Parity conservation reduces this number to 4.

In the following, the 4-momenta of the photon, initial and final baryon and meson are denoted by P_γ, P, P' and P_π. The matrix elements of photoproduction of pseudoscalar mesons may be written as

$$T = \sum_{i=1}^{4} \bar{u}(P')\gamma_5 A_i(s, t) M_i u(P), \tag{6.7}$$

where the A_i are the invariant amplitudes and the M_i are matrices, linear in the photon's polarization vector ε_μ, and free from γ_5 or the antisymmetric tensor $\varepsilon_{\alpha\beta\gamma\delta}$. We can ensure gauge invariance for each M_i by requiring ε_μ to occur only in the combination

$$F^{\mu\nu} = \varepsilon^\mu P_\gamma^\nu - \varepsilon^\nu P_\gamma^\mu, \tag{6.8}$$

which vanishes identically under the replacement $\varepsilon \to P_\gamma$. Four linearly independent M_i are

$$\begin{aligned} M_1 &= \tfrac{1}{2} F^{\mu\nu}\gamma_\mu\gamma_\nu = (\varepsilon \cdot \gamma)(P_\gamma \cdot \gamma), \\ M_2 &= F^{\mu\nu}(P_\mu + P'_\mu)(P_{\pi\nu} - \tfrac{1}{2}P_{\gamma\nu}) = \varepsilon(P+P')P_\gamma \cdot P_\pi - P_\gamma(P+P')\varepsilon \cdot P_\pi, \\ \mathrm{i}M_3 &= F^{\mu\nu}\gamma_\mu P_{\pi\nu} = (\varepsilon \cdot \gamma)P_\gamma \cdot P_\pi - (P_\gamma \cdot \gamma)\varepsilon \cdot P_\pi, \\ \mathrm{i}M_4 &= F^{\mu\nu}\gamma_\mu(P_\nu + P'_\nu - \tfrac{1}{2}(m+m')\gamma_\nu) \\ &= \varepsilon \cdot \gamma P_\gamma(P+P') - P_\gamma \cdot \gamma\varepsilon(P+P') - (m+m')\varepsilon \cdot \gamma P_\gamma \cdot \gamma. \end{aligned} \tag{6.9}$$

The expressions for M_i in terms of $F^{\mu\nu}$ may also be used in electroproduction, e.g. ep → eπN, to the extent that two-photon exchange is negligible. In that case, we have $P_\gamma \equiv P_e - P'_e$, $\varepsilon_\mu = e\bar{u}(P'_e)\gamma_\mu u(P_e)/t$. With $P_\gamma^2 = t \neq 0$, two additional invariant amplitudes appear (DENNERY [1961])

$$M_5 = F^{\mu\nu}P_{\gamma\mu}P_{\pi\nu} = -t\varepsilon \cdot P_\pi, \qquad \mathrm{i}M_6 = F^{\mu\nu}P_{\gamma\mu}\gamma_\nu = -t\varepsilon \cdot \gamma. \tag{6.10}$$

The virtual photon may appear also in "longitudinal" helicity states, $\lambda_\gamma = 0$, which shows that in this case there must be $\frac{1}{2}(3 \times 2 \times 2) = 6$ invariant amplitudes.

10-7. Partial wave expansion of meson photoproduction

In this section, we discuss the helicity partial wave expansion (9-4.4) of reactions such as γp → πN or γp → KΛ. The helicity λ_γ of a real photon assumes only the values ± 1. However, we shall include states with $\lambda_\gamma = 0$, thereby extending the formalism to electroproduction.

The initial proton and the final baryon are taken as particles of "type 1" (see section 9-1). Their helicities are denoted by λ_p and λ'. The total helicity of the initial state is

$$\lambda = \lambda_p - \lambda_\gamma. \tag{7.1}$$

With $\phi = 0$, (9-4.4) reads

$$T(\lambda_p \lambda_\gamma \lambda', \theta) = 8\pi s^{\frac{1}{2}} \sum_J (2J+1) d^J_{\lambda\lambda'}(\theta) T_J(\lambda_p \lambda_\gamma, \lambda'). \tag{7.2}$$

Since both proton and pion have negative intrinsic parity, the total intrinsic parity is $\eta = 1$ as in πN scattering, and parity invariance (9-4.7) reads

$$T_J(-\lambda_p, -\lambda_\gamma, -\lambda') = -T_J(\lambda_p \lambda_\gamma, \lambda'). \tag{7.3}$$

As in πN scattering, the final πN states are completely specified by the total angular momentum J and the parity. In analogy with (3-9.4), we define

$$T_J(\lambda_p \lambda_\gamma, \lambda') = \tfrac{1}{2}(T_{L+} + T_{(L+1)-}), \qquad J \equiv L + \tfrac{1}{2}, \tag{7.4}$$
$$T_J(\lambda_p \lambda_\gamma, -\lambda') = \tfrac{1}{2}(T_{L+} - T_{(L+1)-}),$$

where the states $T_{L\pm}$ have orbital angular momentum L in the final state, i.e. a threshold behaviour $(q')^L$. The orbital angular momentum of the initial state is defined by the decomposition (9-4.14). It may assume the values $J \pm \frac{1}{2}$ and $J \pm \frac{3}{2}$. Since $T_J(\lambda_p \lambda_\gamma, \lambda')$ is antisymmetric under helicity reflection (3), we have instead of (9-4.13)

$$T_{L+} = {}_+\langle \lambda' J | T | J \lambda_p \lambda_\gamma \rangle_- , \qquad T_{(L+1)-} = {}_-\langle \lambda' J | T | J \lambda_p \lambda_\gamma \rangle_+ . \tag{7.5}$$

Denoting the orbital angular momentum of the initial pγ state by L_i, (9-4.15) tells us, that $|J\lambda_p \lambda_\gamma\rangle_+$ ($|J\lambda_p \lambda_\gamma\rangle_-$) contains only even (odd) values of $\frac{3}{2} + L_i - J$. In terms of L, this implies $L_i = L$ or $L+2$ for T_{L+} and $L_i = L \pm 1$ for $T_{(L+1)-}$.

Instead of L_i, one usually classifies the photon-nucleon states by their multipole order, which is the vector sum of the spin of the photon and the orbital angular momentum L_i (see e.g. CHEW, GOLDBERGER, LOW, NAMBU [1957]). This classification is unsymmetrical in the two particles, since the orbital angular momentum L_i is a relative angular momentum between two particles. Only in the limit of static baryons can one interpret L_i as belonging to the photon.

Without proof, we give the multipole decomposition of $T_J(\lambda_p, \lambda_\gamma, \lambda')$:

$$T_J(\tfrac{1}{2}, 0, \pm\tfrac{1}{2}) = (L+1)[\mathscr{L}_{L+} \pm \mathscr{L}_{(L+1)-}], \tag{7.6}$$

$$T_J(\tfrac{1}{2}, 1, \pm\tfrac{1}{2}) = 2^{-\frac{1}{2}} L M_{L+} + 2^{-\frac{1}{2}}(L+2) E_{L+} \pm 2^{-\frac{1}{2}}(L+2) M_{(L+1)-} \mp 2^{-\frac{1}{2}} L \times E_{(L+1)-}, \tag{7.7}$$

$$T_J(\tfrac{1}{2}, -1, \pm\tfrac{1}{2}) = -\sqrt{\tfrac{1}{2} L(L+2)}(M_{L+} - E_{L+} \pm M_{(L+1)-} \pm E_{(L+1)-}). \tag{7.8}$$

The amplitudes $\mathscr{L}$, M and E are called the longitudinal, magnetic and electric multipole amplitudes. The multipole order, i.e. the photon's "total angular momentum", is L for magnetic and $L-1$ for longitudinal and electric amplitudes.

Inserting (6), (7) and (8) and the d-functions from table C-3 into (2), we get explicitly, neglecting terms with $J > \frac{3}{2}$,

$$\begin{aligned} &T(\tfrac{1}{2}, 0, \tfrac{1}{2}, \theta) \\ &= 16\pi\sqrt{s}\cos\tfrac{1}{2}\theta[\mathscr{L}_{0+}+\mathscr{L}_{1-}+(3\cos\theta-1)(\mathscr{L}_{1+}+\mathscr{L}_{2-})], \\ &T(\tfrac{1}{2}, 0, -\tfrac{1}{2}, \theta) \\ &= -16\pi\sqrt{s}\sin\tfrac{1}{2}\theta[\mathscr{L}_{0+}-\mathscr{L}_{1-}+(3\cos\theta+1)(\mathscr{L}_{1+}-\mathscr{L}_{2-})], \end{aligned} \tag{7.9}$$

$$\begin{aligned} &T(\tfrac{1}{2}, 1, \tfrac{1}{2}, \theta) \\ &= 16\pi\sqrt{\tfrac{1}{2}s}\sin\tfrac{1}{2}\theta[2E_{0+}+2M_{1-}+(3\cos\theta+1)(M_{1+}+3E_{1+}+3M_{2-}-E_{2-})], \\ &T(\tfrac{1}{2}, 1, -\tfrac{1}{2}, \theta) \\ &= 16\pi\sqrt{\tfrac{1}{2}s}\cos\tfrac{1}{2}\theta[2E_{0+}-2M_{1-}+(3\cos\theta-1)(M_{1+}+3E_{1+}-3M_{2-}+E_{2-})] \end{aligned} \tag{7.10}$$

$$\begin{aligned} &T(\tfrac{1}{2}, -1, \tfrac{1}{2}, \theta) \\ &= 16\pi\sqrt{\tfrac{1}{2}s}\cdot 3\cos\tfrac{1}{2}\theta\sin\theta(M_{1+}-E_{1+}+M_{2-}+E_{2-}), \\ &T(\tfrac{1}{2}, -1, -\tfrac{1}{2}, \theta) \\ &= 16\pi\sqrt{\tfrac{1}{2}s}\cdot 3\sin\tfrac{1}{2}\theta\sin\theta(-M_{1+}+E_{1+}+M_{2-}+E_{2-}). \end{aligned} \tag{7.11}$$

As in (5-1.4), the differential cross-section of photoproduction may be written in the form

$$\begin{aligned} \frac{d\sigma}{d\Omega} &= \frac{q'}{q}(A+B\cos\theta+C\cos^2\theta+D\cos^3\theta) \\ &= \frac{q'}{q}\cdot\frac{1}{4}\sum_{\lambda_p\lambda_\gamma\lambda'}\left|\frac{T(\lambda_p\lambda_\gamma, \lambda')}{8\pi s^{\frac{1}{2}}}\right|^2. \end{aligned} \tag{7.12}$$

The factor $\frac{1}{4}$ comes from averaging over the four initial spin states. By parity conservation, the summation over λ_p just contributes a factor 2. Insertion of (10) and (11) into (12) yields

$$\begin{aligned} A = |E_{0+}|^2+|M_{1-}|^2+\tfrac{9}{2}|E_{1+}|^2+\tfrac{9}{2}|M_{2-}|^2+\tfrac{5}{2}|M_{1+}|^2+\tfrac{5}{2}|E_{2-}|^2 \\ +\mathrm{Re}\,(M_{1+}^* M_{1-}-E_{0+}^* E_{2-}+3E_{0+}^* M_{2-} \\ -3M_{1+}^* E_{1+}+3E_{2-}^* M_{2-}+3M_{1-}^* E_{1+}), \end{aligned}$$

$$B = 2\,\mathrm{Re}\,(E_{0+}^* M_{1+} - M_{1-}^* E_{2-} - E_{0+}^* M_{1-} + M_{1+}^* E_{2-} + 9E_{1+}^* M_{2-}) \\ + 6\,\mathrm{Re}\,(E_{0+}^* E_{1+} + M_{1-}^* M_{2-} + M_{1+}^* M_{2-} - E_{1+}^* E_{2-}),$$

$$C = \tfrac{3}{2}(3|E_{1+}|^2 + 3|M_{2-}|^2 - |M_{1+}|^2 - |E_{2-}|^2) \\ + 3\,\mathrm{Re}\,(E_{0+}^* E_{2-} - M_{1-}^* M_{1+} + 3E_{1+}^* M_{1+} - 3M_{2-}^* E_{2-} \\ - 3M_{1-}^* E_{1+} - 3E_{0+}^* M_{2-}),$$

$$D = 18\,\mathrm{Re}\,(E_{1+}^* E_{2-} - M_{1+}^* M_{2-} - 2E_{1+}^* M_{2-}). \tag{7.13}$$

These expressions are invariant under the simultaneous exchange (Minami transformation)

$$E_{0+} \leftrightarrow M_{1-}, \qquad E_{1+} \leftrightarrow M_{2-}, \qquad E_{2-} \leftrightarrow -M_{1+}. \tag{7.14}$$

Also, the polarization of the outgoing baryon in photoproduction is given by $-\mathrm{Im}\,\rho_{\frac{1}{2}-\frac{1}{2}}$ according to (9-3.10), with ρ defined by (9-2.8):

$$P_y \frac{\mathrm{d}\sigma}{\mathrm{d}\Omega} = -2\frac{q'}{q}\,\mathrm{Im}\left[\frac{T(\frac{1}{2},1,\frac{1}{2})}{16\pi s^{\frac{1}{2}}}\frac{T^*(\frac{1}{2},1,-\frac{1}{2})}{16\pi s^{\frac{1}{2}}} + \frac{T(\frac{1}{2},-1,\frac{1}{2})}{16\pi s^{\frac{1}{2}}}\frac{T^*(\frac{1}{2},-1,-\frac{1}{2})}{16\pi s^{\frac{1}{2}}}\right]. \tag{7.15}$$

In the approximation (10), (11), this may be written analogous to (8-6.3)

$$P_y \frac{\mathrm{d}\sigma}{\mathrm{d}\Omega} = \frac{q'}{q}\sin\theta(B_0 + B_1\cos\theta + B_2\cos^2\theta),$$

$$B_0 = \mathrm{Im}\,[2E_{0+} M_{1-}^* + E_{0+}(M_{1+}^* + 3E_{1+}^*) + M_{1-}(E_{2-}^* - 3M_{2-}^*) \\ - 4M_{1+} E_{2-}^* - 6M_{1+} M_{2-}^* + 6E_{1+} E_{2-}^*], \tag{7.16}$$

$$B_1 = 3\,\mathrm{Im}\,[E_{0+}(-E_{2-}^* + 3M_{2-}^*) + M_{1-}(-M_{1+}^* - 3E_{1+}^*)],$$

$$B_2 = 18\,\mathrm{Im}\,[M_{1+} M_{2-}^* - E_{1+} E_{2-}^* + 2E_{1+} M_{2-}^*].$$

Note that P_y changes sign under the substitution (14).

10-8. Pion photoproduction at low energies

A theorem by KROLL and RUDERMAN [1954] states that pion photoproduction at threshold is given, to terms of the order m_π/m_p, by the Born terms. In section 10-6, we mentioned that, to ensure gauge invariance, the matrix elements of $\gamma p \to \pi N$ must be proportional to the tensor $F^{\mu\nu}$ defined in (6.8). Neglecting the pion mass, we can put $P_\pi = 0$ at threshold, in which case $P_\gamma + P = P'$ and $m = m'$ implies $P_\gamma = 0$ and therefore $F^{\mu\nu} = 0$. Consequently, $T = \sum \bar{u}(P')\gamma_5 A_i(s = m^2, t = 0) M_i u(P)$ vanishes except for those contributions to A_i which are infinite at $P_\pi^2 = 0$, $s = m^2$, i.e. the poles of A_i. The poles are given by the Born terms, which proves the theorem.

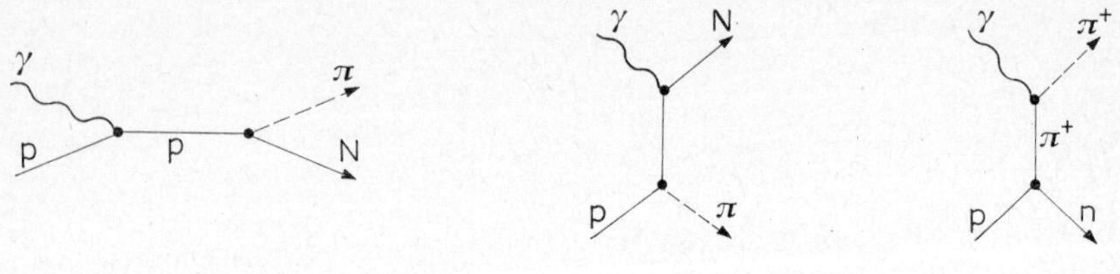

Fig. 10-8.1. The Born terms of pion photoproduction.

The Born terms of $\gamma p \to \pi N$ are shown in fig. 10-8.1. The π-exchange pole,

$$T_{\pi^+} = -2^{\frac{1}{2}} G\bar{u}(P')\gamma_5 u(P) \frac{2e\varepsilon \cdot P_\pi}{m_\pi^2 - t} \tag{8.1}$$

contributes only to π^+ production. The direct (dB) and crossed (cB) nucleon poles are obtained from the corresponding poles in πN scattering by replacing $G\gamma_5$ by the proton vertex $e\varepsilon^\nu[\gamma_\nu - (\kappa/2m)\sigma_{\mu\nu}P_\gamma^\mu]$ of (1.4):

$$T_p(\mathrm{dB}) = G\bar{u}(P')\gamma_5 \frac{(P+P_\gamma)\cdot\gamma + m}{m^2 - s} e\varepsilon^\nu \left(\gamma_\nu - \frac{\kappa}{2m}\sigma_{\mu\nu}P_\gamma^\mu\right) u(P), \tag{8.2}$$

$$T_p(\mathrm{cB}) = G\bar{u}(P')\cdot e\varepsilon^\nu \left(\gamma_\nu - \frac{\kappa}{2m}\sigma_{\mu\nu}P_\gamma^\mu\right) \frac{(P'-P_\gamma)\cdot\gamma + m}{m^2 - u} \gamma_5 u(P). \tag{8.3}$$

These two expressions apply to the reaction $\gamma p \to \pi^0 p$. The anomalous magnetic moment couplings are gauge invariant, but the electric couplings in (2) and (3) are not gauge invariant separately. As in section 10-4, only the sum of the Born terms is gauge invariant. To see this, we replace $\varepsilon^\nu\gamma_\nu$ by $P_\gamma \cdot \gamma = (P+P_\gamma)\cdot\gamma - m$ in (2) and $\varepsilon^\nu\gamma_\nu$ by $P_\gamma\cdot\gamma = -(P'-P_\gamma)\cdot\gamma + m$ in (3).

For the reaction $\gamma p \to \pi^+ n$, (2) and (3) are multiplied by $-2^{\frac{1}{2}}$ (cf. 7-1.7). Since the neutron has no charge, we now omit γ_ν in (3). Gauge invariance is restored by adding (1) to (2).

To apply the Kroll-Ruderman theorem, we compute T(Born) at the physical threshold $\boldsymbol{p}' = -\boldsymbol{p}_\pi = 0$ in the cms. Here (1) vanishes, since ε_μ has no time component. In (2) and (3), we first replace m by $-P'\cdot\gamma$ in (2) and by $-P\cdot\gamma$ in (3), getting

$$T_{\mathrm{p}}(\mathrm{dB}) = Ge\bar{u}(P')\gamma_5 \frac{(P+P_\gamma-P')\cdot\gamma}{m^2-s}\,\varepsilon^\nu\left(\gamma_\nu-\frac{\kappa}{2m}\,\sigma_{\mu\nu}P_\gamma^\mu\right)u(P),$$
$$T_{\mathrm{p}}(\mathrm{cB}) = -Ge\bar{u}(P')\gamma_5\varepsilon^\nu\left(\gamma_\nu+\frac{\kappa}{2m}\,\sigma_{\mu\nu}P_\gamma^\mu\right)\frac{(P+P_\gamma-P')\gamma}{m^2-u}\,u(P). \tag{8.4}$$

At threshold, the non-vanishing components of P_γ are of the order of m_π, which implies that $(\kappa/2m)\sigma_{\mu\nu}P_\gamma^\nu$ may be neglected with respect to γ_ν. Also, $(P+P_\gamma-P')\cdot\gamma$ anticommutes with $\varepsilon\cdot\gamma$, since $\varepsilon\cdot(P+P_\gamma-P') = -\boldsymbol{\varepsilon}\cdot\boldsymbol{p}_\pi = 0$. Therefore, the total Born term T_{p} for $\gamma\mathrm{p}\to\pi^0\mathrm{p}$ at threshold is

$$T_{\mathrm{p}}(\gamma\mathrm{p}\to\pi^0\mathrm{p}) = Ge\bar{u}(P')\gamma_5\,\varepsilon\cdot\gamma(P+P_\gamma-P')\cdot\gamma u(P)\left(\frac{1}{s-m^2}+\frac{1}{u-m^2}\right). \tag{8.5}$$

Inserting $u = 2m^2+m_\pi^2-s$, we find that the last bracket of (5) vanishes to

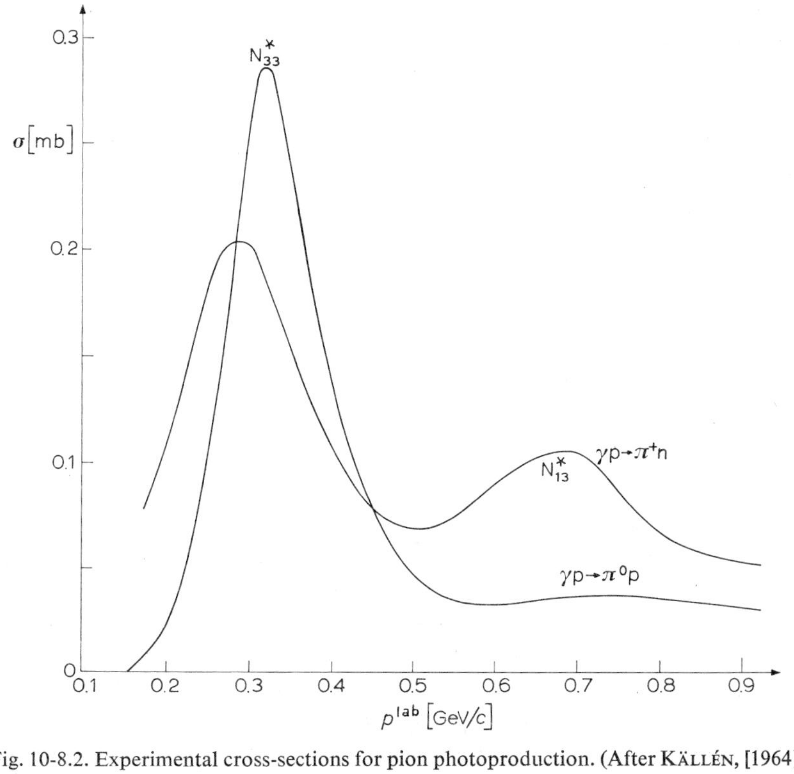

Fig. 10-8.2. Experimental cross-sections for pion photoproduction. (After KÄLLÉN, [1964].)

lowest order in $m_\pi^2/2m^2$. By the Kroll-Ruderman theorem, this implies $T(\gamma p \to \pi^0 p) = 0$ at threshold, i.e. the absence of S-wave π^0 photoproduction at low energies. This agrees with the experimental results (fig. 10-8.2). For $\gamma p \to \pi^+ n$, only the first term of the bracket contributes:

$$T_p(\gamma p \to \pi^+ n) = -2^{\frac{1}{2}} Ge\bar{u}(P')\gamma_5 \varepsilon \cdot \gamma(P+P_\gamma-P')\cdot \gamma u(P)\frac{1}{s-m^2}$$
$$\approx \frac{Ge}{2^{\frac{1}{2}}m}\bar{u}(P')\gamma_5 \varepsilon \cdot \gamma\, \gamma_0 u(P). \tag{8.6}$$

In the last expression, use has been made of the fact that, at threshold, the time component of $P+P_\gamma-P'$ is $s^{\frac{1}{2}}-m$, while the space components are zero. Finally, we may decompose (6) into matrix elements between 2-component spinors (3-5.15), using the approximation $T_p \approx 2m\chi'^+ Q_{bb}\chi$. The Q_{bb}-part of $\gamma_5\gamma\gamma_0$ is $-\boldsymbol{\sigma}$, giving

$$T_p(\gamma p \to \pi^+ n) \approx -Ge2^{\frac{1}{2}}\chi'^+(M_p')\varepsilon(\lambda_\gamma)\cdot \boldsymbol{\sigma}\chi(M_p). \tag{8.7}$$

This predicts uniquely the S-wave π^+ photoproduction near threshold. Historically, (7) has been used to determine the πN coupling constant G. However, the precision is low, mainly due to the theoretical uncertainty. One assumes that the coupling constant of a massless "pion" to the nucleon is identical with the normal coupling constant G.

Next, we try to understand the resonances at $E_\gamma^{\text{lab}} = 330$ MeV in $\gamma p \to \pi^0 p$ and at 300 MeV in $\gamma p \to \pi^+ n$, (fig. 10-8.2), which roughly correspond to the cms energy of the N_{33}^* in elastic πN scattering. The smaller peak in $\gamma p \to \pi^+ n$ (experimentally, the ratio of the peak values in the two reactions is 0.7) indicates a dominance of the amplitude $T^{\frac{3}{2}}$ of isospin $\frac{3}{2}$ (see 5.1). If $T^{\frac{1}{2}}$ and T^0 were zero, we would have $\sigma(\gamma p \to \pi^+ n)/\sigma(\gamma p \to \pi^0 p) = \frac{1}{2}$.

These observations suggest that there is a close connection between photoproduction and elastic πN-scattering. The first part of this connection is known as Watson's theorem [1954], which states that the phases of the amplitudes $E_{L\pm}$ and $M_{L\pm}$ of photoproduction are identical with the phases of the amplitudes $f_{L\pm}$ in elastic πN scattering, as long as inelastic ($\pi\pi$N) channels are negligible. More precisely, $E_{L+}^{\frac{3}{2}}$ and $M_{L+}^{\frac{3}{2}}$ have the phase $\delta_{L+}^{\frac{3}{2}}$, while $E_{L+}^{\frac{1}{2}}$, E_{L+}^{0}, $M_{L+}^{\frac{1}{2}}$ and M_{L+}^{0} have the phase $\delta_{L+}^{\frac{1}{2}}$, and correspondingly for δ_{L-}. The upper index on E and M is defined by (5.1).

The theorem results from an approximate solution of the unitarity equation, $\operatorname{Im} T = \sum q_c TT^+$ (see 2-4.8). For $I = \frac{3}{2}$ and $J = L+\frac{1}{2}$, T is a matrix of the form

$$
(T^{\frac{3}{2}}_{L+})_{\text{if}} = \begin{array}{c|cccc} {}_{\text{i}}\diagdown^{\text{f}} & \pi\text{N} & \gamma\text{N} & \gamma\text{N} & \pi\pi\text{N} \\ \hline \pi\text{N} & f^{\frac{3}{2}}_{L+} & E^{\frac{3}{2}}_{L+} & M^{\frac{3}{2}}_{L+} & \cdots \\ \gamma\text{N} & E^{\frac{3}{2}}_{L+} & 0 & 0 & 0 \\ \gamma\text{N} & M^{\frac{3}{2}}_{L+} & 0 & 0 & 0 \\ \pi\pi\text{N} & \vdots & 0 & 0 & 0 \end{array}, \tag{8.8}
$$

where the points indicate the matrix elements of $\pi\text{N} \to \pi\pi\text{N}$, etc. In the "elastic region" of πN scattering, $|f^{\frac{3}{2}}_{L+}|$ is much larger than any of the other matrix elements. In addition, matrix elements in the first row and column are much larger than those in the remaining rows and columns (referring to reactions such as $\gamma\text{N} \to \gamma\text{N}$, $\gamma\text{N} \to \pi\pi\text{N}$, $\pi\pi\text{N} \to \pi\pi\text{N}$). Then unitarity requires $f^{\frac{3}{2}}_{L+}$ to be approximately of the form (3-9.7) $(1/q)\exp[\text{i}\delta^{\frac{3}{2}}_{L+}]\sin\delta^{\frac{3}{2}}_{L+}$. All other channels are effectively "closed", and the unitarity equations for $E^{\frac{3}{2}}_{L+}$, $M^{\frac{3}{2}}_{L+}$ ... are all of the form (6-5.14), from which the phases follow uniquely.

The second part of the connection between photoproduction and elastic πN scattering is based upon the assumption that the ratios $E^{\frac{3}{2}}_{L\pm}/f^{\frac{3}{2}}_{L\pm}$ and $M^{\frac{3}{2}}_{L\pm}/f^{\frac{3}{2}}_{L\pm}$ are slowly varying functions of the cms energy. Such an assumption is quite plausible for a resonating amplitude. It has been "justified" by CHEW, GOLDBERGER, LOW and NAMBU [1957] by means of dispersion relations. However, the main argument is really nothing but the usual "coupling constant" approximation (see also STICHEL [1965]). In section 5-2, we discussed the decay $\text{N}^* \to \pi\text{N}$, treating the N* as an unstable particle. As a zeroth order approximation, the coupling constant G^* of (5-2.3) could be taken as energy-independent, the corrections being of the form (5-2.8). Similarly, we may write the N* formation in photoproduction as

$$
T(\gamma\text{p} \to \text{N}^*) = \bar{u}_\mu(M^*\left[G_1\left(\varepsilon^\mu - \frac{\varepsilon\cdot\gamma P^\mu_\gamma}{m+m^*}\right) + G_2\frac{P\cdot\varepsilon P^\mu_\gamma - P\cdot P_\gamma\varepsilon^\mu}{(m+m^*)^2}\right]\gamma_5 u(M), \tag{8.9}
$$

and neglect the energy-dependence of G_1 and G_2. In that case, $T(\gamma\text{p} \to \text{N}^* \to \pi\text{N})$ is determined by two coupling constants, the numerical values of which will be calculated by the Kroll-Ruderman theorem.

Let us investigate (9) in detail. P^* and m^* denote the 4-momentum and mass of the N^*_{33}. Gauge invariance is checked by replacing ε by $P_\gamma = P^* - P$ and observing $\bar{u}_\mu P^{*\mu} = 0$ (3-7.4) and $\bar{u}_\mu(P-P^*)\cdot\gamma\gamma_5 u = -\bar{u}_\mu(m^*+m)\gamma_5 u$. There cannot be more than two linearly independent coupling constants, since there are only two linearly independent amplitudes (E_{1+} and M_{1+}). For the time being, we put $G_2 = 0$, getting

$$T(\gamma p \to N^* \to \pi N) = -G^* G_1 \bar{u}' p_i' \cdot \frac{m^*}{3}(1+\gamma_0)\frac{3\delta_{ik}+\gamma_i\gamma_k}{m^{*2}-s}\left(\varepsilon_k - \frac{\varepsilon \cdot \gamma p_k}{m+m^*}\right)\gamma_5 u. \quad (8.10)$$

Here we have inserted (9) for the N* production, (3-7.12) for its propagator, and (5-2.3) for its decay. The momenta of the initial and final nucleons are $\boldsymbol{p} = -\boldsymbol{p}_\gamma$ and $\boldsymbol{p}'$. No distinction is made between m^* and $s^{\frac{1}{2}}$ except in the propagator.

Quite generally, the matrix elements of $\gamma p \to \pi N$ may be written in a form similar to (3-8.1),

$$T(M\lambda_\gamma, M'\theta) = 8\pi s^{\frac{1}{2}} \chi_0'^{+}(M') F \chi_0(M),$$

$$F \equiv F_1 \boldsymbol{\sigma} \cdot \boldsymbol{\varepsilon} - \mathrm{i} F_2 \boldsymbol{\sigma}\hat{\boldsymbol{p}}' \boldsymbol{\sigma}(\hat{\boldsymbol{p}} \times \boldsymbol{\varepsilon}) + F_3(\boldsymbol{\sigma} \cdot \hat{\boldsymbol{p}})(\hat{\boldsymbol{p}}' \cdot \boldsymbol{\varepsilon}) + F_4(\boldsymbol{\sigma} \cdot \hat{\boldsymbol{p}}')(\hat{\boldsymbol{p}}' \cdot \boldsymbol{\varepsilon}). \quad (8.11)$$

We want to express (10) in this form, because we can easily find the connection between the functions F_i and the multipole amplitudes $E_{L\pm}$, $M_{L\pm}$. All we have to do is to take F between helicity states $\chi^+(\lambda', \theta)$ and $\chi(\lambda_p, 0)$. Then we may replace $\boldsymbol{\sigma} \cdot \hat{\boldsymbol{p}}'$ by $2\lambda'$ and $\boldsymbol{\sigma} \cdot \hat{\boldsymbol{p}}$ by $2\lambda_p$. Remembering that the photon has been taken as a "type 2" particle, the argument of $\boldsymbol{\varepsilon}$ is $-\lambda_\gamma$. By (3-2.6), we have

$$\varepsilon_x(-\lambda_\gamma) = 2^{-\frac{1}{2}}\lambda_\gamma, \qquad \varepsilon_y(-\lambda_\gamma) = -\mathrm{i}2^{-\frac{1}{2}}, \qquad \varepsilon_z(\lambda_\gamma) = 0. \quad (8.12)$$

We now find $T(\lambda_p \lambda_\gamma, \lambda'\theta)$ to be

$$\frac{T(\lambda_p\lambda_\gamma, \lambda'\theta)}{8\pi s^{\frac{1}{2}}} = \frac{\chi^+(\lambda'\theta)}{2^{\frac{1}{2}}}\begin{bmatrix}(2\lambda_p F_3 + 2\lambda' F_4)\lambda_\gamma \sin\theta & (F_1 - 2\lambda' F_2)(\lambda_\gamma - 1) \\ (F_1 + 2\lambda' F_2)(1+\lambda_\gamma) & (2\lambda_p F_3 + 2\lambda' F_4)\lambda_\gamma \sin\theta\end{bmatrix}\chi(\lambda_p, 0). \quad (8.13)$$

For $\lambda_p = \frac{1}{2}$, only the first column of the matrix contributes. Inserting $\chi^+(\frac{1}{2}, \theta) = (\cos\frac{1}{2}\theta, \sin\frac{1}{2}\theta)$, $\chi^+(-\frac{1}{2}, \theta) = (-\sin\frac{1}{2}\theta, \cos\frac{1}{2}\theta)$, we get explicitly

$$T(\tfrac{1}{2}, -1, \tfrac{1}{2}\theta) = -8\pi\sqrt{\tfrac{1}{2}s}\cos\tfrac{1}{2}\theta \sin\theta (F_3 + F_4),$$
$$T(\tfrac{1}{2}, -1, -\tfrac{1}{2}\theta) = 8\pi\sqrt{\tfrac{1}{2}s}\sin\tfrac{1}{2}\theta \sin\theta (F_3 - F_4), \quad (8.14)$$

$$T(\tfrac{1}{2}, 1, \tfrac{1}{2}\theta) = 16\pi\sqrt{\tfrac{1}{2}s}\sin\tfrac{1}{2}\theta[F_1 + F_2 + \cos^2\tfrac{1}{2}\theta(F_3 + F_4)],$$
$$T(\tfrac{1}{2}, 1, -\tfrac{1}{2}\theta) = 16\pi\sqrt{\tfrac{1}{2}s}\cos\tfrac{1}{2}\theta[F_1 - F_2 - \sin^2\tfrac{1}{2}\theta(F_3 - F_4)]. \quad (8.15)$$

For a $P_{\frac{3}{2}}$ state such as N^*_{33}, comparison between (14) and (7.11) gives $F_4 = 0$, $F_3 = 6\,(E_{1+} - M_{1+})$, while comparison between (15) and (7.10) gives $F_2 = 4M_{1+}$, $E_1 = 6\cos\theta(M_{1+} + E_{1+})$.

We now return to the evaluation of (10). The factor $1+\gamma_0$ eliminates the lower components of $\bar{u}'$. By (3-5.15), we have

$$T(\gamma p \to N^* \to \pi N) = -G^* G_1 \frac{2m^*/3}{m^{*2} - s} \sqrt{(E+m)(E'+m')}\chi_0'^{+}(M')G\chi_0(M),$$

$$G = p_i'(3\delta_{ik} - \sigma_i\sigma_k)\left(-\frac{\varepsilon\cdot\sigma p_k}{m+m^*} + \frac{p\cdot\sigma\varepsilon_k}{E+m}\right). \tag{8.16}$$

This is easily brought into the form (11). Neglecting terms of order $(m^*-m)/(m^*+m)$, we have

$$G \approx \frac{1}{m+m^*}[-3(p'\cdot p)(\varepsilon\cdot\sigma) + (p'\cdot\sigma)(p\cdot\sigma\varepsilon\cdot\sigma - \varepsilon\cdot\sigma p\cdot\sigma) + 3(p\cdot\sigma)(p'\cdot\varepsilon)]$$

$$= \frac{qq'}{m+m^*}(-3\cos\theta\varepsilon\cdot\sigma + 2i\hat{p}'\cdot\sigma\,\sigma\cdot(\hat{p}\times\varepsilon) + 3\hat{p}\cdot\sigma\hat{p}'\cdot\varepsilon). \tag{8.17}$$

According to our discussion following (15) this implies

$$M_{1+} = \tfrac{1}{4}F_2 \approx G^* G_1 \frac{m^*/3}{m^{*2} - s} qq', \qquad E_{1+} \approx 0. \tag{8.18}$$

The coupling constant G_1 of (9) thus gives a negligible contribution to E_{1+}. Similarly, G_2 gives a negligible contribution to M_{1+}. Experimentally, the differential cross-section of $\gamma p \to N^* \to \pi N$ is of the form $5 - 3\cos^2\theta$, which according to (7.13) implies $E_{1+} \approx 0$ and therefore $G_2 \approx 0$.

Finally, the dominance of M_{1+} follows from the Kroll-Ruderman theorem. To lowest order in m_π/m, only $T_p(\mathrm{cB})$ of (3) contributes to the $I = \frac{3}{2}$ $P_{\frac{3}{2}}$ amplitude. (The Born term $T_p(\mathrm{dB})$ of (2) has $I = \frac{1}{2}$, and the contribution of (1) vanishes to lowest order.) The ratio $M^{\frac{3}{2}}_{1+}/f^{\frac{3}{2}}_{1+}$ of photoproduction to elastic πN scattering amplitudes is calculated from the ratio of the corresponding crossed Born term contributions (CHEW and LOW [1956]) as

$$M^{\frac{3}{2}}_{1+} = \frac{q}{q'}\frac{e}{2m}\frac{1+\kappa_p-\kappa_n}{2f} = \frac{q}{q'}\frac{e(1+\kappa_p-\kappa_n)}{2Gm_\pi/(4\pi)^{\frac{1}{2}}}. \tag{8.19}$$

To see this, one first transforms the bracket $\gamma_\nu - (\kappa/2m)\sigma_{\mu\nu}P^\mu_\gamma$ of (3) into $\gamma_\nu(1+\kappa) + (\kappa/2m)(P_\nu + P_\nu')$ (see 4-8.7) and neglects the second term. Then one observes the similarity between the crossed Born terms for $\pi^0 p \to \pi^0 p$ and $\gamma p \to \pi^0 p$, when the incident π^0 is coupled by pseudovector coupling (6-4.12). In fact, the crossed Born term for $\pi^0 p \to \pi^0 p$ is obtained from that of $\gamma p \to \pi^0 p$ by replacing

$$e\varepsilon^{\nu}(1+\kappa) \to \sqrt{4\pi}\,\frac{f}{m_{\pi}}\,\gamma_5 P^{\nu}_{\pi^0}\,. \tag{8.20}$$

For a review of the second and third πN resonances in photoproduction, see STICHEL [1965].

CHAPTER 11

HIGH-ENERGY INTERACTIONS

11-1. Asymptotic theorems

At high energies, hadron interactions display certain general properties. Among these, the energy-independence of total cross sections σ_T (see fig. 11-1.1) was detected first. For the pp and pn total cross-sections, this constancy appears to continue up to cosmic-ray energies.

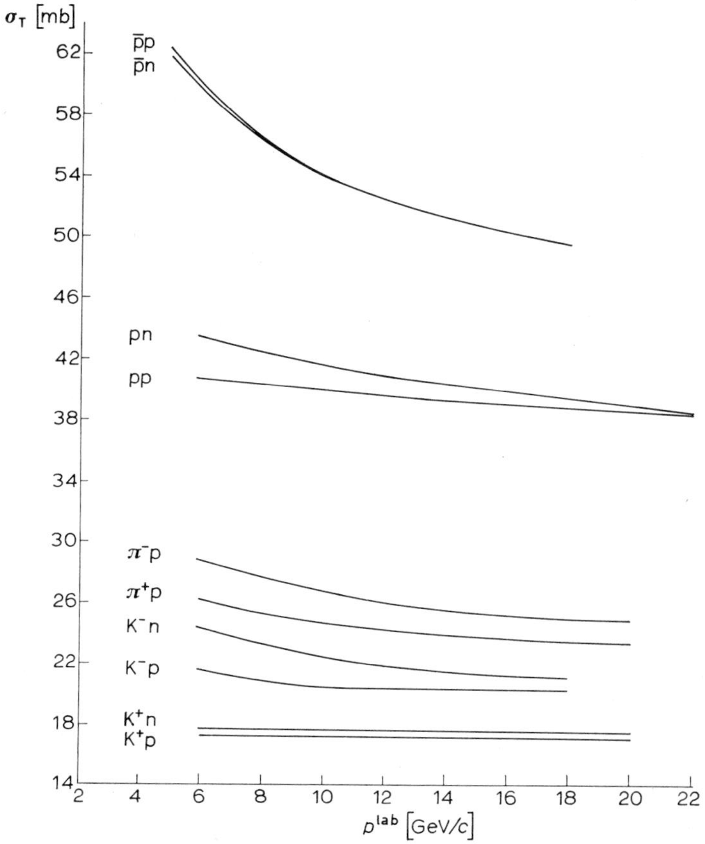

Fig. 11-1.1. The dependence of various total cross-sections on the lab momentum (GALBRAITH *et al.* [1965]. Figure after LINDENBAUM [1964, 1965]).

For elastic cross-sections, the data are less accurate, but it appears that σ_{el}/σ_T also tends to a constant value. For π^-p interactions, σ_{el}/σ_T is 0.2 at 5 GeV/c and 0.17 at 20 GeV/c. (In this interval, the cms energy increases by a factor 2, since $s = (P_a+P_b)^2 \approx 2m_b p^{lab}$.)

The theory of high-energy interactions consists of a number of models of very limited scope and accuracy. In addition, there are a few less model-dependent theorems about the asymptotic form of the interaction, valid for $s \to \infty$. We discuss these theorems first, although their practical use may be as questionable as that of the models.

The first of these theorems is due to POMERANCHUK [1958]: If the total cross-sections for ab collisions and for $\bar{\text{a}}$b collisions both tend to constants, then these constants must be equal,

$$\lim_{s\to\infty} \sigma_T(\text{ab}, s) = \lim_{s\to\infty} \sigma_T(\bar{\text{a}}\text{b}, s). \tag{1.1}$$

It implies common limiting values for $\sigma_T(\pi^+\text{p})$ and $\sigma_T(\pi^-\text{p})$, $\sigma_T(\text{K}^+\text{p})$ and $\sigma_T(\text{K}^-\text{p})$, $\sigma_T(\text{pp})$ and $\sigma_T(\bar{\text{p}}\text{p})$, etc. By isospin invariance, cross-sections should then also be independent of whether the target is a proton or a neutron (this second prediction is in good agreement with the curves of fig. 11-1.1).

Pomeranchuk's proof was based on dispersion relations. It was subsequently extended and refined by many authors. In this context, SUGAWARA and KANAZAWA [1961] discovered the following theorem: A function $f(z)$ which is analytic in the upper half plane (Im $z > 0$) and does not increase exponentially for $|z| \to \infty$ along any direction in the upper half plane, cannot tend to different limits along the positive and negative real z-axes. MEIMAN [1962] mentioned that this is essentially the Phragmèn-Lindelöf theorem (see e.g. TITCHMARSH [1958]). This theorem provided the basis for the further development of asymptotic theorems (for a review, see LOGUNOV *et al.* [1965]). Clearly, any $f(z)$ which satisfies dispersion relations satisfies the conditions of the Phragmèn-Lindelöf theorem, since it must be analytic and polynomial-bounded in the entire complex s-plane, apart from certain cuts.

To apply the theorem, we first consider the elastic scattering amplitude $T(s, t)$. The connection with $\sigma_T(s)$ will be established afterwards, by means of the optical theorem. We assume that for large s and small t, $T(s, t)$ can be expanded in the form

$$T(s, t) = \sum_{n=0}^{\infty} b_n(t) \nu^{\alpha_n(t)}, \qquad \nu = (s - m^2 - \mu^2 + \tfrac{1}{2}t)/2m, \tag{1.2}$$

where the $\alpha_n(t)$ are real functions of t ordered such that, for fixed t,

$$\alpha_0 > \alpha_1 > \alpha_2 \ldots . \tag{1.3}$$

The functions $b_n(t)$ are arbitrary complex functions of t. In the following, we omit the argument t. Obviously, for $\nu \to \infty$, $T(s, t)$ reduces to $b_0 \nu^{\alpha_0}$. Also, for $t = 0$, α_0 cannot be complex, since otherwise Im $T(s, 0)$ would be negative in some regions of s:

$$\nu^{\alpha} = \nu^{\mathrm{Re}\,\alpha} \nu^{\mathrm{i}\,\mathrm{Im}\,\alpha} = \nu^{\mathrm{Re}\,\alpha} \mathrm{e}^{\mathrm{i}\,\mathrm{Im}\,\alpha\,\ln\nu}$$
$$= \nu^{\mathrm{Re}\,\alpha}[\cos(\mathrm{Im}\,\alpha\ln\nu) + \mathrm{i}\sin(\mathrm{Im}\,\alpha\ln\nu)]. \tag{1.4}$$

This would contradict the optical theorem, Im $T = \lambda^{\frac{1}{2}}(s, m^2, \mu^2)\sigma_{\mathrm{T}}$ (see 2-4.2). We should mention here that we only consider the zero-spin case. Constant σ_{T} corresponds to $\alpha_0(0) = 1$.

The variable ν has been chosen instead of s because of the simpler crossing relation. Crossing from the s-channel to the u-channel (e.g. from π^+p to π^-p scattering) implies $T(s, t) = \overline{T}(u, t)$, where $\overline{T}$ is the u-channel amplitude. However, to apply the Phragmèn-Lindelöf theorem, we must remain above the cuts along the real axis (see fig. 6-7.2). We therefore use crossing symmetry in the form

$$T(\nu + \mathrm{i}\varepsilon, t) = \overline{T}^*(-\nu + \mathrm{i}\varepsilon, t). \tag{1.5}$$

In general, $\overline{T}^*(-\nu + \mathrm{i}\varepsilon, t)$ is related to $\overline{T}(-\nu - \mathrm{i}\varepsilon, t)$ by Hermitean analyticity. For the inclusion of spin in (5), see BIAŁAS and SVENSSON [1965]. The amplitude for the crossed reaction is assumed to have an expansion similar to (2),

$$\overline{T}(\nu) = \sum_{n=0}^{\infty} \bar{b}_n(t) \nu^{\alpha_n(t)}. \tag{1.6}$$

The fact that α_n is the same in (2) and (6) is purely formal, because $\bar{b}_n$ may be zero whenever $b_n \neq 0$ and vice versa. However, by means of (5) and the Phragmèn-Lindelöf theorem, we can now demonstrate that

$$\bar{b}_n^* = b_n \mathrm{e}^{\mathrm{i}\pi\alpha_n}. \tag{1.7}$$

As a first step, we define the function

$$T_0 = (\mathrm{i} + \nu)^{-\alpha_0} T, \tag{1.8}$$

which has a non-zero limit for $\nu \to \infty$, namely $b_0(t)$. In fact, with T given by (2), this is also the limit for $\nu \to -\infty$, which proves the the Phragmèn-Lindelöf theorem for our purpose. The combination $\nu + \mathrm{i}$ has been chosen in (8) to move the new singularity of T_0 into the lower half-plane. Next, we observe that

$$b_0 = \lim_{\nu\to\infty} T_0(\nu) = \lim_{\nu\to\infty} T_0(-\nu) = \lim_{\nu\to\infty} \frac{\overline{T}^*(\nu)}{((-\nu-\mathrm{i})^{\alpha_0})^*} = \frac{\overline{b}_0^*}{(-1)^{\alpha_0}}, \quad (1.9)$$

from which (7) follows by $(-1)^{\alpha_0} = \mathrm{e}^{\mathrm{i}\pi\alpha_0}$. The positive sign $+(\mathrm{i}\pi\alpha_0)$ appears in the exponent since ν is rotated in the upper half plane.

Having demonstrated (7) for $n = 0$, we now apply the same type of argument to

$$T_1 = (\nu+1)^{\alpha_1}[T(\nu) - b_0\nu^{\alpha_0}], \quad (1.10)$$

which has the limit b_1, and so on. If, for some $n = N > 0$, the α_0 should be complex, then (7) applies only for the first $N-1$ terms.

Actually, the theorem can be proven under slightly more general circumstances. The expansion (2) may include terms such as

$$b_n\nu^{\alpha_n}(\ln \nu - \tfrac{1}{2}\mathrm{i}\pi)^{\beta_n}, \quad (1.11)$$

in which case one considers functions of the type

$$T(\nu+1)^{-\alpha_0}(\ln(\nu+\mathrm{i}))^{-\beta_0} \quad (1.12)$$

instead of (8), etc. In the limited energy-interval studied at present, terms proportional to $\ln \nu$ have not been determined.

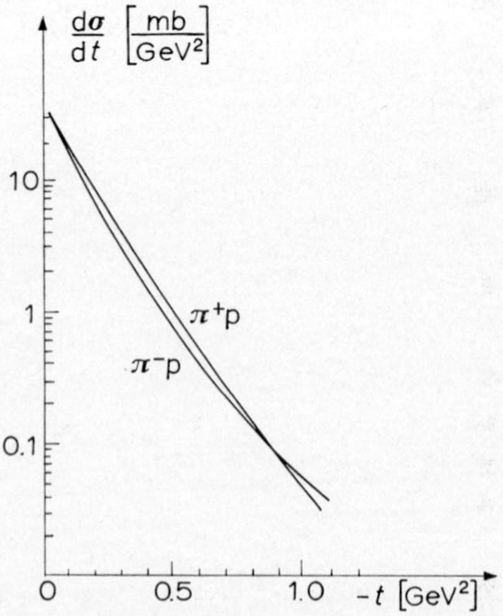

Fig. 11-1.2. Differential cross sections for elastic π^+p and π^-p scattering at 8.5 GeV/c (after CALDWELL *et al.* [1964, 1965]).

We now examine the main consequences of (7). From $|\bar{b}_0| = |b_0|$, we get in the asymptotic region $s \to \infty$,

$$\frac{d\sigma}{dt}(s, t) = \frac{d\bar{\sigma}}{dt}(s, t), \tag{1.13}$$

i.e. equality of the elastic differential cross-sections. A necessary condition is of course that $\alpha_0(t)$ remains real down to some finite negative value of t. Experimentally, (13) is well satisfied for $\pi^{\pm}$p scattering (see fig. 11-1.2).

From the constancy of total cross-sections, we conclude $\alpha_0(t = 0) = 1$, in which case (7) yields for b_0

$$\text{Im}\, b_0 = \text{Im}\, \bar{b}_0, \qquad \text{Re}\, b_0 = -\text{Re}\, \bar{b}_0. \tag{1.14}$$

This now implies Pomeranchuk's theorem (1). The real part of $T(s, t)$ for $\pi^{\pm}$p scattering has been obtained from its interference with Coulomb scattering at small angles; it is small and negative both for π^+p and π^-p scattering. This allows the conclusion that $\text{Re}\, b_0 = 0$, i.e. that $\text{Re}\, T(t = 0)$ comes from the next term in the expansion. We therefore expect

$$\lim_{s\to\infty} \frac{\text{Re}\, T(s, t)}{\text{Im}\, T(s, t)} = 0 \qquad \text{for small} \quad t. \tag{1.15}$$

Finally, by using $T(\pi^-\text{p} \to \pi^0\text{n}) = T - \bar{T}$, we find that the ratio of the charge exchange to the elastic cross-sections should tend to zero, in good agreement with experiment. We shall return to elastic scattering in section 11-5.

11-2. Peripheral collisions, one-pion exchange

The second general feature of high-energy interactions is the peripheral nature of collisions. For meson-nucleon reactions of the type ab → cd, the differential cross-sections has a sharp peak near $t = 0$ (t is the momentum transfer from the initial to the final meson), which drops exponentially for increasing $-t$. This is most evident for elastic scattering (fig. 11-1.2), but it applies by and large also to charge exchange and inelastic reactions. The "particles" b and d in the final state may be resonances such as N*, ρ, ω, f and A_2 (see fig. 11-2.1. A_1 and A_2 are peaks in the $\pi\rho$ effective mass distribution). In fact, it applies also to reactions with three or more "uncorrelated" particles or resonances in the final state. The momentum transfer from the initial to the final baryon or baryon resonance nearly always prefers very small values.

The first theoretical considerations were mainly concerned with the "two-fireball" or "two-jet" structure of high-energy pp collisions. In these collisions, the produced particles frequently form two well-separated

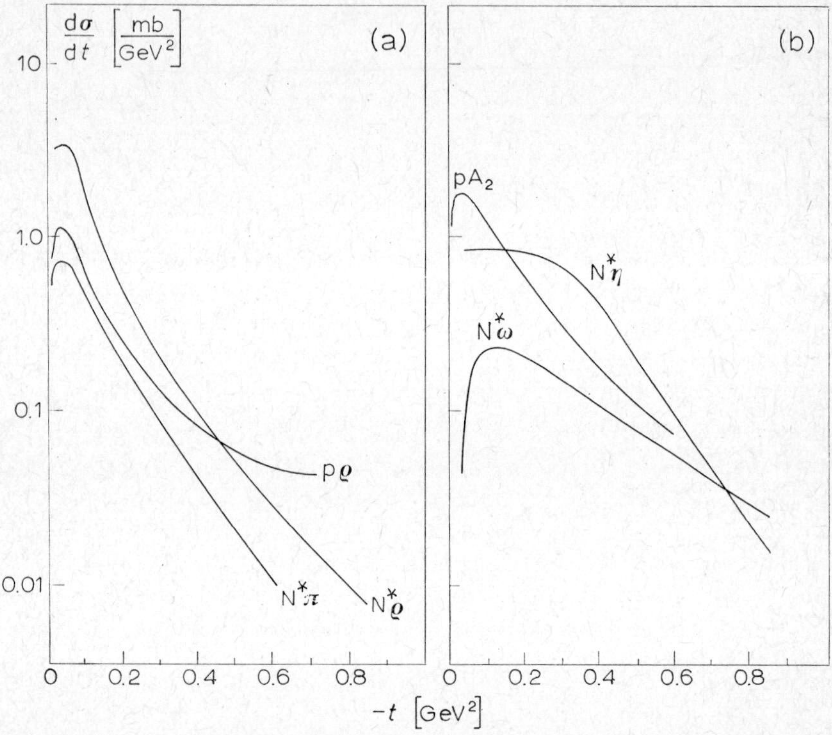

Fig. 11-2.1. Differential cross-sections for various channels of 8 GeV/c π^+p collisions, (a) pρ^+, $N^{*++}\rho^0$, $N^{*++}\pi^0$; (b) pA_2(p$\rho^0\pi^+$), $N^{*++}\eta$ and $N^{*++}\omega$ (after AACHEN-BERLIN-CERN collaboration, [1965]).

groups. In the cms, the momenta in each group lie close to the direction of the incident particles. This may be interpreted classically as an effect of peripheral collisions (fig. 11-2.2). The baryons are pictured as bullets of

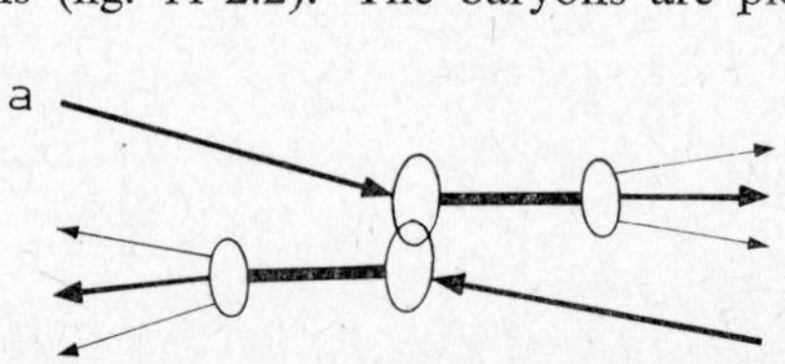

Fig. 11-2.2. The classical picture of a peripheral collision.

finite radius (note the Lorentz contraction), which collide with a certain impact parameter. For large impact parameters, the momentum of each bullet changes only by a small fraction. However, the bullets are excited in the collision, disintegrating shortly afterwards. The final particles are emitted isotropically in each fireball rest system, and the unisotropic cms momentum distribution merely reflects the cms momentum of each fireball.

To some extent, the fireballs were the predecessors of the resonances. With increasing accuracy and statistics, most fireballs could be identified with the resonances found at lower energies. However, the question whether fireballs exist for a short time, or whether the particles are emitted directly in the peripheral collision is of secondary importance.

The next step in the development of the "peripheral model" was the idea of single pion exchange (GOEBEL [1958], BONSIGNORI and SELLERI [1960], SALZMAN and SALZMAN [1960, 1961], DRELL [1960, 1961]). By the uncertainty principle, the "outer parts" of the nucleon contain mainly pions. Therefore, pion exchange is the most likely mechanism of peripheral collisions.

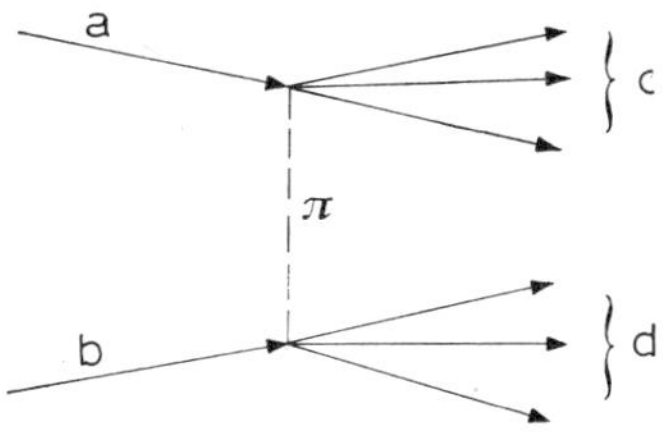

Fig. 11-2.3. The one-pion exchange diagram.

Let us now formulate the matrix element T_π of π-exchange processes in momentum space. Denoting the total momenta of the two jets of particles by P_c and P_d (fig. 11-2.3), we have

$$T_\pi(\mathrm{ab} \to \mathrm{cd}) = \frac{1}{\mu^2 - t}\, T(\pi\mathrm{a} \to \mathrm{c})T(\bar{\pi}\mathrm{b} \to \mathrm{d}), \tag{2.1}$$

where μ is the pion mass and $t = (P_a - P_c)^2$, as in a two-particle reaction. The matrix elements $T(\pi\mathrm{a} \to \mathrm{c})$ and $T(\bar{\pi}\mathrm{b} \to \mathrm{d})$ refer to collisions of a virtual pion (antipion) with particle a (b). By crossing, we have of course $T(\bar{\pi}\mathrm{b} \to \mathrm{d}) = T(\mathrm{b} \to \pi\mathrm{d})$. However, in the simplest version of the peripheral model (the so-called "pole approximation"), the pion is treated like a *real* incoming particle both at the upper $(\pi\mathrm{a} \to \mathrm{c})$ and the lower $(\bar{\pi}\mathrm{b} \to \mathrm{d})$

vertices. SALZMAN and SALZMAN [1960, 1961] stress that the pion is kinematically an incoming particle at each vertex, when viewed in the rest system of each jet. Since t is negative, E_π can be positive in one Lorentz frame and negative in another one. This of course cannot justify the assumption that $T(\pi a \to c)$ and $T(\bar{\pi} b \to d)$ are independent of t over a range much larger than μ^2. In fact, we shall see later that such an assumption is incorrect. In any case, replacing t by μ^2 in $T(\pi a \to c)$ and $T(\bar{\pi} b \to d)$, (1) leads to the differential cross-section

$$\frac{d\sigma}{dt\,ds_c\,ds_d} = \frac{1}{64\pi q^2 s}\,\frac{C(s_c)C(s_d)}{(\mu^2 - t)^2}\,. \tag{2.2}$$

By means of the recurrence relation (1-8.10) for the Lorentz-invariant phase space, we find

$$\begin{aligned} C(s_c) &= \frac{1}{2\pi}\int d\,\mathrm{Lips}(s_c;\, P_1, \ldots, P_m)|T(a\pi \to c)|^2 \\ &= \frac{1}{\pi}\sqrt{\lambda(s_c, m_a^2, t)}\,\sigma(a\pi \to c), \end{aligned} \tag{2.3}$$

and a similar expression for $C(s_d)$.

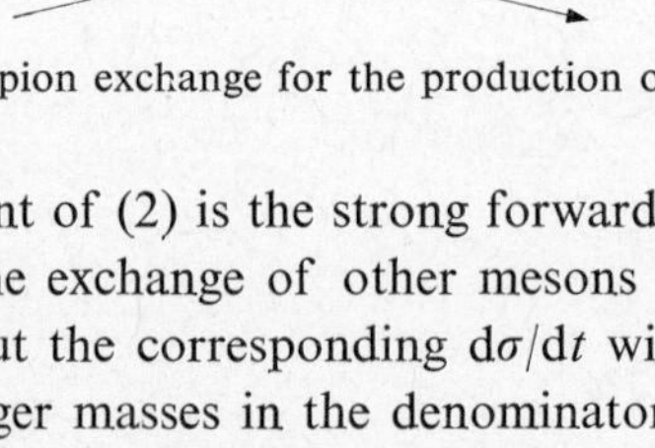

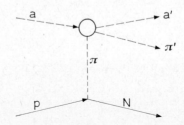

Fig. 11-2.4. One-pion exchange for the production of a single pion.

The main achievement of (2) is the strong forward peak in t, due to the pion pole at $t = \mu^2$. The exchange of other mesons or meson resonances will also contribute, but the corresponding $d\sigma/dt$ will be smaller and less peaked, due to the larger masses in the denominators. However, the pole approximation is much more doubtful in such cases, since these poles are far from the physical region of negative t.

CHEW and LOW [1959] considered a similar problem from a different point of view. They wanted to determine matrix elements of meson-meson collisions from a careful analysis of peripheral interactions. As the simplest example, consider the reaction $\pi p \to \pi\pi N$ (fig. 11-2.4), the matrix element of which may be written as

$$T(\text{ap} \to \text{a}'\pi'\text{N}) = \bar{u}(N)\gamma_5 \left[\frac{G}{\mu^2 - t} T(\text{a}\pi \to \text{a}'\pi'; t, s_{\text{a}\pi}, t_{\text{aa}'}) + X \right] u(p). \quad (2.4)$$

The first term contains the Born approximation for the lower vertex, the pion propagator, and the matrix element $T(\text{a}\pi \to \text{a}'\pi')$ for the scattering of a virtual pion of $(\text{mass})^2 = t$. The second term, which contains everything else, has no pole at $t = \mu^2$. Extrapolating to $t = \mu^2$, one finds the cross-section of meson-meson collision,

$$\frac{1}{\pi} \sqrt{\lambda(s_{\text{a}\pi}, m_\text{a}^2, \mu^2)}\sigma(\text{a}\pi \to \text{a}'\pi') = \frac{1}{64\pi q^2 s} \frac{4\pi}{G^2} \lim_{t \to \mu^2} \left[\frac{(\mu^2 - t)^2}{-t} \frac{\text{d}\sigma}{\text{d}s_{\text{a}\pi}\text{d}t} \right]. \quad (2.5)$$

Only the second order pole of $\text{d}\sigma/(-t\text{d}s_{\text{a}\pi}\text{d}t)$ has been used, since the first order pole contains interference with the unknown function X of (4). The factor $-1/t$ comes from the spin average of $|\bar{u}(N)\gamma_5 u(p)|^2$, which just gives a factor $-t$. Because of the importance of meson-exchange for high-energy models, we discuss this last point in some detail. In the rest system of one baryon (the lab system in case of the initial baryon), the momentum of the other baryon is used as the common spin quantization axis of both baryons. Then the scalar and pseudoscalar couplings reduce to

$$\bar{u}(P'M')u(P, M) = k_+ \delta_{MM'}, \quad (2.6)$$

$$\bar{u}(P'M')\gamma_5 u(P, M) = -2Mk_- \delta_{MM'}, \quad (2.7)$$

$$k_\pm = \sqrt{2m(E' \pm m')} = \sqrt{(m \pm m')^2 - t}. \quad (2.8)$$

These formulae follow from (3-5.16), with $Q_{\text{bb}} = 1$, $Q_{\text{sb}} = 0$ for scalar coupling and $Q_{\text{bb}} = 0$, $Q_{\text{sb}} = 1$ for pseudoscalar coupling. The connection between E' and t is given by (1-3.17). In the equal-mass case, we have $k_- = (-t)^{\frac{1}{2}}$. This proves our remark above.

Quantitatively, the Chew-Low extrapolation has not been particularly successful. This is partly due to the "spin-factor" $-t$, which turns $\text{d}\sigma/\text{d}t$ through the zero before reaching the pole. More seriously, there is the extremely violent t-variation of X in (4), which eventually must cause the nearly exponential decrease of $\text{d}\sigma/\text{d}t$. Finally, one should not forget that for these inelastic reactions, the physical t-region extends only up to $t_{\text{max}} < 0$, where t_{max} is given by (1-3.16).

11-3. Born term model and form factors

With increasing experimental accuracy, more and more inelastic high-energy reactions were recognized as being of the "quasi-two-particle" type ab → cd, where c and/or d are resonances. Knowing the spins and parities of the resonances, one may improve the pole approximation (2.1) by including the appropriate spin factors. The Born term model consists of approximating the remaining invariant amplitude at each vertex by its value at the pole of the exchanged particle, i.e. by the pertinent coupling constant. The Born terms of ab → cd for π-exchange are of the general form

$$T_{\pi}^{\text{Born}}(s, t, M_a, \ldots, M_d) = B_{a\pi c}(t, M_a, M_c) \frac{1}{\mu^2 - t} B_{b\pi d}(t, M_b, M_d). \tag{3.1}$$

The functions $B_{a\pi c}$ and $B_{b\pi d}$ are the vertex functions in the Born approximation. Resonances are usually treated as unstable particles, neglecting all finite-width effects.

We now review the various vertex factors in the Born approximation. Most cases have already been discussed in connection with the decays of resonances. $B(a\pi \to c)$ describes the inverse of the decay $c \to a\pi$, taken in the Born approximation (see e.g. fig. 6-4.2). The only difference is that the pion is now virtual, with $(\text{mass})^2 = t$. When particle a is spinless (π or K), the decay matrix element has been given in (3-2.13), for the decay of a resonance of spin L. We now replace the decay momentum p by the corresponding initial momentum, which is $a_c = [\lambda(m_c^2, m_a^2, t)/4m_c^2]^{\frac{1}{2}}$ as given by (9-8.5). We also quantize the spin states $\langle M|$ of the resonance along the momentum of particle a, in which case (3-2.13) gives

$$\begin{aligned} B_{a\pi c}(t, M_a = 0, M_c) &= G a_c^L L! \sqrt{\frac{2^L 4\pi}{(2L+1)!}}\, Y_{M_c}^L(0,0) \\ &= G a_c^L L! \sqrt{\frac{2^L}{(2L)!}}\, \delta_{0, M_c}. \end{aligned} \tag{3.2}$$

For $L = 1$ (ρ or K* production), the corresponding covariant expression is $-GP_a \cdot \varepsilon^*(M)$ (cf. 5-8.1); for $L = 2$ (f^0-production), it is $GP_a^{\mu} P_a^{\nu} \varepsilon_{\mu\nu}^*(M)$ (cf. 5-8.1). For these cases, (2) reduces to

$$G a_c \delta_{0, M_c} \text{ for spin 1}, \qquad G a_c^2 \sqrt{\tfrac{2}{3}}\, \delta_{0, M_c} \text{ for spin 2}. \tag{3.3}$$

For the baryon vertex, scalar and pseudoscalar coupling have been given in (2.6) and (2.7). They are of the same form as the two terms of (3-4.17) for the decay $\Lambda \to p\pi$, provided we put $\vartheta = 0$. Similarly, the Born vertex factor $B(p\pi N^*)$ for N^* production is analogous to (5-2.3), (5-2.4):

$$B_{p\pi N^*}(t, M_p, M^*) = G^* \bar{u}_\mu(M^*) P_p^\mu u(M_p) = \sqrt{\tfrac{2}{3}}\, G^* k_+ b_d \delta_{M_p, M^*}. \tag{3.4}$$

(Unless otherwise specified, the spin states of the final resonance are quantized along the momentum of the incident particle at the same vertex.) Finally, the production of a meson-baryon resonance of spin j has a vertex factor

$$B_{b\pi d}(t, M_b, M_d) = G C^{\frac{1}{2} j - \frac{1}{2} j}_{\frac{1}{2}\ 0\ \frac{1}{2}} k_\pm b_d^{j-\frac{1}{2}} \delta_{M_b, M_d}, \tag{3.5}$$

where C is a Clebsch-Gordan coefficient, and $k_+ (k_-)$ appears for even (odd) intrinsic parity. For a πN resonance of orbital angular momentum L, k_+ and k_- are associated with odd and even L, respectively. Notice in this connection the identity

$$b_d = \frac{1}{2m_d} k_+ k_-, \tag{3.6}$$

which follows from the decomposition (1-2.9) of the triangle function $\lambda(t, m_b^2, m_d^2)$.

We now discuss the implications of (1), (2), and (5). First of all, the dependence on the magnetic quantum numbers $M_a, \ldots, M_d$ allows us to compute decay distributions of the resonances. By (2) and (5), the joint decay density matrix (9-6.3) of resonances produced in meson-baryon collisions via π-exchange has the form

$$\rho_{NN'}^{MM'} = \delta_{M0} \delta_{M'0} (\delta_{\frac{1}{2}N} \delta_{\frac{1}{2}N'} + \delta_{-\frac{1}{2}N} \delta_{-\frac{1}{2}N'}). \tag{3.7}$$

It is simply the product $\rho_{MM'}(c)\rho_{NN'}(d)$ of the single-decay density matrices. Therefore, all joint decay distributions are of the product form (9-6.1). Moreover, for unpolarized initial particles, the decay distributions are independent of the azimuthal decay angles φ (TREIMAN and YANG [1962]). In peripheral interactions where π-exchange is not excluded by selection rules, these predictions of the π-exchange model are usually well satisfied, at least if one omits the tail of the peripheral peak, $-t > 0.2$ GeV^2 say. Of course, this agreement gives no support to the Born approximation, since it permits any amplitude, the spin dependence of which factorizes:

$$T(s, t, M_a, \ldots, M_d) = T_1(s, t, M_a, M_c) T_2(s, t, M_b, M_d). \tag{3.8}$$

The next important prediction of the π-exchange model is that T is independent of s. Consequently, the differential cross-section should decrease as $(p^{\mathrm{lab}})^{-2}$:

$$\frac{\mathrm{d}\sigma(s,t)}{\mathrm{d}t} = \frac{\pi}{4q^2 s}\left|\frac{T(t)}{4\pi}\right|^2 = \frac{\pi}{(2m_{\mathrm{b}}p^{\mathrm{lab}})^2}\left|\frac{T(t)}{4\pi}\right|^2. \tag{3.9}$$

This also agrees with experiment, provided the above "Treiman-Yang test" is fulfilled. In many reactions, the angular distribution of resonance decay does develop an azimuthal asymmetry at higher energies. In such cases, the fraction of π-exchange cannot be larger than $\rho^{00}_{\frac{1}{2}\frac{1}{2}}+\rho^{00}_{-\frac{1}{2}-\frac{1}{2}}$, according to (7). Moreover, it is frequently possible to split

$$T = T_\pi + T_\mathrm{v} + \ldots, \tag{3.10}$$

where T_v (the vector-meson exchange part) does not contribute to $\rho^{00}_{NN'}$ (see eq. (4.8) below), and the contribution of the rest is negligible. Then (9) appears to be satisfied in the form

$$(\rho^{00}_{\frac{1}{2}\frac{1}{2}}+\rho^{00}_{-\frac{1}{2}-\frac{1}{2}})\frac{\mathrm{d}\sigma}{\mathrm{d}t} = \frac{\pi}{(2m_{\mathrm{b}}p^{\mathrm{lab}})^2}\left|\frac{T_\pi(t)}{4\pi}\right|^2. \tag{3.11}$$

On the other hand, this energy-dependence makes it clear that the importance of π-exchange for reactions ab $\rightarrow$ cd is restricted to intermediate energies, between 2 and 10 GeV, say.

Finally, we come to a specific test of the Born term model, namely the detailed shape of the peripheral peak. In the pole approximation (2.1), the maximum always occurs at $t_{\max}$, i.e. at the beginning of the physical region (when c and d are broad resonances such as ρ or N*, the variation of $t_{\max}$ with the effective masses must be included). In the Born term model (1), the maximum of the peripheral peak is shifted to higher values of $-t$, due to the functions $k_\pm$, a_c and b_d, which all increase with increasing $-t$. The reason for this increase is easily understood, if one remembers that a_c is the common magnitude of the momenta of particle a and the virtual pion in the resonance rest frame. At fixed resonance energy, this magnitude increases with decreasing (mass)^2 of the virtual particle.

We mentioned already that the peripheral peak has roughly an exponentail shape,

$$\frac{\mathrm{d}\sigma}{\mathrm{d}t} \approx \text{constant}\cdot \mathrm{e}^{bt}. \tag{3.12}$$

In many reactions, b is of the order of 5/GeV^2. It is clear that the pole approximation (2.2) gives a flatter $\mathrm{d}\sigma/\mathrm{d}t$, except possibly for very small $-t$. From our above discussion, it follows that the Born term model is even worse. For $-t\rightarrow\infty$, T_π^{Born} diverges like $t^{j_\mathrm{c}+j_\mathrm{d}-1}$ ($j_\mathrm{c} = L$ in (2)).

Despite this failure, the Born term model is usually not abandoned completely. Instead, the general π-exchange matrix element (2.1) is rewritten in the form (FERRARI and SELLERI [1961, 1962, 1963])

$$T_\pi(\mathrm{ab} \to \mathrm{cd}) = T_\pi^{\mathrm{Born}}(\mathrm{ab} \to \mathrm{cd}) F(m_\mathrm{a}^2, s_\mathrm{c}, t) F(m_\mathrm{b}^2, s_\mathrm{d}, t), \qquad (3.13)$$

where the F's are "form factors" associated with the two vertices (for stable particles or narrow resonances, $s_\mathrm{c} = m_\mathrm{c}^2$, $s_\mathrm{d} = m_\mathrm{d}^2$). In fact, since one of the colliding particles is always a nucleon, any matrix element which leads to (7) and (9) can be written in this form. The use of (13) lies in the fact that for $t \to \mu^2$, T_π must reduce to T_π^{Born}:

$$F(m_\mathrm{a}^2, s_\mathrm{c} = m_\mathrm{c}^2, t = \mu^2) = F(m_\mathrm{b}^2, s_\mathrm{d} = m_\mathrm{d}^2, t = \mu^2) = 1. \qquad (3.14)$$

Since $t = \mu^2$ lies outside the physical domain, (14) is of little practical importance, except for extrapolations of the Chew-Low type.

One may go one step further by splitting each F into a "kinematical" and a "dynamical" form factor (DÜRR and PILKUHN [1965]). The factor a_c^L in $B_{\mathrm{a}\pi\mathrm{c}}$ (2) is the threshold behaviour for the creation of the resonance, just as p^L is the threshold behaviour for its decay. In section 5-1 we saw that the threshold behaviour is a poor approximation already for the N*, which is the resonance of smallest p. Instead of p^{2L}, the penetration factor $v_L(pR)$ of (5-1.11) gave a satisfactory fit for the shape of the resonance (fig. 5-1). The same penetration factor may be inserted for the production of the resonance, with p replaced by a_c. For a p-wave resonance, the kinematical form factor thus becomes

$$F(m_\mathrm{a}^2, s_\mathrm{c}, t) = \sqrt{\frac{1+R^2 a_\mathrm{c}^2(m_\mathrm{a}^2, m_\mathrm{c}^2, \mu^2)}{1+R^2 a_\mathrm{c}^2(m_\mathrm{a}^2, s_\mathrm{c}, t)}} = \sqrt{\frac{4m_\mathrm{c}^2+R^2\lambda(m_\mathrm{a}^2, m_\mathrm{c}^2, \mu^2)}{4s_\mathrm{c}+R^2\lambda(m_\mathrm{a}^2, s_\mathrm{c}, t)}}. \qquad (3.15)$$

For $Ra_\mathrm{c} \gg 1$, the Born term model including the kinematical form factor regains the simple t-dependence of the pole approximation (2.2). At the baryon vertex, the functions $k_\pm$ cause a minor complication. In view of the small t-region to which the model applies, one may approximate

$$k_+ \approx m_\mathrm{b}+m_\mathrm{d}, \qquad k_- \approx b_\mathrm{d}\frac{2m_\mathrm{d}}{m_\mathrm{b}+m_\mathrm{d}} \approx b_\mathrm{d} \qquad (3.16)$$

according to (2.8) and (6). Then the factor $k_\pm b_\mathrm{d}^{j-\frac{1}{2}}$ reduces to b_d^L, where L is the orbital angular momentum of the resonance. An interesting special case is the NπN vertex, for which we get $L = 1$. This shows that the nucleon pole is mainly coupled to the P-wave πp system, which agrees with our considerations of sections 7-5 and 7-6.

11-4. Vector meson exchange

In πp collisions of the quasi-two-particle type, single-pion exchange is allowed for ρ and f production but not for π, η and ω production. Similarly, in K^+p collisions, π exchange is allowed for K* production but not for K production. Nonetheless, reactions such as $\pi p \to \pi N$, $\pi p \to \pi N^*$, $\pi p \to \omega N^*$, $Kp \to Kp$, $Kp \to KN^*$ are about as peripheral as π-exchange reactions. In these reactions, vector meson (ρ and/or ω) exchange is allowed and it is tempting to assume that these peripheral reactions are in fact related to the vector meson resonances in the t-channel. Remember in this context our discussion of σ and ρ exchange in low-energy πN scattering (section 7-8).

In the Born model, the matrix element of vector meson exchange is of the general form (6-4.6)

$$T_{\mathrm{v}}^{\mathrm{Born}}(s, t, M_{\mathrm{a}}, \ldots, M_{\mathrm{d}})$$

$$= B_{\mathrm{avc}}^{\mu}(t, M_{\mathrm{a}}, M_{\mathrm{c}}) \frac{-g_{\mu\nu}+\Delta_{\mu}\Delta_{\nu}/m_{\mathrm{v}}^2}{m_{\mathrm{v}}^2-t} B_{\mathrm{bvd}}^{\nu}(t, M_{\mathrm{b}}, M_{\mathrm{d}}). \tag{4.1}$$

Here m_{v} and Δ are the mass and 4-momentum of the exchanged vector particle, with $\Delta^2 = t$. The vertex functions are 4-vectors as in the case of photon exchange. They should not be proportional to $\Delta = P_{\mathrm{b}}-P_{\mathrm{d}} = P_{\mathrm{c}}-P_{\mathrm{a}}$, because, for a real vector meson, $\varepsilon(M)\Delta = 0$ (see 3-3.1). In fact, if we put e.g. $B_{\mathrm{avc}}^{\mu} = \Delta^{\mu}B_{\mathrm{avc}}$, (1) reduces to $-B_{\mathrm{avc}}\Delta_{\nu}B_{\mathrm{bvd}}^{\nu}/m_{\mathrm{v}}^2$, which has the form of spin-zero exchange (except for the absence of the pole, which turns out to be unimportant anyway). In particular, the density matrix would again assume the form (3.7). Experimentally, couplings of this type appear to be small compared to the "proper" vector meson couplings.

Taking particle a as pseudoscalar, we have, for pseudoscalar (π or K) and vector (ω, ρ, ϕ, K*) particles c,

$$B_{\mathrm{av}\pi}^{\mu} = \tfrac{1}{2}G(P_{\mathrm{a}}+P_{\mathrm{c}}), \tag{4.2}$$

$$B_{\mathrm{av}\omega}^{\mu} = -g\varepsilon^{\mu\nu\lambda\rho}\Delta_{\nu}\varepsilon_{\lambda}^{*}(M_{\mathrm{c}})P_{\mathrm{c},\rho}. \tag{4.3}$$

These are the crossed versions of (3-3.5) and (4-8.2) or (5-6.8). On the baryon side, the Born term vertex is given by (4-8.7), if d is also a baryon:

$$B_{\mathrm{bvd}}^{\nu} = \bar{u}'(M_{\mathrm{d}}) \left[(G_{\mathrm{v}}+G_{\mathrm{t}})\gamma^{\nu} - \frac{(P_{\mathrm{b}}+P_{\mathrm{d}})^{\nu}}{m_{\mathrm{b}}+m_{\mathrm{d}}} G_{\mathrm{t}}\right] u(M_{\mathrm{b}}). \tag{4.4}$$

If d is a $\frac{3}{2}^+$ resonance, B^{ν} may be written as

$$\bar{u}_\mu(M^*)\left[G_1 g^{\mu\nu} + \frac{G'\gamma^\nu\Delta^\mu}{m+m^*} + G_2\frac{-P^\nu\Delta^\mu + P\cdot\Delta g^{\mu\nu}}{(m+m^*)^2}\right]\gamma_5 u(M), \qquad (4.5)$$

which is an extension of (10-8.9). This is the first time we have encountered more than two coupling constants for a given vertex. Quite generally, the number of independent couplings is found from helicity considerations. For three-particle couplings as in the Born term model, we apply (9-2.2) to the decay of that particle which has the largest spin. Then the number of independent couplings is given by the number of independent helicity amplitudes $T(\lambda_1, \lambda_2)$. In NρN coupling, the ρ meson has the largest spin. The "decay" $\rho \to \mathrm{N}\bar{\mathrm{N}}$ contains four helicity amplitudes, of which only two are linearly independent, due to parity conservation. In NρN* coupling, the N* has the largest spin, and the number of independent helicity amplitudes $T(\lambda_\rho, \lambda_\mathrm{N})$ for N* $\to \rho$N is three. Also for nucleon isobars of spin $\frac{5}{2}$, $\frac{7}{2}$, etc., exactly three independent couplings exist for N* $\to \rho$N. The photon, however, has only two couplings, since the photon state of zero helicity is excluded by gauge invariance (in other cases such as $\omega \to \rho\pi$, $\lambda = 0$ is excluded by parity conservation 9-2.14).

We now discuss some implications of vector meson exchange for the decay distribution of resonances, beginning with (3) for the production of a 1^- resonance. In the resonance rest frame, only the time-component of P_c contributes, which is m_c. Also, taking the z-axis along the momentum of particle a, we have

$$\boldsymbol{\Delta} = (\Delta_x, \Delta_y, \Delta_z) = (0, 0, -a_\mathrm{c}), \qquad (4.6)$$

and (3) reduces to

$$B^\mu_{\mathrm{av}\omega} = g\varepsilon^{\mu 3\lambda 0}\varepsilon^*_\lambda(M_\mathrm{c})a_\mathrm{c}m_\mathrm{c} = g\sqrt{\lambda(m_\mathrm{a}^2, m_\mathrm{c}^2, t)}(\varepsilon^*_y(M_\mathrm{c}), -\varepsilon^*_x(M_\mathrm{c}), 0, 0), \quad (4.7)$$

i.e. the z- and time-components are zero. This implies

$$B^\mu_{\mathrm{av}\omega}(M_\mathrm{c} = 0) = 0. \qquad (4.8)$$

Consequently, in reactions such as πp $\to \rho$p, Kp $\to$ K*N or Kp $\to$ K*N*, where both π- and vector-exchange contribute, there is no interference between T_π and T_v. Moreover, in the matrix element for the over-all process including the resonance decay, the polarization vector $\boldsymbol{\varepsilon}^*(M_\mathrm{c})$ is replaced by

$$\sum_M \boldsymbol{\varepsilon}^*(M)(\boldsymbol{\varepsilon}(M)\cdot\boldsymbol{n}) = \boldsymbol{n} = (\sin\vartheta\cos\varphi, \sin\vartheta\sin\varphi, \cos\vartheta), \qquad (4.9)$$

where ϑ and φ characterize the direction of resonance decay (eq. (9) follows from the remark following (3-2.14)). Inserting this into (7), we see that 1^-

resonances produced by vector exchange have a polar decay angular distribution of the form $\sin^2 \vartheta$. For the reaction $K^+p \to K^*p$, this fact was mentioned after (5-6.12).

Next, we discuss the production of $\frac{3}{2}^+$ resonances via vector exchange. Here, a simple model has been amazingly successful. One assumes (STODOLSKY and SAKURAI [1963], STODOLSKY [1964]) that the $N\rho N^*$ and NK^*Y^* couplings have the same form as the $N\gamma N^*$ coupling, i.e.

$$G_1 = G', \qquad G_2 = 0, \tag{4.10}$$

which corresponds to M_{1+} excitation. In this model, production of resonance states of magnetic quantum number $\pm\frac{3}{2}$ along the *normal to the production plane* is negligible. The remaining two states are decomposed into the orbital angular momentum states $Y^1_{M_\pi}(\vartheta', \varphi')$ of the decay pion (ϑ' and φ' refer to the normal to the production plane), and the spin states $|M_B\rangle$ of the decay baryon, according to

$$\begin{aligned} |N^*, \pm\tfrac{1}{2}\rangle &= (\tfrac{2}{3})^{\frac{1}{2}} Y^1_0 |\pm\tfrac{1}{2}\rangle + 3^{-\frac{1}{2}} Y^1_{\pm 1} |\mp\tfrac{1}{2}\rangle \\ &= (4\pi)^{-\frac{1}{2}} [2^{\frac{1}{2}} \cos\vartheta' |\pm\tfrac{1}{2}\rangle \mp 2^{-\frac{1}{2}} \sin\vartheta' e^{\pm i\varphi'} |\mp\tfrac{1}{2}\rangle]. \end{aligned} \tag{4.11}$$

Denoting the complex amplitudes for the production of $M^* = \pm\frac{1}{2}$ by $A_\pm$, we obtain the final π-baryon states as

$$\begin{aligned} &(4\pi)^{-\frac{1}{2}} \langle\tfrac{1}{2}| (A_+ 2^{\frac{1}{2}} \cos\vartheta' + 2^{-\frac{1}{2}} A_- \sin\vartheta' e^{i\varphi'}) \\ &\qquad + (4\pi)^{-\frac{1}{2}} \langle -\tfrac{1}{2}| (2^{\frac{1}{2}} \cos\vartheta' A_- - 2^{\frac{1}{2}} A_+ \sin\vartheta' e^{-i\varphi'}). \end{aligned} \tag{4.12}$$

The angular distribution of the decay pion is given by the sum of the absolute squares of $\langle\frac{1}{2}|$ and $\langle -\frac{1}{2}|$,

$$W(\theta'\varphi') = \frac{1}{8\pi} (1 + 3\cos^2 \vartheta'), \tag{4.13}$$

independent of A_+, A_- and φ'.

It remains to show that the matrix elements for the $M^* = \pm\frac{3}{2}$ states are negligible. The spinor $\bar{u}_\mu(\frac{3}{2})$ is $\bar{u}(\frac{1}{2}) \cdot \varepsilon^*_\mu(1)$ according to (3-7.1). In the resonance rest frame, only the x- and y-components of $\varepsilon^*_\mu(1)$ ($-2^{-\frac{1}{2}}$ and $i2^{-\frac{1}{2}}$) are non-zero. Denoting by V_ν the 4-vector with which (5) is contracted, we get, in the Stodolsky-Sakurai model (10),

$$G_1 \bar{u}_\mu(\tfrac{3}{2}) \left[V^\mu + \frac{V \cdot \gamma \Delta^\mu}{m + m^*} \right] \gamma_5 u(M) = 2^{-\frac{1}{2}} G_1 \bar{u}(\tfrac{1}{2}) \left[V_- + \frac{V \cdot \gamma \Delta_-}{m + m^*} \right] \gamma_5 u(M), \tag{4.14}$$

where $V_- = V_x - iV_y$, $\Delta_- = \Delta_x - i\Delta_y$. The big components of $\bar{u}(\frac{1}{2})$ are

$(2m^*)^{\frac{1}{2}}\chi_0^+(\frac{1}{2})$, while the small ones are zero. Decomposing γ_5 and $\gamma_\mu\gamma_5$ into its "bb" and "bs" parts, we find from (3-5.15),

$$G_1\sqrt{m^*}\chi_0^+(\tfrac{1}{2})\left[-\boldsymbol{V}\cdot\boldsymbol{\sigma}\frac{\Delta_-}{m+m^*}+\left(V_-+\frac{V_0\Delta_-}{m+m^*}\right)\frac{\boldsymbol{\sigma}\cdot\boldsymbol{p}}{E+m}\right]\chi_0(M). \tag{4.15}$$

Orienting both $\chi_0(M)$ and $\chi_0^+(\frac{1}{2})$ along the normal to the production plane (states 3-2.1), we see that for $M=\frac{1}{2}$, $\chi_0^+(\frac{1}{2})\boldsymbol{\sigma}\cdot\boldsymbol{p}\chi_0(\frac{1}{2})=0$, since $p_z=0$. Also, if particles a and c are spinless, V^μ is proportional to $P_a^\mu+P_c^\mu$ (2), which has no z-component either. Therefore, (15) is zero for $M=\frac{1}{2}$. (For double resonance production such as $\pi p\to\omega N^*$, V^μ is proportional to (3), which does have a z-component from $\varepsilon^*(M_c=0)$.)

For $M=-\frac{1}{2}$, the evaluation of (15) is slightly more complicated, since $\boldsymbol{\sigma}\cdot\boldsymbol{p}$ transforms $\chi_0(-\frac{1}{2})$ into $\chi_0(\frac{1}{2})$, with coefficient $p_-=p_x-ip_y=\Delta_-$ ($\boldsymbol{p}=\boldsymbol{\Delta}$ in the resonance rest frame). Consequently, the value of (15) for $M=-\frac{1}{2}$ is

$$G_1\sqrt{m^*}\left[-V_-\frac{P_-}{m+m^*}+\left(V_-+\frac{V_0P_-}{m+m^*}\right)\frac{P_-}{E+m}\right]. \tag{4.16}$$

For small momentum transfer, $p_-/(m+m^*)\ll 1$, $(E+m)/(m+m^*)\approx 1$, the coefficient of V_0 is negligible, and the remaining terms cancel. Therefore, (15) vanishes approximately for peripheral collisions.

With these two examples, we conclude our discussion of decay distributions in peripheral reactions due to vector meson exchange.

Before proceeding to the energy-dependence of T_v^{Born}, we remark that (1) is "gauge invariant" in most cases. By this we mean that the term $\Delta_\mu\Delta_\nu/m_v^2$ in the propagator may be omitted, since either $B_{\text{avc}}^\mu\Delta_\mu=0$ or $B_{\text{bvd}}^\nu\Delta_\nu=0$ (or both). From the discussion of section 4-8, we remember that the coupling (3) is always gauge-invariant, while (2) is gauge-invariant for $m_a^2=m_c^2$. Of the vector-baryon coupling (4), the tensor coupling is always gauge-invariant, while the vector coupling is gauge-invariant in the case of equal baryon masses (see 4-8.8). Finally, the Stodolsky-Sakurai model is gauge-invariant since it is analogous to the $N\gamma N^*$ interaction. Therefore, all reactions mentioned at the beginning of this section have gauge invariant T_v. Only in hyperon production such as $\pi p\to KY$ or $K^-p\to\pi Y$, is the vector coupling part not gauge invariant. Apart from such cases, (1) may be rewritten as

$$T_v^{\text{Born}}(s,t,M_a,\dots,M_d)=B_{\text{avc},\nu}(t,M_a,M_c)B_{\text{bvd}}^\nu(t,M_b,M_d)\cdot\frac{1}{m_v^2-t}. \tag{4.17}$$

We now come to the s-dependence of T_v or rather of $|T_v|^2$. The differential transition probability for unpolarized particles is a second degree polynomial in s,

$$\sum_{M_a, \ldots, M_d} |T_v(s, t, M_a, \ldots, M_d)|^2 = A(t)s^2 + B(t)s + C(t), \tag{4.18}$$

with $A(t) \neq 0$. For reactions with one outgoing baryon, this can be seen from e.g. (10-2.9), with ε given by $B_{avc}/(m_v^2 - t)$. The term $\varepsilon^* \varepsilon$ is independent of s, while $\sum (P \cdot B_{avc}(M_c)(P \cdot B^*_{avc}(M_c))$ is quadratic in s, which may be verified for (2) and (3). Also, a coupling $B_{avc}(M_c) = G \cdot \varepsilon(M_c)$ which simply consists of the outgoing particle's polarization vector (this would be appropriate for the $\sigma\rho\rho$ vertex), leads to quadratic terms, since by (3-3.6)

$$\sum_{M_c} P \cdot \varepsilon(M_c) P \cdot \varepsilon^*(M_c) = P^\mu(-g_{\mu\nu} + P_{c\mu} P_{c\nu})P^\nu = (P \cdot P_c)^2 - P^2. \tag{4.19}$$

For a general derivation of (18), we consider the helicity amplitudes $T_t(\lambda_a \lambda_{\bar{b}} \lambda_{\bar{c}} \lambda_d)$ in the t-channel $a\bar{b} \to \bar{c}d$. Here, the vector exchange produces a pole only in the $J = 1$ partial wave amplitude, which according to (9-4.4) is of the form ($\varphi_t = 0$),

$$T_v(\lambda_a \lambda_{\bar{b}} \lambda_{\bar{c}} \lambda_d) = 8\pi t^{\frac{1}{2}} \cdot 3 d^1_{\lambda\lambda'}(\theta_t) T_1(\lambda_a \lambda_{\bar{b}} \lambda_{\bar{c}} \lambda_d, t), \tag{4.20}$$

where $t^{\frac{1}{2}}$ is the cms energy and θ_t is the cms scattering angle. From table C-3 we see that the $(d^1_{\lambda\lambda'})^2$ are second order polynomials in $\cos \theta_t$. By (1-3.10), the cosine of the s-channel cms scattering angle is linear in t. Therefore, $\cos \theta_t$ is linear in s, which proves our theorem for the t-channel helicity amplitudes. Finally, the result applies also to the s-channel, since the transformation (9-8.2) from the t-channel to the s-channel amplitudes is unitary.

For $s \to \infty$, (18) implies constant $d\sigma/dt$ (cf. 3.9). Experimentally, the cross-section for each inelastic reaction ab $\to$ cd tends to zero with increasing energy, at least for reactions such as $\pi^- p \to \omega N^*$, which do not have $I = 0$ and positive G-parity in the t-channel. This energy-dependence is a serious difficulty with the Born term model for vector exchange. Finally, the t-dependence of T_v^{Born} encounters similar difficulties to those of T_π^{Born}. Also, it appears difficult to extend the penetration factor model to vector exchange. Nonetheless, the vector exchange model is of some value, partly because of the predicted decay angular distributions, and partly as a starting point for more complicated models (see next section).

11-5. Diffraction scattering, Regge poles

The π- and vector-exchange models for reactions ab $\to$ cd give purely real matrix elements. Elastic scattering, on the other hand, has a large imaginary part, which may be ascribed, via unitarity, to the total inelastic cross-section. In fact, with $d\sigma_{el}/dt$ given by const $\cdot$ e^{bt} (3.12), the constant is well approximated by the "optical point" at $t = 0$,

$$\frac{d\sigma}{dt} = \pi \left(\frac{\sigma_T}{4\pi}\right)^2 e^{bt}. \tag{5.1}$$

For $t = 0$, (1) follows from (2-2.16), if we insert $(\mathrm{Im}\, T)^2 = \lambda\sigma_T^2$ according to (2-4.2) and neglect $(\mathrm{Re}\, T)^2$. Since the total cross-section is approximately equal to the inelastic cross-section, one may interpret σ_{el} as "shadow" scattering, caused by the "absorption" of incoming particles into inelastic final states. A more common name is "diffraction scattering". The exponential peak (fig. 11-1.2) is called the "diffraction peak", and the region of t where (1) applies ($-t < 1\ \mathrm{GeV}^2$, say) the "diffraction region". Outside this region, $d\sigma/dt$ is very small, except for a backward peak in π^+p scattering, which appears to be due to neutron exchange.

We now consider the partial wave expansion of $T(s, t)$ for elastic meson-nucleon or nucleon-nucleon scattering. We neglect the nucleon spin, which is consistent with the other approximations which we shall make below. We assume that $T(s, t)$ is purely imaginary for all t, in which case we have, according to (1) and the optical theorem,

$$T(s, t) = i\lambda^{\frac{1}{2}}\sigma_T e^{\frac{1}{2}bt} = 8\pi s^{\frac{1}{2}} \sum_L (2L+1) P_L(x) T_L(s). \tag{5.2}$$

Since a sharp peak in the differential cross-section requires constructive interference of many partial waves, we are interested in (2) for large L and small $x = \cos\theta = 1 + t/2q^2$. In this region, $P_L(x)$ may be approximated by the Bessel function of zero order,

$$P_L(x) = P_L(1 + t/2q^2) \approx J_0\left(\frac{L}{q}\sqrt{-t}\right). \tag{5.3}$$

The quotient L/q corresponds classically to the impact parameter ρ. The summation over L is now approximated by an integration,

$$T(s, t) \approx 8\pi s^{\frac{1}{2}} \int_0^\infty 2L\, dL\, J_0\left(\frac{L}{q}\sqrt{-t}\right) T(L, s)$$
$$= 16\pi s^{\frac{1}{2}} \int_0^\infty \rho\, d\rho\, J_0(\rho\sqrt{-t}) q^2 T(\rho, s). \tag{5.4}$$

An alternative point of view is to *define* the last expression of (4) as the "impact parameter representation" of $T(s, t)$. Then one would say that $T(\rho, s)$ is approximately equal to $T_L(s)$, for $\rho = L/q$.

To obtain $T(\rho, s)$, we need the inversion of (4). Since (4) is a Fourier-Bessel transform (see e.g. WHITTAKER and WATSON [1963], p. 385), one has

$$16\pi s^{\frac{1}{2}} q^2 T(\rho, s) = \int_0^\infty \sqrt{-t}\, d(\sqrt{-t}) J_0(\rho\sqrt{-t}) T(s, t), \tag{5.5}$$

which is of the same form as (4). Moreover, inserting $\mathrm{i}\lambda^{\frac{1}{2}}\sigma_T \exp[\frac{1}{2}bt]$ for $T(s, t)$, integral (5) gives (WHITTAKER and WATSON [1963], p. 384)

$$\begin{aligned} 16\pi s^{\frac{1}{2}} q^2 T(\rho, s) &= \mathrm{i}\lambda^{\frac{1}{2}}\sigma_T \int_0^\infty \sqrt{-t}\, d(\sqrt{-t}) J_0(\rho\sqrt{-t}) \mathrm{e}^{-\frac{1}{2}b(\sqrt{-t})^2} \\ &= \mathrm{i}\lambda^{\frac{1}{2}}\sigma_T \frac{1}{b}\, \mathrm{e}^{-\rho^2/2b}. \end{aligned} \tag{5.6}$$

Inserting $\lambda^{\frac{1}{2}} = 2qs^{\frac{1}{2}}$, we find

$$T(\rho, s) = \frac{\mathrm{i}\sigma_T}{8\pi q b}\, \mathrm{e}^{-\rho^2/2b} \quad \text{or} \quad T_L(s) \approx \frac{\mathrm{i}\sigma_T}{8\pi q b}\, \mathrm{e}^{-L^2/2q^2 b}. \tag{5.7}$$

This gives an inelasticity coefficient η_L of the Lth partial wave (see section 2-7),

$$\eta_L \approx S_L = 1 + 2\mathrm{i}qT_L \approx 1 - \frac{\sigma_T}{4\pi b}\, \mathrm{e}^{-L^2/2q^2 b}. \tag{5.8}$$

For $L = \infty$, (8) gives $\eta_L = 1$, i.e. no scattering, while $L = 0$ gives maximal inelasticity, $\eta_0 = 1 - \sigma_T/4\pi b$. Equation (8) is used in models such as the absorption model (see e.g. JACKSON [1965], JACKSON *et al.* [1965]). However, one should remember that (8) is derived only for $L \gg 1$. The lowest partial waves are excluded from the beginning, since they depend essentially on elastic scattering outside the diffraction peak.

Sometimes, (1) is analysed in terms of an optical model with an absorptive (i.e. imaginary) potential. In the simplest version, the nucleon corresponds to an absorbing disc of radius $R = 2b^{\frac{1}{2}}$.

In contrast to most other peripheral interactions, diffraction scattering is nearly independent of s. At 10 GeV/c, b is of the order of 6/GeV^2 for K^+p, 9/GeV^2 for $\pi^{\pm}p$, 10/GeV^2 for pp and 12/GeV^2 for $\bar{p}p$. It increases with s for K^+p and pp scattering (the diffraction peak "shrinks"), while it decreases for $\bar{p}p$ (expanding peak). For $\pi^{\pm}p$ scattering, it is fairly constant.

The energy dependence of the diffraction peak, in particular the shrinking pp peak, played an important role in the early development of the so-called Regge-pole model. In potential theory, REGGE [1959, 1960] investigated the analytic properties of the partial wave amplitudes $T_L(s)$, taken as functions of *complex angular momentum* L (see also DE ALFARO and REGGE [1965]). In the Schrödinger equation (2-5.3), $L(L+1)$ appears as a parameter just like q^2, which may be varied at will. This formalism provided the bases for the model of CHEW and FRAUTSCHI [1960, 1961], who suggested that high-energy reactions of the type ab → cd are governed by the exchange of a few Regge poles, which reduce to the appropriate meson exchange Born terms at t = (meson mass)^2. This model is attractive for the following reason. From (4.20) we conclude that the Born term for exchange of a meson or meson resonance of arbitrary spin L is proportional to $d^L_{\lambda\lambda'}(\theta_t)$, which, for fixed t and $s \to \infty$, diverges like s^L. On the other hand, if the spin L is a complex function $\alpha(t)$, with

$$\alpha(t = m^2_{\text{res}}) = L_{\text{res}}, \tag{5.9}$$

then the Born term is replaced by a Regge pole term, which behaves as $s^{\alpha(t)}$ for $s \to \infty$. It is not difficult to show that for $t < 0$, $\alpha(t)$ is real and $\leqq 1$ (FROISSART [1961]). Hence, for vector mesons etc., the Regge pole model is an extension of the Born term model, which avoids the high-energy divergence s^L. In fact, for all reactions considered so far, it has been possible to parametrize the energy-dependence by a few Regge poles, or equivalently by expansions of the type (1.2). The function $\alpha(t)$ is usually called the Regge trajectory.

Returning now to diffraction scattering, we may approximate $\lambda^{\frac{1}{2}} \approx s$, in which case (2) is of the form (1.2)

$$T(s,t) = b_0(t)s^{\alpha_0(t)}, \qquad b_0(t) = \mathrm{i}\sigma_{\mathrm{T}}\mathrm{e}^{\frac{1}{2}bt}, \qquad \alpha_0(t) = 1. \tag{5.10}$$

In view of the constancy of the "Pomeranchuk trajectory" $\alpha_0(t)$, the Regge pole model does not provide a particularly elegant description of diffraction scattering.

In other reactions also, the Regge pole model meets with some difficulties. Whereas the Born terms are real, the exchange of Regge particles produces complex amplitudes. However, the phase of $T(s, t, M_{\mathrm{a}}, \ldots, M_{\mathrm{d}})$ is independent of the magnetic quantum numbers $M_{\mathrm{a}}, \ldots, M_{\mathrm{d}}$, which means that a single Regge pole produces no polarization. Measurements of $\pi^-\mathrm{p} \to \pi^0\mathrm{n}$ with polarized protons have revealed almost constant polarization effects at high energies (BONAMY *et al.* [1966]), which is difficult to reconcile even if interference between two Regge poles is assumed.

11-6. Multiperipheral interactions and diffraction dissociation

The first evidence for multiperipheral interactions came from the interactions of cosmic ray protons, say in the energy range 100–100 000 GeV. Here, the average number of charged particles produced in a collision (not counting the "heavy tracks" from the destruction of the target nucleus) is

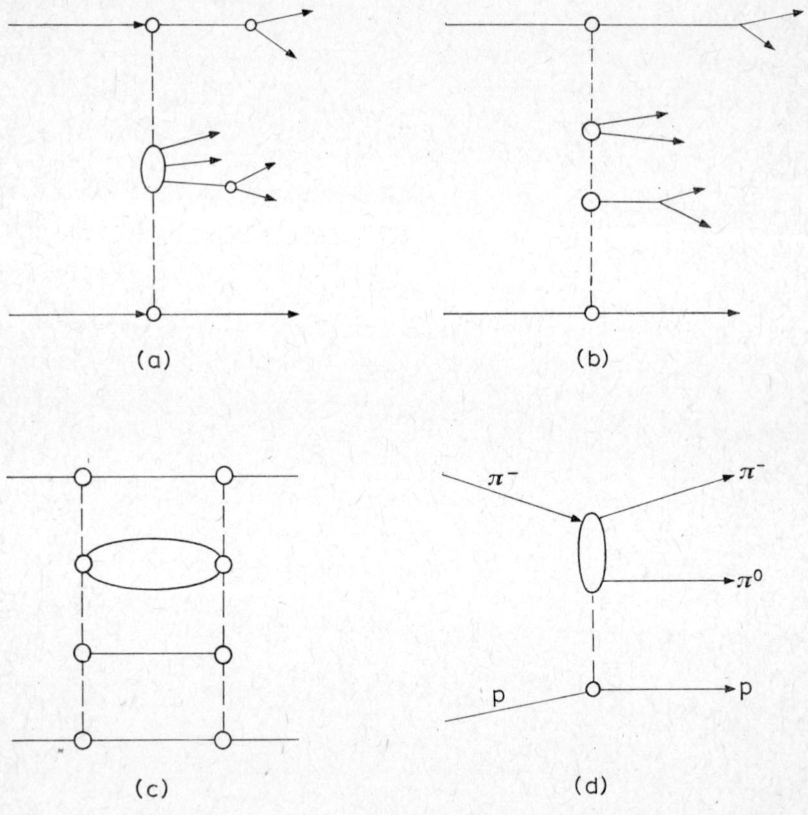

Fig. 11-6. Multiperipheral graphs; (a) double-peripheral structure with many particles from one bubble; (b) multiperipheral structure with at most two particles from each bubble; (c) elastic diffraction scattering, (d) diffraction dissociation of the proton.

23, for an average incident energy of 5000 GeV (PERKINS [1960]). The multiplicities of individual collisions fluctuate between 5 and 100 particles, most of which are pions. Despite these large fluctuations, the transverse momentum of the produced particles (i.e. the momentum component orthogonal to the momentum of the incident proton) remains fairly constant, at about 400 MeV/c. Moreover, one of the produced particles usually carries away a large fraction of the total lab energy, sometimes up to 90%. It is quite likely that this particle is either the "original" incident proton, or else a proton or π^+ from the decay of a baryon resonance (neutral particles are not detected). Finally, in cases where an identification of the slowest final state particle has been possible, this particle turned out to be a baryon. These observations indicate that each baryon transfers only a small amount of its 4-momentum, despite the fact that many particles are produced. Classically, this would correspond to "double-peripheral" collisions, where a pion from the "cloud" of the cosmic-ray proton collides with a pion from the cloud of the target proton (fig. 11-6a). However, to ensure that the produced pions get small transverse momenta, it appears to be necessary to assume that $\pi\pi$ collisions are also peripheral. This leads one to consider multiperipheral collisions (fig. 11-6b). A multiperipheral model of this type was proposed by AMATI, FUBINI and STANGHELLINI [1962], as an extension of the single-pion exchange model (fig. 11-2.3). The chain of exchanged particles between the vertices was assumed to consist of pions. The shadow scattering of the multiperipheral model (illustrated in fig. 11-6c) turned out to be similar to the diffraction scattering caused by the Pomeranchuk trajectory of the Regge pole model.

Another extremely peripheral interaction is the so-called diffraction dissociation (FEINBERG and POMERANCHUK [1956], GOOD and WALKER [1960]), which may be viewed as a diffraction scattering, during which one of the particles "breaks up". More precisely, the exchanged system has zero isospin and positive G-parity, as in elastic diffraction scattering. So far as quasi-two-particle reactions ab → cd are concerned, it appears that these interactions are as little energy-dependent as the diffraction scattering itself (see e.g. MORRISON [1966]). Examples of such reactions are pp → $pN^*_{\frac{1}{2}}$ of πp → A_1p, πp → A_2p.

Finally, reactions such as $\pi^-p \to \pi^-\pi^0p$, with all effective masses above the corresponding resonance regions, are double-peripheral at high energies. Here, the main effect appears to be diffraction scattering of the incident π^- on a π^0 coming from the proton (RAZMI [1964], JOSEPH and PILKUHN [1964]). These reactions thus contain single-pion exchange as one peripheral interaction, and diffraction scattering as the other one (see fig. 11-6d). However, very few "proper" three-particle final states have been investigated so far. Nevertheless, it is clear that these reactions are as "peripheral" as the quasi-two-particle reactions.

CHAPTER 12

WEAK INTERACTIONS BETWEEN HADRONS AND LEPTONS

12-1. Neutron decay. Energy spectrum of allowed beta decay

The neutron decays with a half-life of $t_0 = 11.7 \pm 0.3$ min (SOSNOWSKY *et al.* [1958]). With an exponential decay law $e^{-\Gamma t}$, this corresponds to a lifetime

$$\Gamma^{-1} = t_0/\ln 2 = (1.01 \pm 0.3) \times 10^3 \text{ sec}, \tag{1.1}$$

which is the value given in table 4-1. The decay products are proton, electron and neutrino, i.e. $n \to pe\nu$. Later, this neutrino will be called an antineutrino $\bar{\nu}$, but in the beginning we omit this distinction.

Direct observation of neutrinos is extremely difficult. The first indirect evidence for the existence of the neutrino comes from the energy balance of the decay. The mass difference between neutron and proton is 1.293 MeV. Therefore, if the neutron decay were a two-body decay, $n \to ep$, the energy of the electrons should be equal to this mass difference (the recoil energy of the proton is negligible). Experimentally, the electron energy shows a distribution typical of a three-body decay, instead of a sharp line at $m_n - m_p$. Let us investigate this distribution in detail. From (2-3.3), we have

$$d\Gamma = \frac{1}{2m_n} \, d \operatorname{Lips}(m_n^2, P_p, P_\nu, P_e)|T^2|, \tag{1.2}$$

where d Lips is given by (1-7.9),

$$d \operatorname{Lips}(m_n^2, P_p, P_\nu, P_e) = \frac{d\Omega_e \, d\Omega_\nu}{(2\pi)^5 16 m_n s_d^{\frac{1}{2}}} \, p_e p_\nu ds_d, \qquad s_d = m_p^2 + m_e^2 + 2E_e m_p . \tag{1.3}$$

It is customary to plot $(d\Gamma/dp_e)^{\frac{1}{2}}/p_e$ as a function of the electron energy E_e (the "Kurie plot"). Let us therefore calculate the differential width,

$$\frac{d\Gamma}{dp_e} = \frac{d\Gamma}{ds_d}\frac{ds_d}{dp_e} = \frac{d \operatorname{Lips}}{ds_d}\frac{p_e}{E_e}|T|^2 =$$

$$= \frac{p_e^2 p_\nu}{(2\pi)^5 \cdot 16 m_n (s_d E_e)^{\frac{1}{2}}} \int d\Omega_e \, d\Omega_\nu |T|^2. \tag{1.4}$$

In this expression, two approximations are appropriate. First, the proton recoil may be neglected. This implies that p_e and p_ν both refer to the lab system, and that $s_d^{\frac{1}{2}}$ is replaced by m_p. Experimentally, the maximum electron energy is

$$E_{\max} = m_n - m_p, \tag{1.5}$$

which shows that the neutrino mass is negligible. This allows us to write

$$E_\nu = p_\nu = E_{\max} - E_e. \tag{1.6}$$

Then (4) may be rewritten as

$$\frac{d\Gamma}{dp_e} = \frac{p_e^2(E_{\max}-E_e)^2}{(2\pi)^5 \cdot 4m_n m_p} \int d\Omega_e d\Omega_\nu \frac{|T|^2}{4E_e E_\nu}. \tag{1.7}$$

The reason for writing $d\Gamma/dp_e$ in this peculiar form is that experimentally the Kurie plot gives almost a straight line in neutron decay. Therefore, $|T|^2/4E_e E_\nu$ is roughly energy-independent. The main residual energy-dependence occurs for small p_e, and is due to the Coulomb interaction between the electron and the proton in the final state. In the non-relativistic approximation, $p_e \ll m_e$, this increases the intensity of the wave function for small electron-proton distance by a factor C_0^2 as given by (10-1.18). As a first approximation, the decay probability of the neutron will increase by the same amount. We therefore obtain the momentum dependence of Γ,

$$\begin{aligned} \frac{d\Gamma}{dp_e} &= \frac{2\pi\eta}{e^{2\pi\eta}-1} p_e^2(E_{\max}-E_e)^2 \frac{\xi}{2\pi^3}, \\ \xi &\equiv \frac{1}{(4\pi)^2} \int d\Omega_e d\Omega_\nu \frac{|T|^2}{4E_e E_\nu 4m_i m_f}. \end{aligned} \tag{1.8}$$

For the neutron, we have $\eta = -\alpha E_e/p_e$, and the first factor is well approximated by $(1-\pi\alpha E_e/p_e)^{-1}$ according to (10-1.13).

Experimentally, (8) applies not only to the neutron decay, but to a large number of nuclear beta decays. Quite generally, there are two types of beta decay. In the β^- decays, a nucleus emits an electron and an (anti) neutrino, thereby transforming into a nucleus with one more proton and one less neutron. The lightest nucleus which decays in this way is ^3H, which decays according to $^3H \to e\bar{\nu}\,^3He$. In the β^+-decays, a nucleus emits a positron and a neutrino, thereby transforming into a nucleus with one more neutron and one less proton. Neglecting the nuclei ^8B and ^9C, the β^+ decay of which leads to highly unstable nuclei, the first example of β^+-decay is

$^{10}C \to e^+ \nu^{10}B$. Clearly, the phase space factors of (8) apply to any β-decay, if E_{max} is defined as the mass difference between the parent and the daughter nucleus, generalizing (5). Similarly, η of (8) is defined as $\mp Z\alpha E_e/p_e$, where Z is the electric charge of the daughter nucleus and the plus sign applies for positron emission. With these conventions, (8) applies both to ^3H decay and to ^{10}C decay, but not e.g. to the decay $^{38}Cl \to e\bar{\nu}\,^{38}Ar$. Roughly speaking, β-decays may be classified into "allowed" and "forbidden" decays, according to whether (8) applies or not (for refinements of (8) for allowed decays, see e.g. SCHOPPER [1966], KONOPINSKI [1966]). The allowed decays have zero orbital angular momentum in the emission of the electron (positron) and neutrino.

For completeness, we mention electron capture (also called K-capture), which is an alternative to β^+ decay. The lightest nucleus decaying this way is ^7Be, $e^7Be \to \nu^7Li$. In this case, β^+-decay is impossible because E_{max} is less than m_e.

We conclude this section by calculating the total decay width Γ, by integrating (7) over the decay momentum. From (8), we introduce the so-called Fermi integral,

$$f = \int_{m_e}^{E_{max}} dE_e \frac{2\pi\eta}{e^{2\pi\eta}-1} p_e E_e (E_{max}-E_e)^2 m_e^{-5}. \tag{1.9}$$

Here we have made use of $p\,dp = E\,dE$. The factor m_e^{-5} has been included to make f dimensionless. For neutron decay, the Coulomb correction is small, and (9) becomes, for $\eta = 0$,

$$f = \frac{1}{4m_e}\left[E_{max} \log \frac{E_{max}+p_{max}}{m_e} - p_{max} - \frac{1}{3}\frac{p_{max}^3}{m_e^2}\left(1-\frac{2p_{max}^2}{5m_e^2}\right)\right]. \tag{1.10}$$

In terms of f, the total width becomes, according to (8),

$$\Gamma = \frac{m_e^5}{2\pi^3} f\xi. \tag{1.11}$$

Whereas f contains the phase space factors (apart from the factor $(4E_eE_\nu)^{-1}$) and the Coulomb effects, ξ measures the strength of the weak interactions. It is customary to define the reduced half-life or ft-value,

$$ft_0 = 2\pi^3 \frac{\ln 2}{m_e^5 \xi}, \tag{1.12}$$

where $t_0 = \ln 2/\Gamma$ is the half-life. For allowed transitions, ft values range between 10^3 and 10^6 sec. Forbidden reactions have considerably larger ft

values. Forbidden transitions to the ground state of the daughter nucleus are frequently only a small fraction of allowed transitions to some excited state of that nucleus. For example, the decay $^{22}\mathrm{Na} \to \mathrm{e}^+\nu\, ^{22}\mathrm{Ne}$ goes only in 0.06% to the ground state of $^{22}\mathrm{Ne}$. The corresponding ft value is 10^{14}.

12-2. General form of the matrix elements

In the last section, we neglected the spins of the particles. Since neutron, proton and electron have each spin-$\frac{1}{2}$, the neutrino must also have half-integer spin. The magnitude $S_\nu = \frac{1}{2}$ follows e.g. from the decay $\pi^+ \to \mathrm{e}^+\nu$. For a particle of negligible rest-mass, only the two helicity states $\lambda_\nu = \pm S_\nu$ are populated. Conservation of J_z in π-decay requires $\lambda_\mathrm{e} = \lambda_\nu$ and therefore $S_\nu = \frac{1}{2}$.

The number of invariant amplitudes for the interaction of four spin-$\frac{1}{2}$ particles (usually called a "four-fermion interaction") is $2^4 = 16$. For neutron decay, 8 amplitudes are immediately excluded by the form of the electron energy spectrum. Since ξ in (1.8) is energy-independent, the matrix element $T(\mathrm{n} \to \mathrm{pe}\bar{\nu})$ cannot contain $P_\mathrm{n} - P_\mathrm{p}$, the momentum transfer from the initial to the final nucleon. The remaining 8 amplitudes are commonly defined in the form

$$T = 2^{-\frac{1}{2}} \sum_i \bar{u}_\mathrm{p} O_i u_\mathrm{n} \bar{u}_\mathrm{e} O_i (G_i - \gamma_5 G_i') u_\nu, \tag{2.1}$$

where the index i assumes the "values" S = scalar ($O_\mathrm{S} = 1$), V = vector ($O_\mathrm{V} = \gamma_\mu$), A = axial vector ($O_\mathrm{A} = \gamma_\mu \gamma_5$) and T = tensor ($O_\mathrm{T} = \sigma_{\mu\nu}$). Summation over the indices μ and ν is understood in (1). The operators O_i have been defined in (3-6.1). Note in particular that γ_5 as given by (3-5.13) is real and positive, whereas in most textbooks it is either imaginary or negative.

Among the excluded operators we have the "anomalous magnetic moment" operator $\sigma_{\mu\nu}(P_\mathrm{n} - P_\mathrm{p})^\nu$ and the pseudoscalar operator γ_5. The latter operator would induce an energy-dependence $k_- = (2m_\mathrm{n}(E_\mathrm{p} - m_\mathrm{p}))^{\frac{1}{2}}$ into ξ. Of course, since $P_\mathrm{n} - P_\mathrm{p}$ is so small in β-decay, the upper limits on the 8 excluded amplitudes are really poor. (Nonetheless, some of these amplitudes have been identified in "forbidden" decays and in muon capture.) Similarly, the empirical fact that $G_\mathrm{S}, G_\mathrm{S}', G_\mathrm{V}, G_\mathrm{V}', G_\mathrm{A}, G_\mathrm{A}'$, and G_T, G_T' are independent of $s = (P_\mathrm{n} - P_{\bar{\nu}})^2$ and $t = (P_\mathrm{n} - P_\mathrm{p})^2$ merely indicates that the variation of s and t in β-decay is negligible except in the phase space. In the following, G_i and G_i' are called "coupling constants".

We now turn to the matrix elements of β^+-decay. For the time being, we neglect the complications of nuclear physics and assume that the "basic" process of β^+-decay is the decay of a proton, $p \to e^+ \nu n$, or electron capture $ep \to \nu n$:

$$T^{\mathscr{T}} = 2^{-\frac{1}{2}} \sum_i \bar{u}_n O_i u_p \bar{u}_\nu O_i (G_i^{\mathscr{T}} - \gamma_5 G_i'^{\mathscr{T}}) u_e . \tag{2.2}$$

The index $\mathscr{T}$ stands for "time-reversed", since reaction $ep \to \nu n$ is in fact the inverse of reaction $\nu n \to ep$. An important point about weak interactions is that the coupling constants $G_i^{\mathscr{T}}$ and $G_i'^{\mathscr{T}}$ may be expressed in terms of G_i and G_i' even if time-reversal invariance does not hold. Since the matrix T of weak interactions is so small, unitarity of $S = 1 + iT$ requires T to be Hermitean, $T = T^+ = T^{\mathscr{T}*}$. The complex conjugate of (2) is calculated by the method of section 3-6,

$$\begin{aligned}[\bar{u}_n O_i u_p \bar{u}_\nu O_i (G_i^{\mathscr{T}} - \gamma_5 G_i'^{\mathscr{T}}) u_e]^* &= \bar{u}_p \gamma_0 O_i^+ \gamma_0 u_n \bar{u}_e \gamma_0 (G_i^{\mathscr{T}*} - \gamma_5 G_i'^{\mathscr{T}*}) O_i^+ \gamma_0 u_\nu \\ &= \bar{u}_p \bar{O}_i u_n \bar{u}_e (G_i^{\mathscr{T}*} + \gamma_5 G_i'^{\mathscr{T}*}) \bar{O}_i u_\nu = \bar{u}_p O_i u_n \bar{u}_e (G_i^{\mathscr{T}*} + \gamma_5 G_i'^{\mathscr{T}*}) O_i u_\nu . \end{aligned} \tag{2.3}$$

The matrix $\bar{O}_i$ has been defined in (3-6.8). It differs from O_i by at most a sign. Since (3) is quadratic in $\bar{O}_i$, we may in fact replace $\bar{O}_i$ by O_i in (3). Finally, commuting $G_i^{\mathscr{T}*} + \gamma_5 G_i'^{\mathscr{T}*}$ with the second O_i, we get $T^{\mathscr{T}*} = T$ as given by (1) for

$$G_i^{\mathscr{T}} = G_i^*, \quad G_i'^{\mathscr{T}} = \eta_i G_i'^*, \qquad \eta_i = \begin{cases} 1 & \text{for } i = \text{V and A}, \\ -1 & \text{for } i = \text{S and T}. \end{cases} \tag{2.4}$$

If we now require time-reversal invariance in addition to $T = T^+$, we find that all G_i and G_i' must be real. The formal operation of time reversal has been explained in section 4-5. For the two-component spinors of section 3-4, this implies complex conjugation and multiplication by σ_2:

$$\mathscr{T} \chi(M) = \sigma_2 \chi^*(M). \tag{2.5}$$

The Pauli matrix σ_2 ensures that $\chi^+ P_\mu \sigma^\mu \chi$ is time-reversal invariant:

$$\begin{aligned}\mathscr{T}[\chi^+(M') P_\mu \sigma^\mu \chi(M)] &= \chi(M')_{\text{tr}} \sigma_2 P^\mu \sigma^\mu \sigma_2 \chi^*(M) \\ &= \chi(M')_{\text{tr}} P^\mu (\sigma_\mu)_{\text{tr}} \chi^*(M) = \chi^+(M) P^\mu \sigma_\mu \chi(M'). \end{aligned} \tag{2.6}$$

Here we have used the property

$$\sigma_2 \sigma^\mu \sigma_2 = (\sigma_\mu)_{\text{tr}} . \tag{2.7}$$

The index tr stands for transposed. Note the raising and lowering of μ in (6) and (7). For the Dirac spinors (3-5.12), σ_2 is replaced by the matrix

$$\Sigma_2 = \begin{pmatrix} \sigma_2 & 0 \\ 0 & \sigma_2 \end{pmatrix} = \gamma_5 \gamma_0 \gamma_2 = \gamma_5 C, \tag{2.8}$$

where C is the charge conjugation matrix (4-7.3). Now time-reversal invariance requires that the matrix $T^{\mathcal{T}}$ for the inverse reaction should be identical with the matrix T, taken between time-reversed states. To make the calculation analogous to that of the Hermiticity requirement, we apply a second time inversion to the states. Then $T^{\mathcal{T}}$, taken between time-reversed states, must be identical with the original T. The matrix elements of (2) between the time-reversed states consist of the terms

$$\begin{aligned} u_{\mathrm{n,tr}} \Sigma_2 \gamma_0 O_i \Sigma_2 u_{\mathrm{p}}^* u_{\nu,\mathrm{tr}} \Sigma_2 \gamma_0 O_i (G_i^{\mathcal{T}} - \gamma_5 G_i'^{\mathcal{T}}) \Sigma_2 u_{\mathrm{e}}^* \\ = \bar{u}_{\mathrm{p}} \gamma_0 \Sigma_2 O_{i,\mathrm{tr}} \gamma_0 \Sigma_2 u_{\mathrm{n}} \bar{u}_{\mathrm{e}} \gamma_0 \Sigma_2 (G_i^{\mathcal{T}} - \gamma_5 G_i'^{\mathcal{T}}) O_{i,\mathrm{tr}} \gamma_0 \Sigma_2 u_\nu \\ = \bar{u}_{\mathrm{p}} O_i u_{\mathrm{n}} \bar{u}_{\mathrm{e}} (G_i^{\mathcal{T}} + \gamma_5 G_i'^{\mathcal{T}}) O_i u_\nu . \end{aligned} \tag{2.9}$$

The plus sign in the last bracket comes from commutating $\gamma_0 \Sigma_2$ through the expression. By (4-7.4), we have

$$\gamma_0 \Sigma_2 O_{i,\mathrm{tr}} \gamma_0 \Sigma_2 = \gamma_0 \gamma_5 C O_{i,\mathrm{tr}} C \gamma_5 \gamma_0 = \pm O_i . \tag{2.10}$$

Again, the sign in front of O_i does not matter in (9).

The only difference between (9) and (3) is the star on $G_i^{\mathcal{T}}$ and $G_i'^{\mathcal{T}}$. Therefore time-reversal invariance requires

$$G_i^{\mathcal{T}} = G_i, \qquad G_i'^{\mathcal{T}} = \eta_i G_i', \tag{2.11}$$

analogous to (4). When this is combined with the Hermiticity requirement (4), one gets

$$G_i = G_i^*, \qquad G_i' = G_i'^*, \tag{2.12}$$

i.e. the coupling constants must be real.

Usually, the results of this section, mainly the form (1) of T and the reality condition (12), are derived from local field theory, to lowest order in the interaction Hamiltonian H. That method is less satisfactory for two reasons. Firstly, (1) is more or less postulated by appealing to "simplicity" (non-occurrence of derivative coupling). Only the pseudoscalar coupling is excluded on the basis of the argument at the beginning. Secondly and more seriously, the perturbation theory of weak interactions is internally inconsistent because the theory is "unrenormalizable". It is therefore important to realize that the analysis of β-decay is in fact independent of perturbation theory.

Finally, we introduce the static approximation for the nucleon spinors

u_n and $\bar{u}_p$ into (1). According to (3-5.16), the nucleon part of (1) reduces to

$$\bar{u}_p(M_p)O_i u_n(M_n) = \sqrt{4m_p m_n}\,\chi_0'^{+}(M_p)O_{i,\,\mathrm{bb}}\chi_0(M_n). \qquad (2.13)$$

The bb-components of 1 and γ_μ are 1 and $\delta_{\mu 0}$. Of the axial vector operator $\gamma^\mu\gamma_5$, only $\boldsymbol{\gamma}\gamma_5$ has a bb-component, which is $\boldsymbol{\sigma}$. For the tensor $\sigma_{\mu\nu}$, only space-components contribute:

$$(\sigma_{ik})_{\mathrm{bb}} = \tfrac{1}{2}(\gamma_i\gamma_k)_{\mathrm{bb}} - \tfrac{1}{2}(\gamma_k\gamma_i)_{\mathrm{bb}} = \tfrac{1}{2}(\sigma_k\sigma_i - \sigma_i\sigma_k) = -\mathrm{i}\sigma_l, \quad \text{cyclic.} \qquad (2.14)$$

With these approximations, (1) is rewritten as

$$T = \sqrt{2m_p m_n}\,\chi_0'^{+}(M_p)\chi_0(M_n)T_F + \sqrt{2m_p m_n}\,\chi_0'^{+}(M_p)\sigma_l\chi_0(M_n)T_{l,\,\mathrm{GT}}, \qquad (2.15)$$

$$T_F = \bar{u}_e[G_S - \gamma_5 G_S' + \gamma_0(G_V - \gamma_5 G_V')]u_\nu = \bar{u}_e \begin{bmatrix} G_S + G_V & -G_S' - G_V' \\ -G_S' + G_V' & G_S - G_V \end{bmatrix} u_\nu, \qquad (2.16)$$

$$T_{l,\,\mathrm{GT}} = \bar{u}_e\left[-G_A\gamma_l\gamma_5 + G_A'\gamma_l + \begin{pmatrix}\sigma_l & 0\\ 0 & \sigma_l\end{pmatrix}(G_T - \gamma_5 G_T')\right]u_\nu$$

$$= \bar{u}_e \begin{pmatrix}\sigma_l & 0\\ 0 & \sigma_l\end{pmatrix}\begin{bmatrix} G_T - G_A & G_A' - G_T' \\ -G_A' - G_T' & G_T + G_A \end{bmatrix} u_\nu. \qquad (2.17)$$

T_F and $T_{l,\,\mathrm{GT}}$ are associated with the so-called Fermi- and Gamow-Teller transitions, which will be discussed in the next section.

12-3. Determination of the coupling constants

An enormous amount of work has gone into the determination of the constants G_i and G_i'. Before 1957, the G_i' were postulated to be zero by parity conservation. After 1957, 8 complex numbers (minus a common phase) had to be determined. Finally, the possibility of lepton-non-conservation doubled the number of parameters once more. This last point will be discussed in section 5. In this section, we restrict ourselves to β-decays in which either only T_F (2.16) or only $T_{l,\,\mathrm{GT}}$ (2.17) contributes. Such decays are called pure Fermi-transitions and pure Gamow-Teller transitions, respectively. Since $\chi_0'^{+}\chi_0$ is a scalar, it contributes only to decays where initial and final nucleus have identical spins and parities. Similarly, since $\chi'^{+}_0\sigma_l\chi_0$ is a vector, it contributes only to decays where the $\mathrm{e}\bar{\nu}$ or $\mathrm{e}^+\nu$ pair carries away one unit of angular momentum. In these (Gamow-Teller) transitions, initial and final nuclei also have equal parities, but the nuclear spin may change by one unit or by zero, excluding however $0 \to 0$ transitions.

The connection between (2.15) for neutron decay and the matrix elements for nuclear β-decay is found in many textbooks (see e.g. KÄLLÉN [1964], SCHOPPER [1966], KONOPINSKI [1966], WU and MOSZKOWSKI [1966]). For our purpose, it is more elegant to treat the nuclei as elementary particles, thereby avoiding the complications of nuclear structure. To be specific, consider the β^+-decay $^{14}O \rightarrow \bar{e}\nu^{14}N$. Both nuclear states are spinless. (The nitrogen final state is not the ground state of ^{14}N, which is 1^+.) Therefore, the crossed reaction $e^{14}O \rightarrow \nu^{14}N$ (electron capture) has the spin structure of meson-nucleon scattering, which has been discussed in section 3-8. Including parity-violating terms, the matrix elements for $eO \rightarrow \nu N$ are of the form (cf. 3-9.14)

$$T = \bar{u}_\nu[G_S^* + \gamma_5 G_S'^* + \tfrac{1}{2}(P_O + P_N)\gamma(G_V^* - \gamma_5 G_V'^*)]u_e C_N, \tag{3.1}$$

where the constant C_N contains the effects of nuclear structure. In the static limit, (1) reduces to

$$\begin{aligned} T &= C_N m_N \bar{u}_\nu[G_S^* + \gamma_5 G_S'^* + \gamma_0(G_V^* - \gamma_5 G_V'^*)]u_e \\ &= C_N m_N \bar{u}_\nu \begin{bmatrix} G_S^* + G_V^* & G_S'^* - G_V'^* \\ G_S^{*\prime} + G_V'^* & G_S^* - G_V^* \end{bmatrix} u_e, \end{aligned} \tag{3.2}$$

which is T_F (2.16) for the inverse reaction, apart from the constant factor. The basic assumption is, of course, that nuclear structure effects do not change the *ratios* of the β-decay coupling constants. Fortunately, the structure of weak interactions turns out to be of such a simple type, that this assumption will be justified a posteriori. In fact, in the special case of ^{14}O decay, even the constant C_N will be calculated without detailed knowledge of nuclear structure.

The matrix in the last expression of (2) refers to the small and big components of the Dirac spinors, i.e. to the matrix Q of (3-5.14), (3-5.15). For the computation of differential cross-sections and polarizations, it is advantageous to put T into the form (3-8.1). The transformation is particularly simple since (2) is free from $\boldsymbol{\sigma}$. With $m' = m_\nu = 0$, $m = m_e$ we find, neglecting the common factor $C_N m_N$,

$$\begin{aligned} 8\pi s^{\frac{1}{2}} f_1 &= \sqrt{E_\nu(E+m)}(G_V^* + G_S^*), \\ 8\pi s^{\frac{1}{2}} f_2 &= \sqrt{E_\nu(E-m)}(G_V^* - G_S^*), \\ 8\pi s^{\frac{1}{2}} f_3 &= \sqrt{E_\nu(E-m)}(-G_V'^* + G_S'^*), \\ 8\pi s^{\frac{1}{2}} f_4 &= \sqrt{E_\nu(E+m)}(-G_V'^* - G_S'^*). \end{aligned} \tag{3.3}$$

The first conclusion we can draw from (3) is that $|T|^2/E_\nu$ is independent of E_ν. This agrees with the energy-independence of ξ (1.8). Next, we calculate the differential longitudinal polarization of the electrons (i.e. the helicity expectation value)

$$P_{e,l}(\theta) \equiv \frac{\sum_{\lambda'} (|T(E, \theta, \frac{1}{2}, \lambda')|^2 - |T(E, \theta, -\frac{1}{2}, \lambda')|^2}{\sum_{\lambda\lambda'} |T(E, \theta, \lambda, \lambda')|^2}, \tag{3.4}$$

where θ is the scattering angle between electron and neutrino. By crossing symmetry, this is π minus the opening angle between positron and neutrino in β^+ decay. By (3-8.3) and $d^{\frac{1}{2}}_{\frac{1}{2}\frac{1}{2}} = d^{\frac{1}{2}}_{-\frac{1}{2}-\frac{1}{2}} = \cos\frac{1}{2}\theta$, $d^{\frac{1}{2}}_{-\frac{1}{2}\frac{1}{2}} = -d^{\frac{1}{2}}_{\frac{1}{2}-\frac{1}{2}} = \sin\frac{1}{2}\theta$, we get

$$\begin{aligned} P_{e,l} &= \frac{2\cos^2\frac{1}{2}\theta\, \mathrm{Re}\,(f_1+f_2)(f_3^*+f_4^*) + 2\sin^2\frac{1}{2}\theta\, \mathrm{Re}\,(f_1-f_2)(f_3^*-f_4^*)}{\cos^2\frac{1}{2}\theta(|f_1+f_2|^2+|f_3+f_4|^2)+\sin^2\frac{1}{2}\theta(|f_1-f_2|^2+|f_3-f_4|^2)} \\ &= \frac{2\,\mathrm{Re}\,(f_1 f_3^* + f_2 f_4^*) + 2\cos\theta\, \mathrm{Re}\,(f_1 f_4^* + f_2 f_3^*)}{|f_1|^2+|f_2|^2+|f_3|^2+|f_4|^2+2\cos\theta\,\mathrm{Re}\,(f_1 f_2^* + f_3 f_4^*)} \\ &= \frac{-2p\,\mathrm{Re}\,(G_V G_V'^* - G_S G_S'^*) - 2(E+m)\cos\theta\,\mathrm{Re}\,(G_V G_V'^* + G_S G_S'^*)}{E(|G_V|^2+|G_S|^2+|G_V'|^2+|G_S'|^2)+2m\,\mathrm{Re}\,(G_V G_S^* + G_V' G_S'^*) + p\cos\theta(|G_V|^2+|G_V'|^2-|G_S|^2-|G_S'|^2)}. \end{aligned} \tag{3.5}$$

This formula is lengthy, but it is sufficient to determine the four complex constants G_V, G_V', G_S and G_S'. From the first expression, we note that for parity-conserving interactions, $f_3 = f_4 = 0$, the longitudinal polarization vanishes. Experimentally, in β^- decay the average of $P_{e,l}$ over $\cos\theta$ is $-p/E$, which requires

$$G_V = G_V', \qquad G_S = -G_S'. \tag{3.6}$$

This is confirmed by the fact that $\mathrm{Re}\,(G_V G_S^* + G_V' G_S'^*)$ (the "Fierz interference term") vanishes. If it were non-zero, then $\int \mathrm{d}\cos\theta |T|^2/4E_\nu E_e$ would contain a term proportional to m_e/E_e. Thus, the magnitude of the average longitudinal polarization explains the energy-independence of ξ (1.8).

The ratio $|G_V/G_S|$ is determined by the coefficient of $p\cos\theta$ in the denominator of (5). This coefficient is obtained from the distribution of the opening angle between the positron and neutrino momenta. The measurement is difficult, since the only information about the direction of the neutrino comes from the recoil of the daughter nucleus. Accurate measurements exist only for the decays of the noble gases (ALLEN *et al.* [1959]). The differential decay rate is proportional to the denominator of (5). Because of (6), we have

$$\frac{\mathrm{d}\Gamma}{\mathrm{d}E\,\mathrm{d}\cos\theta} = \text{const.}(E + pa\cos\theta), \qquad a = \frac{|G_V|^2 - |G_S|^2}{|G_V|^2 + |G_S|^2}. \tag{3.7}$$

Experimentally, $a = 1$ and therefore $G_S = 0$.

Next, we discuss decays such as $^{12}\text{B} \to \text{e}\bar{\nu}\,^{12}\text{C}$, where the initial and final nuclear states have spin 1 and 0, respectively. Decays of this type are pure Gamow-Teller transitions. In the static approximation, the matrix elements are of the form

$$T = \text{const.}\ \varepsilon(M)\bar{u}_e \left[-G_A \gamma\gamma_5 + G'_A \gamma + \begin{pmatrix} \sigma & 0 \\ 0 & \sigma \end{pmatrix} (G_T - \gamma_5 G'_T) \right] u_\nu, \tag{3.8}$$

where $\varepsilon(M)$ is the polarization vector of ^{12}B. Again, the constant factor is uninteresting for our purpose. Instead of repeating the calculation of the electron polarization, we exploit a similarity between T_F and $T_{l,\,GT}$. Namely, the square bracket of $T_{l,\,GT}$ (2.17) is obtained from the corresponding square bracket of T_F (2.16) by the replacement

$$\begin{aligned} G_S &\to G_T, & G_V &\to -G_A, \\ G'_S &\to G'_T, & G'_V &\to -G'_A. \end{aligned} \tag{3.9}$$

Of course, the factor $\varepsilon(M) \cdot \boldsymbol{\sigma}$ (which acts between two-component spinors) makes the expression more complicated. However, if the initial nucleus is unpolarized, the following simple argument applies. The electron polarization is defined by (4), provided the summations in numerator and denominator include averaging over M. Quantizing the initial nuclear spin along the z-axis, we have

$$\varepsilon(M) \cdot \boldsymbol{\sigma} = \begin{cases} \sigma_3 & \text{for } M = 0, \\ \begin{pmatrix} 0 & 2^{\frac{1}{2}} \\ 0 & 0 \end{pmatrix} & \text{for } M = -1 \text{ and } \begin{pmatrix} 0 & 0 \\ -2^{\frac{1}{2}} & 0 \end{pmatrix} \text{ for } M = 1. \end{cases} \tag{3.10}$$

Therefore, expressions of the type $\frac{1}{3}\sum_{M\lambda'} |\chi'^{+}(\lambda')\varepsilon(M)\chi(\lambda)|^2$ will lead to (5) in $\frac{1}{3}$ of the cases (corresponding to $M = 0$), and to (5) with $\cos^2 \frac{1}{2}\theta$ and $\sin^2 \frac{1}{2}\theta$ exchanged, in $\frac{2}{3}$ of the cases. In the final formula, this affects only the coefficient of $\cos\theta$, which is multiplied by $-\frac{1}{3}$:

$$P_{e,l} = \frac{-2p\,\mathrm{Re}\,(G_A G_A'^* - G_T G_T'^*) + \frac{2}{3}(E+m)\cos\theta\,\mathrm{Re}\,(G_A G_A'^* + G_T G_T'^*)}{E(|G_A|^2+|G_T|^2+|G_A'|^2+|G_T'|^2) - 2m\,\mathrm{Re}\,(G_A G_T^* + G_A' G_T'^*) - \frac{1}{3}p\cos\theta(|G_A|^2+|G_A'|^2-|G_T|^2-|G_T'|^2)}. \tag{3.11}$$

Experimentally, the polarization (averaged over $\cos\theta$) is $-p/E$ as in Fermi transitions, and the coefficient a of (7) is $-\frac{1}{3}$. This term implies

$$G_A = G_A', \qquad G_T = G_T' = 0, \tag{3.12}$$

in complete analogy with the Fermi transitions. Taken together, the electron polarizations and differential decay rates in Fermi and Gamow-Teller transitions show that the matrix element (2.1) for the basic neutron decay is of the simple form

$$T(n \to \mathrm{pe}\bar{\nu}) = 2^{-\frac{1}{2}}\bar{u}_p\gamma_\mu(G_V - G_A\gamma_5)u_n\bar{u}_e\gamma^\mu(1-\gamma_5)u_\nu(-P_{\bar{\nu}}). \tag{3.13}$$

The minus sign in front of G_A comes from writing on the lepton side $-\gamma_\mu(1-\gamma_5)$ instead of $\gamma_\mu\gamma_5(1-\gamma_5)$.

So far, we have only discussed electron polarization. To obtain the positron polarization in the ^{14}O decay, we need the crossed version of (5). The helicity does not change under crossing, and replacing $(E_\nu(E\pm m))^{\frac{1}{2}}$ by $(E_\nu(-E\pm m))^{\frac{1}{2}} = \mathrm{i}(E_\nu(E\mp m))^{\frac{1}{2}}$ in (3) affects only the terms proportional to m in (5). It thus appears that also the positron should have average polarization $-p/E$, which however is of the wrong sign. The error comes from the relative signs of the square roots. To eliminate it, we go back to the first form of (3-5.15), where only one square root appears as a common factor. Inserting $Q = \gamma_\mu(1-\gamma_5)$, we get

$$\bar{u}_\nu\gamma_\mu(1-\gamma_5)u_e = \sqrt{(E+m)(E_\nu+m_\nu)}\,\chi_0'^+(M')\left(1-\frac{\boldsymbol{\sigma}\cdot\boldsymbol{p}_\nu}{E_\nu+m_\nu}\right)\sigma^\mu\left(1-\frac{\boldsymbol{\sigma}\cdot\boldsymbol{p}}{E+m}\right)\chi_0(M). \tag{3.14}$$

Here we have included a small neutrino mass m_ν. Note also the raising of the index μ. For helicity states, (14) becomes

$$\bar{u}_\nu\gamma_\mu(1-\gamma_5)u_e = \sqrt{(E+m)(E_\nu+m_\nu)}\left(1-\frac{2\lambda' p_\nu}{E_\nu+m_\nu}\right)\left(1-\frac{2\lambda p}{E+m}\right)\chi_0'^+(\lambda')\sigma^\mu\chi_0(\lambda)$$
$$= 2\sqrt{(E_\nu-2\lambda' p_\nu)(E-2\lambda p)}\,\chi_0'^+(\lambda')\sigma^\mu\chi_0(\lambda). \tag{3.15}$$

The last expression follows from (3-4.8). For a positron in the final state, we make the replacements $\boldsymbol{p}\to-\boldsymbol{p}$, $E\to -E$, $M\to -M$ in (14). Clearly, the helicity is not changed by this replacement, since $\boldsymbol{\sigma} \cdot (-\boldsymbol{p})\chi_0(-M)$ has the same eigenvalue $2Mp$ as $\boldsymbol{\sigma} \cdot \boldsymbol{p}\chi_0(M)$. Thus the matrix element for $\mathrm{p} \to \mathrm{e}^+ \nu \mathrm{n}$ is

$$\bar{u}_\nu \gamma_\mu (1-\gamma_5) u_e(-P, \lambda) = 2\sqrt{(E_\nu - 2\lambda' p_\nu)(-E-2\lambda p)}\chi_0'^+(\lambda')\sigma^\mu \chi_0(\lambda)$$
$$= 2\mathrm{i}\sqrt{(E_\nu - 2\lambda' p_\nu)(E+2\lambda p)}\chi_0'^+(\lambda')\sigma^\mu \chi_0(\lambda). \quad (3.16)$$

Apart from the uninteresting factor i, the square root is the same as (15) for $p = -p_{\bar{e}}$ or $\lambda = -\lambda_{\bar{e}}$. Therefore, at the same energy E, the longitudinal polarizations of electrons and positrons are opposite. Note, however, that the positron spinor $\chi_0(\lambda) = \chi_0(-M)$ is still quantized along the electron momentum, so that $\chi_0'^+(\lambda')\chi_0(\lambda) = \delta_{\lambda'\lambda}$ when neutrino and positron have antiparallel momenta.

Exactly the same argument applies to the neutrino. In the limit $m_\nu \to 0$, only neutrinos of negative helicity and antineutrinos of positive helicity are produced in β-decay. We shall return to this point later.

Finally, we calculate the parameter ξ defined in (1.8). Inserting $G_S = G_S' = 0$, $G_V = G_V'$ into (3.3), we get

$$\xi = \frac{1}{(4\pi)^2} \sum_{\lambda\lambda'} \int \mathrm{d}\Omega_e \mathrm{d}\Omega_\nu \frac{|T|^2}{16 E_e E_\nu m_N^2} = (8\pi s^{\frac{1}{2}})^2 \frac{|f_1|^2 + |f_2|^2}{4 E_e E_\nu m_N^2} = \tfrac{1}{2} C_N^2 |G_V|^2. \quad (3.17)$$

The constant C_N will be given in section 12-7. Once it is known, $|G_V|^2$ may be calculated from the decay rate of ^{14}O.

12-4. Decay of polarized neutrons

To measure the phase between G_V and G_A, one needs a decay in which Fermi- and Gamow-Teller matrix elements interfere. The simplest example is the neutron decay itself. Here, the phase between G_V and G_A has been determined from the electron angular distribution relative to the neutron's polarization (Burgy, Krohn, Novey, Ringo and Telegdi [1958]). To calculate this distribution, we choose our coordinate system such that the neutron's polarization vector points along the z-axis. Then the electron distribution is given by

$$\frac{\mathrm{d}\Gamma}{\mathrm{d}p_e \mathrm{d}\cos\vartheta} = C \sum_M \rho_M \int \mathrm{d}\Omega_\nu \sum_{M'\lambda\lambda'} |T(n \to e\bar{\nu}p)|^2. \quad (4.1)$$

The constant C still depends on E; by (1.7), we have

$$C = \frac{p^2(E_{\max}-E)^2}{(2\pi)^4 \cdot 16 m_p m_n E E_{\bar{\nu}}}. \tag{4.2}$$

The sum $\rho_{\frac{1}{2}}+\rho_{-\frac{1}{2}}$ is 1, while the difference is the degree of polarization, P. From (3.13), we get in the static approximation

$$T = \sqrt{2m_p m_n} \cdot 2\sqrt{-E_{\bar{\nu}}-2\lambda' p_{\bar{\nu}}}\, \sqrt{E-2\lambda p}\, \chi_0'^{+}(\lambda)$$
$$\times [G_V \chi_0'^{+}(M')\chi_0(M) - G_A \chi_0'^{+}(M')\boldsymbol{\sigma}\chi_0(M)\boldsymbol{\sigma}]\chi_0(\lambda'). \tag{4.3}$$

Here we have inserted (3.15) with electron and neutrino spinors interchanged, and with E_ν replaced by $-E_{\bar{\nu}}$. If both proton and neutron spin states are quantized along the z-axis, the square bracket of (3) becomes

$$\delta_{MM'}(G_V - 2MG_A\sigma_z) - \delta_{M,-M'}\, G_A(\sigma_x + 2\mathrm{i}M\sigma_y), \tag{4.4}$$

where the σ-matrices act on the neutrino helicity spinor $\chi_0(\lambda')$. Actually, because of $p_{\bar{\nu}} = E_{\bar{\nu}}$, only $\lambda' = \frac{1}{2}$ contributes, and (3) becomes

$$T = 4\mathrm{i}\sqrt{m_p m_n}\sqrt{E_{\bar{\nu}}}\sqrt{E-2\lambda p}\, \chi_0'^{+}(\lambda)$$
$$\times \left[\delta_{MM'}\begin{pmatrix}(G_V-2MG_A)\cos\frac{1}{2}\vartheta_\nu \\ (G_V+2MG_A)\sin\frac{1}{2}\vartheta_\nu \mathrm{e}^{\mathrm{i}\varphi_\nu}\end{pmatrix} - G_A\delta_{M,-M'}\begin{pmatrix}(1+2M)\sin\frac{1}{2}\vartheta_\nu \mathrm{e}^{\mathrm{i}\varphi_\nu} \\ (1-2M)\cos\frac{1}{2}\vartheta_\nu\end{pmatrix}\right]. \tag{4.5}$$

(Strictly speaking, the antineutrino is emitted with angles $\pi-\vartheta_\nu$ and $\varphi_\nu+\pi$.) In the absolute square (1), the two column vectors of (5) do not interfere, since the first contributes only for $M = M'$ and the second only for $M = -M'$. After integration over Ω_ν, the two components of each column vector do not interfere either and we may replace

$$\int \mathrm{d}\Omega_\nu \cos^2\tfrac{1}{2}\vartheta_\nu = \int \mathrm{d}\Omega_\nu \sin^2\tfrac{1}{2}\vartheta_\nu = 2\pi. \tag{4.6}$$

Therefore, the electron distribution (1) has the following form:

$$\frac{\mathrm{d}\Gamma}{\mathrm{d}p_e \mathrm{d}\cos\vartheta} = C \cdot 16 m_p m_n E_{\bar{\nu}} \sum_\lambda (E-2\lambda p)\cdot 2\pi A(\lambda), \tag{4.7}$$

$$A(\lambda) = d^2_{\frac{1}{2}\lambda}\sum_M \rho_M[|G_V-2MG_A|^2+|G_A|^2(1+2M)^2]$$
$$+ d^2_{-\frac{1}{2}\lambda}\sum_M \rho_M[|G_V+2MG_A|^2+|G_A|^2(1-2M)^2]$$
$$= d^2_{\frac{1}{2}\lambda}[|G_V|^2+3|G_A|^2+2P\,\mathrm{Re}\,(G_A-G_V)G_A^*]$$
$$+ d^2_{-\frac{1}{2}\lambda}[|G_V|^2+3|G_A|^2-2P\,\mathrm{Re}\,(G_A-G_V)G_A^*]$$
$$= |G_V|^2+3|G_A|^2+2\lambda\cos\vartheta\cdot 2P\,\mathrm{Re}\,(G_A-G_V)G_A^*. \tag{4.8}$$

Remember that $P = \rho_{\frac{1}{2}} - \rho_{-\frac{1}{2}}$ is the degree of neutron polarization. Finally, inserting (8) into (7), we find the following electron distribution with respect to the neutron polarization direction:

$$\frac{\mathrm{d}\Gamma}{\mathrm{d}p_e \mathrm{d}\cos\vartheta} = C \cdot 16 m_p m_n E_{\bar{\nu}} E_e \cdot 4\pi$$

$$\times \left[|G_V|^2 + 3|G_A|^2 - \frac{p_e}{E_e} \cos\vartheta \cdot 2P \operatorname{Re}(G_A - G_V) G_A^* \right]. \quad (4.9)$$

From this relation, the phase between G_A and G_V may be determined, once the absolute values of G_V and G_A are known. G_V may be determined e.g. from the decay of ^{14}O:

$$G_V = (1.415 \pm 0.0002) \times 10^{-49} \text{erg cm}^3 = 1.150 \frac{10^{-5}}{\text{GeV}^2} = 3.002 \frac{10^{-12}}{m_e^2}. \quad (4.10)$$

(We have erg cm^3 = $0.8125 \times 10^{38}/\text{MeV}^2$ by 1-1.1 and 1-1.6.) G_A may be determined from the neutron decay rate. Inserting (2) into (9), we obtain

$$\Gamma = \frac{m_e^5}{2\pi^3} f[|G_V|^2 + 3|G_A|^2], \quad (4.11)$$

where the Fermi integral f is defined by (1.10). A decay rate of 6.5×10^{-19} eV gives

$$G_A = (1.18 \pm 0.02) G_V. \quad (4.12)$$

Then the relative phase between G_V and G_A, as measured by (9), turns out to be 0°, as anticipated by the notation in (12). However, the uncertainty in the phase is rather large.

In the literature using imaginary or negative γ_5, our G_A is called $-G_A$, which is unfortunate in view of the particularly simple result (12). Inserting (10) and (12) into (3.13), we obtain the final form of the β-decay interaction,

$$T(n \to \mathrm{p}e\bar{\nu}) = 2^{-\frac{1}{2}} G_V \bar{u}_p \gamma_\mu (1 - 1.18\gamma_5) u_n \bar{u}_e \gamma^\mu (1 - \gamma_5) u_\nu. \quad (4.13)$$

This formula is surprisingly simple. Approximating (1.18) by (1), we see that both the lepton and the nucleon spinors are multiplied by $1 - \gamma_5$. In the high-energy representation (3-5.3), $1 - \gamma_5$ eliminates the χ-components of u (see 3-5.11). For this reason, the β-decay interaction is said to contain "maximum" parity violation.

12-5. Lepton number conservation

In the previous sections, we have distinguished between the antineutrino in β^- decay and the neutrino in β^+ decay. This allows us to define a new invariance principle, the conservation of lepton number. We assign lepton number $+1$ to the electron and neutrino and lepton number -1 to the positron and antineutrino, in which case the total lepton number is conserved in any process.

Actually, the new invariance principle has few consequences for the theory of β-decay. Suppose for example that the neutrino is its own antiparticle ("Majorana" neutrino). Then reactions such as $\bar{\nu}\,{}^{37}\mathrm{Cl} \to {}^{37}\mathrm{Ar}\,\mathrm{e}$, in which the lepton number changes by two units, should be possible in principle. (A convenient source for antineutrinos is a nuclear reactor.) However, such processes are forbidden by the complete polarization of neutrinos, which is $+1$ in β^- decay and -1 in β^+ decay. Since the above reaction is a crossed version of the β^+ decay ${}^{37}\mathrm{Ar} \to {}^{37}\mathrm{Cl}\,\mathrm{e}^+\nu$, it requires neutrinos or antineutrinos of negative polarization. Thus, only for $G_\mathrm{V} \neq G'_\mathrm{V}$ or $G_\mathrm{A} \neq G'_\mathrm{A}$ may one hope to detect this reaction. The situation would have been better if the neutrino had a large mass, of the order of the electron mass. Then the neutrino polarization would be only p_ν/E_ν, and the process could occur with a small probability even for $G_\mathrm{V} = G'_\mathrm{V}$, $G_\mathrm{A} = G'_\mathrm{A}$, if lepton number conservation does not hold. The same argument applies to neutrinoless double β-decay, e.g. ${}^{48}\mathrm{Ca} \to \mathrm{ee}{}^{48}\mathrm{Ti}$. (The single β-decay ${}^{48}\mathrm{Ca} \to {}^{48}\mathrm{Sc}\,\mathrm{e}\bar{\nu}$ is forbidden by energy-conservation.) So far, neutrinoless double β-decay has not been found. The same process containing two neutrinos, ${}^{48}\mathrm{Ca} \to \mathrm{ee}\bar{\nu}\bar{\nu}{}^{48}\mathrm{Ti}$, is of course always possible, but it has a smaller probability.

Next, one could imagine that neutrinos and antineutrinos are different particles, but that both are produced in β-decay. To account for this possibility, we replace u_ν in (2.1) by

$$u'_\nu = \alpha u_\nu + \beta u_{\nu,\mathrm{c}}, \qquad \alpha^2 + \beta^2 = 1, \tag{5.1}$$

where u_c is the charge conjugate spinor (4-7.3), and α and β are real numbers (TOUSCHEK [1957], PAULI [1957]). There is no point in taking α or β complex, since phases between amplitudes referring to different particles cannot be measured. On the other hand, each of the eight matrix elements S, S′, V, V′, A, A′, T, T′ could have a different α, so that in general, (1) doubles the number of coupling constants. However, it is not difficult to see that the results of section 3, namely $G_\mathrm{S} = G'_\mathrm{S} = G_\mathrm{T} = G'_\mathrm{T} = 0$, $G_\mathrm{A} = G'_\mathrm{A}$, $G_\mathrm{V} = G'_\mathrm{V}$, remain true if u_ν is replaced by (1). To find possible deviations from lepton number conservation, one must look at interference between G_A and G_V, e.g. in the decay of polarized neutrons. Instead of (3.13), we now have

$$T = 2^{-\frac{1}{2}} G_V \bar{u}_p \gamma_\mu u_n \bar{u}_e \gamma^\mu (1-\gamma_5)(\alpha_V u_\nu + \beta_V u_{\nu,c}) - 2^{-\frac{1}{2}} G_A \bar{u}_p \gamma^\mu \gamma_5 u_n \bar{u}_e \gamma^\mu (1-\gamma_5)(\alpha_A u_\nu + \beta_A u_{\nu,c}). \quad (5.2)$$

Here too, no effect arises for $\alpha_V = \alpha_A$. In fact, if the replacement (1) is universal, i.e. independent of the interaction, it merely redefines neutrinos and antineutrinos. Therefore, we may put $\alpha_V = 1$, $\beta_V = 0$, without loss of generality. The only remaining parameter is α_A, which may be determined from the electron distribution (4.9). If $u_\nu(-P_\nu)$ and $u_{\nu,c}(-P_\nu)$ really describe the production of two different particles, then β_A cannot interfere with the vector coupling, and the interference term $2P \operatorname{Re} G_V G_A^*$ in (4.9) is reduced by a factor α_A. Thus, if one had found $\operatorname{Re} G_V G_A^* < |G_V||G_A|$, this could have been due to lepton non-conservation, and not only to violation of time-reversal invariance. Fortunately, experiment gives $\operatorname{Re} G_V G_A^* = |G_V||G_A|$ and therefore both time-reversal invariance and lepton conservation appear to be valid. Remember, however, that the possibility $u_\nu = u_{\nu,c}$ (Majorana neutrino) has not been excluded.

Lepton number conservation becomes much more interesting when the interactions of muons are included. Muons are produced in the decays of charged pions and of kaons (see table 4-1); they decay into electrons and neutrinos. From the absence of the decay $\mu \to e\gamma$, we conclude that muons and electrons of equal charges have opposite lepton number, i.e. μ^+ is a lepton and μ^- is an antilepton (KONOPINSKI and MAHMOUD [1953]). Consequently, we shall write $\mu \to \bar{e}\nu\nu$ for the decay of the muon (μ^+) and $\bar{\mu} \to e\bar{\nu}\bar{\nu}$ for the decay of the antimuon (μ^-). From the energy spectrum, polarization and angular distribution of positrons from the decay of μ^+, one finds that μ-decay is accurately described by

$$T(\mu^+ \to \bar{e}\nu\nu) = 2^{-\frac{1}{2}} G_\mu \bar{u}_\nu \gamma^\sigma (1+\gamma_5) u_\mu \bar{u}_\nu \gamma^\sigma (1-\gamma_5) u_e . \quad (5.3)$$

The value of G_μ has been given in (4-1.2). Coulomb corrections have been included. One may also compute "radiative corrections", getting (BERMAN [1958], KINOSHITA and SIRLIN [1959])

$$(G_\mu)_{\text{corrected}} = G_\mu \left[1 + \frac{\alpha}{4\pi}\left(\pi^2 - \tfrac{25}{4}\right)\right] = 1.166 \times 10^{-5}/\text{GeV}^2, \quad (5.4)$$

which is approximately 2% larger than G_V (4.10). Here we shall not discuss the theory of μ-decay, since it has little to do with the interactions of hadrons. The interaction (3) is similar to that of β^+-decay $p \to n\bar{e}\nu$, the main difference being the factor $(1+\gamma_5)$ in front of the muon spinor, as compared to the factor (1-1.18 γ_5) in front of the proton spinor.

An immediate consequence of the factors $1+\gamma_5$ and $1-\gamma_5$ in (3) is that the two neutrinos have opposite polarizations. For many years, this was taken as a confirmation of the ill-fated "two-component neutrino" theory of LEE and YANG [1957] (see however KAWAKAMI [1957]). In this theory, it was postulated that neutrinos of positive helicity (and antineutrinos of negative helicity) do not exist in nature. Such a postulate does not violate Lorentz invariance, if the neutrino mass is zero. In the two-component theory, the neutrino associated with the factor $(1+\gamma_5)$ in (3) was automatically interpreted as an antineutrino, in which case μ^+ had to be taken as an antilepton to maintain lepton conservation. Since this excluded the Konopinski-Mahmoud scheme, the absence of the decay $\mu \to \gamma e$ was then a puzzle. An even greater puzzle was the discovery (DANBY *et al.* [1962]), that neutrinos from the decays $\pi \to \mu\bar{\nu}$ and $\bar{\pi} \to \bar{\mu}\nu$ do not produce electrons ($\nu n \to ep$) or positrons ($\bar{\nu}p \to \bar{e}n$) when sent upon a heavy target. Instead, they only produce muons ($\nu p \to \mu n$ and $\bar{\nu}n \to \bar{\mu}p$). We shall discuss these reactions in connection with π-decay. They show that the neutrino of negative polarization cannot be identical to the antineutrino of β^--decay. Of course, one may still call the negative helicity neutrino an antineutrino, in which case one must introduce an additional quantum number, the "muonic charge", to explain why this neutrino does not interact in β-interactions. In such a formalism, the mass degeneracy of the two types of neutrinos is accidental.

Although the Konopinski-Mahmoud scheme was rehabilitated in 1962 by many authors (ISO [1962], BLUDMAN [1963], KABIR [1963], SOKOLOV [1963]), it is seldom used in the literature. A direct exclusion of the two-component neutrino theory would follow from the observation of neutrinoless muon capture, $\mu^- pp \to e^+ nn$, which could occur in heavy nuclei. However, if the antineutrino emitted in the ordinary muon capture process $\mu^- p \to \bar{\nu}n$ is completely forward-polarized, the reaction is ruled out by the polarization properties of β-interactions.

The two-component neutrino theory can also be formulated for a finite neutrino mass, in which case it merely postulates a factor $(1-\gamma_5)$ in front of the neutrino spinor. The average neutrino polarization is $-p_\nu/E_\nu < 1$. However, the original attractive feature is then lost, namely the one-dimensional irreducible representation of the Lorentz-group, for a particle of nonzero spin.

The experimental upper limit on m_ν is 2×10^{-4} MeV (see table 12-5). If we remember that the electron mass is only 5×10^{-4} of the proton mass, it is not surprising that a particle which has only weak interactions has a mass smaller than 4×10^{-4} electron masses.

Finally, it is amusing to note that the mean life of the neutrino is not known, simply because its mass is not known (cf. the discussion following 2-1.7). On the other hand, no particles are known into which neutrinos could decay.

TABLE 12-5

Masses, widths and weak interactions of leptons

lepton	anti-lepton	m [MeV] m^2 [MeV^2]	Γ^{-1}[sec] Γ [eV]	weak interaction average polarization
e^-	e^+	0.511006 0.261127	stable	$\bar{u}_\nu\gamma_\sigma(1-\gamma_5)u_e$ $-p/E$
μ^+	μ^-	105.659 11163.8	2.200×10^{-6} 2.992×10^{-10}	$\bar{u}_\nu\gamma_\sigma(1+\gamma_5)u_\mu$ $+p/E$
ν	$\bar{\nu}$	$< 2\times 10^{-4}$	no information	∓ 1

12-6. Decays of charged pions

Charged pions decay according to $\pi^+ \to \mu^+\bar{\nu}$ and $\pi^- \to \mu^-\nu$; the corresponding electron and positron decays $\pi^- \to e\bar{\nu}$ and $\pi^+ \to e^+\nu$ are $(1.24\pm 0.03)\times 10^{-4}$ times smaller. This might seem surprising since the phase space for $\pi \to \mu\bar{\nu}$ is the smaller one. From (2-3.4), we have

$$\Gamma = \frac{p}{4m_\pi^2}\frac{1}{2\pi}\sum_{\lambda\lambda'}|T|^2, \qquad p = \frac{1}{2m_\pi}(m_\pi^2 - m^2), \tag{6.1}$$

where $m = m_\mu$ or m_e is the lepton mass. The smallness of $\Gamma(\pi \to e\bar{\nu})/\Gamma(\pi \to \mu\bar{\nu})$ is a consequence of the principle of *muon-electron universality.* This empirical rule says that the weak interactions of electrons and muons are of the vector-exchange type,

$$B^\mu_{(l\nu)} = \bar{u}_l(P, \lambda)\gamma^\mu(1\pm\gamma_5)u_\nu(P'\lambda'), \tag{6.2}$$

where P and λ are the 4-momentum and helicity of the charged lepton ($l = \mu^+$ or e^-), and P' is the 4-momentum of the incoming neutrino, or minus the 4-momentum of the outgoing antineutrino. The factor $1+\gamma_5$

appears for muons, while $1-\gamma_5$ appears for electrons. The "coupling constant" is the same for electrons and muons. This rule was proposed by PUPPI [1948] on the basis of a comparison between β-decay, muon decay and muon capture. In particular, the muon decay (5.3) is of the form $2^{-\frac{1}{2}}G_\mu B^\sigma_{(e\nu)} g_{\sigma\tau} B^\tau_{(\mu\nu)}$, apart from an exchange of in- and outgoing particles, and muon capture $\mu^- p \to n\bar{\nu}$ is of the form $B^\lambda_{(\mu\nu)} g_{\lambda\nu} B^\nu_{(pn)}$,

$$B^\nu_{(pn)} = 2^{-\frac{1}{2}}\bar{u}_n \gamma^\nu (G_V - G_A\gamma_5) u_p \,. \tag{6.3}$$

The coupling constants G_V and G_A are roughly the same as (4.10) and (4.12).

For the pion decays, muon-electron universality requires the matrix element to be of the form

$$T(\pi \to l\bar{\nu}) = g_\pi P_\pi \cdot B_{(l\nu)} \,. \tag{6.4}$$

where P_π, the pion 4-momentum, is the only available 4-momentum on the hadron side, and g_π is another coupling constant. We first calculate (4) for the decay $\pi^+ \to e^+\nu$. The corresponding B^μ has been calculated in (3.16). In the pion rest frame, we have $p_\nu = p$, $P_\pi = (m_\pi, 0, 0, 0)$, and therefore

$$T(\lambda, \lambda' = -\tfrac{1}{2}) = 2ig_\pi \sqrt{2p(E+2\lambda p)}\, m_\pi \chi_0'^{+}(\lambda' = -\tfrac{1}{2})\chi_0(\lambda). \tag{6.5}$$

The amplitude for $\lambda' = \frac{1}{2}$ vanishes, i.e. the neutrino has negative helicity. Moreover, since the momenta of neutrino and positron are antiparallel, (5) simplifies to (cf. the remark after 3.16)

$$T(\lambda, \lambda') = 2ig_\pi \sqrt{2p(E-p)}\, m_\pi \delta_{-\frac{1}{2},\lambda'}\delta_{\lambda\lambda'} = 2ig_\pi m \sqrt{m_\pi^2 - m^2}\, \delta_{-\frac{1}{2},\lambda'}\delta_{\lambda\lambda'} \,. \tag{6.6}$$

Inserting this into (1), we find the decay rate for $\pi^+ \to e^+\nu$,

$$\Gamma = \frac{g_\pi^2}{4\pi}\frac{m^2}{m_\pi^3}(m_\pi^2 - m^2)^2 . \tag{6.7}$$

Actually, (6) and (7) are also valid for decay into muons, $\pi^+ \to \mu^+\bar{\nu}$. We know already that the antineutrino associated with the muon has negative helicity, i.e. the same helicity as the electron-neutrino. Therefore, the muon must also have negative helicity, which goes with the factor $(E-p)^{\frac{1}{2}}$. Thus the fraction of $\pi \to e\bar{\nu}$ decay is given by (7) for $m = m_e$, divided by (7) for $m = m_\mu$:

$$\frac{\Gamma(\pi^+ \to e^+\nu)}{\Gamma(\pi^+ \to \mu^+\bar{\nu})} = \frac{m_e^2}{m_\mu^2}\left(\frac{m_\pi^2 - m_e^2}{m_\pi^2 - m_\mu^2}\right)^2 \approx 1.28 \times 10^{-4}, \tag{6.8}$$

in agreement with experiment. This result is a very accurate test of the factor $1-\gamma_5$ for the weak interaction of electrons. Suppose for example that $1+\gamma_5$ occurred with an amplitude of 10^{-3}, i.e. with a probability of 10^{-6}. This probability would be multiplied by $E+p = m_\pi$ instead of $E-p = m_e^2/m_\pi$, i.e. it would gain a factor $(m_\pi/m_e)^2 \approx 75\,000$ relative to (7). For the muon, of course, the test is less sensitive.

The specific form (2) of electron-muon universality implies that in the limit of zero neutrino mass, the muon interaction may be rewritten in the form of the two-component theory, with $1-\gamma_5$ and lepton number $+1$ for the negative muon. This is useful because it allows one to treat the muon as a heavy electron of the same charge. Only when secondary interaction of their neutrinos are observed do significant differences appear. Consider for example the nuclear interactions of neutrinos from the decays $\pi^- \to \bar{\mu}\nu$. The reaction $\nu n \to pe$ is forbidden by the polarization $+1$ of the neutrino, while $\nu p \to ne^+$ is forbidden by lepton conservation. In the two-component theory, this neutrino is called an antineutrino, in which case $\bar{\nu} n \to pe$ is forbidden both by polarization and by lepton conservation, whereas $\bar{\nu} p \to ne^+$ is not forbidden at all. Experimentally, both reactions are absent for neutrinos from π-decay and also from K-decay, whereas the reactions $\nu p \to n\mu^+$ and $\bar{\nu} n \to p\mu^-$ do occur.

Two more decay modes of charged pions have been observed, namely $\pi \to \mu\bar{\nu}\gamma$ and $\pi \to \pi^0\bar{e}\nu$. We shall not discuss the first of these, which differs from the ordinary decay $\pi \to \mu\bar{\nu}$ only by an electromagnetic interaction. The second decay, $\pi \to \pi^0\bar{e}\nu$, may be called the β^+-decay of the pion. Its general spin structure is identical with (3.1) for the decay of ^{14}O. Further, the coupling constant and the constants of nuclear structure C_N are identical to those of ^{14}O-decay. Consequently, $\pi \to \pi^0\bar{e}\nu$ and $^{14}\text{O} \to {}^{14}\text{N}\bar{e}\nu$ have identical *ft*-values (1.12). The reason for this surprising equality is given in the next section. Insertion of ξ from ^{14}O-decay into (1.11) gives a partial mean life of 2.4 sec, which corresponds to a fraction

$$\frac{\Gamma(\pi \to \pi^0\bar{e}\nu)}{\Gamma(\pi \to \mu\bar{\nu})} = \frac{2.60 \times 10^{-8}}{2.4} \approx 1.1 \times 10^{-8}, \tag{6.9}$$

in good agreement with experiment (see table 4-1).

12-7. Conserved vector current

The electron-muon universality (6.2) allows one to write the weak interaction between hadrons and lepton pairs in a form analogous to the Born term of vector exchange (6-4.6)

$$T(l\nu, \text{hadrons}) = g_l B^{\mu}_{(l\nu)} \frac{-g_{\mu\nu} + \Delta_\mu \Delta_\nu / m_W^2}{m_W^2 - t} g_h B^{\nu}(\text{hadrons}), \tag{7.1}$$

provided the mass m_W of the exchanged "vector boson" W is considerably larger than the momentum transfer from the hadrons to the leptons. In this case, the vector propagator is approximately $-g_{\mu\nu}/m_W^2$, and the leptonic coupling constant g_l is given by the dimensionless constant

$$g_l = m_W \sqrt{2^{-\frac{1}{2}} G_\mu}, \tag{7.2}$$

by the form (5.3) of μ-decay. The vector part of the hadronic coupling constant is determined by the form (6.3) of β-decay,

$$g_h = -m_W G_V / \sqrt{2^{\frac{1}{2}} G_\mu} \approx -g_l, \tag{7.3}$$

and so on. So far, no charged vector bosons $W^{\pm}$ decaying into lepton pairs with a coupling constant (2) have been observed. Also, the relatively precise measurements of the electron spectrum in μ-decay (characterized by the so-called Michel parameter ρ) put a lower limit on m_W, of the order of 1 GeV. Nevertheless, (1) is convenient for the formulation of a certain analogy between weak and electromagnetic interactions. We thus denote by W^+ the pairs $\mu^+\bar{\nu}$ and $e^+\nu$, and by W^- the pairs $\mu^-\nu$ and $e\bar{\nu}$.

The analogy is known as the "conserved vector current hypothesis", in short CVC. It is based on the observation (GERSTEIN and ZELDOWITCH [1955], FEYNMAN and GELL-MANN [1958]) that the hadronic vector coupling constant g_h (3) has approximately the same value as the leptonic coupling constant g_l. In electromagnetic interactions, the proton has the same coupling constant as the muon and positron. This suggests that gauge invariance (section 10-4) and the principle of minimal interaction (section 10-5) apply not only to the electromagnetic, but also to the vector part of the weak interactions of hadrons. By gauge invariance, we mean

$$\Delta_\nu B_V^\nu(\text{hadrons}) = 0, \tag{7.4}$$

where B_V is the vector part of the hadron-W coupling, and Δ is the 4-momentum of W. For the axial vector part, gauge invariance is excluded by the decay of the pion (6.4), with $\Delta = P_\pi$. In addition, for the vector part, (4) is satisfied only if the proton-neutron mass difference is neglected. From (4-8.8), we remember that the vector coupling is gauge invariant only in the equal-mass case. In the following, we neglect mass differences within isospin multiplets. Then the vector coupling is allowed in $n \to pe\bar{\nu}$ but forbidden in $\Sigma \to \Lambda e\bar{\nu}$. (Hypercharge changing decays such as $\Lambda \to e\bar{\nu}p$ are excluded for the time being.)

As with the electric charge, gauge invariance implies conservation of the total "weak vector charge" g_h. For example, the two Born terms of the reaction $\pi^- n \to W^- n$ are shown in fig. 12-7.1. In the first term, W^- is emitted by the neutron, with coupling constant g_h. In the second term, W^- is emitted by the pion. The corresponding coupling constant must be $2^{\frac{1}{2}} g_h$, if the sum of the two Born terms is to be gauge invariant. The situation is analogous to photoproduction, where the corresponding Born terms are (10-8.2) and (10-8.1). In the terminology of local field theory, gauge invariance corresponds to a conserved vector current.

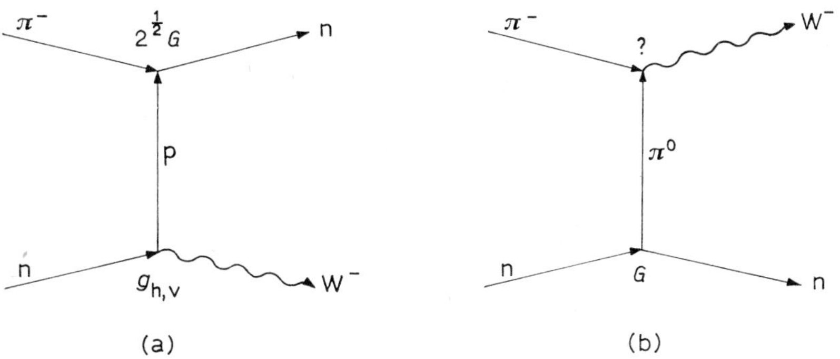

Fig. 12-7.1. The two Born terms of $\pi^- n \to W^- n (W^- = e\bar{\nu}$ or $\mu^-\nu)$.

The argument is immediately generalized to any decay from one member of an isospin multiplet to another member of the same multiplet. In particular, the ground state of ^{14}O belongs to an isospin triplet, together with the excited state of ^{14}N to which it decays. The third member of the triplet is ^{14}C. With 8 protons and 6 neutrons, ^{14}O has $I_3 = 1$ and therefore a nuclear structure constant

$$C_N = 2^{\frac{1}{2}}, \tag{7.5}$$

exactly the same as the pion. This is the origin of the identical ft-values of $^{14}O \to e^+\nu^{14}N$ and $\pi^+ \to e^+\nu\pi^0$. For any isospin multiplet, C_N in β^+-decay is given by C_- of (C-1.13),

$$C_N^2 = I(I+1) + I_3(I_3 - 1), \tag{7.6}$$

where I_3 refers to the initial nuclear state.

We get more results if we assume the principle of minimal weak interaction. Loosely speaking, this principle states that in the absence of strong interactions, the vector part of the hypercharge-conserving weak interaction is given simply by $\bar{u}'\gamma_\mu u$, without any anomalous magnetic moment coupling or form factors, which are secondary effects of the strong interactions. Since the strong interactions conserve isospin, they do not change the isospin properties of the basic interaction. Consequently, W^+ and W^- behave like the charged components of an isovector particle in their hypercharge-conserving interactions with hadrons.

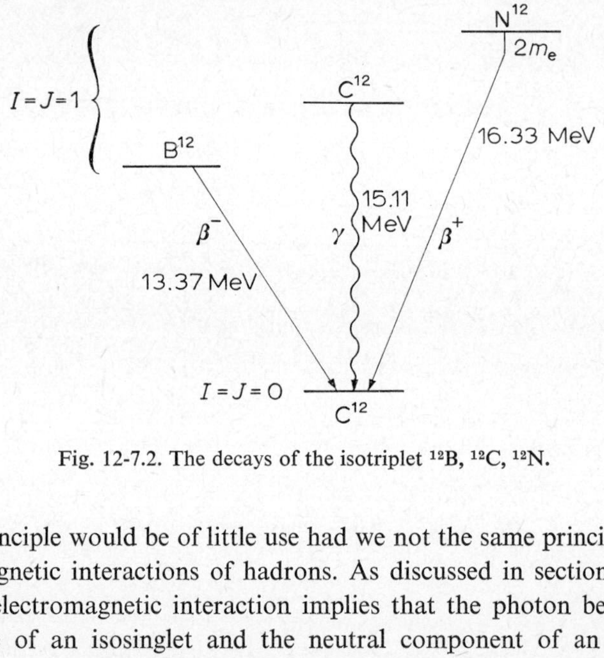

Fig. 12-7.2. The decays of the isotriplet ^{12}B, ^{12}C, ^{12}N.

The principle would be of little use had we not the same principle for the electromagnetic interactions of hadrons. As discussed in section 10-5, the minimal electromagnetic interaction implies that the photon behaves like a mixture of an isosinglet and the neutral component of an isotriplet. Consequently, the isovector photon is the neutral member of the "W triplet", if the electric charge e is replaced by g_h:

$$\frac{1}{e}\, B^{v}(\gamma h \to h', \text{isovector}) = B^{v}_{v}(Wh \to h'), \tag{7.7}$$

for any transition $h \to h'$ between hadrons. In particular, we obtain from (10-2.1)

$$B^{v}_{v}(W^{-}p \to n) = \bar{u}_{n}(P'M') \left[F^{v}_{1}(t)\gamma^{v} + \frac{\kappa^{v}}{2m} F^{v}_{2}(t)\sigma^{\mu v}(P-P')_{\mu} \right] u_{p}(P, M), \tag{7.8}$$

where $\kappa^{v} = \kappa_{p} - \kappa_{n}$ is the isovector anomalous magnetic moment, and F^{v}_{i}

are the isovector electromagnetic form factors (10-3.1). At present, little is known about the form factors of weak interactions, but the "weak magnetism" $\kappa^{v}\sigma^{\mu\nu}\Delta_{\mu}/(2m)$ has been identified in some decays. (For a review see WU [1964], WU and MOSZKOWSKI [1966].) The best studied example is the pair of decays $^{12}B \rightarrow e\nu^{12}C$ and $^{12}N \rightarrow e^{+}\nu^{12}C$ (LEE, MO and WU [1963]). Together with an excited state of ^{12}C, ^{12}B and ^{12}N form an isotriplet with $J = 1$, while the ground state of ^{12}C has $I = J = 0$ (see fig. 12-7.2). As discussed in section 3, these decays are Gamow-Teller transitions, for which the ordinary vector coupling is "forbidden". The main correction comes just from the anomalous magnetic moment coupling, the interference of which with the axial vector coupling is opposite in sign in the two decays. Finally, the magnitude of the magnetic moment coupling is known from the γ-decay of the excited state of ^{12}C.

12-8. Partially conserved axial current

For the axial vector coupling, the most general W-baryon interaction (7.1) is of the form

$$B^{\nu}_{A}(\text{baryons}) = \bar{u}_{n}\left[-F^{A}_{1}\gamma^{\nu} + \frac{\kappa^{A}F^{A}_{2}}{2m}\sigma^{\mu\nu}\Delta_{\mu} + H(t)\Delta^{\nu}\right]\gamma_{5}u_{p}, \tag{8.1}$$

where κ^{A} is the axial anomalous magnetic moment, and F_1, F_2 are form factors of $\Delta^2 = t$, normalized such that

$$F^{A}_{1}(0) = F^{A}_{2}(0) = G_{A}/G_{V} = 1.18. \tag{8.2}$$

The coupling $H(t)\Delta_{\nu}$, usually called the "induced pseudoscalar" coupling, corresponds to the exchange of a zero-spin particle, as discussed at the beginning of section 11-4. It has no pole at the mass of the W meson, since (7.1) has been constructed such that a real W has spin 1. Nevertheless, we must include it, since we know from pion decay that the coupling $\pi \rightarrow W$ does exist.

We now assume that $H(t)$ is well approximated by the contribution from π-exchange, fig. 12-8. Inserting (6.4) for the $\pi \rightarrow W$ coupling and (7-1.7) for $p \rightarrow \pi^{+}n$, we get

$$H(t) = -2^{\frac{1}{2}}GF_{\pi}(t)\frac{1}{m_{\pi}^{2}-t}\,g_{\pi}\frac{2^{\frac{1}{2}}}{G_{V}}, \tag{8.3}$$

where $F_{\pi}(t)$ is the NπN form factor defined by (11-3.13).

Next, we may determine $F_1^A(t)$ and g_π by requiring the gauge invariance of (1),

$$\Delta_\nu B_A^\nu = \bar{u}_n[F_1^A(t) \cdot 2m + tH(t)]\gamma_5 u_p = 0. \tag{8.4}$$

This relation cannot be satisfied exactly, since $H(t)$ has no pole at $t = 0$. However, we can rewrite $-t/(m_\pi^2 - t)$ as $1 - m_\pi^2/(m_\pi^2 - t)$ and require that all terms except the pion pole cancel in (4). We then obtain

$$F_1^A(t) \cdot 2m + 2GF_\pi(t)g_\pi/G_V = 0, \tag{8.5}$$

which for $t = 0$ gives

$$g_\pi = -\frac{G_A m}{GF_\pi(0)}. \tag{8.6}$$

Experimentally, (6) is surprisingly well satisfied. With $G = 2(\pi)^{\frac{1}{2}}(14.9)^{\frac{1}{2}} = 13.7$ and $G_A = 1.36 \times 10^{-5}/\text{GeV}^2$, we get $g_\pi = 932/\text{eV}\ F_\pi(0)$, whereas the experimental width of 2.53×10^{-8} eV for π^+ gives $g_\pi = 1.060 \times 10^{-6}/\text{GeV}$. This coincides with (6) for $F_\pi(0) = 0.88$.

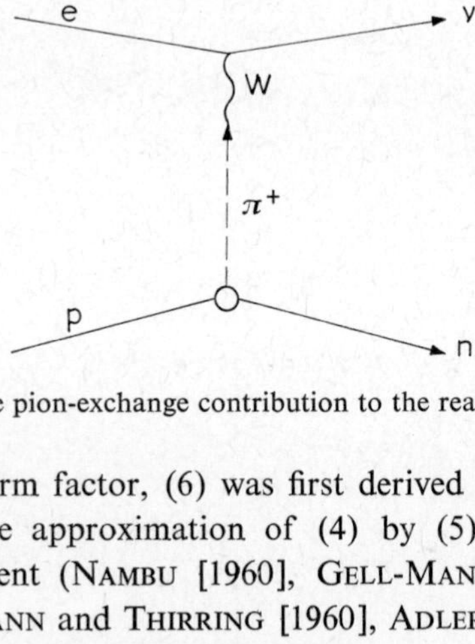

Fig. 12-8. The pion-exchange contribution to the reaction ep → νn.

Apart from the form factor, (6) was first derived by GOLDBERGER and TREIMAN [1958]. The approximation of (4) by (5) implies a partially conserved axial current (NAMBU [1960], GELL-MANN and LEVY [1960], BERNSTEIN, GELL-MANN and THIRRING [1960], ADLER [1965]). In the limit $-t/m_\pi^2 \to \infty$, the gauge invariance becomes exact.

The success of the Goldberger-Treiman relation suggests that $W^\pm$ has the isospin properties of $\pi^\pm$ for the whole axial vector coupling (1) (LEE and YANG [1962]). For p → nW, this would imply $\kappa^A = 0$. To see this, we first rewrite the pseudotensor coupling by means of the Dirac equation,

$$\sigma^{\mu\nu}\Delta_\mu\gamma_5 = \tfrac{1}{2}[(P-P')\gamma\gamma^\nu - \gamma^\nu(P-P')\gamma]\gamma_5 \to (m-m')\gamma^\nu\gamma_5 + (P+P')^\nu\gamma_5. \tag{8.7}$$

By the method of section 12-2, we then find that Hermiticity and time-reversal invariance require

$$-\kappa^{A\mathcal{T}} = \kappa^{A*} = \kappa^{A}. \tag{8.8}$$

On the other hand, according to the discussion following (7-1.7), the direct and inverse processed should have equal coupling constants, $\kappa^{A\mathcal{T}} = \kappa^{A}$, which agrees with (8) only for $\kappa^{A} = 0$. The final form of (1) for $p \to nW$ thus becomes

$$B^{\nu}_{A}(p \to nW) = -F^{A}_{1}\bar{u}_{n}\left[\gamma^{\nu} + \frac{2m\Delta^{\nu}}{m_{\pi}^{2}-t}\right]\gamma_{5}u_{p}. \tag{8.9}$$

Direct observation of the induced pseudoscalar interaction requires large momentum transfers, because of the factors $\Delta^{\nu}\gamma_5$. For this reason, muon capture is the most suitable reaction (for a review, see LEE and WU [1965]).

For the hypercharge-conserving decays $\Sigma^{-} \to \Lambda e\bar{\nu}$ and $\Sigma^{+} \to \Lambda\bar{e}\nu$, the isovector hypothesis of the axial vector coupling implies equal matrix elements, according to (8-1.8). The ratio of the two decays is therefore determined by the ratio of the corresponding phase spaces, which is 1.6 according to (9.5) below. This agrees with the experimental ratio 2 : 1 of table 4-1.

12-9. Cabibbo's theory

All experimental evidence on the leptonic decays of kaons and hyperons is consistent with muon-electron universality (6.2). This lets us use the vector-exchange form (7.1) for these decays; only the coupling constants will be different. When use is made of SU_3 invariance, it turns out that all coupling constants can be expressed in terms of two constants in addition to G_V and G_A of neutron decay (CABIBBO [1963]). The first of these constants is the "Cabibbo angle" θ

$$\tan\theta = \frac{S_V}{G_V} \approx \frac{S_A}{G_A} \approx \frac{g_K}{g_\pi} \approx 0.27, \tag{9.1}$$

or $\theta = 0.26 = 15°$. S_V and S_A are the vector and axial vector coupling constants of hypercharge-changing decays; their exact definitions are given below. The coupling constant g_K is the analogue of (6.4) for the decay $K^{+} \to \mu\bar{\nu}$; from (6.7) we find

$$\frac{\Gamma(K^{+} \to \mu\bar{\nu})}{\Gamma(\pi^{+} \to \mu\bar{\nu})} = \left(\frac{g_K}{g_\pi}\right)^{2} \frac{m_K}{m_\pi} \left(\frac{1-m^{2}/m_K^{2}}{1-m^{2}/m_\pi^{2}}\right)^{2}. \tag{9.2}$$

We now come to the vector part of the weak interaction. We saw that in hypercharge-conserving decays, W^+ and W^- have the isospin (and vector) properties of ρ^+ and ρ^-. Then in the larger frame of SU_3 transformations, W^+ and W^- must in addition have the SU_3 properties of K^{*+} and K^{*-} in hypercharge-changing decays, i.e. W "imitates" the charged members of an octet. More precisely, W imitates a ρ with amplitude $G^0 \cos\theta$, and a K^* with amplitude $G^0 \sin\theta$:

$$G_V = G^0 \cos\theta, \qquad S_V = G^0 \sin\theta. \tag{9.3}$$

It is interesting that the coupling constant G^0 defined by (3) is very close to the coupling constant (5.4) of μ-decay. With $\cos 15^\circ = 0.966$, G^0 is 3.4% larger than G_V. In some sense, it is possible that all weak interactions are governed by one "universal" coupling constant G_W, and that the deviations of the actual coupling constants from G_W are due to electromagnetic and strong interactions.

The couplings baryon $\to$ W+baryon are now analogous to the couplings baryon $\to$ meson+baryon, which have been discussed in section 8-7. There are two independent coupling constants, namely the "D-type coupling" αG_V for $\Sigma \to W\Lambda$ and the "F-type coupling" $(1-\alpha)G_V$ for $\Sigma \to W\Sigma$. However, since the vector coupling for $\Sigma \to W\Lambda$ is forbidden in the conserved vector current theory (section 12-7), we need $\alpha = 0$. In this case, hypercharge-conserving decays remain gauge invariant, while hypercharge-changing decays become gauge invariant in the limit of exact SU_3 symmetry.

For the axial part of the W coupling, none of above arguments applies, since the axial current is only partially conserved. Nonetheless, the approximate equality of the Cabibbo angle (1) for vector and axial coupling (which is not a consequence of SU_3 invariance) suggests that even in the axial couplings, W may imitate the charged members of an octet ($\pi^\pm$ and $K^\pm$, say). This would explain the "spurious kaon" rule of section 4-9, as far as the leptons are concerned. The only difference to the vector coupling is that this time the D-type coupling $G_A \alpha_A$ need not be zero. In fact, its magnitude may be determined from the decays $\Sigma^+ \to W^+\Lambda$ and $\Sigma^- \to W^-\Lambda$. Thus the two parameters of Cabibbo's theory are θ and $\alpha \equiv \alpha_A$.

In table 12-9, we have collected the SU_3-predictions for the leptonic decays of baryons. The equations from which these are obtained are quoted in the last column. Some care is necessary with the charge states. In particular, the coupling constant of $n \to \pi^- p$ is $2^{\frac{1}{2}}G$ instead of G, which shows that $G \to 2^{-\frac{1}{2}}G_V$ and $G \to -2^{-\frac{1}{2}}G_A$ are the corresponding coupling constants of weak interactions. Thus, the coupling constants of table 12-9 are a factor $2^{-\frac{1}{2}}$ smaller than the corresponding constants of section 8-7, except for charge combinations which require an extra $2^{\frac{1}{2}}$, as for example $n \to Wp$ and $\Sigma^- \to Wn$.

TABLE 12-9

SU_3-predictions for the leptonic baryon decays. $W^- = e^-\bar{\nu}$ or $\mu^-\nu$

decay	Matrix element	from eqs.
$n \to pW^-$	$G_V\gamma_\mu - G_A\gamma_\mu\gamma_5$	
$\Sigma^- \to \Lambda W^-$	$(\frac{2}{3})^{\frac{1}{2}}\alpha G_A\gamma_\mu\gamma_5$	(8—7.4)
$\Sigma^+ \to \Lambda W^+$	$(\frac{2}{3})^{\frac{1}{2}}\alpha G_A\gamma_\mu\gamma_5$	+(8—1.8)
$\Sigma^- \to \Sigma^0 W^-$	$2^{\frac{1}{2}}G_V\gamma_\mu - 2^{\frac{1}{2}}(1-\alpha)G_A\gamma_\mu\gamma_5$	(8—7.6)
$\Xi^- \to \Xi^0 W^-$	$-G_V\gamma_\mu + (1-2\alpha)G_A\gamma_\mu\gamma_5$	(8—7.18)+(8—7.9)
$\Lambda \to pW^-$	$(\frac{3}{2})^{\frac{1}{2}}S_V\gamma_\mu - (\frac{1}{6})^{\frac{1}{2}}(3-2\alpha)S_A\gamma_\mu\gamma_5$	(8—7.10)
$\Sigma^- \to nW^-$	$-S_V\gamma_\mu + (1-2\alpha)S_A\gamma_\mu\gamma_5$	(8—7.9)+(8—1.12)
$\Xi^- \to \Lambda W^-$	$-(\frac{3}{2})^{\frac{1}{2}}S_V\gamma_\mu + (\frac{1}{6})^{\frac{1}{2}}(3-4\alpha)S_A\gamma_\mu\gamma_5$	(8—7.16)+(8—7.14)
$\Xi^- \to \Sigma^0 W^-$	$(\frac{1}{2})^{\frac{1}{2}}S_V\gamma_\mu - (\frac{1}{2})^{\frac{1}{2}}S_A\gamma_\mu\gamma_5$	(8—7.16)
$\Xi^0 \to \Sigma^+ W^-$	$S_V\gamma_\mu - S_A\gamma_\mu\gamma_5$	

For the known leptonic decays of baryons (see table 4-1), good agreement with experiment is obtained with θ given by (1) and with

$$\alpha = 0.63, \tag{9.4}$$

which is somewhat smaller than the value $\alpha = 0.71$ of the baryon-meson coupling (see section 8-7).

In hyperon decays, the electron mass is negligible, and the Fermi integral (1.10) is well approximated by its last term, $(p_{max})^5/30m_e^5$. However, the recoil of the final baryon should be included in the calculation. To lowest order in p_{max}/m_f, this contributes a correction factor $(1-3p_{max}/2m_f)$, where m_f is the mass of the final baryon. With $p_{max} \approx m_i - m_f = \Delta m$, we get the final formula for the decay widths of hyperons from (4.11),

$$\Gamma(\text{if}) = \frac{(\Delta m)^5}{60\pi^3}\left(1 - \frac{3\Delta m}{2m_f}\right)(G_V^2(\text{if}) + 3G_A^2(\text{if})), \tag{9.5}$$

where G_V (if) and G_A (if) are the vector and axial vector coupling constants appropriate to the decay $i \to f$. This formula, with G(if) given by table 12-9, describes the electronic hyperon decays. For muonic decays such as $\Lambda \to p\bar{\mu}\nu$, the formula is more complicated.

In the leptonic decays of kaons also, SU_3 symmetry works surprisingly well. The main decay mode $K^+ \to \mu\bar{\nu}$ has been calculated in (2). The next important leptonic decay modes are $K^+ \to \mu\bar{\nu}\pi^0$ and $K^+ \to \bar{e}\nu\pi^0$, which are analogous to the beta decay of π^+. Their matrix elements are of the form

$$T(K^+ \to W^+\pi^0) = f_+(P_K+P_\pi)\cdot B + f_-(P_K-P_\pi)\cdot B, \tag{9.6}$$

with the 4-vector B given by (6.2). For the decay $\pi^+ \to W^+\pi^0$, the f_- coupling was negligible because of the smallness of the momentum transfer $P_K - P_\pi$. Actually, this coupling is also negligible for the decay $K^+ \to e^+\nu\pi^0$, since it has the same structure as the pion decay matrix element (6.4). Evaluating $f_-(P_K-P_\pi)\cdot B$ in the lepton's cms, we obtain (6.6) with g_π replaced by f_- and m_π by the effective mass of the lepton pair. For the decay $K^+ \to \mu^+\bar{\nu}\pi^0, f_-$ may of course contribute.

For f_+, SU_3 invariance requires (we may use e.g. (5-7.9), since the vector coupling is pure F-type)

$$f_+(K^+)\sin\theta = \tfrac{1}{2}f_+(\pi^+)\cos\theta, \tag{9.7}$$

which agrees with experiment for $\theta = 0.22$. In principle, f_+ is a function of the effective mass $t^{\frac{1}{2}}$ of the lepton pair. However, parametrizing

$$f_+(t) = f_+(0)\,\frac{M^2}{M^2-t}, \tag{9.8}$$

one finds that M is at least of the order of 1 GeV, and (7) can in fact be tested from the decay rates.

CHAPTER 13

NEUTRAL KAONS

13-1. Lifetimes and masses of K_L^0 and K_S^0

The existence of two neutral kaons of different lifetimes and masses was predicted by GELL-MANN and PAIS [1955]. At that time, the weak interactions were still believed to be invariant under $\mathscr{C}$ and $\mathscr{P}$ separately. Only the short-living K_S^0 (then called θ_1^0) had been observed. The long-living K_L^0 (then called θ_2^0) was detected in 1956 (Lande *et al.*). At about the same time, the non-conservation of $\mathscr{C}$ and $\mathscr{P}$ in weak interactions was suggested. With the product $\mathscr{C}\mathscr{P}$ still intact, the two neutral kaon states were K_1^0 and K_2^0 as given by (4-9.6), i.e. the two eigenstates of $\mathscr{C}\mathscr{P}$ with eigenvalues ± 1. The decays of these states into pions have been mentioned in section 4-9. In particular, the short lifetime of K_1^0 is due to the decay into two pions, which is forbidden for K_2^0.

The detection of the rare decay $K_L^0 \to \pi^+\pi^-$ (CHRISTENSON *et al.*, [1964]) indicated a weak violation of $\mathscr{C}\mathscr{P}$, thereby changing the theory of K^0 decays once more. However, these changes are negligible for most experiments on the lifetimes and masses of K_S^0 and K_L^0, as we shall see below.

Apart from production of neutral kaon pairs such as $\bar{p}p \to K_S^0 K_S^0$ or $\phi \to K_L^0 K_S^0$, the neutral kaons produced in strong interactions are K^0 or $\bar{K}^0$, i.e. states of hypercharge ± 1. A convenient method of producing K^0 is charge exchange of a K^+ beam, e.g. $K^+ d \to K^0 pp$.

Since the weak interactions do not conserve hypercharge, the time dependence of the states K^0 and $\bar{K}^0$ cannot be of the exponential type (2-3.6). By definition, those linear combinations of K^0 and $\bar{K}^0$ which do have exponential time dependence are called K_S^0 and K_L^0. Denoting by $\psi_S(\tau)$ and $\psi_L(\tau)$ the corresponding Schrödinger wave functions, we thus have

$$\psi_S(\tau) = \psi_S(0)e^{-(im_S + \frac{1}{2}\Gamma_S)\tau}, \qquad \psi_L(\tau) = \psi_L(0)e^{-(im_L + \frac{1}{2}\Gamma_L)\tau}, \tag{1.1}$$

where τ is the kaon's proper time, i.e. the laboratory time, multiplied by m/E_{lab}. From the energy release in K_L^0 and K_S^0 decays, one finds $m_S = m_L$ to within 0.2 MeV. The actual value of $m_S - m_L$ is much smaller; it can be measured from the time dependence of certain decays or secondary collisions of K^0 (PAIS and PICCIONI [1955]). To obtain this time dependence, we invert (4-3.4),

$$|K^0\rangle = \frac{s|K_L^0\rangle - q|K_S^0\rangle}{sp-qr}, \qquad |\overline{K}^0\rangle = \frac{-r|K_L^0\rangle + p|K_S^0\rangle}{sp-qr}, \tag{1.2}$$

and insert the time dependence (1) for $|K_L^0\rangle$ and $|K_S^0\rangle$. Introducing for convenience the complex masses

$$M_S = m_S - \tfrac{1}{2}i\Gamma_S, \qquad M_L = m_L - \tfrac{1}{2}i\Gamma_L, \tag{1.3}$$

we find

$$\begin{aligned}(sp-qr)\psi_K(\tau) &= e^{-iM_L\tau}s\psi_L(0) - e^{-iM_S\tau}q\psi_S(0)\\ &= (e^{-iM_L\tau}sp - e^{-iM_S\tau}qr)\psi_K(0) + (e^{-iM_L\tau} - e^{-iM_S\tau})qs\psi_{\overline{K}}(0),\end{aligned} \tag{1.4}$$

$$\begin{aligned}(sp-qr)\psi_{\overline{K}}(\tau) &= e^{-iM_S\tau}p\psi_S(0) - e^{-iM_L\tau}r\psi_L(0)\\ &= (e^{-iM_S\tau} - e^{-iM_L\tau})rp\psi_K(0) + (e^{-iM_S\tau}ps - e^{-iM_L\tau}rq)\psi_{\overline{K}}(0).\end{aligned} \tag{1.5}$$

From (5), we see that even if the particle produced at $\tau = 0$ is a pure K^0 (i.e. $\psi_{\overline{K}}(0) = 0$), the state will develop a $\overline{K}$-component at later times. This component manifests itself in reactions of the type $\overline{K}^0 p \to \Lambda\pi^+$, which are forbidden for the K^0-component. One thus observes sequences in which the total hypercharge changes by two units, e.g. $\pi^- p \to K\Lambda$, $Kp \to \pi^+\Lambda$, which is the double-scattering approximation of the reaction $\pi^- pp \to \pi^+\Lambda\Lambda$. Alternatively, one may measure the $\overline{K}^0$ probability by the $\pi^+ e\bar{\nu}$ and $\pi^+\bar{\mu}\nu$ decay modes. For the K^0-component, these modes are forbidden by the $\Delta Y = \Delta Q$ rule (4-9.3).

Before discussing the time dependence of these processes, we simplify the functions (4) and (5) by assuming *CPT* invariance. By definition, $\overline{K}^0$ is the antiparticle of K^0. Therefore *CPT* invariance requires that at any time τ, the coefficient of $\psi_K(0)$ in $\psi_K(\tau)$ equals the coefficient of $\psi_{\overline{K}}(0)$ in $\psi_{\overline{K}}(\tau)$. Comparing the relevant coefficients in (4) and (5), we see that this requires

$$sp = -qr. \tag{1.6}$$

In principle, *CPT* invariance can be tested separately, but we shall not discuss this. Note that (6) eliminates two real parameters of K^0 decay, since p, q, r, and s could be complex. Only one parameter remains. To see this, we first observe that the normalization of $|K_L^0\rangle$ and $|K_S^0\rangle$ in (4-3.4) requires

$$|p|^2 + |q|^2 = |r|^2 + |s|^2 = 1. \tag{1.7}$$

Moreover, three of the four phases of p, q, r, and s are unobservable and may be fixed by definition. The over-all phases of the states $|K_L^0\rangle$ and $|K_S^0\rangle$ as well as the relative phase between the states $|K^0\rangle$ and $|\bar{K}^0\rangle$ do not appear in any of the observable distributions. Thus p, q, and r may be taken as real parameters, and (6) and (7) lead to

$$r = p, \; s = -q = \sqrt{1-p^2}. \tag{1.8}$$

With these equalities, (2), (4) and (5) assume the simpler forms

$$|K^0\rangle = \frac{1}{2p}(|K_L^0\rangle + |K_S^0\rangle), \qquad |\bar{K}^0\rangle = \frac{1}{2q}(|K_L^0\rangle - |K_S^0\rangle), \tag{1.9}$$

$$\psi_K(\tau) = \frac{1}{2}\left[(e^{-iM_L\tau} + e^{-iM_S\tau})\psi_K(0) + \frac{q}{p}(e^{-iM_L\tau} - e^{-iM_S\tau})\psi_{\bar{K}}(0)\right], \tag{1.10}$$

$$\psi_{\bar{K}}(\tau) = \frac{1}{2}\left[\frac{p}{q}(e^{-iM_L\tau} - e^{-iM_S\tau})\psi_K(0) + (e^{-iM_L\tau} + e^{-iM_S\tau})\psi_{\bar{K}}(0)\right]. \tag{1.11}$$

The probability $|\psi_{\bar{K}}(\tau)|^2$ of finding a $\bar{K}^0$ at proper time τ can easily be calculated. If the initial particle at $\tau = 0$ is a pure K^0 as in $\pi^- p \to K^0 \Lambda$, we have $\psi_K(0) = 1$, $\psi_{\bar{K}}(0) = 0$. The corresponding probability is

$$\begin{aligned} W(K \to \bar{K}, \tau) &= \frac{1}{4}\frac{p^2}{q^2}|e^{-iM_L\tau} - e^{-iM_S\tau}|^2 \\ &= \frac{1}{4}\frac{p^2}{q^2}(e^{-\Gamma_L\tau} + e^{-\Gamma_S\tau} - 2e^{-\frac{1}{2}(\Gamma_L+\Gamma_S)\tau}\cos(m_L - m_S)\tau). \end{aligned} \tag{1.12}$$

This formula may be simplified in two respects. Since the $\mathscr{CP}$-violating effects are very small, we have $p^2/q^2 \approx 1$. Secondly, the proper times τ needed in experiments are usually negligible with respect to the lifetime Γ_L^{-1} of K_L^0. Therefore, (12) may be approximated by

$$W(K \to \bar{K}, \tau) = \tfrac{1}{4}(1 + e^{-\Gamma_S\tau} - 2e^{-\frac{1}{2}\Gamma_S\tau}\cos\Delta m\tau), \qquad \Delta m \equiv m_L - m_S. \tag{1.13}$$

In fig. 13-1, (13) is shown for $\Delta m = 0.6\,\Gamma_S$, which is close to the experimental value. For comparison, the curve for $\Delta m = 0$ is also shown.

Note that (13) does not determine the sign of Δm. To measure this sign, one needs three successive interactions of K^0, for example production, elastic scattering and decay. A simple method of this type is due to CAMERINI, FRY and GAIDOS [1963]; it consists of measuring the $\pi^+\pi^-$ decay mode of elastically scattered kaons, as a function of the proper time τ between production and scattering of the neutral kaons.

As before, we start from (10) and (11), setting $\psi_K(0) = 1$ and $\psi_{\bar{K}}(0) = 0$. Immediately before the elastic scattering, the states $|K^0\rangle$ and $|\bar{K}^0\rangle$ occur with amplitudes

$$\tfrac{1}{2}(e^{-iM_L\tau}+e^{-iM_S\tau}) \quad \text{and} \quad \left(\frac{p}{2q}\right)(e^{-iM_L\tau}-e^{-iM_S\tau}),$$

respectively. Let f and $\bar{f}$ denote the scattering amplitudes of K^0p and $\bar{K}^0p$ scattering. In the scattered state, $|K^0\rangle$ and $|\bar{K}^0\rangle$ thus occur with amplitudes

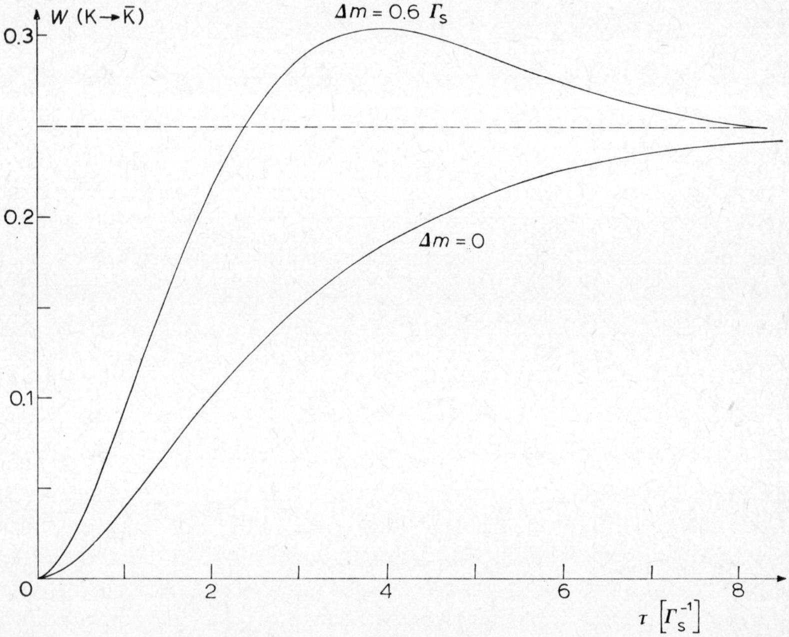

Fig. 13-1. The probability (1.13) of the $\bar{K}^0$-component, as a function of the proper time τ after K^0-production.

f and $\bar{f}$, multiplied by the amplitudes of the corresponding initial states:

$$\psi_K(\tau, \tau' = 0) = \tfrac{1}{2}f(e^{-iM_L\tau}+e^{-iM_S\tau}), \qquad \psi_{\bar{K}}(\tau, \tau' = 0) = \tfrac{1}{2}\bar{f}(e^{-iM_L\tau}-e^{-iM_S\tau}) \tag{1.14}$$

(the factor p/q is again approximated by 1). The proper time of the scattered kaon has been denoted by τ'. The probability of decay into $\pi^+\pi^-$ is now obtained from the exponential time dependence of the K^0_S-amplitude of the scattered state. We invert (9),

$$|K^0_S\rangle = p|K^0\rangle - q|\bar{K}^0\rangle, \qquad |K^0_L\rangle = p|K^0\rangle + q|\bar{K}^0\rangle, \tag{1.15}$$

and find the amplitude

$$\psi_S(\tau, \tau') = e^{-iM_S\tau'}[p\psi_K(\tau, \tau' = 0) - q\psi_{\bar{K}}(\tau, \tau' = 0)]$$
$$\approx e^{-iM_S\tau'} \frac{1}{2\sqrt{2}} [e^{-iM_L\tau}(f-\bar{f}) + e^{-iM_S\tau}(f+\bar{f})]. \tag{1.16}$$

The absolute square of (16) is

$$|\psi_S(\tau, \tau')|^2 = e^{-\Gamma_S\tau'}\tfrac{1}{8}[e^{-\Gamma_L\tau}|f-\bar{f}|^2 + e^{-\Gamma_S\tau}|f+\bar{f}|^2$$
$$+2e^{-\frac{1}{2}(\Gamma_L+\Gamma_S)\tau}(|f|^2-|\bar{f}|^2)\cos \Delta m\tau + 4e^{-\frac{1}{2}(\Gamma_L+\Gamma_S)\tau}\,\mathrm{Im}\,(f\bar{f}^*)\sin \Delta m\tau]. \tag{1.17}$$

This distribution depends on the sign of Δm through the coefficient of $\sin \Delta m\tau$. The functions f and $\bar{f}$ are obtained from an isospin analysis of K^+p, K^+n, K^-p and K^-n interactions. In particular, the $\bar{K}^0p$ states have $I_3 = 1$ and therefore $I = 1$. Of course, f and $\bar{f}$ depend on the cms scattering angle. Also, for a given scattering angle, two final states exist, corresponding to the two spin states of the scattered proton. Therefore, if f denotes the non-spinflip amplitude $T(\frac{1}{2}, \frac{1}{2}, \theta)$ of (3-9.20), we have in addition to (17) a probability

$$|\psi'_S(\tau, \tau')|^2 = e^{-\Gamma_S\tau'}\tfrac{1}{8}[e^{-\Gamma_L\tau}|g-\bar{g}|^2 + e^{-\Gamma_S\tau}|g+\bar{g}|^2 + \ldots] \tag{1.18}$$

where g is the spin-flip amplitude $T(\frac{1}{2}, -\frac{1}{2}, \theta)$. The observed probability is the sum of (17) and (18).

Two effects have been neglected in our derivation, namely the decays $K^0_L \to \pi^+\pi^-$ and elastic scattering at zero angle, i.e. forward scattering. These effects do not change our previous conclusions, but they can be exploited in other experiments. Forward scattering will be discussed in section 3. The decay $K^0_L \to \pi^+\pi^-$ is negligible as long as K^0_S and K^0_L occur with comparable intensities. Now consider times $\tau = \tau_0 + \tau'$ at which the K^0_S-component is already very small, and let

$$\rho = \psi_S(\tau_0)/\psi_L(\tau_0) \tag{1.19}$$

denote the ratio of the two amplitudes at $\tau = \tau_0$. The probability of finding $\pi^+\pi^-$ pairs at later times $\tau_0 + \tau'$ is proportional to

$$|\rho T(K^0_S \to \pi^+\pi^-)e^{-iM_S\tau'} + T(K^0_L \to \pi^+\pi^-)e^{-iM_L\tau'}|^2$$
$$= |\rho T(K^0_S \to \pi^+\pi^-)|^2 e^{-\Gamma_S\tau'} + |T(K^0_L \to \pi^+\pi^-)|^2 e^{-\Gamma_L\tau'}$$
$$+2e^{-\frac{1}{2}(\Gamma_S+\Gamma_L)\tau'}\,\mathrm{Re}\,[\rho T(K^0_S \to \pi^+\pi^-)T^*(K^0_L \to \pi^+\pi^-)e^{i\Delta m\tau'}]. \tag{1.20}$$

For very large τ', only the second term survives. This is the region from which $\Gamma(K_L^0 \to \pi^+\pi^-)$ is determined. There is also a region in which all three terms of (20) contribute. Introducing the ratio

$$\eta_{+-} \equiv \frac{T(K_L^0 \to \pi^+\pi^-)}{T(K_S^0 \to \pi^+\pi^-)}, \tag{1.21}$$

this region is characterized by $\Gamma_S\tau' \approx 2 \ln |\rho/\eta_{+-}|$. Factoring out $|T(K_L^0 \to \pi^+\pi^-)|^2$ and writing $\rho = |\rho|e^{i\varphi_\rho}$, $\eta_{+-} = |\eta_{+-}|e^{i\varphi_\eta}$ we see that the time dependence of $\pi^+\pi^-$ decays is given by

$$|\rho|^2 e^{-\Gamma_S\tau'} + |\eta_{+-}|^2 e^{-\Gamma_L\tau'} + 2e^{-\frac{1}{2}(\Gamma_L+\Gamma_S)\tau'}|\rho\eta_{+-}| \cos(\varphi_\rho - \varphi_\eta + \Delta m\tau'). \tag{1.22}$$

If Δm and φ_ρ are known, this function allows a determination of φ_η.

13-2. Isospin in $K \to \pi\pi$ decays

The isospin analysis of $K_L^0 \to \pi\pi$ and $K_S^0 \to \pi\pi$ has been given by Wu and Yang [1964] and by Wolfenstein [1966]. We shall present it here with some important simplifications. In addition to *CPT* invariance, we shall assume that the states K_L^0 and K_S^0 are orthogonal to each other, i.e.

$$p = q = 2^{-\frac{1}{2}}, \qquad |K_S^0\rangle = |K_1^0\rangle, \qquad |K_L^0\rangle = |K_2^0\rangle, \tag{2.1}$$

according to (1.15) and (4-9.6). By (1), we really mean that $|K_S^0\rangle$ and $|K_L^0\rangle$ are eigenstates of $\mathscr{CP}$, with eigenvalues ± 1 (Truong [1964], Bowen [1966]). The $\mathscr{CP}$-violating effects thus occur only in the decay matrix elements, not in the states.

To justify (1), we first observe that the $\pi^+\pi^-$ and $\pi^0\pi^0$ final states occur roughly with ratios 2 : 1 in K_S^0-decay and 1 : 2 in K_L^0-decay (see table 4-1). This means that the two-pion final state has $I = 0$ in K_S^0-decay and $I = 2$ in K_L^0-decay (the states $\boxed{1|2}$ of table 4-2. The states $I = 1$ are excluded for S-waves). If the final states are orthogonal, the initial states must be orthogonal, too.

The formal derivation of (1) goes as follows (see e.g. Bell and Steinberger [1966], Lee and Wu [1966]). For arbitrary linear combinations

$$\psi(\tau) = Xe^{-iM_L\tau}|K_L^0\rangle + Ye^{-iM_S\tau}|K_S^0\rangle, \tag{2.2}$$

M_L and M_S being the complex masses defined by (1.3), the norm is given by

$$N = |X|^2e^{-\Gamma_L\tau} + |Y|^2e^{-\Gamma_S\tau} + X^*Ye^{i(M_L^*-M_S)\tau}\langle K_L^0|K_S^0\rangle + Y^*Xe^{i(M_S^*-M_L)}\langle K_S^0|K_L^0\rangle. \tag{2.3}$$

At $\tau = 0$, the rate of decrease of the norm is

$$-\frac{dN}{d\tau} = \Gamma_L|X|^2+\Gamma_S|Y|^2+2\,\mathrm{Im}\,[(M_L^*-M_S)X^*Y\langle K_L^0|K_S^0\rangle]. \tag{2.4}$$

This must equal the total transition rate, which according to (2) and (2-3.3) is

$$\frac{1}{2m}\sum_F\int d\,\mathrm{Lips}|X\langle F|T|K_L^0\rangle+Y\langle F|T|K_S^0\rangle|^2, \tag{2.5}$$

where the sum extends over all final channels.

Comparison between the coefficients of X^*Y in (4) and (5) gives

$$-i(M_L^*-M_S)\langle K_L^0|K_S^0\rangle = \frac{1}{2m}\sum_F\int d\,\mathrm{Lips}\langle F|T|K_L^0\rangle^*\langle F|T|K_S^0\rangle. \tag{2.6}$$

Similarly, the coefficients of $|X|^2$ and $|Y|^2$ provide the definition of Γ_S and Γ_L. By (1.3) and (1.15), the lhs. of (6) is

$$[-i(m_L-m_S)+\tfrac{1}{2}(\Gamma_S+\Gamma_L)](p^2-q^2). \tag{2.7}$$

Since the square bracket is known from experiment, (6) can be used for estimating p^2-q^2. The long lifetime of K_L^0 alone guarantees $p^2-q^2 \ll 1$. However, this is not enough for the subsequent analysis; a detailed discussion of the rhs. of (6) is necessary. Three categories of final states occur in (6): two-pion states, three-pion states and states containing lepton pairs. The last category does not contribute to

$$\sum_F \langle F|T|K_L^0\rangle^*\langle F|T|K_S^0\rangle$$

because of the $\Delta Y = \Delta Q$ rule (eliminating $|K_L^0\rangle$ and $|K_S^0\rangle$ by (1.15), one sees that the "leptonic" contribution is proportional to p^2-q^2, which is certainly negligible). The contribution of the three-pion states is small because of the phase-space in (6). If in addition the amplitude $\langle\pi\pi\pi|T|K_S^0\rangle$ is of the same order of magnitude as $\langle\pi\pi|T|K_L^0\rangle$, it is negligible. Thus the decisive states are the $\pi\pi$-states. Here, the product is zero if K_S^0 decays only to $I = 0$ states and K_L^0 only to $I = 2$ states. A small admixture of $I = 2$ in K_S^0 decay or $I = 0$ in K_L^0 decay does not affect our conclusion (1).

Consider now the decomposition of the two-pion isospin states into $\pi^+\pi^-$ and $\pi^0\pi^0$ states. Denoting by T_I the matrix elements of $K^0 \to \pi\pi$ for pion-isospin I, table 4-2 yields

$$3^{-\frac{1}{2}}[\sqrt{2}\,T(K^0\to\pi^+\pi^-)-T(K^0\to\pi^0\pi^0)] = T_0, \tag{2.8}$$

$$3^{-\frac{1}{2}}[T(K^0\to\pi^+\pi^-)+\sqrt{2}\,T(K^0\to\pi^0\pi^0)] = T_2. \tag{2.9}$$

The matrix elements of $\overline{\mathrm{K}}^0 \to \pi\pi$ will be denoted by $\overline{T}_I$. The *CPT* theorem requires

$$\overline{T}_I(\overline{\mathrm{K}} \to \pi\pi) = T_I(\pi\pi \to \mathrm{K}), \tag{2.10}$$

since $\pi^0\pi^0$ and $\pi^+\pi^-$ states transform into themselves under *CPT*. The amplitude $T_I(\pi\pi \to \mathrm{K})$ may be related to $T_I^*(\mathrm{K} \to \pi\pi)$ by the partial-wave unitarity (2-4.8). As in the derivation of Watson's theorem, all intermediate channels except the elastic (two-pion) channel are negligible. The result is

$$\overline{T}_I = T_I^* \mathrm{e}^{2\mathrm{i}\delta_I} \tag{2.11}$$

where δ_I is the phase-shift (2-4.12) of $\pi\pi$-scattering. $\mathscr{CP}$ invariance (or $\mathscr{T}$ invariance) would require $\overline{T}_I = -T_I$ (the minus sign comes from $\mathscr{CP}|\mathrm{K}^0\rangle = -|\overline{\mathrm{K}}^0\rangle$ and $\mathscr{CP}|\bar{\pi}\pi\rangle = |\pi\bar{\pi}\rangle$, which is the same as $|\bar{\pi}\pi\rangle$ for symmetric states). In view of the approximate validity of $\mathscr{CP}$-invariance for T_0, it is convenient to introduce

$$T_I = \mathrm{i}A_I \mathrm{e}^{\mathrm{i}\delta_I}, \qquad \overline{T}_I = -\mathrm{i}A_I^* \mathrm{e}^{\mathrm{i}\delta_I}. \tag{2.12}$$

The second equation follows from (11). Inversion of (8) and (9) now yields the final expressions

$$T(\pi^+\pi^-) = \frac{1}{\sqrt{6}}\mathrm{i}[\sqrt{2}(A_0 \pm A_0^*)\mathrm{e}^{\mathrm{i}\delta_0} + (A_2 \pm A_2^*)\mathrm{e}^{\mathrm{i}\delta_2}], \tag{2.13}$$

$$T(\pi^0\pi^0) = \frac{1}{\sqrt{6}}\mathrm{i}[-(A_0 \pm A_0^*)\mathrm{e}^{\mathrm{i}\delta_0} + \sqrt{2}(A_2 \pm A_2^*)\mathrm{e}^{\mathrm{i}\delta_2}], \tag{2.14}$$

where the upper (lower) sign applies to K_S^0 (K_L^0) decay. In order to obtain branching ratios $\pi^+\pi^-/\pi^0\pi^0 \approx 2$ for K_S^0 and $\frac{1}{2}$ for K_L^0, we must have

$$\mathrm{Re}\, A_0 \gg \mathrm{Re}\, A_2, \qquad \mathrm{Im}\, A_2 \gg \mathrm{Im}\, A_0. \tag{2.15}$$

Then the matrix elements for the $\pi^+\pi^-$ final state are approximately

$$T(\mathrm{K}_\mathrm{S}^0 \to \pi^+\pi^-) \approx \frac{2\mathrm{i}}{\sqrt{3}}\mathrm{e}^{\mathrm{i}\delta_0}\,\mathrm{Re}\, A_0, \qquad T(\mathrm{K}_\mathrm{L}^0 \to \pi^+\pi^-) \approx -\sqrt{\tfrac{2}{3}}\mathrm{e}^{\mathrm{i}\delta_2}\,\mathrm{Im}\, A_2. \tag{2.16}$$

Finally, the small branching ratio of $(\mathrm{K}_\mathrm{L}^0 \to \pi^+\pi^-)/(\mathrm{K}_\mathrm{S}^0 \to \pi^+\pi^-)$ requires $\mathrm{Re}\, A_0 \gg \mathrm{Im}\, A_2$. By (15), this implies that A_0 is real, as expected.

The phase of η_{+-} (1.21) follows from (16):

$$\varphi_\eta = \delta_2 - \delta_0 \pm \tfrac{1}{2}\pi. \tag{2.17}$$

We conclude our analysis by discussing a possible connection with the decay $\mathrm{K}^+ \to \pi^+\pi^0$. As mentioned in section 4-9, the two pions can only have $I = 2$. Since the kaon has isospin $\frac{1}{2}$, the possible changes in $\mathrm{K} \to \pi\pi$

decays are $\Delta I = \frac{1}{2}, \frac{3}{2}$ or $\frac{5}{2}$. Let us denote the corresponding decay amplitudes by $T_{\frac{1}{2}}, T_{\frac{3}{2}}$ and $T_{\frac{5}{2}}$. To find their connection with the amplitudes T_0, T_2 and $T_+ \equiv T(K^+ \to \pi^+\pi^0)$, we decompose the states $|I, I_3\rangle$ into kaon-antispurion states of definite charges:

$$|0, 0\rangle = T_{\frac{1}{2}} \frac{1}{\sqrt{2}} (|\bar{K}^0_{\frac{1}{2}}, K^0\rangle - |\bar{K}^-_{\frac{1}{2}}, K^+\rangle), \tag{2.18}$$

$$|2, 0\rangle = T_{\frac{3}{2}} \frac{1}{\sqrt{2}} (|\bar{K}^0_{\frac{3}{2}}, K^0\rangle + |\bar{K}^-_{\frac{3}{2}}, K^+\rangle) + T_{\frac{5}{2}} \frac{1}{\sqrt{2}} (|\bar{K}^0_{\frac{5}{2}}, K^0\rangle - |\bar{K}^-_{\frac{5}{2}}, K^+\rangle), \tag{2.19}$$

$$|2, 1\rangle = T_{\frac{3}{2}} \tfrac{1}{2} (|\bar{K}^+_{\frac{3}{2}}, K^0\rangle + \sqrt{3} |\bar{K}^0_{\frac{3}{2}}, K^+\rangle) + T_{\frac{5}{2}} \frac{1}{\sqrt{3}} (\sqrt{2} |\bar{K}^+_{\frac{5}{2}}, K^0\rangle - |\bar{K}^0_{\frac{5}{2}}, K^+\rangle). \tag{2.20}$$

The symbols $\bar{K}_{\frac{1}{2}}, \bar{K}_{\frac{3}{2}}$ and $\bar{K}_{\frac{5}{2}}$ denote "antispurions" of isospin $\frac{1}{2}$, $\frac{3}{2}$ and $\frac{5}{2}$. Here we only need the neutral antispurion states (the charged ones occur in the leptonic decays, according to the spurions-kaon rule of section 4-9). Comparing (18) and (19) with (8) and (9), we obtain

$$T_0 = \frac{1}{\sqrt{2}} T_{\frac{1}{2}}, \qquad T_2 = \frac{1}{\sqrt{2}} (T_{\frac{3}{2}} + T_{\frac{5}{2}}). \tag{2.21}$$

From (20), we have

$$T_+ \equiv T(K^+ \to \pi^+\pi^0) = \tfrac{1}{2}\sqrt{3}\, T_{\frac{3}{2}} - \sqrt{\tfrac{1}{3}}\, T_{\frac{5}{2}}. \tag{2.22}$$

In view of the approximate validity of the $\Delta I = \frac{1}{2}$ rule, it is tempting to assume $T_{\frac{5}{2}} = 0$, in which case one obtains

$$T_2 = \sqrt{\tfrac{2}{3}}\, T_+ . \tag{2.23}$$

If this assumption is correct, then (12) and (23) imply

$$\left| \frac{\operatorname{Im} A_2}{A_2} \right| = \frac{3}{2} \left(\frac{\Gamma(K^0_L \to \pi^+\pi^-)}{\Gamma(K^+ \to \pi^+\pi^-)} \right)^{\frac{1}{2}} \approx 0.28, \tag{2.24}$$

which shows that also A_2 is approximately real.

13-3. Coherent regeneration

The strong interactions of K^0_L with matter "regenerate" a K^0_S-component. In section 13-1, we discussed this in connection with elastic non-forward scattering. The case of elastic forward scattering must be studied separately, due to the fact that scattering amplitudes from nuclei of different atoms may add coherently. This "coherent regeneration" of K_S^0 may be studied in different ways. One way is to put a slab of material into an "old" beam, consisting of K_L^0 only. Behind the slab one then observes $\pi^+\pi^-$ decays. For a thick slab, these decays are dominated by the K_S^0 amplitude (PAIS and PICCIONI [1955]). For a thin slab, interference with the K_L^0 amplitude cannot be neglected.

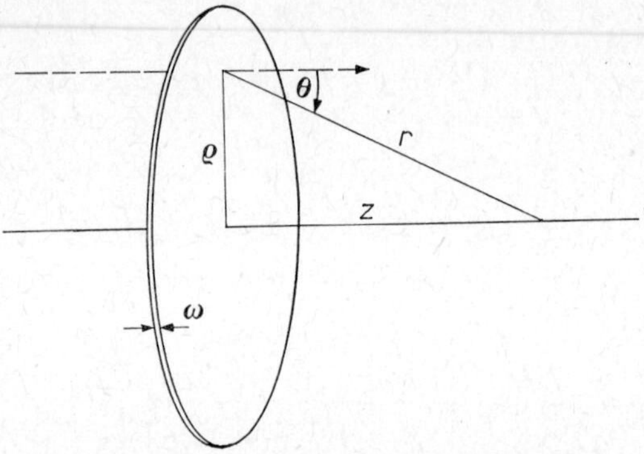

Fig. 13-3. The scattering by a thin slab.

As in optics, the behaviour of K^0 waves in matter may be described by an index of refraction. (See e.g. the reviews of LEE and WU [1966], BELL and STEINBERGER [1966].) We first consider a pure K^0 state of hypercharge $+1$ and neglect the weak interactions. For a single scatterer, the space dependence of the wave function is given by (2-5.5), where r is the distance from the scatterer, and the scattering angle θ is determined by $\sin\theta = \rho/r$ (see fig. 13-3). For a slab of thickness $\omega \ll z$ and atom density N, the corresponding wave function is

$$\begin{aligned}\psi &= e^{iqz} + 2\pi \int_0^\infty \rho \, d\rho \, e^{iqr} \frac{f(\theta)}{r} \omega N \\ &= e^{iqz} + 2\pi\omega N \int_z^\infty dr \, e^{iqr} f(\theta) \\ &= e^{iqz} \left[1 + 2\pi\omega N \frac{i}{q} f(0) \right]. \end{aligned} \tag{3.1}$$

Strictly speaking, q needs a small imaginary part (from inelastic scattering or decay) to damp the integrand for $r \to \infty$. The approximation $\theta = 0$ requires $f(\theta)$ to be nearly constant over many oscillations of e^{iqr}.

For a slab of finite thickness ω, (1) is replaced by

$$\psi(\omega, z) = e^{iqn\omega} e^{iq(z-\omega)}, \tag{3.2}$$

where n is the index of refraction of the medium. Comparing (2) with (1), we find

$$iq(n-1) = 2\pi i \frac{N}{q} f(0), \qquad \frac{d\psi}{d\omega} = 2\pi i \frac{N}{q} f(0)\psi. \tag{3.3}$$

We now turn to the time dependence of K_L^0 and K_S^0 states in matter. This is related to the space dependence through ω = velocity × time (all quantities referring to the lab system). The kaon velocity is q/E and the lab time is $\tau \cdot E/m$, which gives the simple relation

$$d\omega = d\tau \cdot q/m. \tag{3.4}$$

The total time dependence of the Schrödinger wave function $\psi(\tau)$ is given by

$$\frac{d\psi}{d\tau} = \left(\frac{d\psi}{d\tau}\right)_{\text{weak}} + \left(\frac{d\psi}{d\tau}\right)_{\text{strong}}, \tag{3.5}$$

where the first term describes the time dependence in vacuum (which is governed by the weak interactions), and the second term contains the changes due to the (strong) interactions with the medium. From (1.1) and (1.15), we have

$$\begin{aligned} \frac{d}{d\tau}\psi_S &= -iM_S\psi_S + \frac{d}{d\tau}(p\psi_K - q\psi_{\bar{K}})_{\text{strong}}, \\ \frac{d}{d\tau}\psi_L &= -iM_L\psi_L + \frac{d}{d\tau}(p\psi_K + q\psi_{\bar{K}})_{\text{strong}}. \end{aligned} \tag{3.6}$$

The decomposition of the second terms into K and $\overline{K}$ components is necessary, since only these components do not mix in strong interactions. Equation (3) applies to ψ_K and $\psi_{\bar{K}}$ separately. Denoting the corresponding forward scattering amplitudes by f and $\bar{f}$, we find for the second terms

$$\begin{aligned} 2\pi i \frac{N}{m}(pf\psi_K - q\bar{f}\psi_{\bar{K}}) &= i\pi \frac{N}{m}(f+\bar{f})\psi_S + i\pi \frac{N}{m}(f-\bar{f})\psi_L, \\ 2\pi i \frac{N}{m}(pf\psi_K + q\bar{f}\psi_{\bar{K}}) &= i\pi \frac{N}{m}(f+\bar{f})\psi_L + i\pi \frac{N}{m}(f-\bar{f})\psi_S. \end{aligned} \tag{3.7}$$

Thus, unless $f-\bar{f} = 0$, K_S^0 is regenerated from K_L^0 (due to the short lifetime of K_S^0, the inverse regeneration $K_S^0 \to K_L^0$ is negligible). However, there exist linear combinations of K_L^0 and K_S^0 which again have the exponential time dependence:

$$\psi'_S(\tau) = \psi'_S(0)e^{-iM'_S\tau}, \qquad \psi'_L(\tau) = \psi'_L(0)e^{-iM'_L\tau}, \tag{3.8}$$

where $M'_S = m'_S - \frac{1}{2}i\Gamma'_S$ and $M'_L = m'_L - \frac{1}{2}i\Gamma'_L$ are two new complex masses. Differentiating (8) and comparing it with (6) and (7), we find, to lowest order in $N(f-\bar{f})$,

$$M'_L = M_L - \pi\frac{N}{m}(f+\bar{f}), \qquad |K'_L\rangle = |K_L^0\rangle - \pi\frac{N}{m}\frac{f-\bar{f}}{M_L-M_S}|K_S^0\rangle, \tag{3.9}$$

$$M'_S = M_S - \pi\frac{N}{m}(f+\bar{f}), \qquad |K'_S\rangle = |K_S^0\rangle + \pi\frac{N}{m}\frac{f-\bar{f}}{M_L-M_S}|K_L^0\rangle. \tag{3.10}$$

Remember that both $f-\bar{f}$ and M_L-M_S are complex. In a thin extended regenerator (e.g. a bubble chamber), only $|K'_L\rangle$ survives at large enough τ, and the transition rate to a particular final state $|F\rangle$ is proportional to

$$|\langle F|T|K_L^0\rangle - \pi\frac{N}{m}\frac{f-\bar{f}}{\Delta m - \frac{1}{2}i(\Gamma_L-\Gamma_S)}\langle F|T|K_S^0\rangle|^2. \tag{3.11}$$

For materials where $f-\bar{f}$ is not known, useful information may be obtained by varying the density N.

APPENDIX A

FUNCTIONS ASSOCIATED WITH THE PARTIAL WAVE EXPANSION

A-1. Legendre polynomials

We define a Legendre polynomial $P_L(x)$ as a polynomial of degree L in x, which obeys the orthogonality relation

$$\int_{-1}^{1} \mathrm{d}x(L+\tfrac{1}{2})P_L(x)P_{L'}(x) = \delta_{LL'}. \tag{1.1}$$

For $L = 0$ and $L = 1$, the solution of (1) is

$$P_0(x) = 1, \quad P_1(x) = x. \tag{1.2}$$

The signs have been defined such that $P_L(1) = +1$. Similarly, we can compute P_2 from the condition that P_2 is orthogonal to P_0 and P_1 and normalized such that $\frac{5}{2}\int \mathrm{d}xP_2^2(x) = 1$, giving $P_2(x) = \frac{1}{2}(3x^2-1)$. For $L > 1$, P_L satisfies the recurrence relation

$$P_L(x) = \left(2-\frac{1}{L}\right) xP_{L-1} - \left(1-\frac{1}{L}\right) P_{L-2}. \tag{1.3}$$

The polynomial condition is obviously satisfied. Also, if P_{L-2} contains only even powers of x, P_{L-1} only odd powers, then P_L contains only even powers, P_{L+1} only odd powers etc. This implies $\int P_L P_{L-1} = 0$. The ratio of the coefficients of xP_{L-1} and P_{L-2} in (3) is fixed by the requirement that P_L is orthogonal to P_{L-2}. Multiplying the r.h.s. of (3) by P_{L-2} and integrating, we get

$$\left(2-\frac{1}{L}\right)\int P_{L-1}xP_{L-2}\mathrm{d}x - \left(1-\frac{1}{L}\right)\int P_{L-2}^2\mathrm{d}x. \tag{1.4}$$

The second integral is $2/(2L-3)$ according to (1). For the first integral, we use the recurrence relation (3) in the form

$$xP_{L-2} = \frac{P_{L-1}}{2-1/(L-1)} - \text{const.}\ P_{L-3}. \tag{1.5}$$

Since we assume that P_{L-1} and P_{L-3} are already orthogonal, we have

$$\int P_{L-1} x P_{L-2} = \frac{L-1}{2L-3}\int P_{L-1}^2 = \frac{L-1}{2L-3}\,\frac{1}{L-\frac{1}{2}}, \tag{1.6}$$

and (4) is in fact zero. The absolute values of the two coefficients in (3) are determined similarly from the normalization $\int (L+\frac{1}{2})P_L^2 = 1$. Finally, P_L is automatically orthogonal to $P_{L'}$ for $L' < L-2$, since

$$\int x P_{L-1} P_{L-3} = 0, \qquad \int P_{L-2} P_{L-3} = 0, \qquad \text{etc.} \tag{1.7}$$

There exist various recurrence relations involving the derivatives of P_L. The basic relation of this type is

$$P'_{L+1} - xP'_L = (L+1)P_L. \tag{1.8}$$

It is proven by integration by parts. Other relations are obtained by differentiating (3) and combining it with (8). Later we shall need

$$(1-x^2)P'_L = LP_{L-1} - LxP_L. \tag{1.9}$$

From these equations, one derives the orthogonality relation

$$\frac{1}{2}\int_{-1}^{1} \mathrm{d}x\, P'_{L'}(x)\left(P_{L-1}(x) - P_{L+1}(x)\right) = \delta_{LL'}. \tag{1.10}$$

A-2. Legendre functions of the second kind

Legendre functions of the second kind may be defined by means of Heine's expansion (see e.g. WHITTAKER and WATSON, section 15.4):

$$\frac{1}{z-x} = \sum_{L=0}^{\infty} (2L+1)P_L(x)Q_L(z), \tag{2.1}$$

valid for complex z and x. The expansion converges for x in the interior of the ellipse which has the points ± 1 as foci and which passes through the point z. From the orthogonality relations (1.1) of the Legendre polynomials $P_L(x)$, one finds

$$Q_L(z) = \frac{1}{2}\int_{-1}^{1} \frac{\mathrm{d}x}{z-x} P_L(x). \tag{2.2}$$

If z is real, it should not lie between $+1$ and -1. Insertion of (1.2) and (1.3) gives

$$Q_0(z) = \tfrac{1}{2}\ln\frac{z+1}{z-1}, \qquad Q_1(z) = zQ_0(z)-1, \tag{2.3}$$

$$Q_L(z) = \left(2-\frac{1}{L}\right) zQ_{L-1}(z) - \left(1-\frac{1}{L}\right) Q_{L-2}(z) \qquad \text{for} \quad L > 1. \tag{2.4}$$

This recurrence relation is identical with that of P_L. For $|z| \gg 1$, the following expansion is useful:

$$\begin{aligned} Q_0(z) &= \frac{1}{z} + \frac{1}{3z^3} + \frac{1}{5z^5} + \ldots, \\ Q_1(z) &= \frac{1}{3z^2} + \frac{1}{5z^4} + \frac{1}{7z^6} + \ldots, \\ Q_2(z) &= \frac{2}{3\cdot 5z^3} + \frac{4}{5\cdot 7z^5} + \frac{6}{7\cdot 9z^7} + \ldots. \end{aligned} \tag{2.5}$$

The expansion for $L > 1$ follows from the recurrence relation (4). The leading term is proportional to z^{-1-L}.

A-3. Spherical Bessel and Neuman functions

The spherical Bessel and Neuman functions $j_L(\rho)$ and $n_L(\rho)$ of order L satisfy the differential equation

$$j_L''(\rho) + \frac{2}{\rho} j_L'(\rho) + \left[1 - \frac{L(L+1)}{\rho^2}\right] j_L(\rho) = 0, \tag{3.1}$$

which is obtained from (2-5.3) by setting $V(r) = 0$ and $u_L(r) /= rj_L(qr)$; n_L is a solution of (1) which is infinite at $\rho = 0$. For $L = 0$, 1 and 2, we have

$$j_0 = \frac{\sin\rho}{\rho}, \qquad j_1 = \frac{\sin\rho}{\rho^2} - \frac{\cos\rho}{\rho}, \qquad j_2 = \left(\frac{3}{\rho^2} - \frac{1}{\rho}\right)\sin\rho - \frac{3}{\rho^2}\cos\rho, \tag{3.2}$$

$$n_0 = \frac{\cos\rho}{\rho}, \qquad n_1 = \frac{\cos\rho}{\rho^2} + \frac{\sin\rho}{\rho}, \qquad n_2 = \left(\frac{3}{\rho^2} - \frac{1}{\rho}\right)\cos\rho + \frac{3}{\rho^2}\sin\rho. \tag{3.3}$$

The following recurrence relation is valid for both j_L and n_L:

$$j_{L+1} = \frac{2L+1}{\rho} j_L - j_{L-1}. \tag{3.4}$$

The j's and n's are related by

$$n_L j_{L-1} - n_{L-1} j_L = \frac{1}{\rho^2}. \tag{3.5}$$

For $\rho \to 0$ and $\rho \to \infty$, we have

$$j_L \underset{(\rho\to 0)}{\longrightarrow} \frac{\rho^L}{1\cdot 3\cdot 5\ldots(2L+1)} \equiv \frac{\rho^L}{(2L+1)!!}, \qquad n_L \underset{(\rho\to 0)}{\longrightarrow} \frac{(2L-1)!!}{\rho^{L+1}}, \tag{3.6}$$

$$j_L \underset{(\rho\to\infty)}{\longrightarrow} \frac{1}{\rho}\sin(\rho-\tfrac{1}{2}\pi L), \qquad n_L \underset{(\rho\to\infty)}{\longrightarrow} \frac{1}{\rho}\cos(\rho-\tfrac{1}{2}\pi L). \tag{3.7}$$

APPENDIX B

GROUPS OF UNITARY MATRICES

B-1. Unitary matrices

Let M^+, M^* and M_{tr} denote the Hermitean conjugate, complex conjugate and transpose of a matrix M, respectively. A square matrix S is said to be unitary if

$$S^+ \equiv S^*_{tr} = S^{-1} \quad \text{or} \quad S^+S = SS^+ = 1, \tag{1.1}$$

where 1 is the unit matrix. The matrix equation $SS^+ = 1$ has the components

$$\sum_m S_{im}(S^+)_{mf} = \sum_m S_{im} S^*_{fm} = \delta_{if}. \tag{1.2}$$

Any unitary matrix may be written as

$$S = e^{iH} \equiv 1 + iH - \tfrac{1}{2}H^2 - \frac{i}{3!}H^3 + \ldots \tag{1.3}$$

where H is Hermitean:

$$H^+ = H, \qquad S^+ = e^{-iH^+} = e^{-iH} = S^{-1}. \tag{1.4}$$

The advantage of representation (3) is that a general Hermitean matrix may be constructed as a superposition of fixed, linearly independent Hermitean matrices. The construction of unitary matrices is more complicated. Instead of (3), one may use the algebraic expression

$$S = \frac{1+iK}{1-iK}, \qquad 2K = \operatorname{tg} H = H + \tfrac{1}{3}H^3 + \tfrac{2}{15}H^5 + \ldots \tag{1.5}$$

Obviously K is also Hermitean. Unitary matrices are important in quantum mechanics, because the scalar product of two quantum mechanical state vectors

$$\langle b|a\rangle = \sum_i a_i b_i^* \tag{1.6}$$

is invariant under unitary transformations:

$$\langle bS|Sa\rangle = \sum_{ijk} S_{ij} a_j (S_{ik} b_k)^* = \sum_{ijk} (S^+)_{ki} S_{ij} a_j b_k^*$$
$$= \sum_{jk} \delta_{kj} a_j b_k^* = \langle b|a\rangle. \tag{1.7}$$

Unitary transformations of state vectors have some properties of coordinate transformations of ordinary 3-component vectors. Such transformations leave the scalar product invariant. The product of two unitary matrices is also unitary, and a unitary matrix is diagonalized by another unitary matrix U,

$$(U^+SU)_{mn} = \mathrm{e}^{\mathrm{i}\phi_m}\delta_{mn}. \tag{1.8}$$

Both properties are obviously true for coordinate transformations.

In connection with time-reversal invariant interactions, symmetric matrices S are needed, $S = S_{\mathrm{tr}}$. The corresponding matrices H and K are also symmetric by (3) and (5), and since they are Hermitean, they are in fact real, $H = H^*$, $K = K^*$. The matrix U of (8) which diagonalizes S is then also real. This follows from the fact that U diagonalizes not only S, but also H and K, and that real symmetric matrices are diagonalized by real matrices.

B-2. Unitary groups

As mentioned in the last section, the product of two unitary matrices is also unitary (if $C = UV$, then $C^{-1} = (UV)^{-1} = V^{-1}U^{-1} = V^+U^+ = C^+$). Since the inverse of any unitary matrix is also unitary, the manifold of unitary matrices of a given dimension forms a group. In the physics of elementary particles, the groups U_2 of 2×2 and U_3 of 3×3 unitary matrices are the most important ones.

Any unitary matrix $U_n(\alpha)$ may be written as the product of a phase and a "special" or "unimodular" unitary matrix $\mathrm{SU}_n(\alpha)$ which has determinant $+1$.

$$U_n(\alpha) = \mathrm{e}^{\mathrm{i}\phi}\mathrm{SU}_n(\alpha). \tag{2.1}$$

Since the determinant of a product of matrices is the product of the determinants of these matrices, the matrices SU_n also form a group. It is convenient to neglect the phase factors and discuss only the groups SU_n.

Unitary matrices of dimension n are parametrized by n^2 real parameters. For SU_n, one has one parameter less (the phase ϕ). For example, one may write

$$\mathrm{SU}_n(\alpha_1, \ldots, \alpha_{n^2-1}) = \mathrm{e}^{\mathrm{i}H_n}, \qquad H_n = \sum_{i=1}^{n^2-1} \alpha_i\lambda_i, \tag{2.2}$$

where the fixed, linearly independent Hermitean matrices λ_i are called the generators of the unitary matrices. The condition det $(\mathrm{SU}_n) = 1$ implies trace $(\lambda_i) = 0$. For SU_2 for example, $n^2-1 = 3$, and the three generators

λ_i are taken in the form σ_i of the Pauli spin matrices (3-2.2). The three parameters α_i form a "rotation vector", $\frac{1}{2}\boldsymbol{\omega} = (\alpha_1, \alpha_2, \alpha_3)$, by means of which (2) is rewritten as

$$\mathrm{SU}_2(\omega) = \mathrm{e}^{\frac{1}{2}\mathrm{i}\boldsymbol{\omega}\cdot\boldsymbol{\sigma}}. \tag{2.3}$$

This rotation vector is not the only possible parametrization of SU_2 matrices. In this book, the Euler angles α, β, γ are used instead.

The application of group theory to physics consists of studying the irreducible representations of group. A representation D_k of the group SU_n is again a group of unitary matrices of dimension k (which may be different from n), which has the same number of parameters as SU_n. Moreover, the coordination of parameters to the D matrices preserves the multiplication properties of the SU_n matrices. If, for example, $\mathrm{SU}_2(\omega) = \mathrm{SU}_2(\omega_1)\cdot \mathrm{SU}_2(\omega_2)$, then $D(\omega) = D(\omega_1)\cdot D(\omega_2)$. For this property, it is both necessary and sufficient that D may be written in the form

$$D(\alpha_1, \ldots, \alpha_{n^2-1}) = \exp\left[\mathrm{i}\sum_{i=1}^{n^2-1} \alpha_i F_i\right], \tag{2.4}$$

where the generators F_i have the same *commutation relations* as the λ_i. Thus the "structure constants" f_{ijk} in the commutation relations

$$[F_i, F_j] = 2\mathrm{i}\sum_k f_{ijk} F_k \tag{2.5}$$

should be identical with the constants in the commutation relations of the corresponding λ_i. This is the basic property of Lie groups. For the group SU_2 we have $F_i = 2J_i$, where J_i are the angular momentum operators.

Let $|\xi\rangle$ with components ξ_α, $\alpha = 1, \ldots, n$, denote a vector on which the matrices SU_n act. The direct product of r such vectors, $\xi^a \ldots \xi^r$, transforms under U_n like a tensor of rank r. Consider for example the transformation law of the second-rank tensor $T_{\alpha\beta}$,

$$T_{\alpha\beta} \equiv \xi^a_\alpha \xi^b_\beta, \qquad (V\cdot T)_{\alpha\beta} = U_{\alpha\alpha'} U_{\beta\beta'} T_{\alpha'\beta'}. \tag{2.6}$$

The matrix V is the "direct product" $U \otimes U$. It is a $n^2 \times n^2$ unitary matrix, the first (second) index of which is given by the index pair $\alpha\beta$, $(\alpha'\beta')$. The group of V matrices which are of the form $U_n \otimes U_n$ form a representation of U_n. For $n > 1$, this representation is reducible, which means that T may be split into two parts such that V never mixes components of different parts. The reduction is accomplished by spitting T into a symmetric and an antisymmetric part

$$T_{\alpha\beta} = T_{\{\alpha\beta\}} + T_{[\alpha\beta]}, \qquad T_{\{\alpha\beta\}} = \tfrac{1}{2}(\xi^a_\alpha \xi^a_\beta + \xi^a_\beta \xi^b_\alpha),$$
$$T_{[\alpha\beta]} = \tfrac{1}{2}(\xi^a_\alpha \xi^b_\beta - \xi^a_\beta \xi^b_\alpha), \tag{2.7}$$

which have $\frac{1}{2}n(n+1)$ and $\frac{1}{2}n(n-1)$ non-zero components, respectively. Since the symmetric tensor remains symmetric under the transformation law (6), while the antisymmetric tensor remains antisymmetric, it follows that a division of each index pair into symmetric and antisymmetric form brings V into the reduced form

$$V = \begin{pmatrix} V_{\{\alpha\beta\},\{\alpha'\beta'\}} & 0 \\ 0 & V_{[\alpha\beta],[\alpha'\beta']} \end{pmatrix} \begin{matrix} \leftarrow \frac{1}{2}n(n+1) \text{ comp.} \\ \leftarrow \frac{1}{2}n(n-1) \text{ comp.} \end{matrix} \Bigg\} \; n^2 \text{ comp.} \tag{2.8}$$

Symbolically, one writes $2 \otimes 2 = 3 \oplus 1$ in the case of SU_2, $3 \otimes 3 = 6 \oplus \bar{3}$ in the case of SU_3, etc. (The symbol "$\bar{3}$" is used to distinguish the transformation law of the antisymmetric tensor from that of the 3-vector. In SU_3, $\bar{V}$ denotes the complex conjugate representation of V, see D-2.4 below.)

Similarly, the tensor product $\xi^a_\alpha \xi^b_\beta \xi^c_\gamma$ of rank three may be decomposed into one totally symmetric part, one totally antisymmetric part, and two parts of mixed symmetry. The totally symmetric and antisymmetric parts are of dimensions $\frac{1}{6}n(n+1)(n+2)$ and $\frac{1}{6}n(n-1)(n-2)$, respectively, whereas the remaining parts are of dimension $\frac{1}{3}n(n^2-1)$ each. By forming tensors of arbitrary rank and reducing them with respect to their permutation properties, all irreducible representations of SU_n are found. This method will be used for SU_3. For SU_2, we shall follow the more familiar approach of studying the commutation relations (5).

B-3. Schur's lemma and orthogonality relations

If D^1 and D^2 are two irreducible sets of $n_1 \times n_1$ and $n_2 \times n_2$ matrices, then any fixed $n_1 \times n_2$ matrix A for which

$$D^1(\alpha_i) \cdot A = A \cdot D^2(\alpha_i), \tag{3.1}$$

for all values of the parameters α_i, is either zero or non-singular. This statement is the first part of Schur's lemma. The term "non-singular" means $\det A \neq 0$. Since only square matrices can be non-singular, the latter possibility implies $n_1 = n_2$.

Without loss of generality, we take $n_1 \geqq n_2$. The matrix multiplication on the l.h.s. of (1),

$$\sum_{k=1}^{n_1} D_{ik} A_{kl},$$

may be viewed as the transformation of n_2 different vectors A_l of n_1 components A_{kl}. The r.h.s. of (1) states that the transformed vectors are linear combinations of the old vectors A_l. If this is true for all matrices D^1, then these matrices leave the space spanned by the A_l invariant. For $n_1 > n_2$, this would be a proper subspace, which is inconsistent with our assumption that the D^1 are irreducible, unless of course

$$A_l = 0 \quad \text{for} \quad l = 1, \ldots, n_2. \tag{3.2}$$

For $n_1 = n_2$, the space spanned by the A_l is the full space, provided that the A_l are linearly independent, i.e. det $A \neq 0$. This proves the first part of Schur's lemma.

The second part investigates in more detail the case $n_1 = n_2$. We exclude the trivial possibility $A = 0$, in which case (1) may be written as

$$D^2(\alpha_i) = A^{-1} \cdot D^1(\alpha_i) \cdot A \text{ for all } \alpha_i. \tag{3.3}$$

This is a similarity transformation which does not affect the matrix elements between state vectors. Representations D^2 and D^1 which are connected by (3) are called equivalent. The second part of Schur's lemma states that for $D^2 = D^1$, A must be a multiple of the unit matrix. This is proven as follows: In the relation $AD = DA$, we may add to A any $\mu \cdot 1$ multiple of the unit matrix 1, since this matrix certainly commutes with any D. Specifically, we now choose μ such that

$$\det(A - \mu \cdot 1) = 0. \tag{3.4}$$

If we allow complex values for μ, this equation has always a solution. By the first part of Schur's lemma, we find

$$A - \mu \cdot 1 = 0, \tag{3.5}$$

since the other possibility, det $(A - \mu \cdot 1) \neq 0$ is barred by construction.

As an application of Schur's lemma, we derive the orthogonality relations of the matrix elements of irreducible representations. For this purpose, we choose an arbitrary fixed $n_1 \times n_2$ matrix B and construct

$$A = \int d\Omega_i D^1(\alpha_i) B \cdot D^{2+}(\alpha_i), \tag{3.6}$$

where the integration covers the whole parameter space Ω_i. Since $D(\alpha_i') \cdot D(\alpha_i)$ gives another matrix $D(\alpha_i'')$ of the same representation, we have

$$D^1(\alpha_i') \cdot AD^{2+}(\alpha_i') = \int d\Omega_i'' D^1(\alpha_i'') B \cdot D^{2+}(\alpha_i'') = A. \tag{3.7}$$

Actually, we have assumed that the integral (6) is finite (compact groups), and that the Jacobian determinant of the transformation of variables $\alpha_i \to \alpha_i''$ is one. The latter requirement restricts the form of the differential $\mathrm{d}\Omega_i$. For SU_1, we have $\mathrm{d}\Omega_1 = \mathrm{d}\alpha_1$. For SU_2, the differential of the three Euler angles α, β, γ is $\mathrm{d}\alpha\,\mathrm{d}(\cos\beta)\mathrm{d}\gamma$. For a differential $\mathrm{d}\alpha\,\mathrm{d}\beta\,\mathrm{d}\gamma$ for example, (7) would be false.

From (7), we conclude that A has the property (1). Now Schur's lemma requires $A = 0$ for inequivalent irreducible representations. Since the matrix B was completely arbitrary, we conclude that

$$\int \mathrm{d}\Omega_i D^1_{ik}(\alpha_i) D^{2*}_{lm}(\alpha_i) = 0. \tag{3.8}$$

On the other hand, for $D^1 = D^2$, A is a multiple of the unit matrix, which implies

$$\int \mathrm{d}\Omega_i D_{ik}(\alpha_i) D^*_{lm}(\alpha_i) = \delta_{il}\, d_{km}. \tag{3.9}$$

Setting $i = l$ and summing, we get from the unitarity of the D-matrices.

$$\int \mathrm{d}\Omega_i D_{ik}(\alpha_i) D^*_{im}(\alpha_i) = \delta_{km} \int \mathrm{d}\Omega_i = n d_{km}, \tag{3.10}$$

where n is the dimension of the D-matrices. Equations (8), (9) and (10) may be combined into one single equation:

$$\int \mathrm{d}\Omega_i D^a_{ik}(\alpha_i) D^{b*}_{lm}(\alpha) = \delta_{ab}\,\delta_{il}\,\delta_{km} \frac{1}{n_a} \int \mathrm{d}\Omega_i . \tag{3.11}$$

Of course, we must assume that the integral over the parameter space is finite. For the group SU_2, with the Euler angles α, β, γ as parameters, (11) reads

$$\int \mathrm{d}\alpha\ \mathrm{d}\cos\beta\,\mathrm{d}\gamma\ D^{j*}_{\lambda\mu}(\alpha\beta\gamma) D^{j'}_{\lambda'\mu'}(\alpha\beta\gamma) = \frac{8\pi^2}{2j+1}\,\delta_{jj'}\,\delta_{\lambda\lambda'}\,\delta_{\mu\mu'} . \tag{3.12}$$

For a finite group such as the permutation group, the integral is replaced by the sum over all elements of the group.

APPENDIX C

REPRESENTATIONS OF SU_2

C-1. The matrix elements of J

The irreducible representations of SU_2 are usually given in the form

$$D(\alpha\beta\gamma) = e^{-i\alpha J_z} e^{-i\beta J_y} e^{-i\gamma J_z}. \tag{1.1}$$

They are constructed from the commutation relations of the three generators

$$[J_x, J_y] = iJ_z, \qquad \text{cyclic,} \tag{1.2}$$

which are obviously true for the generators $\frac{1}{2}\boldsymbol{\sigma}$ of 2×2 unitary matrices. Representations of higher dimensions may be found in two different ways. One can reduce the direct product of two SU_2 matrices into one three-dimensional and one one-dimensional representation, $(2\otimes 2 = 3+1)$. Then one can reduce the direct product of the three-dimensional matrices with the SU_2 matrices $(3\otimes 2 = 4+2)$ and so on. This method has the advantage of giving the Clebsch-Gordan coefficients at the same time. The other method is to determine first the matrices $\boldsymbol{J}$ for any dimension. This is the method found in the books of Edmonds [1957] and Rose [1957]. We review it briefly.

From (2) one concludes that the matrix

$$\boldsymbol{J}^2 = J_x^2 + J_y^2 + J_z^2 \tag{1.3}$$

commutes with all three generators. According to Schur's lemma, it must be a multiple of the unit matrix. We call its eigenvalue η_j, where $2j+1$ is the dimension of the matrices. The matrix J_z is chosen in diagonal form, with eigenvalues m_j. Then the matrix

$$J_x^2 + J_y^2 = \boldsymbol{J}^2 - J_z^2 \tag{1.4}$$

must also be diagonal, with eigenvalues $\eta_j - m_j^2$. All eigenvalues of the square of a Hermitean matrix are non-negative. For fixed η_j, this restricts the range of m. The next step is to show that the matrices

$$J_\pm = J_x \pm iJ_y \tag{1.5}$$

transform one eigenstate $|jm\rangle$ of $\boldsymbol{J}^2$ and J_z into another eigenstate with eigenvalue $m' = m \pm 1$:

$$J_{\pm}|jm\rangle = C_{\pm}(j, m)|j, m\pm 1\rangle, \tag{1.6}$$

where $C_{\pm}(j, m)$ are constants. This follows from the commutation relations

$$[J_z, J_{\pm}] = \pm J_{\pm}. \tag{1.7}$$

$$J_z J_{\pm}|jm\rangle = (J_{\pm}J_z + [J_z, J_{\pm}])|jm\rangle = J_{\pm}(J_z \pm 1)|jm\rangle$$
$$= (m\pm 1)J_{\pm}|jm\rangle. \tag{1.8}$$

Sucessive application of $J_+ (J_-)$ increases (decreases) the value of m without limit, unless there exist two values $m_{\max}, m_{\min}$, for which

$$J_+|j, m_{\max}\rangle = 0, \qquad J_-|j, m_{\min}\rangle = 0. \tag{1.9}$$

Multiplying the first of these equations by J_- and the second by J_+ and observing

$$J_{\mp}J_{\pm} = \boldsymbol{J}^2 - J_z(J_z \pm 1) = \eta_j - m(m\pm 1), \tag{1.10}$$

we find

$$\eta_j = m_{\max}(m_{\max}+1) = m_{\min}(m_{\min}-1). \tag{1.11}$$

The only solution of (11) is

$$m_{\max} = -m_{\min} = j, \qquad \eta_j = j(j+1). \tag{1.12}$$

Finally, since the Hermitean conjugate of J_+ is J_-, the absolute squares of $C_{\pm}(j, m)$ are given by (10). The phase is now fixed arbitrarily by the convention of CONDON and SHORTLEY [1935],

$$C_{\pm} = +\sqrt{j(j+1)-m(m\pm 1)} = +\sqrt{(j\mp m)(j\pm m+1)}. \tag{1.13}$$

This is in agreement with the choice $\boldsymbol{J} = \frac{1}{2}\boldsymbol{\sigma}$ for $j = \frac{1}{2}$. The calculation of the matrices $\boldsymbol{J}$ is now complete. We have found exactly one representation for every dimension.

C-2. The *d*-functions and their symmetries

With J_z in diagonal form, the matrix elements of $e^{-i\alpha J_z}$ are given by

$$(e^{-i\alpha J_z})_{mm'} = e^{-i\alpha m}\delta_{mm'}. \tag{2.1}$$

Thus the only nontrivial part of the rotation matrices (1.1) are the matrices $e^{-i\beta J_y}$. Their elements are denoted by $d^j_{mm'}(\beta)$. We thus have

$$D^j_{mm'}(\alpha\beta\gamma) = e^{-i\alpha m}d_{mm'}(\beta)e^{-i\gamma m'}. \tag{2.2}$$

In the text, we need only rotations with rotation axis in the xy-plane. The angle between the rotation axis and the y-axis is called φ or ϕ and the angle of rotation itself is called ϑ or θ. This corresponds to the Euler angles $\beta = \theta$, $\alpha = -\gamma = \phi$,

$$D^j_{mm'}(\phi, \theta, -\phi) = e^{i(m'-m)\phi} d_{mm'}(\theta). \tag{2.3}$$

In the previous section, we defined the matrix elements $C_\pm(j, m)$ of $J_\pm$ to be real. Then all matrix elements of J_y are imaginary, and the d-functions are real. From this a nice symmetry property follows. The rotation by an angle $-\theta$ is the inverse of the rotation by θ. Since the rotation matrices are unitary, the inverse equals the Hermitean conjugate, which, for a real matrix is simply the transpose:

$$d_{mm'}(-\theta) = d_{m'm}(\theta). \tag{2.4}$$

In order to derive more symmetry properties, we write $e^{-i\theta J_y}$ in the form

$$e^{-i\theta J_y} = e^{-\frac{1}{2}\theta(J_+ - J_-)}. \tag{2.5}$$

From (1.13) we find that all matrix elements of J_y are invariant under the exchange $m \to -m'$, $m' \to -m$. Consequently, the d-functions have the symmetry

$$d_{mm'} = d_{-m'-m}. \tag{2.6}$$

Next, the fact that the matrix $J_+ - J_-$ is antisymmetric and has non-zero matrix elements only if m and m' differ by one, leads to the following property: An even (odd) power of J_y is symmetric (antisymmetric) and has non-zero matrix elements only if m and m' differ by an even (odd) number. This can be summarized as

$$d_{mm'} = (-1)^{m-m'} d_{m'm}. \tag{2.7}$$

Finally, the fact that $d(2\pi)$ equals $d(0)$ $(-d(0))$ for integer (halfinteger) value of j is enough to determine $d(\pi)$ as

$$d^j_{mm'}(\pi) = (-1)^{j+m} \delta_{m,-m'}. \tag{2.8}$$

The basic symmetries (4), (6) and (7) may be combined into new relations. For example, combination of (6) and (7) yields

$$d_{mm'} = (-1)^{m-m'} d_{-m,-m'}. \tag{2.9}$$

For the matrix $D^j_{mm'}(\phi, \theta, -\phi)$, this implies,

$$D^j_{mm'} = (-1)^{m-m'} D^{j*}_{-m,-m'}. \tag{2.10}$$

C-3. Calculation of the *d*-functions

The explicit calculation of *d*-functions proceeds most conveniently by means of recurrence relations. The starting point is the famous Clebsch-Gordan series (see (10) below),

$$D^{j_1}_{m_1 m'_1} \cdot D^{j_2}_{m_2 m'_2} = \sum_j C^{j_1 j_2 j}_{m_1 m_2 m}\, C^{j_1 j_2 j}_{m'_1 m'_2 m'} \cdot D^{j}_{mm'}\,, \tag{3.1}$$

where C are the Clebsch-Gordan coefficients. Many different recurrence relations are possible. We transform (1) by means of the orthogonality relations of the Clebsch-Gordan coefficients into

$$C^{j_1 j_2 j}_{m'_1 m'_2 m'} \cdot D^{j}_{mm'} = \sum_{m_1} C^{j_1 j_2 j}_{m_1 m_2 m} \cdot D^{j_1}_{m_1 m'_1}\, D^{j_2}_{m_2 m'_2}\,. \tag{3.2}$$

All these formulae are valid for the *d*-functions as well. We start by calculating $d^{\frac{1}{2}}$ directly from its definition $e^{-\frac{1}{2} i\theta\sigma_y}$. The result is found in table C-3.

TABLE C-3

The functions $d^{s}_{mm'}(\theta)$ for $s=\frac{1}{2}$, 1, $\frac{3}{2}$ and 2

(Sign convention of ROSE [1957])

$m \backslash m'$	$+\frac{1}{2}$	$-\frac{1}{2}$
$+\frac{1}{2}$	$\cos\frac{1}{2}\theta$	$-\sin\frac{1}{2}\theta$
$-\frac{1}{2}$	$\sin\frac{1}{2}\theta$	$\cos\frac{1}{2}\theta$

$m \backslash m'$	$+1$	0	-1
$+1$	$\cos^2\frac{1}{2}\theta$	$-2^{-\frac{1}{2}}\sin\theta$	$\sin^2\frac{1}{2}\theta$
0	$2^{-\frac{1}{2}}\sin\theta$	$\cos\theta$	$-2^{-\frac{1}{2}}\sin\theta$
-1	$\sin^2\frac{1}{2}\theta$	$2^{-\frac{1}{2}}\sin\theta$	$\cos^2\frac{1}{2}\theta$

$m \backslash m'$	$+\frac{3}{2}$	$+\frac{1}{2}$	$-\frac{1}{2}$	$-\frac{3}{2}$
$+\frac{3}{2}$	$\cos^3\frac{1}{2}\theta$	$-3^{\frac{1}{2}}\cos^2\frac{1}{2}\theta\sin\frac{1}{2}\theta$	$3^{\frac{1}{2}}\cos\frac{1}{2}\theta\sin^2\frac{1}{2}\theta$	$-\sin^3\frac{1}{2}\theta$
$+\frac{1}{2}$	$3^{\frac{1}{2}}\cos^2\frac{1}{2}\theta\sin\frac{1}{2}\theta$	$\cos\frac{1}{2}\theta(1-3\sin^2\frac{1}{2}\theta)$	$-\sin\frac{1}{2}\theta(3\cos^2\frac{1}{2}\theta-1)$	$3^{\frac{1}{2}}\cos\frac{1}{2}\theta\sin^2\frac{1}{2}\theta$
$-\frac{1}{2}$	$3^{\frac{1}{2}}\cos\frac{1}{2}\theta\sin^2\frac{1}{2}\theta$	$\sin\frac{1}{2}\theta(3\cos^2\frac{1}{2}\theta-1)$	$\cos\frac{1}{2}\theta(1-3\sin^2\frac{1}{2}\theta)$	$-3^{\frac{1}{2}}\cos^2\frac{1}{2}\theta\sin\frac{1}{2}\theta$
$-\frac{3}{2}$	$+\sin^3\frac{1}{2}\theta$	$3^{\frac{1}{2}}\cos\frac{1}{2}\theta\sin^2\frac{1}{2}\theta$	$3^{\frac{1}{2}}\cos^2\frac{1}{2}\theta\sin\frac{1}{2}\theta$	$\cos^3\frac{1}{2}\theta$

$m \backslash m'$	2	1	0	-1	-2
2	$\cos^4\frac{1}{2}\theta$	$-2\cos^3\frac{1}{2}\theta\sin\frac{1}{2}\theta$	$6^{\frac{1}{2}}\cos^2\frac{1}{2}\theta\sin^2\frac{1}{2}\theta$	$-2\cos\frac{1}{2}\theta\sin^3\frac{1}{2}\theta$	$\sin^4\frac{1}{2}\theta$
1	$2\cos^3\frac{1}{2}\theta\sin\frac{1}{2}\theta$	$\cos^2\frac{1}{2}\theta(\cos^2\frac{1}{2}\theta-3\sin^2\frac{1}{2}\theta)$	$-\frac{3}{2}^{\frac{1}{2}}\sin\theta\cos\theta$	$\sin^2\frac{1}{2}\theta(3\cos^2\frac{1}{2}\theta-\sin^2\frac{1}{2}\theta)$	
0	$6^{\frac{1}{2}}\cos^2\frac{1}{2}\theta\sin^2\frac{1}{2}\theta$	$\frac{3}{2}^{\frac{1}{2}}\sin\theta\cos\theta$	$\frac{1}{2}(3\cos^2\theta-1)$		

Then in (2) we put $j_2 = \frac{1}{2}$, and $j_1 = j-\frac{1}{2}$. The relevant Clebsch-Gordan coefficients are

$$C^{j_1\frac{1}{2}j}_{m_1m_2m} = \sqrt{\frac{j\pm m}{2j_1+1}} \quad \text{for} \quad m_2 = \pm\tfrac{1}{2}. \tag{3.3}$$

We set $m_2' = +\frac{1}{2}$ in (2), and get

$$\sqrt{j+m'}\,d^j_{mm'} = \sqrt{j+m}\,d^{j-\frac{1}{2}}_{m-\frac{1}{2},\,m'-\frac{1}{2}} \cdot \cos\tfrac{1}{2}\theta + \sqrt{j-m}\,d^{j-\frac{1}{2}}_{m+\frac{1}{2},\,m'-\frac{1}{2}} \cdot \sin\tfrac{1}{2}\theta. \tag{3.4}$$

If we apply this formula twice, we obtain

$$2\sqrt{(j+m')(j+m'-1)}\,d^j_{mm'} = \sqrt{(j+m)(j+m-1)}(1+\cos\theta)d^{j-1}_{m-1,\,m'-1}$$
$$+2\sqrt{j^2-m^2}\sin\theta\, d^{j-1}_{m,\,m'-1} + \sqrt{(j-m)(j-m-1)}(1-\cos\theta)d^{j-1}_{m+1,\,m'-1}. \tag{3.5}$$

In the theory of scattering of particles with spin, one needs the d-functions for arbitrary values of j but for small values of m and m'. For that case, a convenient recurrence relation in m has been given by JACOB and WICK [1959].

$$d^j_{m',\,m\pm1} = [(j\pm m+1)(j\mp m)]^{-\frac{1}{2}}\left(\frac{-m'}{\sin\theta} + m\cot\theta \mp \frac{\partial}{\partial\theta}\right) d^j_{m'm}. \tag{3.6}$$

The proof of this formula makes use of the relation

$$\mathrm{e}^{-\mathrm{i}\theta J_y} J_z \mathrm{e}^{\mathrm{i}\theta J_y} = \cos\theta J_z + \sin\theta J_x. \tag{3.7}$$

This relation is evident from the geometrical interpretation in terms of rotations. It allows one to express $J_x \mathrm{e}^{-\mathrm{i}\theta J_y}$ in terms of J_z and $\mathrm{e}^{-\mathrm{i}\theta J_y}$. Using the relation

$$-\mathrm{i}J_y \mathrm{e}^{-\mathrm{i}\theta J_y} = \frac{\partial}{\partial\theta}\mathrm{e}^{-\mathrm{i}\theta J_y}, \tag{3.8}$$

we obtain

$$(J_x \pm \mathrm{i}J_y)\mathrm{e}^{-\mathrm{i}\theta J_y} = \frac{1}{\sin\theta}\mathrm{e}^{-\mathrm{i}\theta J_y}J_z - \cot\theta J_z \mathrm{e}^{-\mathrm{i}\theta J_y} \mp \frac{\partial}{\partial\theta}\mathrm{e}^{-\mathrm{i}\theta J_y}. \tag{3.9}$$

Now we get (6) by inserting the matrix elements (1.13) into this last equation.

The Clebsch-Gordan coefficients $C^{j_1j_2j}_{m_1m_2m}$ are defined by the expansion of product states $|j_1m_1\rangle|j_2m_2\rangle$ in terms of the basic states of irreducible representations,

$$|j_1m_1\rangle|j_2m_2\rangle = \sum_{jm} C^{j_1j_2j}_{m_1m_2m}|jm\rangle. \tag{3.10}$$

By considering the transformation of these states under rotations (3-1.1), one immediately obtains (1). The symmetries and orthonormality relations of the Clebsch-Gordan coefficients all follow from the corresponding properties of the D-functions.

C-4. *D*-functions for integer *j*

The functions $d^L_{00}(\theta)$ are identical with the Legendre polynomials $P_L(\cos\theta)$. To show this, we first notice from (3.5) that $d^L_{mm'}$ is a polynomial of degree L in $\cos\theta$ and $\sin\theta$. For $m = m' = 0$, the symmetry (2.4) shows that d^L_{00} is a polynomial in $\cos\theta$ only. The orthogonality relations for d-functions follow from (B-3.12) and the decomposition (1.1):

$$\int_{-1}^{1} \mathrm{d}(\cos\theta) d^j_{mm'} d^{j'}_{mm'} = \frac{2}{2j+1}\delta_{jj'}, \tag{4.1}$$

which coincides with the orthogonality relation (A-1.1) for the P_L.

Next, the spherical harmonics are defined by

$$Y^L_M(\theta,\phi) = \sqrt{\frac{2L+1}{4\pi}}\, D^{L*}_{M0}(\phi,\theta,-\phi) = \sqrt{\frac{2L+1}{4\pi}}\, d^L_{M0}(\theta)\mathrm{e}^{\mathrm{i}M\phi}. \tag{4.2}$$

From (1), it is obvious that these functions are orthonormal on a unit sphere:

$$\int \mathrm{d}\Omega\, Y^{L*}_M(\Omega) Y^{L'}_{M'}(\Omega) = \delta_{LL'}\delta_{MM'}. \tag{4.3}$$

The spherical harmonics addition theorem,

$$P_L(\cos\theta'') = \frac{4\pi}{2L+1}\sum_M Y^{L*}_M(\theta,\phi) Y^L_M(\theta',\phi'), \tag{4.4}$$

$$\cos\theta'' \equiv \cos\theta\cos\theta' + \sin\theta\sin\theta'\cos(\phi-\phi'),$$

is a consequence of the group property of the D-functions,

$$D_{m'm''}(\alpha''\beta''\gamma'') = \sum_m D_{m'm}(\alpha\beta\gamma)\cdot D_{mm''}(\alpha'\beta'\gamma'), \tag{4.5}$$

for $m' = m'' = 0$. Finally we compute the functions $d^L_{M0} = d^L_{0,-M}$ by means of the recurrence relation (3.6) for $m' = 0$:

$$d^L_{0,M-1} = [(L-M+1)(L-M)]^{-\frac{1}{2}}\left(M\cot\theta + \frac{\partial}{\partial\theta}\right) d^L_{0M} \tag{4.6}$$

Starting with $M = 0$, the d^L_{0M} may be expressed in terms of P_L and its derivatives. The first two cases are

$$d^L_{0,-1} = d^L_{10} = \frac{-1}{\sqrt{L(L+1)}} \sin\theta P'_L(x), \tag{4.7}$$

$$d^L_{20} = [L(L^2-1)(L+2)]^{-\frac{1}{2}}[2P'_{L-1}(x) - L(L-1)P_L(x)]. \tag{4.8}$$

The prime means derivation with respect to $x = \cos\theta$. In deriving (8) from (6), we have applied (A-1.9) to eliminate the second derivative.

From (7) and (8) we can now construct $d^j_{MM'}$ for small values of M and M'. The values given in table C-4 are taken from the recurrence relation (3.4).

TABLE C-4

Some d-functions for half-integer j

$$(j+\tfrac{1}{2})d^j_{\frac{1}{2}\frac{1}{2}} = \cos\tfrac{1}{2}\theta(P'_{j+\frac{1}{2}} - P'_{j-\frac{1}{2}})$$

$$(j+\tfrac{1}{2})d^j_{-\frac{1}{2}\frac{1}{2}} = \sin\tfrac{1}{2}\theta(P'_{j+\frac{1}{2}} + P'_{j-\frac{1}{2}})$$

$$(j+\tfrac{1}{2})d^j_{\frac{1}{2}\frac{3}{2}} = \frac{\sin\frac{1}{2}\theta}{\sqrt{(j-\frac{1}{2})(j+\frac{3}{2})}}[(j-\tfrac{1}{2})P'_{j+\frac{1}{2}} + (j+\tfrac{3}{2})P'_{j-\frac{1}{2}}]$$

$$(j+\tfrac{1}{2})d^j_{-\frac{1}{2}\frac{3}{2}} = \frac{\cos\frac{1}{2}\theta}{\sqrt{(j-\frac{1}{2})(j+\frac{3}{2})}}[-(j-\tfrac{1}{2})P'_{j+\frac{1}{2}} + (j+\tfrac{3}{2})P'_{j-\frac{1}{2}}]$$

APPENDIX D

THE GROUP SU_3

D-1. The generators of SU_3

The most general 3×3 unimodular unitary matrix may be written as

$$\mathrm{SU}_3 = \mathrm{e}^{\mathrm{i}H_3}, \qquad H_3 = \sum_{i=1}^{8} \alpha_i \lambda_i, \tag{1.1}$$

where the α_i are real numbers and the λ_i are linearly independent traceless Hermitean matrices. It is useful to take λ_1, λ_2 and λ_3 in the form

$$\lambda_i = \begin{pmatrix} \sigma_i & 0 \\ 0 & 0 \end{pmatrix} \qquad \text{for} \quad i = 1, 2, 3. \tag{1.2}$$

The matrices (2) are explicitly

$$\lambda_1 = \begin{pmatrix} 0 & 1 & 0 \\ 1 & 0 & 0 \\ 0 & 0 & 0 \end{pmatrix}, \quad \lambda_2 = \begin{pmatrix} 0 & -i & 0 \\ i & 0 & 0 \\ 0 & 0 & 0 \end{pmatrix}, \quad \lambda_3 = \begin{pmatrix} 1 & 0 & 0 \\ 0 & -1 & 0 \\ 0 & 0 & 0 \end{pmatrix}. \tag{1.3}$$

They generate SU_2 transformations of the eigenstates of λ_3. By analogy with isospin transformations of proton, neutron and Λ, such states are occasionally called $\underline{\mathrm{p}}$, $\underline{\mathrm{n}}$ and $\underline{\Lambda}$:

$$\underline{\mathrm{p}} = \begin{pmatrix} 1 \\ 0 \\ 0 \end{pmatrix}, \quad \underline{\mathrm{n}} = \begin{pmatrix} 0 \\ 1 \\ 0 \end{pmatrix}, \quad \underline{\Lambda} = \begin{pmatrix} 0 \\ 0 \\ 1 \end{pmatrix}. \tag{1.4}$$

In addition to λ_3, there is one more linearly-independent diagonal matrix of zero trace. It is chosen as

$$\lambda_8 = \frac{1}{\sqrt{3}} \begin{pmatrix} 1 & 0 & 0 \\ 0 & 1 & 0 \\ 0 & 0 & -2 \end{pmatrix} \tag{1.5}$$

Finally, the matrices λ_4, λ_5, (λ_6, λ_7) may be taken as σ_1 and σ_2, but this time with zeros in the second row and column (first row and column):

$$\lambda_4 = \begin{pmatrix} 0 & 0 & 1 \\ 0 & 0 & 0 \\ 1 & 0 & 0 \end{pmatrix}, \quad \lambda_5 = \begin{pmatrix} 0 & 0 & -\mathrm{i} \\ 0 & 0 & 0 \\ \mathrm{i} & 0 & 0 \end{pmatrix},$$

$$\lambda_6 = \begin{pmatrix} 0 & 0 & 0 \\ 0 & 0 & 1 \\ 0 & 1 & 0 \end{pmatrix}, \quad \lambda_7 = \begin{pmatrix} 0 & 0 & 0 \\ 0 & 0 & -\mathrm{i} \\ 0 & \mathrm{i} & 0 \end{pmatrix}. \tag{1.6}$$

This exhausts the list of generators. The matrix

$$\begin{pmatrix} 0 & 0 \\ 0 & \sigma_3 \end{pmatrix}$$

for example is composed as

$$\begin{pmatrix} 0 & 0 \\ 0 & \sigma_3 \end{pmatrix} = \tfrac{1}{2}(-\lambda_3 + \sqrt{3}\lambda_8) \equiv \lambda_9 . \tag{1.7}$$

Together with λ_6 and λ_7, it generates matrices

$$\begin{pmatrix} 1 & 0 \\ 0 & \mathrm{SU}_2 \end{pmatrix}$$

which leave the p̲ state of (4) invariant. Such transformations are called *U*-spin transformations. In analogy to *I*-spin, the eigenvalues of λ_9 are called $2U_3$. The states (4) have $U_3 = 0, \frac{1}{2}$ and $-\frac{1}{2}$, respectively.

The normalization of the generators $\lambda_1, \ldots, \lambda_8$ is such that

$$\operatorname{trace}(\lambda_i \lambda_j) = 2\delta_{ij} . \tag{1.8}$$

The commutation relations are

$$[\lambda_i, \lambda_j] = 2\mathrm{i} f_{ijk} \lambda_k . \tag{1.9}$$

The structure constants f_{ijk} are antisymmetric in all three indices. The antisymmetry in i and j follows directly from the definition (9). The antisymmetry in i and k follows from the insertion of (9) into (8):

$$\begin{aligned} 4\mathrm{i} f_{ijk} &= \operatorname{trace} \lambda_k [\lambda_i, \lambda_j] = \operatorname{trace} \lambda_k (\lambda_i \lambda_j - \lambda_j \lambda_i) \\ &= \operatorname{trace} (\lambda_k \lambda_i \lambda_j - \lambda_i \lambda_k \lambda_j) = -\operatorname{trace} [\lambda_i, \lambda_k] \lambda_j . \end{aligned} \tag{1.10}$$

The non-zero elements of f_{ijk} are

ijk	123	147	156	246	257	345	367	458	678
f_{ijk}	1	$\frac{1}{2}$	$-\frac{1}{2}$	$\frac{1}{2}$	$\frac{1}{2}$	$\frac{1}{2}$	$-\frac{1}{2}$	$\sqrt{\frac{3}{4}}$	$\sqrt{\frac{3}{4}}$

(1.11)

An even (odd) permutation of the listed indices corresponds to multiplication of f_{ijk} by $+1$ (-1). An easy way of deriving (11) is to compute $[\lambda_i, \lambda_j]$ first for $i, j = 1, 2, 3$, then for $i, j = 6, 7, 9$, and to eliminate λ_9 by (7).

D-2. Representations of SU_3

We now construct irreducible representations of SU_3 by the method outlined in B-2. The second rank tensor was already reduced according to (7). The reduction of the third rank tensor is

$$3\otimes 3\otimes 3 = (\bar{3}+6)\otimes 3,\ \bar{3}\otimes 3 = 1+8,\ 6\otimes 3 = 8+10. \tag{2.1}$$

From our general formula following (B-2.8), we find 10 and 1 as the dimensions of the totally symmetric and anti-symmetric representations, respectively, and 8 as the dimension of the two remaining representations.

For the construction of the representations, it is useful to introduce a vector with an upper index η^α by means of the totally antisymmetric tensor $\varepsilon_{\alpha\beta\gamma}$ in three indices,

$$\eta^\alpha = \varepsilon_{\alpha\beta\gamma} \cdot T_{[\beta\gamma]}. \tag{2.2}$$

Under the transformation (B-2.6), η transforms into

$$\eta'^\alpha = \varepsilon_{\alpha\beta\gamma} U_{\beta\beta'} U_{\gamma\gamma'} T_{[\beta'\gamma']}. \tag{2.3}$$

In this equation, we insert a factor $\delta_{\alpha\lambda}$ by means of the unitarity

$$\delta_{\alpha\lambda} = U^*_{\alpha\alpha'} U_{\lambda\alpha'},$$

$$\begin{aligned}\eta'^\alpha &= \delta_{\alpha\lambda}\varepsilon_{\lambda\beta\gamma} U_{\beta\beta'} U_{\gamma\gamma'} T_{[\beta'\gamma']} = U^*_{\alpha\alpha'}\varepsilon_{\lambda\beta\gamma} U_{\lambda\alpha'} U_{\beta\beta'} U_{\gamma\gamma'} T_{[\beta'\gamma']} \\ &= \det(U)\cdot U^*_{\alpha\alpha'}\varepsilon_{\alpha'\beta'\gamma'}\cdot T_{[\beta'\gamma']} = U^*_{\alpha\alpha'}\cdot\eta^{\alpha'},\end{aligned} \tag{2.4}$$

since $\det U = 1$. The matrices U^* are said to form the *conjugate* representation of the matrices U. The product $\bar{3}\otimes 3$ is now easily reduced. The transformation law (4) can be summarized as $\eta' = \eta U^+ = \eta U^{-1}$, which shows that $\eta^\alpha \xi_\alpha$ is invariant under unitary transformations. It therefore belongs to the representation 1. The remaining part,

$$T^\beta_\alpha = \eta^\alpha \xi_\beta - \tfrac{1}{3}\delta_{\alpha\beta}\eta^\gamma \xi_\gamma \tag{2.5}$$

gives the unitary octet. The reduction of the product $6\otimes 3$ proceeds along similar lines. The totally symmetric part of

$$T_{\{\alpha\beta\}\gamma} = T_{\{\alpha\beta\}}\xi_\gamma \tag{2.6}$$

may be written down directly; it is $\frac{1}{6}$ of the sum of all permutations of the three indices. The part which is anti-symmetric in β and γ is

$$T_\alpha^\delta = T_{\{\alpha\beta\}\gamma} \cdot \varepsilon_{\beta\gamma\delta}. \tag{2.7}$$

The trace of this mixed tensor is again zero, which shows that it belongs to the representation 8.

Instead of (7), we now consider the combinations

$$T_i = \tfrac{1}{2}\,\mathrm{Trace}\,(T \cdot \lambda_i) = \tfrac{1}{2}T_\alpha^\beta(\lambda_i)_{\alpha\beta} = \tfrac{1}{2}\eta^\alpha(\lambda_i)_{\alpha\beta}\,\xi_\beta\,, \tag{2.8}$$

where the λ_i are the eight generators of the previous section. Under infinitesimal unitary transformations, ξ and η are multiplied by $1+\mathrm{i}\alpha_k\lambda_k$ and $1-\mathrm{i}\alpha_k\lambda_k$, respectively. The effect on the combination (8) is

$$\begin{aligned} T_i' &= \eta^{\alpha'}(\delta_{\alpha\alpha'} - \mathrm{i}\alpha_k(\lambda_k)_{\alpha\alpha'})(\tfrac{1}{2}\lambda_i)_{\alpha\beta}(\delta_{\beta\beta'} + \mathrm{i}\alpha_k(\lambda_k)_{\beta\beta'})\xi_{\beta'} \\ &= \eta^\alpha(\tfrac{1}{2}\lambda_i)_{\alpha\beta}\,\xi_\beta - \tfrac{1}{2}i\alpha_k\eta^\alpha[\lambda_k, \lambda_i]_{\alpha\beta}\,\xi_\beta = T_i + 2\alpha_k f_{kij}\,T_j\,. \end{aligned} \tag{2.9}$$

Comparing this with (B-2.4), we find the result that in the form (8) of the 8-dimensional representation, the generators are related with the structure constants:

$$(T_k)_{ij} = -\mathrm{i}f_{kij}\,. \tag{2.10}$$

APPENDIX E

TRACES OF γ-MATRICES

Of the 16 linearly independent γ-matrices enumerated in (3-6.1), only the unit matrix has a non-vanishing trace. From the definition (3-5.11), we see that γ_5 has zero trace. Moreover, γ_5 anticommutes with the four Dirac matrices γ_μ. With trace (ABC) = trace (CAB), we have

$$\text{trace}\,\gamma_\mu = \text{trace}\,\gamma_\mu\gamma_5^2 = \text{trace}\,\gamma_5\gamma_\mu\gamma_5 = -\text{trace}\,\gamma_\mu\gamma_5^2 = -\text{trace}\,\gamma_\mu, \quad (1.1)$$

i.e. trace $\gamma_\mu = 0$. The same proof applies to any product of an odd number of γ_μ-matrices, and also to the pseudovector matrices $\gamma_\mu\gamma_5$. The traces of the tensor matrices $\sigma_{\mu\nu}$ vanish because of the antisymmetry of $\sigma_{\mu\nu}$. From the relations

$$\gamma_\mu\gamma_\nu = 1\cdot g_{\mu\nu}+\sigma_{\mu\nu}, \qquad \text{trace}\ (1) = 4, \quad (1.2)$$

we find

$$\text{trace}\ \gamma_\mu\gamma_\nu = 4g_{\mu\nu}. \quad (1.3)$$

In the applications, matrices γ_μ are frequently contracted with 4-vectors P^μ. For such cases, it is useful to define a generalized scalar product

$$(P_1 P_2 \ldots P_n) \equiv \tfrac{1}{4}\,\text{trace}\,(P_1^\alpha\gamma_\alpha P_2^\beta\gamma_\beta \ldots P_n^\nu\gamma_\nu), \quad (1.4)$$

which by (3) reduces to the normal scalar product $P_1 \cdot P_2$ for $n = 2$. In general, (4) obeys the recurrence relation

$$(P_1P_2 \ldots P_n) = P_1\cdot P_2(P_3 \ldots P_n) - P_1\cdot P_3(P_2 \ldots P_n) + - \ldots + P_1\cdot P_n(P_2 \ldots P_{n-1}). \quad (1.5)$$

To prove (5), one iterates the relation

$$P_1^\mu\gamma_\mu P_x^\nu\gamma_\nu = 2P_1\cdot P_x - P_x^\nu\gamma_\nu P_1^\mu\gamma_\mu \quad (1.6)$$

$n-1$ times, until the $P_1^\mu\gamma_\mu$ has been transferred to the last position in the bracket. (4) We assume that n is even, otherwise the trace vanishes. After $n-1$ iterations, one thus ends up with an expression of the form

$$(P_1P_2 \ldots P_n) = 2(n-1\ \text{terms}) - (P_2 \ldots P_nP_1). \quad (1.7)$$

The invariance of the trace under cyclic permutations implies $(P_1 P_2 \dots P_n) = (P_2 \dots P_n P_1)$, and the final results is (5).

An important special case of (5) is

$$\tfrac{1}{4}\,\text{trace}\,(P_1^\alpha \gamma_\alpha P_2^\beta \gamma_\beta P_3^\gamma \gamma_\gamma P_4^\delta \gamma_\delta) = (P_1 P_2)(P_3 P_4) - (P_1 P_3)(P_2 P_4) + (P_1 P_4)(P_2 P_3). \qquad (1.8)$$

LIST OF FREQUENTLY USED SYMBOLS

A = first scalar amplitude of meson-nucleon scattering (3-9.14), scattering length (2-6.3), complex parameters of K^-p interactions (8-3.5), (8-3.7)

a = incident particle, πN scattering length (7-2.7)

B = second scalar amplitude of meson-nucleon scattering (3-9.14), vertex factor in Born approximation (6-4.4)

b = target particle

C = charge conjugation and charge conjugation matrix (4-7.3)

$C^{J_1 J_2 J}_{M_1 M_2 M}$ = Clebsch-Gordan coefficient (C-3.10)

c = outgoing particle;

cms = centre-of-momentum system (1-2.1)

D = D-matrix (C-1.1)

$D_{M'M}$ = its elements

d = outgoing particle, decaying particle, or particle with secondary scattering;

$d_{M'M}(\theta)$ = d-function (C-2.2)

d Lips = phase space element

dσ = differential cross-section,

dΓ = differential decay rate

E = energy (1-1.3)

e = electron, exchanged (virtual) particle

e = electric charge

F = form factor

f = Fermi integral (12-1.9)

f = final state, coupling constant (6-4.12), $\pi\pi$-resonance; f_1, f_2 = scattering amplitudes (3-8.1), $f_{L\pm}$ = their partial-wave component (3-9.4)

fm = fermi (1-1.7)

G = coupling constant, G-parity

g = coupling constant

g_L = logarithmic derivative of wave function (2-5.12)

$g_{\mu\nu}$ = metric tensor, $g_{00} = 1$, $g_{ik} = -\delta_{ik}$ (1-1.13)

H = Hamiltonian, Hermitean matrix

I	=	isospin, I_3 its third component
i	=	initial state
J, j	=	total angular momentum
K	=	kaon
K	=	partial-wave K-matrix
$k_\pm$	=	(11-2.8)
L	=	integer angular momentum;
Lips	=	Lorentz invariant phase space (sect. 1-5)
l	=	lepton
M	=	magnetic quantum number
m	=	mass
N	=	nucleon (p or n)
N*	=	pion-nucleon resonance
n	=	neutron
O	=	any of the 16 Dirac matrices (3-6.1)
P	=	P^μ, principle value
$\mathscr{P}$	=	parity operator
P^μ	=	total 4-momentum (E, $\boldsymbol{p}$)
$\boldsymbol{P}$	=	polarization vector (9-3.9)
P_L	=	Legendre polynomial
P	=	P-wave: $L = 1$
p	=	proton, $\lvert\boldsymbol{p}\rvert$; $\hat{\boldsymbol{p}} = \boldsymbol{p}/p$; $\boldsymbol{p} = (p_x, p_y, p_z)$
Q	=	electric charge (in units of e), 4×4 matrix containing Dirac matrices (3-5.10, 3-5.14)
Q_L	=	Legendre functions of second kind
q	=	magnitude of cms momentum in two-particle reactions (in inelastic reactions, q' for the final state)
R	=	radius, range of interaction
r	=	distance
S	=	spin, S-matrix (elements S_{if}), S-wave ($L = 0$)
s	=	(total cms energy)^2, s_{ik} = (effective mass of particles i and k)^2
s_{d}	=	P_{d}^2
T	=	T-matrix (elements T_{if}); T_J = partial wave T-matrix (T_{L} for spinless one-channel scattering)
$\mathscr{T}$	=	time reversal
t	=	square of 4-momentum transfer (1-3.3), time in sections 2-2, 2-3
U	=	unitary matrix, U-spin
u	=	$\sum m^2 - s - t$ (1-3.5), radial wave function (2-5.2), Dirac spinor, usually (3-5.12)

V = 2μ times potential (2-5.1)
v = velocity p/E
v_L = penetration factor (5-1.9)
W = probability, fictitious vector boson in weak interactions (W^- represents $e\bar{\nu}$ and $\mu^-\nu$)
x = $\cos\theta$
Y = hypercharge
Y^* = pion-hyperon resonance; Y_M^L = spherical harmonics
$\mathscr{Y}$ = inversion of the y-axis (9-1.9)
z = extension of s to complex values, argument of the Legendre functions of second kind (2-6.6)

α = $e^2/4\pi$, α-particle, fraction of D-type coupling
Γ = width, decay rate, gamma function
γ = photon, reduced width (5-1.9)
γ_μ, γ_5 = Dirac matrices (usually 3-5.15), $\gamma_\mu\gamma_\nu + \gamma_\nu\gamma_\mu = 2g_{\mu\nu}$
δ = delta function, δ_L = phase shift
ε = $m\Gamma$ for $\Gamma \to 0$ (6-1.7); $\varepsilon^\mu = (\varepsilon_0, \boldsymbol{\varepsilon})$ = polarization vector
η = eta meson, intrinsic parity
η_c = charge parity (4-7.1)
θ = cms scattering angle (1-3.7), Cabibbo angle (12-9.1)
ϑ = polar angle of some momentum, other angle
κ = anomalous magnetic moment (10-2.1)
Λ = lambda hyperon
λ = helicity, triangle function (1-2.8)
μ = muon, reduced mass, pion mass in πN-scattering
ν = neutrino
Ξ = cascade particle
π = pion or 3.14...
ρ = $\pi\pi$-resonance, density matrix
Σ = Sigma hyperon, summation
σ = cross-section, $\pi\pi$-resonance; $\boldsymbol{\sigma} = (\sigma_x, \sigma_y, \sigma_z)$ = Pauli matrices
τ = proper time
Φ = propagator; ϕ = $\overline{\text{K}}$K resonance, azimuthal scattering angle
φ = azimuthal angle, any angle
χ = two-component spinor, χ_0 for particles at rest
ψ = Schrödinger wave function
Ω = Omega particle, solid angles
ω = omega vector meson

REFERENCES *

Aachen-Berlin-Birmingham-Bonn-Hamburg-London (I.C.)-München collaboration, 1964, Nuovo Cim. **34**, 495-(*11*); 1965, Phys. Rev. **138** B897-(*11, 20*)

Aachen-Berlin-CERN Collaboration, 1965, Phys. Letters **19**, 608-(*278*)

ADLER, S. L., 1965, Phys. Rev. **137** B, 1022-(*320*)

ALLEN, J. S., R. L. BURMAN, W. B. HERRMANSFELDT, T. STÄHELIN and T. H. BRAID, 1959, Phys. Rev. **116**, 134-(*305*)

ALSTON, M., L. W. ALVAREZ, P. EBERHARD, M. L. GOOD, W. GRAZIANO, H. K. TICHO and S. G. WOJCICKI, 1960, Phys. Rev. Letters **5**, 520-(*129*); 1961, Phys. Rev. Letters **6**, 300-(*143*)

ALVÄGER, T., F. J. M. FARLEY, J. KJELLMAN and I. WALLIN, 1964, Phys. Letters **12**, 260-(*2*)

AMATI, D., S. FUBINI and A. STANGHELLINI, 1962, Nuovo Cim. **26**, 896-(*295*)

ANDERSON, C. D., 1933, Phys. Rev. **43**, 491-(*104*)

ARNOLD, R. C. and J. L. URETSKY, 1967, Phys. Rev. **153**, 1443-(*206*)

AUVIL, P. R. and J. J. BREHM, 1966, Phys. Rev. **145**, 1152-(*72*)

BADE, W. L. and H. JEHLE, 1953, Rev. Mod. Phys. **25**, 714-(*68*)

BALL, J. S., A. SCOTTI and D. Y. WONG, 1966, Phys. Rev. **142**, 1000-(*140*)

BAREYRE, P., C. BRICKMAN, A. V. STIRLING and G. VILLET, 1965, Phys. Letters **18**, 342-(*47, 125*)

BARTON, G., 1965, *Introduction to Dispersion Techniques in Field Theory*, (Benjamin, New York)-(*199*)

BELL, J. S. and J. STEINBERGER, 1966, *Proc. Oxford Int. Conf. on Elem. Particles* 1965 (Rutherford High Energy Laboratory)-(*330, 334*)

BERLEY, D., S. HERZBACH, R. KOFLER, S. YAMAMOTO, W. HEINTZELMAN, M. SCHIFF, J. THOMPSON and W. WILLIS, 1966, Phys. Rev. Letters **17**, 1071-(*240*)

BERMAN, S. M., 1958, Phys. Rev. **112**, 267-(311)

BERNSTEIN, J., M. GELL-MANN and W. THIRRING, 1960, Nuovo Cim. **16**, 560-(*320*)

BERTANZA, L., V. BRISSON, P. L. CONNOLLY, E. L. HART, I. S. MITTRA, G. C. MONETI, R. R. RAU, N. P. SAMIOS, I. O. SKILLICORN, S. S. YAMAMOTO, M. GOLDBERG, C. GRAY, J. LEITNER, S. LICHTMAN and J. WESTGARD, 1963, Phys. Rev. Letters **10**, 176-(*131*)

BIAŁAS, A. and B. E. Y. SVENSSON, 1965, Nuovo Cim. **42**, 672-(*275*)

BJORKEN, J. D. and S. D. DRELL, 1964, *Relativistic Quantum Mechanics*; 1965, *Relativistic Quantum Fields*, (McGraw-Hill, New York)-(*247*)

BLATT, J. M. and V. F. WEISSKOPF, 1952, *Theoretical Nuclear Physics*, (John Wiley & Sons, New York)-(*121*)

BLUDMAN, S. A., 1963, Nuovo Cim. **27**, 751-(*312*)

* The numbers in parentheses appearing at the end of the reference indicate the pages of this book.

BONAMY, P., P. BORGEAUD, C. BRUNETON, P. FALK-VAIRANT, O. GUISAN, P. SONDEREGGER, C. CAVERZASIO, J. P. GUILLAUD, J. SCHNEIDER, M. YVERT, I. MANELLI, F. SERGIAMPIETRI and L. VINCELLI, 1966, Phys. Letters **23**, 501-(*293*)

BONSIGNORI, F. and F. SELLERI, 1960, Nuovo Cim. **15**, 465-(*279*)

BOWEN, T., 1966, Phys. Rev. Letters **16**, 112-(*330*)

BURGY, M. T., V. E. KROHN, T. B. NOVEY, G. R. RINGO and V. L. TELEGDI, 1958, Phys. Rev. **110**, 1214-(*307*)

BYERS, N. and S. FENSTER, 1963, Phys. Rev. Letters **11**, 52-(*131*)

CABIBBO, N., 1963, Phys. Rev. Letters **10**, 531-(*321*)

CALDWELL, *et al.*, 1964, CERN-Bologna-Liverpool-Ann Arbor collaboration, Phys. Letters **8**, 288; 1965, Nuovo Cim. **38**, 60(-*276*)

CAMERINI, U., W. F. FRY and J. GAIDOS, 1964, Nuovo Cim. **38**, 1096-(*327*)

CAP, F., 1954, Fortschritte der Physik **2**, 207(-*68*)

CARTER, A. A., 1967, Nuovo Cim. **48**, 15-(*140*)

CARTWRIGHT, W. F., C. RICHMAN, M. N. WHITEHEAD and H. A. WILCOX, 1953, Phys. Rev. **91**, 677-(*102*)

CHAMBERLAIN, O., E. SEGRÉ, C. WIEGAND and T. YPSILANTIS, 1955, Phys. Rev. **100**, 947; 1956, Nature **177**, 11-(*103*)

CHAN, L. H., K. W. CHEN, J. R. DUNNING, N. F. RAMSEY, J. K. WALKER and R. WILSON, 1966, Phys. Rev. **141**, 1298-(*254*)

CHEW, G. F., 1962, *S-Matrix Theory of Strong Interactions* (Benjamin, New York)-(*30, 181, 201*); 1966, *The Analytic S-Matrix* (Benjamin, New York)-(*179*)

CHEW, G. F. and S. C. FRAUTSCHI, 1960 (1961), Phys. Rev. Letters **7**, 394; **8**, 41-(*293*)

CHEW, G. F., M. L. GOLDBERGER, F. E. LOW and Y. NAMBU, 1957, Phys. Rev. **106**, 1345-(*263, 269*)

CHEW, G. F. and F. E. LOW, 1956, Phys. Rev. **101**, 1570 (photoproduction p. 1579)-(*191, 196*)

CHEW, G. F. and F. E. LOW, 1959, Phys. Rev. **113**, 1640-(*13, 280*)

CHEW, G. F. and S. MANDELSTAM, 1960, Phys. Rev. **119**, 467-(*199*); 1961, Nuovo Cim. **19**, 752-(*200*)

CHINOWSKY, W., G. GOLDHABER, S. GOLDHABER, W. LEE and T. O'HALLORAN, 1962, Phys. Rev. Letters **9**, 330; 1963, Phys. Letters **6**, 62-(*21*)

CHINOWSKY, W. and J. STEINBERGER, 1954, Phys. Rev. **95**, 1561; 1955, Phys. Rev. **100**, 1476-(*99*)

CHRISTENSON, J. H., J. W. CRONIN, V. L. FITCH and R. TURLAY, 1964, Phys. Rev. Letters **13**, 138-(*117, 325*)

CLARK, D. L., A. ROBERTS and R. WILSON, 1951, Phys. Rev. **83**, 649-(*102*)

COESTER, F., 1951, Phys. Rev. **84**, 1259-(*102*)

COHEN, E. R. and J. W. M. DUMOND, 1965, Rev. Mod. Phys. **37**, 537-(*1*)

COLEMAN, S. and S. L. GLASHOW, 1961, Phys. Rev. Letters **6**, 423-(*259, 260*)

COLEMAN, S. and R. E. NORTON, 1965, Nuovo Cim. **38**, 438-(*170*)

CONDON, E. U. and G. H. SHORTLEY, 1935, *The Theory of Atomic Spectra* (Cambridge University Press)-(*91, 348*)

COURANT, H., H. FILTHUTH, P. FRANZINI, R. G. GLASSER, A. MINGUZZI-RANZI, A. SEGAR and W. WILLIS, 1963, Phys. Rev. Letters **10**, 409-(*100*)

CUTKOSKY, R. E., 1960, J. Math. Phys. **1**, 429-(*170*)

DALITZ, R. H., 1953, Phil. Mag. **44**, 1068-(*11*); 1961, Rev. Mod. Phys. **33**, 471-(*215*); 1962, *Strange Particles and Strong Interactions* (Oxford University Press)-(*210*)

DALITZ, R. H. and S. F. TUAN, 1959, Ann. Phys. **8**, 100; 1960, Ann. Phys. **10**, 307-(*210, 214*)

DANBY, G., J. M. GAILLARD, K. GOULIANOS, L. M. LEDERMAN, N. MISTRY, M. SCHWARTZ and J. STEINBERGER, 1962, Phys. Rev. Letters **9**, 36-(*312*)

DASHEN, R. F. and D. H. SHARP, 1964, Phys. Rev. **133**, B1585-(*146*)

DE ALFARO, V. and T. REGGE, 1965, *Potential Scattering* (North-Holland Publishing Co., Amsterdam)-(*41, 293*)

DECK, R. T., 1964, Phys. Rev. Letters **13**, 169-(*148*)

DENNERY, Ph., 1961, Phys. Rev. **124**, 2000-(*262*)

DE SWART, J. J., 1963, Rev. Mod. Phys. **35**, 916-(*220*)

DIRAC, P. A. M., 1928, Proc. Roy. Soc., **A117**, 610-(*67*)

DIU, B., 1965, *Qu'est-ce qu'une Particule Elémentaire*? (Masson et Cie, Paris)-(*199, 201*)

DONNACHIE, A., J. HAMILTON and A. T. LEA, 1964, Phys. Rev. **135**, B515-(*193*)

DORFAN, D. E., J. EADES, L. M. LEDERMAN, W. LEE and C. C. LING, 1965, Phys. Rev. Letters **14**, 1003-(*103*)

DRELL, S. D., 1960, Phys. Rev. Letters **5**, 278, 342; 1961, Rev. Mod. Phys. **33**, 458-(*279*)

DRELL, S. D., 1963, in *Proc. of the International School of Physics "Enrico Fermi", Course* 26, Varenna, ed. M. Conversi (Academic Press, New York)-(*253*)

DUNNING, J. R., K. W. CHEN, A. A. CONE, G. HARTWIG, N. F. RAMSEY, J. K. WALKER and R. WILSON, 1964, Phys. Rev. Letters **13**, 631-(*254*)

DURAND, L., III, 1961, in *Lectures in Theoretical Physics, Vol. IV*, University of Colorado, Bolder, 1961, ed. Brittin, Downs and Downs (John Wiley & Sons, New York, 1962)-(*222*)

DURBIN, R., H. LOAR and J. STEINBERGER, 1951, Phys. Rev. **83**, 646-(*102*)

DÜRR, H. P. and H. PILKUHN, 1965, Nuovo Cim. **40**, 899-(*285*)

EDEN, R. J., P. V. LANDSHOFF, D. I. OLIVE and J. C. POLKINGHORNE, 1966, *The Analytic S-Matrix* (Cambridge University Press)-(*150, 168*)

EDMONDS, A. R., 1957, *Angular Momentum in Quantum Mechanics* (Princeton University Press)-(*53, 347*)

FABRI, E., 1954, Nuovo Cim. **11**, 479-(*11*)

FEINBERG, E. L. and I. POMERANCHUK, 1956, Nuovo Cim. **3**, 652-(*295*)

FERMI, E., 1950, Progr. Theor. Phys. **5**, 570-(*22*)

FERMI, E. and C. N. YANG, 1949, Phys. Rev. **76**, 1739-(*110*)

FERRARI, E. and F. SELLERI, 1961, Nuovo Cim. **21**, 1028; 1962, Suppl. Nuovo Cim. **24**, 453; 1963, Nuovo Cim. **27**, 1450-(*285*)

FERRO-LUZZI, M., R. D. TRIPP and M. WATSON, 1962, Phys. Rev. Letters **8**, 28; 1963, Phys. Rev. **131**, 2248-(*216*)

FEYNMAN, R. P., 1949, Phys. Rev. **76**, 769-(*38*)

FEYNMAN, R. and M. GELL-MANN, 1958, Phys. Rev. **109**, 193-(*316*)

FRAZER, W. R. and J. R. FULCO, 1960, Phys. Rev. **117**, 1603; 1609-(*203*)

FROISSART, M., 1961, Phys. Rev. **123**, 1053-(*293*)

FROISSART, M. and J. R. TAYLOR, 1967, Phys. Rev. **153**, 1636-(*158*)

GALBRAITH, W., E. W. JENKINS, T. F. KYCIA, B. A. LEONTIC, R. H. PHILLIPS, A. L. READ and R. RUBINSTEIN, 1965, Phys. Rev. **138**, B913-(*273*)

GASIOROWICZ, S., 1960, Fortschritte der Physik **8**, 665; 1966, *Elementary Particle Physics* (John Wiley & Sons, New York)-(*179*)

GELL-MANN, M., 1956, Nuovo Cim. **4**, Suppl. **2**, 848-(*95*); 1961, Report CTSL-20 (reprinted in the book of Gell-Mann and Ne'eman, The Eightfold Way)-(*133*, *138*, *219*); 1964, Phys. Letters **8**, 214-(*135*)

GELL-MANN, M. and M. LÉVY, 1960, Nuovo Cim. **16**, 705-(*320*)

GELL-MANN, M. and Y. NE'EMAN, 1964, *The Eightfold Way* (Benjamin, New York)-(*133*)

GELL-MANN, M. and A. PAIS, 1955, Phys. Rev. **97** 1387-(*325*)

GELL-MANN, M., D. SHARP and W. G. WAGNER, 1962, Phys. Rev. Letters **8**, 261-(*142*)

GERSTEIN, S. S. and J. B. ZELDOVITCH, 1955, Z. Eksperim. Teor. Fiz. **29**, 698-(*316*)

GOEBEL, C., 1958, Phys. Rev. Letters **1**, 337-(*279*)

GOLDBERGER, M. L., H. MIYAZAWA and R. OEHME, 1955, Phys. Rev. **99**, 986-(*187*)

GOLDBERGER, M. L. and S. B. TREIMAN, 1958, Phys. Rev. **110**, 1178; **111**, 354-(*320*)

GOLDBERGER, M. L. and K. M. WATSON, 1964, *Collision Theory* (John Wiley & Sons, New York)-(*32*, *222*, *250*)

GOLDFARB, L. J. B., 1958, Nucl. Phys. **7**, 622-(*230*)

GOLDHABER, G., J. BROWN, S. GOLDHABER, J. KADYK, B. SHEN and G. TRILLING, 1964, Phys. Rev. Letters **12**, 336-(*148*)

GOLDSTEIN, H., 1951, *Classical Mechanics*, (Addison-Wesley, New York)-(*53*)

GOOD, M. L. and W. D. WALKER, 1960, Phys. Rev. **120**, 1857-(*295*)

GOURDIN, M., 1967, *Unitary Symmetries* (North-Holland Publishing Co., Amsterdam)-(*137*)

GUNSON, J., 1965, J. Math. Phys. **6**, 827, 845, 852-(*150*)

HAMILTON, J., 1966, Phys. Letters **20**, 687-(*187*); 1967, in *High Energy Physics*, ed. E. H. S. Burhop (Academic Press, New York)-(*187*, *198*, *204*, *206*)

HAMILTON, J., P. MENOTTI, T. D. SPEARMAN and W. S. WOOLCOCK, 1961, Nuovo Cim. **20**, 519-(*202*)

HAMILTON, J. and T. D. SPEARMAN, 1961, Ann. Phys. **12**, 172-(*188*)

HEISENBERG, W., 1943, Z. für Physik **120**, 513 and 673-(*30*)

HEITLER, W., 1941, Proc. Cambridge Phil. Soc. **37**, 291; 1944, 1954, *The Quantum Theory of Radiation* (Clarendon Press, Oxford)-(*210*, *247*)

IAGOLNITZER, D., 1967, J. Math. Phys. **8**, (*170*)

ISO, C., 1962, Nuovo Cim. **25**, 456-(*312*)

JACKSON, J. D., 1964, Nuovo Cim. **34**, 1644-(*124*)

JACKSON, J. D., 1965, Rev. Mod. Phys. **37**, 484-(*292*)

JACKSON, J. D., J. T. DONOHUE, K. GOTTFRIED, R. KEYSER and B. E. Y. SVENSSON, 1965, Phys. Rev. **139**, B428-(*292*)

JACKSON, J. C. and H. W. WYLD, 1959, Phys. Rev. Letters **2**, 355-(*214*)

JACOB, M., 1961, in *Lectures on High Energy Physics*, ed. B. Jaksic, (Gordon and Breach, New York, 1965)-(*222*)

JACOB, M. and G. F. CHEW, 1964, *Strong Interaction Physics* (Benjamin, New York)-(*179*)

JACOB, M. and G. C. WICK, 1959, Ann. Phys. **7**, 404-(*4*, *58*, *222*, *223*, *232*, *351*)

JAHN, H. and H. VAN WIERINGEN, 1951, Proc. Roy. Soc. **209**, 502-(*93*)

JARLSKOG, C. and H. PILKUHN, 1966, Phys. Letters **20**, 428-(*220*)

JAUCH, J. M. and F. ROHRLICH, 1955, *The Theory of Photons and Electrons* (Addison-Wesley, New York)-(*247*)

JOSEPH, J. and H. PILKUHN, 1964, Nuovo Cim. **33**, 1407-(*295*)

KABIR, P. K., 1963, Nuovo Cim. **28**, 165-(*312*)

KÄLLÉN, G., 1958, *Quantenelektrodynamik, Handbuch der Physik, V*1 (Springer Verlag, Berlin)-(*247*)

KÄLLÉN, G., 1964, *Elementary Particle Physics* (Addison-Wesley, Reading)-(6, *179*, *198*, *303*)

KAWAKAMI, I., 1957, Progr. Theor. Phys. **19**, 459-(312)

KEMMER, N., 1938, Proc. Cambridge Phil. Soc. **34**, 354-(*90*)

KIM, J. K., 1965, Phys. Rev. Letters **14**, 29-(*214*)

KINOSHITO, T. and A. SIRLIN, 1959, Phys. Rev. **113**, 1652-(311)

KITTEL, W., G. OTTER and I. WACEK, 1966, Phys. Letters **21**, 349-(*214*)

KONOPINSKI, E. J., 1966, *The Theory of Beta Radioactivity* (Clarendon Press, Oxford)-(*298*, *303*)

KONOPINSKI, E. J. and H. M. MAHMOUD, 1953, Phys. Rev. **92**, 1045-(*311*)

KOTAŃSKI, A., 1966, Acta Physica Polonica **29**, 699-(*246*)

KROLL, N. M. and M. A. RUDERMAN, 1954, Phys. Rev. **93**, 233-(265)

LANDAU, L. D., 1959, Nucl. Phys. **13**, 181-(*170*)

LANDE, K., E. T. BOOTH, J. IMPEDUGLIA, L. M. LEDERMAN and W. CHINOWSKY, 1956, Phys. Rev. **103**, 1901-(*325*)

LEE, Y. K., L. W. MO and C. S. WU, 1963, Phys. Rev. Letters **10**, 253-(319)

LEE, T. D. and C. S. WU, 1965, Ann. Rev. Nucl. Sci. **15**, 381-(*321*); 1966, Ann. Rev. Nucl. Sci. **16**, Ch. 8 and 9-(*118*, *330*, *334*)

LEE, T. D. and C. N. YANG, 1956, Nuovo Cim. **3**, 749-(*112*); 1957, Phys. Rev. **105**, 1671-(*312*); 1962, Phys. Rev. **126**, 2239-(*320*)

LEPORE, J. V. and R. STUART, 1954, Phys. Rev. **94**, 1724-(*24*)

LINDENBAUM, S. J., 1964, *International Conference of High Energy Physics*, ed. Ya. A. Smorodinsky; *Dubna* 1964; 1965, *Oxford International Conference on Elementary Particles* (The Rutherford High Energy Laboratory, 1966)-(*273*)

LIPKIN, H. J., 1965, *Lie Groups for Pedestrians* (North-Holland Publishing Co., Amsterdam)-(*89*)

LOGUNOV, A. A., NGUYEN VAN HIEU and I. T. TODOROV, 1965, Ann. Phys. **31**, 203-(*274*)

LOVELACE, C., R. M. HEINZ and A. DONNACHIE, 1966, Phys. Letters **22**, 332-(*204*)

LOW, F., 1955, Phys. Rev. **97**, 1392-(*196*)

LU, E. Y. C. and D. I. OLIVE, 1966, Nuovo Cim. **45**, 205-(*158*)

LURÇAT, F. and P. MAZUR, 1964, Nuovo Cim. **31**, 140-(*24*)

MACDOWELL, S., 1960, Phys. Rev. **116**, 774-(*188*)

MAGLIC, B. C., L. W. ALVAREZ, A. H. ROSENFELD and M. L. STEVENSON, 1961, Phys. Rev. Letters **7**, 178-(*141*)

MANDELSTAM, S., 1958, Phys. Rev. **112**, 1344-(*181*)

MARTIN, B. R., 1965, Phys. Rev. **138**, B1136-(*219*)

MARTIN, A., 1966, Nuovo Cim. **42**, A930; **44**, A1219-(*179*)

MASSAM, T., Th. MULLER, B. RIGHINI, M. SCHNEEGANS and A. ZICHICHI, 1965, Nuovo Cim. **39**, 10-(*103*)

MEIMAN, N. N., 1962, JETP **43**, 2277-(*274*)

MICHEL, L., 1953, Nuovo Cim. **10**, 319-(*112*)
MILBURN, R. H., 1955, Rev. Mod. Phys. **27**, 1-(*24*)
MORRISON, D. R. O., 1966, Phys. Letters **22**, 226; 528-(*295*)
MUSHKELISHVILI, N. I., 1946 (1953), *Singular Integral Equations* (Gosudarstvennoye Tekhnicheskoye Izdatelstvo and Noordhoff, Groningen)-(*204*)
MUZINICH, I., 1964, J. Math. Phys. **5**, 1481-(*242*)

NAMBU, Y., 1960, Phys. Rev. Letters **4**, 380-(*320*)
NE'EMAN, Y., 1961, Nucl. Phys. **26**, 222-(*133*)
NISHIJIMA, K., 1955, Progr. Theor. Phys. **13**, 285-(*95*)
NYBORG, P., 1965, Phys. Rev. **140**, B921-(*22*)
NYBORG, P., H. S. SONG, W. KERNAN and R. H. GOOD, Jr., 1965, Phys. Rev. **140**, B914-(22)

OKUBO, S., 1962, Progr. Theor. Phys. **27**, 949-(*138*)
OLIVE, D. I., 1964, Phys. Rev. **135**, B745-(*150*, *152*, *155*, *157*)
OMNES, R., 1958, Nuovo Cim. **8**, 316-(*204*)

PAIS, A., 1960, Ann. Phys. **9**, 548; 1963, Ann. Phys. **22**, 274-(*93*); 1966, Rev. Mod. Phys. **38**, 215-(*139*)
PAIS, A. and R. JOST, 1952, Phys. Rev. **87**, 871-(*112*)
PAIS, A. and O. PICCIONI, 1955, Phys. Rev. **100**, 1487-(*325*, *334*)
PARKER, W. H., B. N. TAYLOR and D. N. LANGENBERG, 1967, Phys. Rev. Letters **18**, 287-(*82*)
PAULI, W., 1957, Nuovo Cim. **6**, 204-(*310*)
PERKINS, D. H., 1960, in *Progress in Elementary Particle and Cosmic Ray Physics*, ed. Wilson and Wouthuysen, Vol. V, North-Holland Publishing Co., Amsterdam-(*294*)
PHAM, F., 1967, Annales de l'Institut Henri Poincaré VI, 89-(*170*)
POIRIER, J. A. and M. PRIPSTEIN, 1963, Phys. Rev. **130**, 1171-(*94*)
POMERANCHUK, I., 1958, JETP **34**, 725-(*274*)
POWELL, C. F., 1950, Reports on Progress in Physics **13**, 350-(*87*)
PRESTON, M. A., 1962, *Physics of the Nucleus* (Addison-Wesley, Reading)-(*250*)
PUPPI, G., 1948, Nuovo Cim. **5**, 505-(*314*)

RARITA, W. and J. SCHWINGER, 1941, Phys. Rev. **60**, 61-(*59*)
RAZMI, M. S. K., 1964, Nuovo Cim. **31**, 615-(*295*)
REGGE, T., 1953 (1960), Nuovo Cim. **14**, 951; **18**, 947-(*293*)
ROMAN, P., 1960, *Theory of Elementary Particles* (North-Holland Publishing Co., Amsterdam)-(*67*)
ROPER, L. D., 1964, Phys. Rev. Letters **12**, 340-(*125*)
ROPER, L. D., R. M. WRIGHT and B. T. FELD, 1965, Phys. Rev. **138**, B190-(*122*)
ROSE, M. E., 1957, *Elementary Theory of Angular Momentum* (John Wiley & Sons, New York)-(*53*, *347*, *350*)
ROSENBLUTH, M. N., 1950, Phys. Rev. **79**, 615-(*251*)
ROSENFELD, A. H., A. BARBARO-GALTIERI, W. J. PODOLSKY, L. R. PRICE, P. SÖDING, C. J. WOHL, M. ROOS and W. J. WILLIS, 1967, Rev. Mod. Phys. **39**, 1-(*84*, *148*)
ROSS, M. H. and G. L. SHAW, 1961, Ann. Phys. **13**, 147-(*211*)

Saclay-Orsay-Bari-Bologna Collaboration, 1965, Nuovo Cim. **35**, 713-(*141*)

Sakata, S., 1956, Progr. Theor. Phys. **16**, 686-(*133*)

Salzman, F. and G. Salzman, 1960, Phys. Rev. Letters **5**, 377; Phys. Rev. **120**, 599; 1961, Phys. Rev. **121**, 1541-(*279, 280*)

Samaranayake, V. K. and W. S. Woolcock, 1965, Phys. Rev. Letters **15**, 936-(*187*)

Schiff, L. I., 1955, *Quantum Mechanics*, 2nd ed. (McGraw-Hill and Kogakusha)-(*250*)

Schopper, H. F., 1966, *Weak Interactions and Nuclear Beta Decay* (North-Holland Publishing Co., Amsterdam)-(*298, 303*)

Schweber, S. S., 1961, *An Introduction to Relativistic Quantum Field Theory*, (Row, Peterson and Co., New York)-(*198*)

Screaton, G. R., 1961, *Dispersion Relations* (Scottish Universities' Summer School 1960) (Oliver and Boyd, Edinburgh, London)-(*204*)

Shapiro, I. S., 1963, in *Selected Topics in Nuclear Theory* (IAEA, Vienna) -(*162*)

Sokolov, A. A., 1963, Phys. Letters **3**, 211-(*312*)

Solmitz, F. T., 1954, Phys. Rev. **94**, 1799-(*249*)

Stevenson, M. L., L. W. Alvarez, B. C. Maglić and A. H. Rosenfeld, 1962, Phys. Rev. **125**, 687-(*141*)

Stichel, P., 1965, Fortschritte der Physik **13**, 73-(*269, 272*)

Stodolsky, L., 1964, Phys. Rev. **134**, B 1099-(*288*)

Stodolsky, L. and J. J. Sakurai, 1963, Phys. Rev. Letters **11**, 90-(*288*)

Streater, R. F. and A. S. Wightman, 1964, *PCT, Spin and Statistics, and all that* (Benjamin, New York)-(*104*)

Sugawara, M. and A. Kanazawa, 1961, Phys. Rev. **123**, 1895-(*274*)

Taylor, J. R., 1966, J. Math. Phys. **7**, 181-(*158*)

Tenner, A. G. and G. F. Wolters, 1965, in *Progress in Elementary Particle and Cosmic Ray Physics*, ed. Wilson and Wouthuysen, Vol. 8 (North-Holland Publishing Co., Amsterdam)-(*148*)

Theis, W. R., 1959, Fortschritte der Physik **7**, 559-(*67*)

Titchmarsh, E. C., 1958, *The Theory of Functions* (Oxford University Press)-(*274*)

Touschek, B. Z., 1957, Nuovo Cim. **5**, 754-(*310*)

Treiman, S. and C. N. Yang, 1962, Phys. Rev. Letters **8**, 140-(*283*)

Tripp, R. D., 1965, CERN report 65-7; 1966, Proc. Intern. School of Physics "Enrico Fermi", Course 33, ed. L. Alvarez, (Academic Press, New York)-(*166*)

Trueman, T. L. and G. C. Wick, 1964, Ann. Phys. **26**, 322-(*175, 242, 243, 246*)

Truong, T. N., 1964, Phys. Rev. Letters **13**, 358a-(*330*)

Tuan, S. F., 1965, Phys. Rev. **139**, B1393-(*205*)

Van der Waerden, B. L., 1929, Göttinger Nachrichten, 100-(*68*)

Watson, K. M., 1952, Phys. Rev. **85**, 852-(*257*); 1954, Phys. Rev. **95**, 228-(*268*)

Weinberg, S., 1964, Phys. Rev. **133**, B1318; **134**, B882-(*61, 74*)

Werle, J., 1966, *Relativistic Theory of Reactions* (North-Holland Publishing Co., Amsterdam)-(*222*)

Whittaker, E. T. and G. N. Watson, 1963, *A Course of Modern Analysis* (Cambridge University Press)-(*292, 338*)

Wick, G. C., 1962, Ann. Phys. **18**, 65-(*242*)

Wigner, E. P., 1955, Phys. Rev. **98**, 145-(*48*)

WOLFENSTEIN, L., 1966, Nuovo Cim. **42**, 17-(*330*)

WU, C. S., 1964, Rev. Mod. Phys. **36**, 618-(*319*)

WU, C. S. and S. A. MOSZKOWSKI, 1966, *Beta Decay* (John Wiley & Sons, New York)-(*303*, *319*)

WU, T. T. and C. N. YANG, 1964, Phys. Rev. Letters **13**, 380-(*330*)

YUKAWA, H., 1935, Proc. Phys. Math. Soc. Japan, **17**, 48-(*87*)

ZOVKO, N., 1966, Phys. Letters **23**, 143-(*220*)

SUBJECT INDEX